Automotive Electrical and Electronic Systems

Fourth Edition

By Chek-Chart

Richard K. DuPuy, *Editor*
Steven D. Schaefer, *Managing Editor*

Automotive Electrical and Electronic Systems, Fourth Edition

Classroom Manual and Shop Manual

Copyright © 2000 by Chek-Chart Publications

International Standard Book Number: 1-57932-245-x
Library of Congress Catalog Card Number: 99-067757

Chek-Chart Publications

320 Soquel Way
Sunnyvale, CA 94086
408-739-2435

"Chek" us out on the web at www.chekchart.com.

General Manager
Peter Monte

Executive Director
Roger Fennema

Technical Publications Manager
Richard K. DuPuy

Managing Editor
Steven D. Schaefer

Contributing Editors
Robert Maddox
William Renke
Dennis L. Shortino

Technical Consultant
Jerry Mullen

Manufacturing Coordinator
Thomas Hedrick

Production Team
Troy Barnes, *Team Supervisor*
Kristy Nash, *Production Coordinator*
Carl Pierce, *Proofreader*

ACKNOWLEDGEMENTS

In producing this series of textbooks for automotive technicians, Chek-Chart has drawn extensively on the technical and editorial knowledge of the vehicle manufacturers and their suppliers. Automotive design is a technical, fast-changing field, and Chek-Chart gratefully acknowledges the help of the following companies and organizations that provided help and information allowing us to present the most up-to-date text and illustrations possible. These companies and organizations are not responsible for any errors or omissions in the instructions or illustrations, or for changes in procedures or specifications made by the manufacturers or suppliers, contained in this book or any other Chek-Chart product:

Allen Testproducts
American Isuzu Motors, Inc.
Automotive Electronic Services
Bear Manufacturing Company
Borg-Warner Corporation
Champion Spark Plug Company
DaimlerChrysler
DeAnza College, Cupertino, CA
Fluke Corporation
Ford Motor Company
Fram Corporation
General Motors Corporation
  Delco-Remy Division
  Rochester Products Division
  Saginaw Steering Gear Division
  Buick Motor Division
  Cadillac Motor Car Division
  Chevrolet Motor Division
  Oldsmobile Division
  Pontiac-GMC Division

Honda Motor Company, LTD
Jaguar Cars, Inc.
Marquette Manufacturing Company
Mazda Motor Corporation
Mercedes-Benz USA, Inc.
Mitsubishi Motor Sales of America, Inc.
Nissan North America, Inc.
The Prestolite Company
Robert Bosch Corporation
Saab Cars USA Inc.
Snap-on Tools Corporation
Toyota Motor Sales, U.S.A., Inc.
Vetronix Corporation
Volkswagen of America
Volvo Cars of North America

The comments, suggestions, and assistance of the following reviewers were invaluable:

Rick Escalambre, *Skyline College, San Bruno CA*
Eugene Wilson, *Mesa Community College, Mesa AZ*

The authors have made every effort to ensure that the material in this book is as accurate and up-to-date as possible. However, neither Chek-Chart nor any related companies are responsible for mistakes or omissions, or for changes in procedures or specifications by the manufacturers or suppliers.

Contents

On the Covers:
Front — Fluke 98 Automotive Scope Meter, Series II

Introduction to Automotive Electrical and Electronic Systems

Automotive Electrical and Electronic Systems is part of the Chek-Chart Automotive Series. The package for each course has two volumes: a *Classroom Manual* and a *Shop Manual*.

Other titles in this series include:

- *Automatic Transmissions and Transaxles*
- *Automotive Brake Systems*
- *Automotive Heating, Ventilation, and Air Conditioning*
- *Automotive Steering, Suspension, and Wheel Alignment*
- *Automotive Engine Repair and Rebuilding*
- *Engine Performance, Diagnosis, and Tune-Up*
- *Fuel Systems and Emission Controls*.

Each book is written to help the instructor teach students to become competent and knowledgeable professional automotive technicians. The two-manual texts are the core of a learning system that leads a student from basic theories to actual hands-on experience.

The entire series is job-oriented, designed for students who intend to work in the automotive service profession. Knowledge gained from these books and the instructors enables the student to get and keep a job in the automotive repair industry. Learning the material and techniques in these volumes is a giant leap toward a satisfying, rewarding career.

The books are divided into a *Classroom Manual* and *Shop Manual* for an improved presentation of the descriptive information and study lessons, along with representative testing, repair, and overhaul procedures. The manuals are to be used together: The descriptive material in the *Classroom Manual* reinforces the application material in the *Shop Manual*.

Each book is divided into several parts and each of these parts is complete by itself. Within each part are several related chapters. Instructors enjoy the complete, readable, and well-thought-out presentation of the chapters. Students benefit from the many learning aids included, as well as from the thoroughness of the presentation.

The series was researched and written by the editorial staff of Chek-Chart. Chek-Chart has been providing vehicle specification, training, and repair information to the professional automotive service field since 1929. Chek-Chart maintains a complete, up-to-date automotive data bank, which was used extensively to prepare this textbook series.

Because of the comprehensive material, the hundreds of high-quality illustrations, and the inclusion of the latest automotive technology, instructors and students alike find that these books maintain their value over the years. Many master technicians form the core of their professional library with Chek-Chart publications.

How To Use This Book

Why Are There Two Manuals?

Unless you are familiar with the other books in this series, *Automotive Electrical and Electronic Systems* is unlike any other textbook you have used before. It is actually two books, the *Classroom Manual* and the *Shop Manual*. They have different purposes and should be used together.

The *Classroom Manual* teaches what a technician needs to know about electrical and electronic theory, systems, and components. The *Classroom Manual* is valuable in class and at home, both for study and for reference. The text and illustrations are used for years to refresh the memory—not only about the basics of automotive electrical and electronic systems but also about related topics in automotive history, physics, and technology.

The *Shop Manual* teaches test procedures, troubleshooting techniques, and how to repair the systems and components introduced in the *Classroom Manual*. The *Shop Manual* provides the practical, hands-on information required for working on automotive electrical and electronic systems. Use the two manuals together to understand fully how the systems work and how to make repairs when something is not working.

What Is In These Manuals?

These key features of the *Classroom Manual* make it easier to learn and remember the material:

- Each chapter is divided into self-contained sections for easier understanding and review. This organization clearly shows which parts make up which systems, and how various parts or systems that perform the same task differ or are the same.
- Most parts and processes are fully illustrated with drawings or photographs. Important topics appear in several different ways, to make sure other aspects of them are seen.
- Important words in the *Classroom Manual* text are printed in boldface type and are defined on the same page and in a glossary at the end of the manual. Use these words to build the vocabulary needed to understand the text.
- Review questions are included for each chapter. Use them to test your knowledge.
- Every chapter has a brief summary at the end to help you review for exams.
- Every so often, sidebars—short blocks of "nice to know" information—are included in addition to the main text.

The *Shop Manual* has detailed instructions on test, service, and overhaul procedures for modern electrical and electronic systems and their components. These are easy to understand and often include step-by-step explanations of the procedure. The *Shop Manual* contains:

- Helpful information on the use and maintenance of shop tools and test equipment
- Safety precautions
- Clear illustrations and diagrams to help you locate trouble spots while learning to read service literature
- Test procedures and troubleshooting hints that help you work better and faster
- Repair tips used by professionals, presented clearly and accurately
- A sample test at the back of the manual that is similar to those given for Automotive Service Excellence (ASE) certification; use this test to help you study and prepare when ready to be certified as an electrical and electronics expert.

Where Should I Begin?

If you already know something about automotive electrical and electronic systems and how to repair them, this book is a helpful review. If you are just starting in automotive repair, then this book provides a solid foundation on which to develop professional-level skills.

Your instructor has designed a course to take advantage of what you already know and what facilities and equipment are available. You may be asked to read certain chapters of these manuals out of order. That is fine. The important thing is to really understand each subject before moving on to the next.

Study the vocabulary words in boldface type and use the review questions to help understand the material. When reading the *Classroom Manual*, be sure to refer to the *Shop Manual* to relate the descriptive text to the service procedures. When working on actual vehicle systems and components, look to the *Classroom Manual* to keep the basic information fresh in your mind. Working on such a complicated piece of equipment as a modern automobile is not easy. Use the information in the *Classroom Manual*, the procedures in the *Shop Manual*, and the knowledge of your instructor to guide you.

The *Shop Manual* is a good book for work, not just a good workbook. Keep it on hand while actually working on a vehicle. It folds flat on the workbench and under the chassis, and is designed to withstand quite a bit of rough handling.

When performing actual test and repair procedures, a complete and accurate source of manufacturer specifications and procedures is needed for the specific vehicle. Most automotive repair shops have either the annual service manuals from the vehicle manufacturer, which list these specifications, or an independent guide, such as the *Chek-Chart Car Care Guide*. This unique book, with ten-year coverage, is updated each year to provide service instructions, capacities, and troubleshooting tips needed to work on specific vehicles.

PART ONE

Electrical Fundamentals

1

Basic Electricity and Circuits

A car may be thought of as a large electrical system on wheels. This is a bit different from the more common conception of cars. But cars use electricity not only to get started, but to keep running.

To know enough about electrical systems to work on them, you will have to know about electricity. Perhaps you already do. If so, these first few chapters will be a good review. If not, study them carefully. You will soon find that some of the best examples of electrical science exist in your own automobile.

Unlike the fuel and oil for your car, electricity cannot be seen, heard, touched, or smelled. We cannot weigh or measure it either. We can, however, measure its actions, and we can see, hear, touch, or smell many of its effects. Our knowledge and use of electricity are based on some scientific theories which describe the features of electricity that we cannot see. When you use a voltmeter to test a circuit, you cannot see the voltage. But, the meter tells you some facts about the circuit based on theories that define voltage.

Because our knowledge of electricity is based on science, we will begin with a quick look at the chemistry and atomic structure of the materials used in electrical systems.

ATOMIC STRUCTURE

"Matter" is the general name given to everything in the physical universe. The only place in the physical universe where matter does not exist is in a total vacuum. Matter is made up of chemical building blocks called **elements.**

An element is matter that cannot be reduced to anything simpler by chemical means. Scientists have so far discovered 103 elements in our world. Of these, 92 exist in nature and the others have been created by scientists. Some are familiar elements such as oxygen, gold, and copper. Others are ones we seldom hear of, such as antimony, lithium, and gallium.

The smallest part of an element that still has all the features, or characteristics, of that element is the **atom.** Atoms of each element are distinctly different from those of any other element.

What makes the atom of one element different from those of another are the same characteristics that cause electricity. To learn more about electricity, we must look inside the atom.

Protons, Electrons, and Neutrons

As small as it is, the atom is made of several other, much smaller units: the **proton,** the **electron,** and the **neutron.** Compare the atom to our solar system. Our earth and the other planets go around (orbit) the sun in fixed paths, figure 1-1.

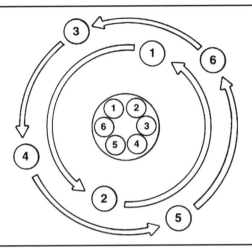

Figure 1-1. In an atom (left), electrons orbit protons in the nucleus just as planets orbit the sun in our solar system (right).

Figure 1-3. A balanced atom.

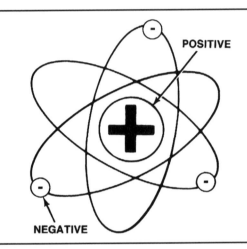

Figure 1-2. The charges within an atom.

In the atom, the electrons orbit in fixed paths around the central core, or **nucleus**, which contains the protons and the neutrons. The only difference between atoms of different kinds of matter is the number of protons and neutrons in the nucleus and the number and spacing of the orbiting electrons.

Positive and Negative Charges

The parts of the atom have different charges. The orbiting electrons are negatively charged, while the protons are positively charged. Positive charges are indicated by the "plus" sign (+), negative charges by the "minus" sign (–), figure 1-2. As you will soon see, we use these same + and – signs to identify parts of an electrical circuit. Neutrons have no charge at all—they are neutral. In a normal, or balanced, atom, the number of negative particles equals the number of positive particles. That is, there are as many electrons as there are protons, figure 1-3. The number of neutrons varies according to the type of atom.

An ordinary magnet has two ends, or poles. One end is called the south pole, and the other is called the

north pole. If two magnets are brought close to each other with like poles together (south to south or north to north), the magnets will push each other apart. This is because like poles repel each other. If the opposite poles of the magnets are brought close to each other, south to north, the magnets will snap together. This is because unlike poles attract each other.

The positive and negative charges within an atom are like the north and south poles of a magnet. Charges that are alike will repel each other, similar to the poles of a magnet, figure 1-4. That is why the negative electrons continue to orbit around the positive protons. They are attracted and held by the opposite charge of the protons. The electrons keep moving in orbit because they repel each other.

When an atom loses any electrons, it becomes unbalanced. It will have more protons than electrons, and therefore will have a positive charge. If it gains more electrons than protons, the atom will be negatively charged. When an atom is not balanced, it becomes a charged particle called an **ion**. Ions try to regain their balance of equal protons and electrons. They do this by exchanging electrons with neighboring atoms, figure 1-5. This is the flow of electric current, or electricity.

Electron Shells

Electrons orbit around the nucleus in definite paths. These paths form shells, like **concentric** rings, around the nucleus. Only a specific number of electrons can orbit within each shell. If there are too many electrons for the first and closest shell to the nucleus, the others will orbit in additional shells until all electrons have an orbit within a shell. There can be as many as seven shells around a single nucleus.

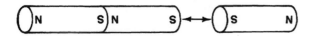

Figure 1-4. Unlike and like charges.

Free and Bound Electrons

The outermost electron shell, or ring, is the most important to our study of electricity. It is called the **valence ring**. The number of electrons in this ring determines the valence of the atom, and indicates its capacity to combine with other atoms. From now on, we will be concerned only with the valence ring and the action of the electrons in that ring.

If the valence ring of an atom has three or fewer electrons in it, the ring has room for more. The electrons there are held very loosely, and it is easy for a drifting electron to join the valence ring and push another electron away. These loosely held electrons are called **free electrons**. When the valence ring has five or more electrons in it, it is fairly full. The electrons are held tightly, and it is hard for a drifting electron to push its way into the valence ring. These tightly held electrons are called **bound electrons**.

The movement of these drifting electrons is called current. Current can be small, with only a few electrons moving, or it can be large, with a tremendous number of electrons moving. However, current only flows in a conductor. Electric current is the controlled, directed movement of electrons from atom to atom within a conductor.

Conductors, Insulators, and Semiconductors

When a material has many free electrons, it is easy for electrons to move from atom to atom. Materials whose atoms have from one to three free electrons and easy electron flow are good **conductors.** That is, electric current can pass through them easily. Many metals are good conductors, especially silver, copper, and aluminum.

When a material has many bound electrons, it is hard for electrons to move from atom to atom. These materials that do not conduct electricity well are called **insulators.** Rubber, glass, and certain plastics are good insulators, as are gaseous elements such as nitrogen and oxygen. Insulators are used in electrical systems to ensure that the electron flow stays within the conductor and is directed to the proper place in the system.

Some materials are neither good conductors nor good insulators. They have just four electrons in the valence ring. These are called **semiconductors.** They are important in some parts of electrical systems, as

Figure 1-5. An unbalanced, positively charged atom will attract electrons from neighboring atoms.

we will see when we study diodes, transistors, and other solid-state electronic devices.

Elements: Chemical building blocks that make up all types of matter in the physical universe.

Atom: The smallest part of a chemical element that still has all the characteristics of that element.

Proton: A positively charged particle within an atom.

Electron: A negatively charged particle within an atom.

Neutron: A particle in an atom that has no charge and is electrically neutral.

Nucleus: The center core of an atom that contains the protons and neutrons.

Ion: An atom which has become unbalanced by losing or gaining an electron. It can be positively or negatively charged.

Concentric: Having the same center, such as two circles drawn around a common centerpoint.

Valence Ring: The outermost electron shell of an atom.

Free Electrons: Three or fewer loosely held electrons in an atom's valence ring.

Bound Electrons: Five or more tightly held electrons in an atom's valence ring.

Conductors: Materials that allow easy electron flow because of their many free electrons.

Insulators: Materials that oppose electron flow because of their many bound electrons.

Semiconductors: Materials that have four electrons in their valence ring and are neither good conductors nor good insulators.

Figure 1-6. Movement of electrons through a wire.

ELECTRON FLOW (CURRENT)

If electrons simply move about in various directions, no electricity will flow. This is called random drift of electrons. Only a directed, concentrated flow of electrons from one point to another is called current flow.

To illustrate the flow of electric current, let's look at a length of copper wire. Copper is a good conductor because it has only one electron in its valence ring. Electrons can be made to move easily from one atom to another. To do this, we must have a positive charge at one end of the wire and a negative charge at the other. How this is done is explained later in this text. For now, assume that these charges do exist and that they remain unchanged.

The outer electron of an atom near the positive end of the wire will be attracted by the positive charge. As it leaves its atom and moves toward the positive charge, the atom becomes unbalanced. It becomes positively charged and attracts the outer electron from a neighboring atom. The outer electrons of neighboring atoms will move in order toward the positive charge. The negative charge at one end of the wire repels the electrons with the same force that the positive charge at the other end attracts them. The net result is a controlled flow of electrons from the negative end of the wire to the positive end, figure 1-6. This flow will continue as long as the positive and negative charges are at the opposite ends of the wire. This brings us back to our definition of electricity, or electric current, namely:

> The controlled, directed flow of electrons
> from atom to atom in a conductor.

Current-Flow Theories

There are two theories that describe electrical current. They are called the conventional theory and the electron theory, figure 1-7. Either theory can be used with equal accuracy, as long as it is used consistently.

Conventional theory

When scientists first began to make discoveries about electricity, they thought it flowed from positive to negative. This became what is now called the **conventional theory** of current flow. In the past, the conventional theory was always used to describe automotive electrical systems.

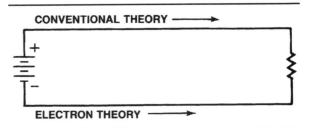

Figure 1-7. Two theories of current flow.

Figure 1-8. A simple circuit.

Electron theory

The **electron theory** of current flow says that current moves from negative to positive. It is this theory we have used so far in talking about basic electricity. It is the theory used in electronic communications, computers, and other areas of the electronics industry.

In recent years, the electron flow theory has been used for the most part to describe systems on automobiles. Whenever the electron flow theory is used in this book, it will be clearly identified. Our continuing study of current, voltage, and resistance in *this* chapter is based on the electron theory.

Current Path (Circuit)

An electrical current needs a path to flow. This path is called a **circuit,** which means around. If there is any break in the circuit, no current travels through it. The electrons have nowhere to go.

One of the simplest circuits contains an energy source (battery), conductors (wires), and a lamp, figure 1-8. The current flows from the negative side, or terminal, of the battery through the wires and the lamp, lighting the lamp, and back to the positive terminal of the battery. If one wire is taken off of its battery terminal, figure 1-9, the circuit is not complete. Current does not flow, and the lamp does not light. Breaking the circuit by removing one wire from its terminal is the same as using a switch to break the circuit.

Figure 1-9. An incomplete (open) circuit.

Figure 1-10. Voltage pushes current flow; force pushes water flow.

Ampere

Current in a conductor can be compared to water flowing in a pipe, figure 1-10. When measuring water flow, we can count how many gallons flow past a point in a certain period of time. When measuring electrical charges, we count electrons instead of gallons. When 6.28 billion electrons pass a point in one second, we say that one **ampere**, or amp, of current is flowing. The ampere is the unit that indicates the rate of electric current. Remember that current (amperes) travels *through* a circuit.

VOLTAGE

Current cannot exist unless some sort of force pushes all the randomly drifting electrons in one direction. This is called electromotive force. It is measured in units called **volts**. The force that pushes current through a conductor is called **voltage**. It can be compared to the force that moves water through a pipe, figure 1-10. Voltage is also the measurement of a **potential** difference in force that exists between two points. One point must be negatively charged, and the other must be positively charged, figure 1-11, such as the two terminals of a battery. The strength of the force depends upon the strength of the charges at each point. If the charges are strong, the voltage is high. If the charges are weak, the voltage is low.

Voltage exists even when there is no current, such as when we disconnect one wire from its battery terminal in our simple circuit. Voltage is present at the terminals of the battery in figure 1-11, but there is no current without a complete circuit.

Voltage Sources

In automobiles, voltage is supplied by the battery and the alternator. In the battery, chemical action creates a difference in electromotive force (potential) between the positive and negative terminals. In an alternator, mechanical energy is converted to electrical energy (electromotive force, or voltage). Remember that voltage is the force applied *to*, or impressed *on*, a circuit.

Figure 1-11. Voltage is a potential difference in electromotive force.

Conventional Theory: The current flow theory that says electricity flows from positive to negative. Also called the positive current flow theory.

Electron Theory: The current flow theory that says electricity flows from negative to positive.

Circuit: A circle or unbroken path through which an electric current can flow.

Ampere: The unit for measuring the rate of electric current flow.

Volt: The unit for measuring the amount of electrical force.

Voltage: The electromotive force that causes current flow. The potential difference in electrical force between two points when one is negatively charged and the other is positively charged.

Potential: Possible, but not yet in use. The voltage between two points.

RESISTANCE TO CURRENT FLOW

Voltage is required to force current through a conductor. All conductive materials oppose current to some extent. This opposition is called **resistance**. More important than the resistance of a conductor is the resistance of an electrical device. The lamp in figure 1-8 is an electrical device that has more resistance than the wire conductors. Other electrical devices, such as starter motors, radios, or ignition coils, also offer resistance.

Resistance can be present in places other than the wires and devices of a circuit. A break in the circuit, such as in figure 1-9, creates infinite resistance. Loose or corroded connections also cause resistance to current. Remember that resistance exists *in* a circuit.

Ohm—The Unit of Resistance

Resistance is measured in units called **ohms**. There is an important relationship between volts (electromotive force), amperes (current), and ohms (resistance) that must be understood in order to troubleshoot an electrical circuit effectively:

> When a force of *one volt* pushes *one ampere* of current through a circuit, the resistance present is *one ohm,* figure 1-12.

This statement is an expression of Ohm's Law, named after the German scientist Georg Simon Ohm. Ohm's Law is one of your most important electrical troubleshooting tools.

Factors of Resistance

Five factors, or characteristics, determine how much resistance is present in any part of an electrical circuit. The examples below refer to wire conductors. Conductors also exist in circuit devices. The filament of a bulb and the windings of a motor are conductors, so the examples apply to all electrical devices. The electrical devices in a circuit, such as bulbs and motors, are also called "loads". These are the devices that do work—produce light, heat, or motion.

- *The atomic structure of the material*—If the material has few free electrons, it is a poor conductor. Resistance to current is high. All conductors have some resistance, but the resistance of a good conductor is so small that a fraction of a volt causes current.
- *The length of the conductor*—Electrons in motion are constantly colliding with the atoms of the conductor. The longer a piece of wire, the greater the number of collisions that occur, and the higher the resistance of the conductor.

Figure 1-12. If this battery provides one volt of pressure, the resistance of the lamp must be one ohm.

- *The cross-sectional area of the conductor*—The thinner a piece of wire is, the higher its resistance.
- *The temperature of the conductor*—In most cases, the higher the temperature of the conducting material, the higher its resistance. That is why alternator regulators are tested at normal operating temperature for accurate readings.
- *The condition of the conductor*—If a wire is partially cut, it acts almost as if the entire wire were of a smaller diameter, offering a high resistance at the damaged point. Loose or corroded connections have the same effect. High resistance at connections is a major cause of electrical problems.

Voltage Drop and Resistance

Because every electrical load in a circuit offers some resistance, voltage is reduced as it moves the current through each load. Voltage is electrical energy, and as it moves current through a load, some of the electrical energy is changed to another form of energy, such as light, heat, or motion.

If you measure the voltage on both sides of a load, you can see how much voltage has been used to move current through the load. This is called **voltage drop**. If you measure the voltage drop at every load in a circuit and add the measurements, they equal the original voltage available. No voltage disappears; it is just changed into a different form of energy by the resistance of the load.

The resistance of any electrical part (load or conductor) can be measured in two ways:

- Direct measurement with an instrument called an **ohmmeter**, which measures the resistance (in ohms) offered by the part.
- Indirect measurement with an instrument called a **voltmeter**, which measures the voltage drop through the part.

These measurements are explained in Chapter Two of the *Shop Manual*, along with the use of an **ammeter** to measure current. While voltage and resistance are measured in different units, they are directly related. As the resistance of a load increases, the voltage drop across the load also increases. If you know either the voltage drop or the resistance (plus the amperage), you can calculate the other, using Ohm's Law, as explained in the next section. If you know *both* the voltage drop and the resistance, you can also calculate the current.

OHM'S LAW

We introduced one way of stating Ohm's Law when we said:

> When a force of *one volt* pushes *one ampere* of current through a circuit, the resistance present is *one ohm,* figure 1-12.

Ohm stated this relationship as a simple mathematical formula that can be written three ways:

- Volts = amperes multiplied by ohms
$$E = I \times R$$
- Amperes = volts divided by ohms
$$I = E \div R$$
- Ohms = volts divided by amperes
$$R = E \div I$$

Traditionally, the equations are shown with amperes (current) abbreviated as I, for "intensity", voltage as E, for "electromotive force", and resistance as R. When any two of the values are known for a circuit, the third can be found using Ohm's Law. The law makes electrical testing easier if you know how to use it. An easy way to remember Ohm's Law is shown in figure 1-13. If you cover the unknown factor, you see the formula to use in finding it.

We now look at the three types of circuits—series, parallel, and series-parallel—and see how to apply Ohm's Law to each of them. We will illustrate these circuits in pictures and use symbols to represent different parts. These illustrations are called diagrams. Some common symbols and their meanings are shown in figure 1-14.

SERIES CIRCUIT

In a **series circuit,** the current has only one path to follow. In figure 1-15, using conventional current flow theory, you see that the current must flow from the battery, through the resistor, and back to the battery. The circuit must be continuous, or have **continuity.** If one wire is disconnected from the battery, the circuit is broken and there is no current. If electrical loads are wired in series, they must all be switched on and

working, or the circuit is broken and none of them work. A simplified example of a series circuit is shown in figure 1-16. Current flows from the battery, through the horn switch, through the horn, and then back to the battery.

Series Circuits and Ohm's Law

Ohm's Law can easily be applied to a series circuit. If any two of the values are known, the third can be

■ **Compounds**

Some of the materials used in electrical systems are pure chemical elements, such as copper. Other materials, like rubber and plastic insulation, are combinations of several elements. These combinations of elements are called compounds.

Just as the atom is the smallest identifiable part of an element, the molecule is the smallest identifiable part of a compound. Atoms join into molecules because they seek to complete their outer (valence) rings of electrons. They do this by sharing their valence electrons with each other.

Some compounds, like water and rubber, exist in nature. Others, like various plastics, are man-made. A molecule of water consists of two atoms of hydrogen joined to one atom of oxygen. Each hydrogen atom has one electron in its valence ring, but each could have two. The oxygen atom has six electrons in its valence ring, but it could have eight. By sharing the electrons of the two hydrogen atoms, the oxygen atom completes its valence ring. Similarly, each atom of hydrogen borrows one electron from the oxygen atom to complete its valence ring.

Resistance: Opposition to electrical current flow.

Ohm: The unit for measuring electrical resistance. When one volt pushes one ampere through a circuit, the resistance present is one ohm.

Voltage Drop: The measurement of the loss of voltage caused by the resistance of a conductor or a circuit device.

Ohmmeter: A meter used to measure resistance to current flow.

Voltmeter: A meter used to measure electromotive force in volts.

Ammeter: A meter used to measure electrical current flow in amperes.

Series Circuit: A circuit that has only one path through which current can flow.

Continuity: Continuous, unbroken. Used to describe a working electrical circuit or component that is not open.

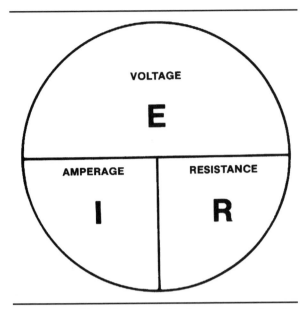

Figure 1-13. This diagram will help you remember the Ohm's Law formula. Cover the unknown value and multiply or divide the other two.

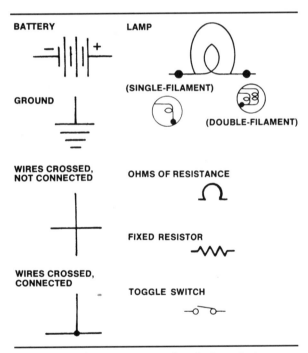

Figure 1-14. Some common electrical symbols.

figured out using Ohm's Law. Some features of a series circuit are:

• Current is the same everywhere in the circuit. Since there is only one path for current, the same amount of current must be available at all points of the circuit.

• Voltage drops may vary from load to load if the individual resistances vary, but the sum of all

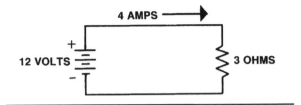

Figure 1-15. A simple series circuit.

Figure 1-16. This horn circuit diagram illustrates a simple series circuit.

the voltage drops in the series equals the original source voltage.

• The total resistance (R~t) is the sum of all the individual resistances in the series.

In figure 1-15, the simple circuit consists of a 3-ohm resistor connected to a 12-volt battery. The amperage is found by using Ohm's Law:

$$E \div R = I$$

$$12 \div 3 = 4 \text{ amperes}$$

When you know the current and the individual resistances of a series circuit, you can calculate the voltage drop across each load. The sum of these drops equals the source voltage. For the 2-ohm resistor in figure 1-17:

$$I \times R = E$$

$$2 \times 2 = 4 \text{ volts}$$

For the 4-ohm resistor in figure 1-17:

$$I \times R = E$$

$$2 \times 4 = 8 \text{ volts}$$

The sum of the voltage drops is 4 volts + 8 volts = 12 volts, which is the source voltage.

PARALLEL CIRCUITS

When current can follow more than one path to complete a circuit, that circuit is called a **parallel circuit**. The points where current paths split and rejoin are called junction points. The separate paths which split and meet at junction points are called branch circuits or **shunt** circuits. A parallel circuit is shown in figure 1-18. In an automobile, the headlamps are wired in parallel with each other, figure 1-19.

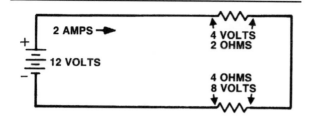

Figure 1-17. A series circuit with more than one resistor.

Figure 1-18. A parallel circuit.

Parallel Circuits and Ohm's Law

The features of a parallel circuit are:

- The voltage applied to, or measured across, each branch of the circuit is the same.
- The total current in a parallel circuit is the sum of the current in each branch.
- The total resistance (R~t) of a parallel circuit is always less than the lowest individual resistance. The reason is that when you add resistors in parallel, you are actually adding more conductors, or paths in which current can flow, which reduces the total resistance.

There are two ways to calculate the total resistance, or **equivalent resistance**, in a parallel circuit. One formula for any number of resistors is:

$$R_t = \cfrac{1}{\cfrac{1}{R_1} + \cfrac{1}{R_2} + \cfrac{1}{R_3} + \ldots + \cfrac{1}{R_n}}$$

For the circuit illustrated in figure 1-18:

$$R = \cfrac{1}{\cfrac{1}{6} + \cfrac{1}{3}} = \cfrac{1}{\cfrac{1}{6} + \cfrac{2}{6}} = \cfrac{1}{\cfrac{3}{6}} = \cfrac{1}{\cfrac{1}{2}} = \cfrac{1}{0.5} = 2 \text{ ohms}$$

Another way to calculate total resistance is the product-over-the-sum method:

$$R_1 = \frac{R_1 \times R_2}{R_1 + R_2}$$

This formula can be used for only two resistances at a time. If more than two are wired in parallel, you must calculate their values in pairs until you determine one total resistance for the circuit. For the circuit in figure 1-18:

Figure 1-19. The headlamps are wired in parallel with each other in all headlamp circuits.

$$R_1 = \frac{6 \times 3}{6+3} = \frac{18}{9} = 2 \text{ ohms.}$$

To apply Ohm's Law to a parallel circuit, sometimes you must treat branches as independent circuits and sometimes you must deal with the entire circuit, depending upon which values are unknown.

To find current, you must treat each branch separately because of the different current in each branch. Voltage is applied equally across all branches, so the source voltage is divided by the branch resistance to determine the current through that branch. Adding the current in all the branches gives the total current in the circuit. In the circuit shown, figure 1-18, current through the 6-ohm resistor is:

$$E \div R = I$$

$$12 \text{ volts} \div 6 \text{ ohms} = 2 \text{ amps}$$

Through the 3-ohm resistor, it is:

$$E \div R = I$$

$$12 \text{ volts} \div 3 \text{ ohms} = 4 \text{ amps}$$

Total circuit current is 2 amps + 4 amps = 6 amps.

If resistance of a branch is unknown, dividing the source voltage by the branch current gives the branch resistance. In figure 1-18, for the first branch:

Parallel Circuit: A circuit that has more than one path through which current can flow.

Shunt: Parallel. An electrical connection or branch circuit in parallel with another branch circuit or connection.

Equivalent Resistance: The total resistance of a parallel circuit. The single mathematical equivalent of all the parallel resistance.

$$R_1 = 12 \text{ volts} \div 2 \text{ amps} = 6 \text{ ohms}$$

For the second branch:

$$R_2 = 12 \text{ volts} \div 4 \text{ amps} = 3 \text{ ohms}$$

Total resistance of the circuit can be calculated using the product-over-the-sum method:

$$R_t = \frac{6 \text{ ohms} \times 3 \text{ ohms}}{6 \text{ ohms} + 3 \text{ ohms}} = \frac{18}{9} = 2 \text{ ohms}$$

Or, if all you need is the equivalent circuit resistance, divide the source voltage by the total circuit amperage as follows:

$$R_t = 12 \text{ volts} \div 6 \text{ amps} = 2 \text{ ohms}$$

To determine source voltage, multiply the total circuit current by the total circuit resistance. Or, since the voltage is the same across all branches, multiply one branch current by the same branch resistance. In figure 1-18:

$$I \times R = E$$

$$6 \text{ amps} \times 2 \text{ ohms} = 12 \text{ volts}$$

Or, (branch I) × (branch R) = E:

$$\text{Branch 1: } 2 \times 6 = 12 \text{ volts}$$

$$\text{Branch 2: } 4 \times 3 = 12 \text{ volts}$$

SERIES-PARALLEL CIRCUITS

As the name suggests, **series-parallel circuits** combine the two types of circuits already discussed. Some of the loads are wired in series, but there are also some loads wired in parallel, figure 1-20. The entire headlamp circuit of an automobile is a series-parallel circuit, figure 1-21. The headlamps are in parallel with each other, but the switches are in series with the battery and with each lamp. Both lamps are controlled by the switches, but one lamp still lights if the other is burned out. Most of the circuits in an automobile electrical system are series-parallel.

Series-Parallel Circuits and Ohm's Law

Values in a series-parallel circuit are figured by reducing the parallel branches to equivalent values for single loads in series. Then the equivalent values and any actual series loads are combined.

To calculate total resistance, first find the resistance of all loads wired in parallel. If the circuit is complex, it may be handy to group the parallel branches into pairs and treat each pair separately. Then add the values of all loads wired in series to the equivalent resistance of all the loads wired in parallel. In the circuit shown in figure 1-20:

$$R_t = \frac{(6 \times 3)}{(6 + 3)} + 2 = \frac{18}{9} + 2 = 4 \text{ ohms}$$

In the illustration, the equivalent resistance of the loads in parallel is:

Figure 1-20. A series-parallel circuit.

Figure 1-21. A complete headlamp circuit, with all bulbs and switches, is a series-parallel circuit.

$$\frac{6 \times 3}{6 + 3} = \frac{18}{9} = 2 \text{ ohms}$$

The total of the branch currents is $1 + 2 = 3$ amps, so the voltage drop is:

$$I \times R = E$$

$$3 \times 2 = 6$$

The voltage drop across the load in series is 2 [×] 3 = 6 volts. Add these voltage drops to find the source voltage:

$$6 + 6 = 12 \text{ volts}$$

To determine the source voltage in a series-parallel circuit, you must first find the equivalent resistance of the loads in parallel, and the total current through this equivalent resistance. Figure out the voltage drop across this equivalent resistance and add it to the voltage drops across all loads wired in series.

To determine total current, find the currents in all parallel branches and add them together. This total is equal to the current at any point in the series circuit. In figure 1-20:

$$I = \frac{E}{R_1} + \frac{E}{R_2} = \frac{6}{6} + \frac{6}{3} = 1 + 2 = 3 \text{ amps}$$

Notice that there are only 6 volts across each of the branch circuits because another 6 volts have already been "dropped" across the 2-ohm series resistor.

WATTS—ELECTRIC POWER

We have learned that voltage is the ability to do work. It is the electromotive force that moves current. Voltage, however, is not the same as power. Power is the *rate* of doing work, or the amount of work done per unit of time. The basic formula for calculating any type of power, mechanical or electrical, is the amount of work divided by the time taken to do the work.

Electric power is calculated easily by multiplying the current by the voltage. The unit for measuring electric power is called the **watt**. The abbreviation for watt is W; however, in power formulas, P is usually used as the symbol for power.

Electric power (watts, or wattage) equals voltage times current. This formula, using abbreviations already defined, is written simply:

$$P = E \times I$$

We can substitute other values from Ohm's Law into the power formula, if necessary. We know that E = IR, so we can substitute IR for E in the power formula and write:

$$P = (IR)I, \text{ or simply, } P = I_2 R$$

Similarly, we know that I = E (R, so we can substitute E (R for I in the power formula and write:

$$P = \frac{EE}{R}, \text{ or simply, } P = \frac{E2}{R}$$

Up to this point, we have talked about resistors and other electrical devices in terms of their resistance in ohms. Electrical devices, particularly resistors, may be rated in two ways: in ohms of resistance, and in watts of power capacity.

Wattage measurement and wattage ratings in an automotive electrical system are most commonly applied to lighting and accessory circuits and to batteries. The wattage formula can be applied to an entire circuit by multiplying the applied voltage by the total current. It can also tell you the power used by one separate part of a circuit, when the voltage drop across that section is multiplied by the current through that section.

CAPACITANCE

There is another important concept for our understanding of electricity; the concept of an **electrostatic field**. Earlier, we learned about positive and negative charges. We saw that like charges repel each other, while unlike charges attract each other. This action of like and unlike charges leads to the assumption that each charged body has an electrostatic field around it consisting of invisible lines of force, figure 1-22. According to the laws affecting charged bodies, the closer they are to each other, the stronger the force becomes between them. As the bodies move farther apart, the force weakens. An electrostatic field results

■ Kirchhoff's Laws

Another 19th-century German physicist, named Gustav Robert Kirchhoff, discovered two laws about the actions of current and voltage. Knowing these laws can help your understanding of electrical circuits. Kirchhoff's *voltage law* says:

> The sum of the voltage drops across all the devices in a series circuit must equal the source voltage.

Remember when you test a circuit that all of the voltage delivered to the circuit by the battery or alternator must be used up in doing work in the circuit. If you have a 12-volt battery connected to one lamp bulb, the voltage drop across the bulb must be the entire 12 volts. If the battery is connected to two or more bulbs, the drops across all the bulbs and the wires and connectors, must add up to 12 volts. No voltage can be left over at the end of the circuit.

Kirchhoff's *current* law deals with current at any point in a circuit. It says:

> The sum of the currents flowing into any point in a circuit equals the sum of the currents flowing out of that point.

This is seen easiest in a parallel circuit. It simply means that the sum of the currents flowing in the branches of a circuit must equal the total current flowing to and from the source. Kirchhoff's current law is a statement of the conservation of matter. Electrical current is electron flow, and electrons are matter. You cannot create or destroy electrons in a circuit. Remember when testing a parallel circuit, all the amperage in the branch circuits must add up to the amperage leaving and returning to the source.

Series-Parallel Circuit: A circuit that has some parts in series with the voltage source and some parts in parallel with each other and with the voltage source.

Watt: The unit of measurement for electric power. One way to measure the rate of doing work. Watts equals volts times amperes.

Electrostatic Field: The area around an electrically charged body resulting from the difference in voltage between two points or surfaces.

Figure 1-22. An electrostatic field exists between two charged bodies.

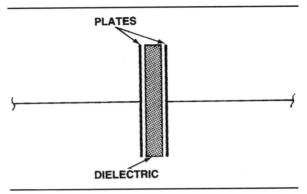

Figure 1-23. A simple capacitor.

from a difference in potential, or voltage, between two points or surfaces.

Capacitance is the ability of two conducting surfaces (charged bodies), separated by some kind of insulator, to store an electric charge (voltage). A capacitor, then, is a device that stores electricity when it is installed in a circuit.

Capacitor Construction and Operation

A capacitor consists of two conductive plates with an insulating material between them, figure 1-23. The insulating material is commonly called a **dielectric**. It may be air, mica, ceramic, glass, paper, plastic, or any similar nonconductive material. When a capacitor is placed in a closed circuit, the voltage source (battery) forces electrons around the circuit, figure 1-24. Because electrons cannot flow through the dielectric of the capacitor, excess electrons collect on what becomes the negatively charged plate. At the same time the other plate loses electrons and becomes, therefore, positively charged.

Current continues until the voltage charge across the capacitor plates becomes the same as the source voltage. At that time, the negative plate of the capacitor and the negative terminal of the battery are at the same negative potential. The positive plate of the capacitor and the positive terminal of the battery are also at equal positive potentials. There is then a voltage charge across the battery terminals and an equal voltage charge across the capacitor plates, figure 1-25. The circuit is in balance, and there is no current. An electrostatic field now exists between the capacitor plates because of their opposite charges. It is this field that stores energy.

At this point, the circuit can be opened, and the capacitor holds its charge until it is connected into an external circuit through which it can discharge, figure 1-26. When the charged capacitor is connected to an external circuit, it discharges. After discharging, both plates of the capacitor are neutral. It is important to

Figure 1-24. As the capacitor is charging, the battery forces electrons through the circuit.

remember that a capacitor does not change any energy or consume any power, as a circuit load does. All the energy from a circuit stored in a capacitor is returned when it is discharged.

Theoretically, a capacitor holds its charge indefinitely. Actually, the charge slowly leaks off the capacitor through the dielectric. The better the dielectric, the longer the capacitor holds its charge. To avoid an electrical shock, any capacitor should be treated as if it were charged until it is proven to be discharged.

Capacitors are also called **condensers**. This term developed because electric charges collect, or condense, on the plates of a capacitor much like water vapor collects and condenses on a cold bottle or glass.

Capacitor Ratings

Capacitors are rated in units called **farads**. The abbreviation for farad is F. In reality, one farad is a very large charge, and a capacitor rated at one farad might be the size of a railroad boxcar. Capacitors used in automotive electrical systems are rated in microfarads, or one-millionth (0.000001) of a farad, abbreviated µF.

Just as resistors are rated in terms of their resistance (ohms) and their power-handling capabilities (watts), capacitors are rated in terms of their

Figure 1-25. When the capacitor is charged, there is equal voltage across the capacitor and the battery. An electrostatic field exists between the capacitor plates. No current flows in the circuit.

Figure 1-26. The capacitor is charged through one circuit (top) and discharged through another (bottom).

maximum safe working voltage, as well as their capacitance.

We learned earlier that resistance is a physical property of a resistor. A single resistor will have the same ohm rating in any circuit in which it is used. Similarly, capacitance is a physical property of a capacitor, and this value does not change in any circuit. We also learned that there are physical factors that affect the resistance of a resistor. There are similar factors that affect the capacitance of a capacitor.

Factors of Capacitance

Capacitance is governed by three factors:

- The surface area of the plates
- The distance between the plates
- The dielectric material.

The larger the surface area of the plates, the greater the capacitance. This is because more electrons collect on a large plate area than on a small one.

The closer the plates are to each other, the greater the capacitance. This is because a stronger electrostatic field exists between charged bodies that are close together.

■ Watts = Metric Horsepower

When it comes to automobiles, the unit traditionally used to measure the rate of doing work has been the horsepower. It does not relate to the work done by a single horse, but it has become a standardized unit of measure.

While "horsepower" is still commonly used, there is another way to describe the rate of doing work, and that is the "watt". Since it is part of the metric system, the watt is beginning to come into use as the system is gradually adopted.

One horsepower contains (equals) 746 watts. A Chevrolet 4.1-liter (250-cid) engine, for example, would be rated at 110 kW at 3,800 rpm. That equals 147 horsepower. The abbreviation "kW" stands for kilowatt (1,000 watts). The prefix "kilo" (k) is used in the metric system to mean 1,000.

Capacitance: The ability of two conducting surfaces, separated by an insulator, to store an electric charge.

Dielectric: The insulating material between the two conductive plates of a capacitor.

Condenser: A capacitor. Usually refers to an automotive capacitor constructed of two pieces of tinfoil, separated by an insulator, within a metal can.

Farad: The unit of measurement of capacitance.

The insulating qualities of the dielectric material also affect capacitance. The capacitance of a capacitor is higher if the dielectric is a very good insulator.

Types of Capacitors

Capacitors are designed with either fixed or variable capacitance. The common symbols for fixed and variable capacitors are shown in figure 1-27. The capacitance of a variable capacitor is usually changed by altering the plate area or the distance between the plates.

Some fixed capacitors used in radio and electronic circuits are small ceramic units with short wire leads that are soldered into a circuit. The most common fixed capacitor found in automotive electrical systems in the days of ignition points was the cylindrical type, figure 1-28. The plates were two layers of metal foil, with a dielectric between them, rolled into a cylinder. Contacts were attached to the plates, and the capacitor sealed in a metal shell. A wire lead was attached to the contact for one plate for connection to the insulated side of the circuit. The contact for the other plate was attached to the capacitor shell and connected to the ground side of the circuit through a mounting clamp.

Capacitor Uses

Because a capacitor stores a voltage charge, it opposes, or slows down, any voltage change in a circuit. Therefore, capacitors are often used as voltage "shock absorbers". You sometimes find a capacitor attached to one terminal of an ignition coil. In this application, it absorbs and damps changes in ignition voltage that interfere with radio reception.

Probably the most familiar capacitor in an automobile is the ignition condenser in breaker-point ignition systems. The condenser is installed in parallel with the ignition breaker points. The points are a rotating switch that opens and closes the circuit to the ignition coil. When the points open, self-induced voltage in the coil tries to maintain current across the opening points. This would cause an arc across the points and burn them up very quickly. However, the condenser, in

Figure 1-27. You will see these capacitor symbols on electrical diagrams. The negative plate is often shown curved.

Figure 1-28. Cylindrical capacitors are the most common fixed capacitors for automotive use.

parallel with the points, provides an easier path for current to follow and reduces or eliminates point arcing.

The self-induced voltage from the coil charges the condenser instead of arcing across the points. As the condenser is charged, coil primary voltage drops. The condenser then discharges back into the coil. This current from the condenser to the coil aids the buildup of the coil magnetic field as the points close and primary current resumes.

SUMMARY

Materials used in electrical systems are conductors, insulators, or semiconductors. Conductors have three or fewer free electrons in the outer shell of their atoms. Electric current is the controlled, directed flow of electrons from atom to atom in a conductor. Insulators have five or more bound electrons in their outer shells. Current does not flow easily in an insulator. Semiconductors have four electrons in their outer shells. Current travels through a semiconductor under certain conditions.

There are two theories of electric current flow. The conventional current flow theory says that current travels from positive to negative. The electron current flow theory says that current travels from negative to positive. Either theory can be used to describe current in a circuit.

A circuit is a complete path from an electrical energy source, through wires and electrical loads, and back to the source. A complete circuit is necessary for current. Current is measured in amperes and travels *through* a circuit. Voltage is *applied to,* or *impressed on* a circuit. Resistance, measured in ohms, opposes current and is *contained within* the circuit.

There are three kinds of electrical circuits: series, parallel, and series-parallel. In a series circuit, there is only one current path. In a parallel circuit, there are two or more current paths. A series-parallel circuit has several current paths in parallel with each other, but in series with other parts of the circuit.

Ohm's Law is the foundation of electrical circuit troubleshooting. It says, "When one volt forces one ampere of current through a circuit, one ohm of resistance is present." Mathematically, Ohm's Law says:

$$\text{Voltage (E)} = \text{Current (I)} \times \text{Resistance (R)}$$
$$\text{Current (I)} = \text{Voltage (E)} \div \text{Resistance (R)}$$
$$\text{Resistance (R)} = \text{Voltage (E)} \div \text{Current (I)}$$

Capacitance is the ability of two conducting surfaces (charged bodies), separated by an insulator, to store an electric charge. A capacitor is a device that stores electricity when it is installed in a circuit. An electrostatic field is formed by the difference in potential between the two charged plates of the capacitor. Because a capacitor stores a voltage charge, it opposes, or slows down, any voltage change in a circuit. Therefore, they are often used as voltage "shock absorbers".

■ Capacitance Is All Around Us

The ignition condenser is probably the most familiar capacitor in an automobile, but the largest is the battery. A 12-volt automotive battery is also a 12-volt capacitor. Because a difference in potential exists between the positive and negative plates of a battery, they act as a capacitor. This is one reason why a battery stores a voltage charge.

High-tension electric power lines can also act as a capacitor. The power lines carry very high voltages and act like the plates of a capacitor. The air space between the lines acts as a dielectric. During a rainstorm, when water vapor reduces the insulating qualities of the air space, you often see a blue halo around power lines. This is the "corona effect" of the electrostatic field between the lines.

A similar halo is sometimes seen around the spark plug cables of an automobile. Spark plug cables carry high ignition voltages and can also act like the plates of a capacitor, particularly when they lie parallel and close to each other. The glow often seen around the cables is another example of an electrostatic field.

Review Questions

1. The general name given every substance in the physical universe is:
   a. Mass
   b. Matter
   c. Compound
   d. Nucleus

2. The smallest part of an element that retains all of its characteristics is:
   a. An atom
   b. A proton
   c. A compound
   d. A neutron

3. The particles that orbit around the center of an atom are:
   a. Electrons
   b. Molecules
   c. Nucleus
   d. Protons

4. An atom which loses or gains one electron is called:
   a. Balanced
   b. An element
   c. A molecule
   d. A charged particle or ion

5. A material with many free electrons is a good:
   a. Compound
   b. Conductor
   c. Insulator
   d. Semiconductor

6. A material with four electrons in the valence ring is a:
   a. Compound
   b. Insulator
   c. Semiconductor
   d. Conductor

7. The conventional theory of current flow says that current flows:
   a. Randomly
   b. Positive to negative
   c. Negative to positive
   d. None of the above

8. An ampere is a measure of:
   a. Charge
   b. Resistance
   c. Current flow
   d. Difference in potential

9. Voltage is:
   a. Applied to a circuit
   b. Flowing in a circuit
   c. Built into a circuit
   d. Flowing out of a circuit

10. The unit that represents resistance to current flow is:
    a. Ampere
    b. Volt
    c. Ohm
    d. Watt

11. In automotive systems, voltage is supplied by the:
    a. Alternator
    b. Battery
    c. Generator
    d. All of the above

12. Which of the following does NOT affect resistance?
    a. Diameter of the conductor
    b. Temperature of the conductor
    c. Atomic structure of the conductor
    d. Direction of current flow in the conductor

13. The resistance in a longer piece of wire is:
    a. Higher
    b. Lower
    c. Unchanged
    d. Higher, then lower

14. According to Ohm's Law, when one volt pushes one ampere of current through a conductor, the resistance is:
    a. Zero
    b. One ohm
    c. One watt
    d. One coulomb

15. What circuit does this figure illustrate?
    a. Series
    b. Parallel
    c. Series-parallel
    d. Broken

16. Which of the following is an example of a series circuit that might be used in an automobile?
    a. Headlamp
    b. Horn
    c. Taillamp
    d. Stereo

17. The amperage in a series circuit is:
    a. Always the same anywhere
    b. Always the same at certain points
    c. Sometimes the same, under some conditions
    d. Never the same anywhere

18. The sum of the voltage drops in a series circuit equals:

    a. The amperage
    b. The resistance
    c. The source voltage
    d. The shunt circuit voltage

19. The total resistance is equal to the *sum* of all the resistance in:
    a. Series circuits
    b. Parallel circuits
    c. Series-parallel circuits
    d. Series and parallel circuits

20. Where E = volts, I = amperes, and R = resistance, Ohm's Law is written:
    a. $I = E \times R$
    b. $E = I \times R$
    c. $R = E \times I$
    d. $E = I_2 \times R$

21. Where current can follow more than one path to complete the circuit, the circuit is called:
    a. Branch
    b. Series
    c. Complete
    d. Parallel

22. If resistance in a parallel circuit is unknown, dividing the voltage by the branch _____ equals branch resistance.
    a. Amperage
    b. Conductance
    c. Voltage drops
    d. Wattage

23. In a closed circuit with a capacitor, current will continue to flow until the voltage charge across the capacitor plates:
    a. Becomes less than the source voltage
    b. Becomes equal to the source voltage
    c. Becomes greater than the source voltage
    d. Becomes equal to the resistance of the plates

24. Capacitors are also called:
    a. Diodes
    b. Resistors
    c. Condensers
    d. Dielectrics

25. Capacitors are rated in:
    a. Microcoulombs
    b. Megawatts
    c. Microfarads
    d. Milliohms

2

Magnetism, Electro-magnetism, and EMI Suppression

SOURCES OF ELECTRICITY

So far, in discussing voltage sources, we have used automobile batteries and alternators as examples. We have not gone into detail on how voltage and current are created. There are several sources of electrical energy, but only a few of them are used in automotive electrical systems.

Friction

When certain different materials are rubbed together, the friction causes electrons to be transferred from one to the other. Both materials become electrically charged. These charges are not in motion, but stay on the surface where they were deposited. Because the charges are stationary, or static, this type of voltage is called **static electricity.** Vehicle tires rolling on pavement often create static electricity that interferes with radio reception. This is one form of electromagnetic interference, or EMI, as we will see later in this chapter.

Heat

When pieces of two metals are joined together at both ends and one junction is heated, current passes through the metals. The current is very small, only millionths of an ampere, but this is enough to use in a temperature-measuring device called a thermocouple. Some engine temperature sensors operate in this manner. This form of voltage is called **thermoelectricity.**

Light

When certain metals are exposed to light, some of the light energy is transferred to the free electrons of the metal. This excess energy breaks the electrons loose from the surface of the metal. They can be collected and made to flow in a conductor. This **photoelectricity** is widely used in light-measuring devices such as photographic exposure meters and automatic head-lamp dimmers.

Pressure

When subjected to pressure, certain crystals, such as quartz, develop a potential difference, or voltage, on the crystal faces. This current is used in phonograph pick-ups, crystal microphones, underwater hydrophones, and certain stethoscopes. The voltage created is called **piezoelectricity.** Many automobile engine control sensors use piezoelectricity to create voltage or to vary resistance and control a computer input signal.

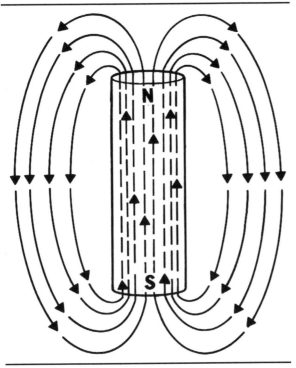

Figure 2-1. Magnetic lines of force surrounding a bar magnet.

Chemistry

Two different materials (usually metals) placed in a conducting and reactive chemical solution create a difference in potential, or voltage, between them. This principle is called **electrochemistry** and is the basis of the automotive battery. We will study this in depth in Chapter Seven.

Magnetism

The lines of force which surround magnetic materials induce current in a conductor. This chapter explains magnetism and electromagnetism in detail, because they are vital parts of the automotive electrical system.

FUNDAMENTALS OF MAGNETISM

Magnetism is a form of energy that is caused by the motion of electrons in some materials. It is recognized by the attraction it exerts on other materials. Like electricity, magnetism cannot be seen. It can be explained in theory, because it is possilble to see the results of magnetism and recognize the actions that it causes.

Iron ore exists as a magnet in nature. Many other materials can be artificially magnetized to some degree, depending upon their atomic structure. Soft

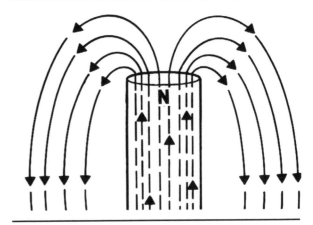

Figure 2-2. Flux density equals the number of lines of force per unit of area.

iron is very easy to magnetize, while some materials—such as aluminum, glass, wood, and plastic—cannot be magnetized at all.

Lines of Force

The lines that create a field of force around a magnet are believed to be caused by the way groups of atoms are aligned in the magnetic material. In a bar magnet, the lines are concentrated at both ends of the bar and form closed, parallel loops in three dimensions around the magnet, figure 2-1. Force does not flow along these lines the way electrical current flows, but the lines *do* have direction. They come out of one end, or **pole,** of the magnet and enter at the other end.

The stronger a magnet, the more lines of force are formed. The magnetic lines of force form a **magnetic field.** These lines of force are also called **magnetic flux,** or **flux lines.** The terms "magnetic field", "lines of force", "flux", and "flux lines" are used interchangeably. In this chapter, "flux lines" is used.

Flux density refers to the number of flux lines per unit of area. To determine flux density, divide the number of flux lines by the area in which the flux exists. For example, 100 flux lines divided by an area of 10 square centimeters equals a flux density of 10, figure 2-2.

Polarity

The poles of a magnet are called north (N) and south (S) because, when a magnet is suspended freely, the poles tend to point toward the north and south magnetic poles of the earth, figure 2-3. The discovery of this property in natural magnets led to the development of the compass.

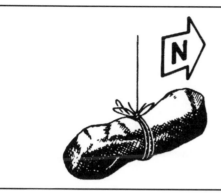

Figure 2-3. A freely suspended natural magnet.

Figure 2-4. Magnetic poles behave like electrically charged particles.

Magnetic flux lines exit from the north pole and bend around to enter the south pole. An equal number of lines exit and enter, so magnetic force is equal at both poles of a magnet. Flux lines are concentrated at the poles, and therefore magnetic force (flux density) is stronger at the ends.

Magnetic poles behave like positively and negatively charged particles. When unlike poles are placed close together, the lines exit from one magnet and enter the other. The two magnets are pulled together by the flux lines. If like poles are placed close together, the curving flux lines meet head-on, forcing the magnets apart. The like poles of a magnet repel and the unlike poles attract, figure 2-4.

Permeability

Magnetic flux lines cannot be insulated. There is no known material through which magnetic force does not pass, if the force is strong enough. However, some materials allow the force to pass through more easily than others. This ease of passage is called **permeability**. Iron allows magnetic flux lines to pass through much more easily than air, so iron is very permeable.

Reluctance

While there is no absolute insulation for magnetism, certain materials resist the passage of magnetic force. This can be compared to resistance within an electrical circuit. Air does not allow easy passage, so air has a high **reluctance**. Magnetic flux lines tend to concentrate in permeable materials and avoid reluctant materials. As with electricity, magnetic force follows the path of least resistance.

Electromagnetism

Scientists did not discover that current-carrying conductors also are surrounded by a magnetic field until 1820. These fields may be made many times stronger

Static Electricity: Voltage resulting from the transfer of electrons from the surface of one material to the surface of another material. The electrons are "static", meaning at rest.

Thermoelectricity: Voltage resulting from an unequal transfer of electrons from one metal to another, when one of the metals is heated.

Photoelectricity: Voltage caused by the energy of light as it strikes certain materials.

Piezoelectricity: Voltage caused by physical pressure applied to the faces of certain crystals.

Electrochemistry: Voltage caused by the chemical action of two dissimilar materials in the presence of a conductive chemical solution.

Magnetism: A form of energy caused by the alignment of atoms within certain materials. The ability of a metal to attract iron.

Pole: The areas of a magnetized body where the lines of magnetic force are concentrated. One end of a magnet.

Magnetic Field: The area surrounding a magnet that is influenced by the magnet's energy.

Magnetic Flux: The invisible directional lines of force which make up a magnetic field.

Flux Lines: Another term for magnetic flux.

Flux Density: The number of flux lines in a magnetic field area. The more flux lines in a unit of area, the stronger the magnetic field at that point.

Permeability: A measure of the ease with which materials are penetrated by magnetic flux lines. Iron is more permeable than air.

Reluctance: The tendency of some materials to resist penetration by magnetic flux lines.

Figure 2-5. A magnetic field surrounds a straight current-carrying conductor.

Figure 2-6. The left-hand rule for field direction, used with the electron-flow theory.

than those surrounding conventional magnets. Also, the magnetic field strength around a conductor may be controlled by changing the current. As current increases, more flux lines are created and the magnetic field expands. As current decreases, the magnetic field contracts, or collapses. These discoveries greatly broadened the practical uses of magnetism and opened an area of study known as **electromagnetics.**

Straight Conductor

The magnetic field surrounding a straight, current-carrying conductor consists of several concentric cylinders of flux the length of the wire, figure 2-5. The strength of the current determines how many flux lines (cylinders) there will be and how far out they extend from the surface of the wire.

Left- and right-hand rules

Magnetic flux cylinders have direction, just as the flux lines surrounding a bar magnet have direction. The **left-hand rule** is a simple way to determine this direction. When you grasp a conductor with your left hand so that your thumb points in the direction of electron flow (- to +) through the conductor, your fingers curl

Figure 2-7. The right-hand rule for field direction, used with the conventional theory of electron flow.

Figure 2-8. Current direction symbols.

around the wire in the direction of the magnetic flux lines, figure 2-6.

It is important to note at this point that if using the conventional theory of current (+ to -), the **right-hand rule** is used to determine the direction of the magnetic flux lines, figure 2-7. For the rest of this chapter, the electron-flow theory, that is negative to positive, and the left-hand rule are used.

Field Interaction

The cylinders of flux surrounding current-carrying conductors interact with other magnetic fields. In the following illustrations, the cross symbol (+) indicates current moving inward, or away from you. It represents the tail of an arrow. The dot symbol (•) represents an arrowhead and indicates current moving outward, or toward you, figure 2-8. If two conductors carry current in opposite directions, their magnetic fields are also in opposite directions (according to the left-hand rule). If they are placed side by side, figure 2-9, the opposing flux lines between the conductors create a strong magnetic field. Current-carrying conductor tend to move out of a strong field into a weak field, so the conductors move away from each other, figure 2-10.

If the two conductors carry current in the same direction, their fields are in the same direction. As seen figure 2-11, the flux lines between the two conductors cancel each other out, leaving a very weak field. The

Figure 2-9. Conductors with opposing magnetic fields.

Figure 2-10. Conductors will move apart into weaker fields.

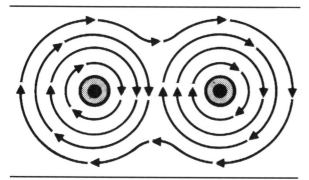

Figure 2-11. Conductors with the same magnetic field direction.

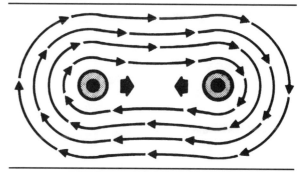

Figure 2-12. Conductors will move together into the weak field.

Figure 2-13. Electric motors use field interaction to produce mechanical energy.

conductors are drawn into this weak field; that is, they move closer together, figure 2-12.

Motor principle

Electric motors, such as automobile starter motors, use this field interaction to change electrical energy into mechanical energy, figure 2-13. If two conductors carrying current in opposite directions are placed between strong north and south poles, the magnetic field of the conductor interacts with the magnetic fields of the poles. The clockwise field of the top conductor adds to the fields of the poles and creates a strong field beneath the conductor. The conductor tries to move up to get out of this strong field. The counterclockwise field of the lower conductor adds to the field of the poles and creates a strong field above the conductor. The conductor tries to move down to get out of this strong field. These forces cause the

Electromagnetics: The study of the relationship of magnetic energy to electrical energy.

Left-Hand Rule: A method of determining the direction of the magnetic flux lines surrounding a current-carrying conductor, when the electron theory of current flow (- to +) is used. If the conductor is grasped with the left hand so the thumb points in the direction of current flow, the fingers point in the direction of magnetic flux.

Right-Hand Rule: A method of determining the direction of magnetic flux lines surrounding a current-carrying conductor, when the conventional theory of current flow (+ to -) is used. If the conductor is grasped with the right hand so the thumb points in the direction of conventional current flow, the fingers point in the direction of magnetic flux.

DIRECTION OF CURRENT FLOW

Figure 2-14. The magnetic field surrounding a looped conductor. (Delco-Remy)

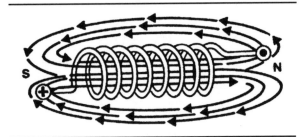

Figure 2-15. The flux lines surrounding a coil look much like those surrounding a bar magnet.

center of the motor, where the conductors are mounted, to turn clockwise.

Loop Conductor

The field around a straight conductor can be strengthened by bending the wire into a loop. This is because, as the wire is bent, the fields which meet in the center of the loop combine their strengths, figure 2-14. The left-hand rule also applies to loop conductors.

Coil Conductor

If several loops of wire are made into a coil, the magnetic flux density is further strengthened. Flux lines around a coil are the same as the flux lines around a bar magnet, figure 2-15. They exit from the north pole and enter at the south pole. Use the left-hand rule to determine the north pole of a coil. If you grasp a coil with your left hand so that your fingers point in the direction of electron flow, your thumb points toward the north pole of the coil, figure 2-16. The magnetic field of a coil can be strengthened by increasing the

Figure 2-16. The left-hand rule for a coil.

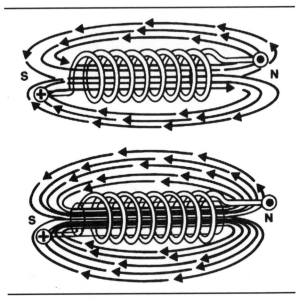

Figure 2-17. An iron core concentrates the magnetic flux lines surrounding a coil.

number of turns in the wire, by increasing the current through the coil, or both.

Electromagnets

There is a third way to strengthen the magnetic field surrounding a current-carrying conductor. Because soft iron is very permeable, magnetic flux lines pass through it easily. If a piece of soft iron is placed inside a coiled conductor, the flux lines concentrate in the iron core, figure 2-17, rather than pass through the air, which is less permeable. This concentration of force greatly increases the strength of the magnetic field inside the coil. Coils with an iron core are called **electromagnets.**

Relays

One common automotive use of electromagnets is in a device called a **relay**. A relay is a control device

Figure 2-18. An electromagnetic relay.

which allows a small amount of current to trigger a large amount of current in another circuit. A simple relay, figure 2-18, contains an electromagnetic coil in series with a battery and a switch. Near the electromagnet is a movable flat blade, or **armature** of some material which is attracted by a magnetic field. The armature pivots at one end and is held a small distance away from the electromagnet by a spring (or by the spring steel of the armature itself). A contact point, made of a good conductor, is attached to the free end of the armature. Another contact point is fixed a small distance away. The two contact points are wired in series with an electrical load and the battery.

When the switch is closed:

1. Current travels from the battery through the electromagnet.
2. The magnetic field created by the current attracts the armature, bending it down until the contact points meet.
3. Closing the contacts allows current in the second circuit from the battery to the load.

When the switch is open:

1. The electromagnet looses its current and its magnetic field.
2. Spring pressure brings the armature back.
3. The second circuit is broken by the opening of the contact points.

Relays may also be designed with normally closed contacts that open when current passes through the electromagnet.

ELECTROMAGNETIC INDUCTION

Only a decade after the discovery of magnetic fields surrounding current-carrying conductors, more discoveries were made about the relationship between electricity and magnetism. The modern automotive electrical system is based in great part upon the principles of **electromagnetic induction**, discovered in the 1830s.

Magnetic flux lines create an electromotive force, or voltage, in a conductor if either the flux lines or the conductor is moving. This movement is called **relative motion**. This process is called induction, and the resulting electromotive force is called **induced voltage**. If the conductor is in a complete circuit, current exists.

Voltage is induced when magnetic flux lines are broken by a conductor. This relative motion can be a conductor moving across a magnetic field (as in a dc generator), or a magnetic field moving across a stationary conductor (as in ac generators and ignition coils), figure 2-19. In both cases, the induced voltage is caused by relative motion between the conductor and the magnetic flux lines.

Voltage Strength

Induced voltage depends upon magnetic flux lines being broken by a conductor. The strength of the

Electromagnet: A soft iron core wrapped in a coil of a current-carrying conductor.

Relay: An electromagnetic switch. A relay uses a small amount of current flow to control the flow of a larger amount of current through a separate circuit.

Armature: The movable part in a relay. The revolving part in a generator or motor.

Electromagnetic Induction: The creation of a voltage within a conductor when relative motion exists between the conductor and a magnetic field.

Relative Motion: Movement of a conductor in relation to magnetic flux lines or movement of magnetic flux lines in relation to a conductor.

Induced Voltage: The voltage which appears in a conductor when relative motion exists between it and magnetic flux lines.

Figure 2-19. Voltage can be induced by the relative motion between a conductor and magnetic flux lines.

Figure 2-20. No voltage is induced if no flux lines are broken.

Figure 2-21. Maximum voltage is induced when the flux lines are broken at a 90-degree angle.

voltage depends upon the rate at which the flux lines are broken. The more flux lines broken per unit of time, the greater the induced voltage. If a single conductor breaks one million flux lines per second, one volt is induced.

There are four ways to increase induced voltage:

• Increase the strength of the magnetic field, so there are more flux lines.
• Increase the number of conductors which are breaking the flux lines.
• Increase the speed of the relative motion between the conductor and the flux lines so that more lines are broken per time unit.
• Increase the angle between the flux lines and the conductor to a maximum of 90 degrees. There is no voltage induced if the conductors move parallel to, and do not break any, flux lines, figure 2-20. Maximum voltage is induced if the conductors break flux lines at 90 degrees, figure 2-21. Induced voltage varies proportionately at angles between 0 and 90 degrees.

We know voltage can be electromagnetically induced, and we can measure it and predict its behavior. Induced voltage creates current. The direction of induced voltage (and the direction in which current moves) is called **polarity** and depends upon the direction of the flux lines and the direction of relative motion.

An induced current moves so that its magnetic field opposes the motion which induced the current. This principle, called Lenz's Law, is based upon Newton's observation that every action has an equal and opposite reaction. The relative motion of a conductor and a magnetic field is opposed by the magnetic field of the current it has induced. This is why induced current

can move in either direction, and it is an important factor in the design and operation of voltage sources such as alternators.

Generator Principles

As explained earlier, voltage may be induced by the motion of a conductor across a stationary magnetic field. This is the principle used to change mechanical energy to electrical energy in a generator. A looped conductor is mechanically moved within the magnetic field created by stationary magnets, figure 2-22. In figure 2-22A, the voltage is zero because the conductor motion is parallel to the flux lines. As the conductor moves from A to B, the voltage increases because it is cutting across the flux lines. At B, the voltage is at a maximum because the conductor is moving at right angles to the flux lines, breaking the maximum number.

From position B to C, the voltage decreases to zero again because fewer lines are broken. At C, the conductor is again parallel to the flux lines. As the conductor rotates from C to D, voltage increases. However, the induced voltage is in the opposite direction because the conductor is cutting the flux lines in the opposite direction. From position D to E, the cycle begins to repeat.

Figure 2-22 shows how voltage is induced in a loop conductor through one complete revolution in a magnetic field. The induced voltage is called **alternating current** (ac) voltage because it reverses direction every half cycle, as shown on the graph at the bottom of the figure.

Because automotive battery voltage is always in one direction, the current it produces always flows in one direction. This is called **direct current** (dc). Alternating current cannot be used to charge the battery, so the ac must be changed, or **rectified** to dc This is done in a generator by the **commutator**. In a simple, single-loop generator, the commutator would be a split ring of conductive material connected to the ends of the conductor. Brushes of conductive material ride on the surface of the two commutator segments. Induced

■ Benjamin Franklin's Theory

When the science of electricity was still young, the men who studied it were able to use electricity without really understanding why and how it worked. In the early 1700s, Benjamin Franklin, the American printer, inventor, writer, and politician brought his famed common sense to the problem.

Although he was not the first to think that electricity and lightning were the same, he was the first to prove it. He also thought that electricity was like a fluid in a pipe that flowed from one terminal to the other. He named the electrical terminals *positive* and *negative* and suggested that current moved from the positive terminal to the negative terminal.

It was Benjamin Franklin who created what we now call the *Conventional Theory of Current Flow.*

Polarity: Having poles, such as the north and south poles of a magnet. The poles of a battery or an electrical circuit are its positive and negative terminals.

Alternating Current: A flow of electricity through a conductor, first in one direction and then in the opposite direction.

Direct Current: A flow of electricity in one direction through a conductor.

Rectify: To change alternating current to direct current.

Commutator: A segmented ring attached to one end of an armature in a dc generator or a motor, providing an electrical connection between the armature and the brushes. In a generator, it rectifies the alternating current. In a motor, it provides a direct current path to the armature.

Figure 2-22. Alternating current voltage generated in a rotating loop conductor.

Figure 2-23. The commutator and brushes conduct pulsating direct current from the looped conductor.

Figure 2-24. A simplified alternator.

current travels from the conductor through the commutator and out through the brushes, figure 2-23A. At the instant the looped conductor is turned so that the induced current changes direction, figure 2-23B, the commutator also rotates under the brushes so that the brushes now contact the opposite commutator segments. Current now flows out of the other

half of the commutator, but the same brush is there to receive it. This design is called a brush-rectified, or commutator-rectified, generator, and the output is called pulsating direct current.

Simple pulsating dc from one generator winding and a pair of commutator segments would not work well to run electrical devices and recharge a battery. Actual dc generators have many armature windings and commutator segments. The dc voltages overlap to create an almost continuous dc output.

Alternator Principles

Since 1960, virtually all automobiles have used an ac. generator, or alternator, in which voltage is generated by the movement of magnetic lines through a stationary conductor, figure 2-24. A magnet called a rotor is turned inside a stationary looped conductor called a stator, figure 2-24. The induced current, like that of a dc generator, is constantly changing its direction. The rotation of the magnetic field causes the stator to be cut by flux lines, first in one direction and then the other. The ac must be rectified to match the battery dc This is done with diodes, small electronic devices which conduct current in only one direction. This design is called a diode-rectified alternator. We will study diodes in Chapter Three and alternators in Chapter Eight.

Self-Induction

Up to this point, our examples have depended upon mechanical energy to physically move either the conductor or the magnetic field. Another form of relative motion occurs when a magnetic field is forming or collapsing. When current begins to flow in a coil, the flux lines expand as the magnetic field forms and strengthens. As current increases, the flux lines continue to expand, cutting through the wires of the coil and actually inducing another voltage within the same coil. Following Lenz's Law, this **self-induced voltage** tends to *oppose* the current that produces it. If the current

Figure 2-25. Mutual induction.

continues to increase, the second voltage opposes the increase. When the current stabilizes, the countervoltage is no longer induced because there are no more expanding flux lines (no relative motion). When current to the coil is shut off, the collapsing magnetic flux lines self-induce a voltage in the coil that tries to maintain the original current. The self-induced voltage *opposes* and *slows down* the *decrease* in the original current. The self-induced voltage that opposes the source voltage is called **counterelectromotive force (cemf)**.

Mutual Induction

When two coils are close together, energy may be transferred from one to the other by magnetic coupling called mutual induction. **Mutual induction** means that the expansion or collapse of the magnetic field around one coil induces a voltage in the second coil.

Usually, the two coils are wound on the same iron core. One coil winding is connected to a battery through a switch and is called the **primary winding**. The other coil winding is connected to an external circuit and is called the **secondary winding**.

When the switch is open, figure 2-25A, there is no current in the primary winding. There is no magnetic field and, therefore, no voltage in the secondary winding. When the switch is closed, figure 2-25B, current is introduced and a magnetic field builds up around both windings. The primary winding thus changes electrical

energy from the battery into magnetic energy of the expanding field. As the field expands, it cuts across the secondary winding and induces a voltage in it. A meter connected to the secondary circuit shows current.

When the magnetic field has expanded to its full strength, figure 2-25C, it remains steady as long as the same amount of current exists. The flux lines have stopped their cutting action. There is no relative

Self-Induced Voltage: Voltage created in a conductor by the magnetic lines of a current through that same conductor.

Counterelectromotive Force (CEMF): An induced voltage that opposes the source voltage and any change (increase or decrease) in the charging current.

Mutual Induction: Creation of voltage in one conductor by the rise and collapse of the magnetic field surrounding another conductor.

Primary Windings: The coil winding made of a few turns of a heavy wire, which uses battery current to create a magnetic field.

Secondary Windings: The coil winding made of many turns of a fine wire, in which voltage is induced by the rise and collapse of the magnetic field of the primary winding.

Figure 2-26. Mutual induction in the ignition coil produces voltage to the spark plugs.

Figure 2-27. Sources of electromagnetic interference (EMI) in an automobile.

motion and no voltage in the secondary winding, as shown on the meter.

When the switch is opened, figure 2-25D, primary current stops, and the field collapses. As it does, flux lines cut across the secondary winding, but in the opposite direction. This induces a secondary voltage with current in the opposite direction, as shown on the meter.

Mutual induction is used in ignition coils, figure 2-26. In an ignition coil, low-voltage primary current induces a very high secondary voltage because of the different number of turns in the primary and secondary windings. We will study ignition coils in detail in Chapter 14.

ELECTROMAGNETIC INTERFERENCE (EMI) SUPPRESSION

Until the advent of the onboard computer, **electromagnetic interference (EMI)** was not a source of real concern to automotive engineers. The problem was mainly one of **radiofrequency interference (RFI),** caused primarily by the use of secondary ignition cables containing a low-resistance metal core. These cables produced electrical impulses that interfered with radio and television reception.

The problem was recognized in the 1950s and brought under control by the use of secondary ignition cables containing a high-resistance, nonmetallic core made of carbon, linen, or fiber glass strands impregnated with graphite. In addition, some manufacturers even installed a metal shield inside their distributors to further reduce RFI radiation from the breaker points, condensers, and rotors.

As the use of electronic components and systems increased, the problem of electromagnetic interference reappeared with broader implications. The low-power digital integrated circuits now in use are extremely sensitive to EMI signals that were of little or no concern before the late 1970s.

Interference Generation and Transmission

Whenever there is current in a conductor, an electromagnetic field is created. When current stops and starts, as in a spark plug cable or a switch that opens and closes, field strength changes. Each time this happens, it creates an electromagnetic signal wave. If it happens rapidly enough, the resulting high-frequency signal waves, or EMI, interfere with radio and television transmission or with other electronic systems such as those under the hood. This is an undesirable side effect of the phenomenon of electromagnetism.

Figure 2-28. Conductive-coupling interference is transmitted by wiring from the source of interference to the receiver.

Figure 2-30. Inductive-coupling interference is transmitted by an electromagnetic field between adjacent wiring.

Figure 2-29. Capacitive-coupling interference is transmitted by a capacitive field between adjacent wiring.

Figure 2-31. Radiation interference occurs when EMI waves travel through space and are picked up by wiring that acts as a receiving antenna.

Figure 2-27 shows common sources of EMI on an automobile.

Static electric charges caused by friction of the tires with the road, or the friction of engine drive belts contacting their pulleys, also produces EMI. Drive axles, drive shafts, and clutch or brake lining surfaces are other sources of static electric charges.

There are four ways of transmitting EMI, all of which can be found in an automobile:

- Conductive coupling through circuit conductors, figure 2-28.
- Capacitive coupling through an electrostatic field between two conductors, figure 2-29.
- Inductive coupling as the magnetic fields between two conductors form and collapse, figure 2-30.
- Electromagnetic radiation, figure 2-31.

EMI Suppression Devices

Just as there are four methods of EMI transmission, there are four general ways in which EMI is reduced:

- By the addition of resistance to conductors that suppresses conductive transmission and radiation

- By the use of capacitors and **radio choke coil** combinations to reduce capacitive and inductive coupling
- By the use of metal or metalized plastic shielding, which reduces EMI radiation in addition to capacitive and inductive coupling
- By an increased use of ground straps to reduce conductive transmission and radiation by bypassing the unwanted signals to ground.

Electromagnetic Interference (EMI): An undesirable form of electromagnetism created by rapid changes in field strength whenever current stops and starts.

Radiofrequency Interference (RFI): A form of electromagnetic interference created in the ignition secondary circuit which disrupts radio and television transmission.

Radio Choke Coil: A coil wound with fine wire and installed in a circuit to absorb oscillations that occur when the circuit is closed or opened.

Figure 2-32. This capacitor attached to an HEI ignition module protects the module from EMI.

Resistance suppression

Adding resistance to a circuit to suppress RFI works only for high-voltage systems (for example, changing the conductive core of ignition cables). The use of resistance to suppress interference in low-voltage circuits creates too much voltage drop and power loss to be efficient.

The only high-voltage system on most vehicles is the ignition secondary circuit. While this is the greatest single source of EMI, it is also the easiest to control. This has been done in large part by the use of resistance spark plug cables, resistor spark plugs, and the silicone grease used on the distributor cap and rotor of some electronic ignitions.

Suppression capacitors and coils

Capacitors are installed across many circuits and switching points to absorb voltage fluctuations. Among other applications, they are used:

- Across the primary circuit of some electronic ignition modules, figure 2-32
- Across the output terminal of most alternators
- Across the armature circuit of electric motors.

Radio choke coils reduce current fluctuations resulting from self-induction. They are often combined with capacitors to act as EMI filter circuits for windshield wiper and electric fuel pump motors, figure 2-33. Filters may also be incorporated in wiring connectors.

Shielding

Metal shields, such as the ones used in breaker point distributors, block the waves from components that create RFI signals. The circuits of onboard computers are protected to some degree from external electromagnetic waves by their metal housings.

Figure 2-33. Interference-suppression capacitors and choke coils are attached to many electric motors, like this wiper motor. (Bosch)

Ground straps

Ground or bonding straps between the engine and chassis of an automobile help suppress EMI conduction and radiation by providing a low-resistance circuit ground path. Such suppression ground straps are often installed between rubber-mounted components and body parts, figure 2-34. On some models ground straps are installed between body parts, such as the hood and a fender panel where no electrical circuit exists, figure 2-34. In such a case, the strap has no other job than to suppress EMI. Without it, the sheet-metal body and hood could function as a large capacitor. The space between the fender and hood could form an electrostatic field and couple with the computer circuits in the wiring harness routed near the fender panel.

EMI Suppression

Interference suppression is now a critical automotive engineering task. The modern automobile has increased the need for EMI suppression. The increasing use of citizens-band (CB) radios and mobile telephones, as well as onboard computer systems, are only a few of the factors that have made interference suppression extremely important.

Even small amounts of EMI can disrupt the operation of an onboard digital computer, which operates on voltage signals of a few millivolts (thousandths of a volt) and milliamperes (thousandths of an ampere) of current.

Any of the interference transmission modes discussed earlier are capable of creating false voltage

ENGINE TO IGNITION
SUPPRESSION CAPACITOR

HOOD TO
FENDER PANEL

RADIATOR
TO ENGINE

FIREWALL TO
CABLES OR
TUBING

FIREWALL TO
SPEEDOMETER
CABLE

ALTERNATOR
TO REGULATOR

Figure 2-34. Ground straps are installed in many areas of late-model engine compartments to suppress EMI. (Bosch)

signals and excessive current in the computer systems. False voltage signals disrupt computer operation, while excessive current causes permanent damage to microelectronic circuitry.

As the complexity and number of electronic systems continues to increase, manufacturers are using multiplex wiring systems to reduce the size and number of wiring harnesses, which also reduces EMI. Multiplexing is a method of sending more than one electrical signal over the same channel. Multiplex circuits are described in detail in Chapter Five.

SUMMARY

Electricity can be generated in several ways. The most important way for automotive use is by magnetism. Magnetism is a form of energy caused by the alignment of atoms in certain materials. It is the ability of metal to attract iron. Some magnetic materials exist in nature; others can be artificially magnetized.

Lines of force, called flux lines, form a magnetic field around a magnet. Flux lines exit the north pole and enter the south pole of a magnet. Electrical conductors are also surrounded by magnetic flux lines. As

current increases, the magnetic field of a conductor becomes stronger. Voltage can be generated by the interaction of magnetic fields around conductors.

Voltage is generated by the relative movement of a conductor and a magnetic field. This process is called induction. Either the conductor or the magnetic field may be moving. The strength of the induced voltage depends on the strength of the magnetic field, the number of conductors, the speed of the relative motion, and the angle at which the conductors cut the flux lines. Electromagnetic induction is used in generators, alternators, electric motors, and coils.

Electromagnetism can also generate electromagnetic interference (EMI) and radiofrequency interference (RFI). Such interference can disrupt radio and television signals, as well as electronic system signals. Many devices are used to suppress this interference in automotive systems.

■ Squeeze a Rock, Get a Volt

In 1880, the French chemists, Pierre and Marie Curie, discovered the phenomenon of piezoelectricity, which means, "electricity through pressure". They found that when pressure is applied to a crystal of quartz, tourmaline, or Rochelle salt, a voltage is generated between the faces of the crystal. Although the effect is only temporary, while the pressure lasts, it can be maintained by alternating the pressure between compression and tension.

Piezoelectricity is put to practical use in phonograph pickups and crystal microphones, where mechanical vibrations (sound waves) are converted into varying voltage signals. Similar applications are used in underwater hydrophones and piezoelectric stethoscopes.

A reverse piezoelectric effect can be created by applying a high-frequency alternating voltage to a crystal. The crystal then produces mechanical vibrations at the same frequency. The vibrations are called ultrasonic sound waves because their vibrations are beyond our range of hearing. These ultrasonic vibrations are used, among other things, to detect sonar reflections from submarines and to drill holes in diseased teeth.

Review Questions

Choose the single most correct answer.
Compare your answers with the correct answers on Page 468.

1. Current flows through a heated thermocouple because of:
   a. The two-way flow of electrons between dissimilar materials
   b. The blockage of free electrons between the metals
   c. The one-way transfer of free electrons between the metals
   d. Random electron flow

2. Which of the following forms of generating electricity is *not* widely used in an automobile?
   a. Heat
   b. Pressure
   c. Chemistry
   d. Magnetism

3. The lines of force of a magnet are called:
   a. Flux lines
   b. Magnetic polarity
   c. Magnetic lines
   d. Flux density

4. A material through which magnetic force can easily flow has a high:
   a. Reluctance
   b. Permeability
   c. Capacitance
   d. Magnetic attraction

5. The "left-hand rule" says that if you grasp a conductor in your left hand with your thumb pointing in the direction of the electron ([-] to +) flow:
   a. Your fingers will point in the direction of the magnetic flux lines.
   b. Your fingers will point in the opposite direction of the magnetic flux lines.
   c. Your fingers will point at right angles to the magnetic flux lines.
   d. Your fingers will point at a 45° angle to the magnetic flux lines.

6. The "left-hand rule" is useful to determine:
   a. The direction of current flow
   b. The length of the magnetic flux lines
   c. The strength of the magnetic field
   d. Flux density

7. When two parallel conductors carry electrical current in opposite directions, their magnetic fields will:
   a. Force them apart
   b. Pull them together
   c. Cancel each other out
   d. Rotate around the conductors in the same direction

8. The motor principle of changing electrical energy into mechanical energy requires:
   a. Two semiconductors carrying current in opposite directions
   b. Two semiconductors carrying current in the same direction
   c. Two conductors carrying current in opposite directions
   d. Two conductors carrying current in the same direction

9. Which of the following will *not* increase induced voltage?
   a. Increase the strength of the magnetic field
   b. Increase the number of conductors cutting flux lines
   c. Increase the speed of the relative motion between the conductor and the fluX lines
   d. Increase the angle between the flux lines and the conductor beyond 90 degrees

10. The _____ in an automobile dc. generator rectifies ac. to dc.
    a. Armature
    b. Commutator
    c. Field coil
    d. Loop conductor

11. In an ignition coil, low-voltage primary current induces a very high secondary voltage because of:
    a. Different number of wire turns in the two windings.
    b. An equal number of turns in the two windings
    c. The constant current flow through the primary winding
    d. Bigger wire in the secondary winding

12. To reduce EMI, manufacturers have done all of the following *except:*
    a. Use low resistance in electrical systems
    b. Install metal shielding in components
    c. Increase the use of ground straps
    d. Use capacitors and choke coils

3

Semiconductors and Solid-State Electronics

SEMICONDUCTORS

In Chapter One, we examined the atom's valence ring, the outermost electron shell. We learned that elements whose atoms have three or fewer electrons in their valence rings are good conductors because the free electrons in the valence ring readily join with the valence electrons of other, similar atoms. We also learned that elements whose atoms have five or more electrons in their valence rings are good insulators (poor conductors) because the valence electrons do not readily join with those of other atoms.

Elements whose atoms have four electrons in their valence rings are neither good insulators nor good conductors. Their four valence electrons cause special electrical properties which give them the name "semiconductors". Germanium and silicon are two widely used semiconductor elements.

When semiconductor elements are in the form of a crystal, they bond together so that each atom has eight electrons in its valence ring. It has its own four electrons and shares four with surrounding atoms, figure 3-1. In this form it is an excellent insulator, because there are no free electrons to carry current flow.

Other elements can be added to silicon and germanium to change this crystalline structure. This is called **doping** the semiconductor. The ratio of doping elements to silicon or germanium is about 1 to 10,000,000. The doping elements are often called **impurities** because their addition to the silicon or germanium makes the semiconductor materials impure.

N-material

If silicon or germanium is doped with an element such as phosphorus, arsenic, or antimony, each of which has five electrons in its valence ring, there will not be enough space for the ninth electron in any of the shared valence rings. This extra electron is free, figure 3-2. This type of doped material is called negative, or **N-material,** because it already has excess electrons and will repel additional negative charges.

P-material

If silicon or germanium is doped with an element such as boron or indium, each of which has only three electrons in its outer shell, some of the atoms will have only seven electrons in their valence rings. There will be a **hole** in these valence rings, figure 3-3. This type of doped material is called positive or **P-material,** because it will attract a negative charge (an electron).

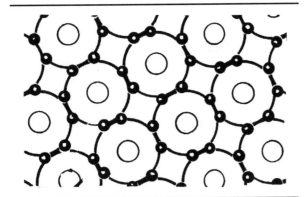

Figure 3-1. Crystalline silicon is an excellent insulator. (Delco-Remy)

EXCESS (FREE) ELECTRON

Figure 3-2. N-material has an extra, or free, electron. (Delco-Remy)

HOLE FLOW

We have explained the electron flow theory of electricity as the movement of electrons from negative to positive. We can also visualize the movement of the holes which these electrons move into and out of. If you imagine a line of cars moving ahead one car length at a time, the car length of empty space can be seen to move from the front to the back of the line, figure 3-4. Just as the car-length of empty space moves in the opposite direction from traffic flow, holes move in the direction opposite from electron flow, or from positive to negative. The hole can be thought of as a positive charge of electricity. Holes can move from atom to atom just as electrons move from atom to atom. The hole flow theory is an easy way to understand the operation of diodes and transistors, as we will see.

VOLTAGE AND SEMICONDUCTORS

Doping silicon or germanium causes it to behave in unusual but predictable ways when voltage is applied to it. The behavior depends upon which charge of the voltage is connected to which type of doped material (P or N). To use this behavior in solid-state devices,

HOLE

Figure 3-3. P-material has a hole in some of its valence rings. (Delco-Remy)

Figure 3-4. Space flow moves opposite to traffic flow just as hole flow moves opposite to electron flow.

P-material and N-material are placed side by side. The line along which they meet is called the **junction.** The application of voltage to the two doped semiconductor materials is called **biasing.** To begin our description of doped material behavior, let us look at a P-material and N-material junction, with positive voltage connected to the P-material and negative voltage connected to the N-material, figure 3-5. A simple device consisting of P-material and N-material joined at a junction is called a **diode.**

Diode Bias Voltage

The negative battery voltage in figure 3-5 will repel the free electrons in the N-material, causing them to move toward the junction. The positive battery voltage will repel the holes in the P-material, moving them toward the junction also. With enough voltage, the electrons of the N-material will move across the junction into the holes of the P-material. This leaves behind positively charged holes in the N-material, which attract more electrons from the negative voltage source. At the same time, the free electrons which moved into the P-material continue to be attracted toward the positive battery voltage, leaving behind holes in the P-material at the junction. This area near the junction where the N-type material is depleted of electrons and the P-material is depleted of holes is called the **depletion region.** As long as battery voltage is maintained, this chain of events will be repeated, and current will flow through

Figure 3-5. Current will flow through this forward-bias connection. (Delco-Remy)

the doped materials. The application of voltage to maintain current flow as described here is called **forward bias.**

A diode cannot withstand unlimited forward bias voltage and current flow. If the forward current flow is too strong or flows for too long, the doped materials can be damaged or destroyed.

If the battery polarity is reversed, so that the negative battery voltage is connected to the P-material and the positive battery voltage is connected to the N-material, the doped materials' behavior changes, figure 3-6. The positive battery voltage attracts the free electrons in the N-material, causing them to move away from the junction. The negative battery voltage attracts the holes in the P-material, causing them to move away from the junction. At the junction, there will be no holes and no free electrons. No current can flow under these conditions. Voltage applied in this way is called **reverse bias,** figure 3-6. If reverse bias voltage is very high, the diode will break down and current will flow. One of the most common ways to rate a diode is in terms of its **peak inverse voltage (piv).** This refers to the amount of voltage a diode can withstand before it breaks down and allows reverse current flow. A diode can withstand reverse bias voltage below its piv rating indefinitely, but reverse current flow caused by voltage higher than the piv rating can quickly damage the diode. This is the reason that diodes in alternators can be damaged if a battery is hooked up backwards or if high voltage from a battery charger is applied to a battery without disconnecting it from a car's electrical system. We will learn more about diode uses when we study charging systems,

ignition systems, and other electronic circuits in an automobile.

Junction Diode Applications

Diodes operate as electrical one-way check valves. They allow current flow in one direction but not in the other. For example, they can allow one-half of an alternating current (a.c.) wave to flow in one direction while blocking flow of the remaining half of the current wave in the other direction, figure 3-7. The diode polarity may be either positive or negative, depending

---

Doping: The addition of a small amount of a second element to a semiconductor element.

Impurities: The doping elements added to pure silicon or germanium to form semiconductor materials.

N-material: A semiconductor material that has excess (free) electrons because of the type of impurity added. It has a negative charge and will repel additional electrons.

Hole: The space in a valence ring where another electron could fit.

P-material: A semiconductor material that has holes for additional electrons because of the type of impurity added. It has a positive charge and will attract additional electrons.

Junction: The area where two types of semiconductor materials (P- and N-material) are joined.

Biasing: Applying voltage to a junction of semiconductor materials.

Diode: An electronic device made of P-material and N-material bonded at a junction. A diode allows current flow in one direction and blocks it in the other.

Depletion Region: An area near the junction of a diode where P-material is depleted of holes and N-material is depleted of electrons.

Forward Bias: The application of a voltage to produce current flow across the junction of a semiconductor.

Reverse Bias: The application of a voltage so that normally no current will flow across the junction of a semiconductor.

Peak Inverse Voltage (PIV): The highest reverse bias voltage that can be applied to a junction of a diode before its atomic structure breaks down and allows current to flow.

Figure 3-6. No current will flow through this reverse-bias connection. (Delco-Remy)

Figure 3-7. A diode blocks one-half of the current wave and transmits the other half. (Chrysler)

Figure 3-8. The electrical symbol for a diode. (Delco-Remy)

Figure 3-9. Alternator diodes (top center and top right) and radio diodes (left and center). At lower right is a diode trio (three diodes in one unit) from a late-model alternator.

upon the direction of forward bias. Bias direction is determined by the direction in which the P-material or N-material is connected into the circuit.

The symbol for a simple PN diode is shown in figure 3-8. The arrowhead represents the P section, and the vertical bar represents the N section. Hole flow, or conventional current flow, is in the direction of the arrowhead. Electron flow is in the *opposite* direction.

One of the first major uses of diodes in automotive electrical systems was in a.c. generators, or alternators, which we will study in Chapter Eight. An early alternator diode is shown in figure 3-9, along with smaller diodes used in radios and other electronic systems.

Zener Diodes

We said before that reverse current can damage a diode. **Zener diodes** are heavily doped to withstand reverse current without damage. The doping can be carefully controlled so that a zener diode will only conduct reverse current if the voltage is higher than a specific level. For instance, a certain zener diode might be designed to conduct reverse current if the voltage is more than six volts. At any voltage below six volts, the zener acts as a normal junction diode and does not conduct reverse flow. At six volts and above,

the zener will conduct reverse current with no damage to the doping materials if the current flow is kept within specified limits. Six volts is then called the diode's **breakdown voltage** or zener voltage.

Zener diodes are often used in control circuits, especially in the charging system, which we will study in Part Two. The symbols for a zener diode are shown in figure 3-10. Like the junction diode symbol, the arrowhead shows the direction in which conventional current is allowed to flow freely. Zener diodes are carefully rated as to the reverse voltage necessary for reverse current to flow. This rating is often expressed as the amount of voltage the zener diode will regulate in a circuit.

SILICON-CONTROLLED RECTIFIERS

The silicon-controlled rectifier (SCR) is basically a four-layer PNPN device which normally allows current flow in both directions. It can be triggered to block current flow in one direction or the other. Its

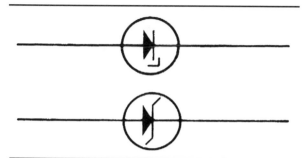

Figure 3-10. A zener diode is represented by either of these symbols.

Figure 3-11. The symbol for a silicon-controlled rectifier (SCR), also called a thyristor.

importance lies in this ability to control current flow. Silicon-controlled rectifiers may be found in some solid-state ignition systems and solid-state regulators for charging systems. An SCR is often called a thyristor. Its symbol is shown in figure 3-11.

LIGHT-EMITTING DIODES

A light-emitting diode (LED), figure 3-12, is a diode made of a particular type of crystal that glows when current is passed through it. Light-emitting diodes are used in the display faces of many "digital" instruments, such as digital clocks and digital tachometers or speedometers. These are called digital instruments because the LEDs are arranged in the display face to light up as numbers (digits) when current is passed through different combinations of the LEDs.

TRANSISTORS

A transistor is a three-element semiconductor, produced by adding another layer of doped material to a basic PN diode. The three materials are combined so that the two outer layers are the same (either P-material or N-material) and are doped with the same impurity. The inner layer is the opposite type of material and doped with a different impurity.

The three parts of a transistor are called the **base,** the **emitter,** and the **collector.** The emitter and the collector are the outer layers, and the base is the inner layer. If the emitter and the collector are N-material, the base is P-material. If the emitter and the collector are P-material, the base is N-material. Transistors are described as either PNP construction or NPN construction. The circuit diagram symbols for the two kinds of transistors are shown in figure 3-13, along with illustrations of how the materials are joined together in their construction. Note that the arrowhead is always shown on the emitter branch of the symbol and indicates the direction of hole flow. The emitter always produces the majority current carriers, either holes (P-material) or free electrons (N-material), and

■ Semiconductor Doping

Adding impurities to a semiconductor material, or doping, must be a carefully controlled process. Manufacturing methods are constantly changing as better doping processes are developed. Early semiconductor technology called for painting layers of doping elements onto either side of a semiconductor wafer and baking it at temperatures above 2,000°F (1,093°C). The ratio of impurity to the pure semiconductor was not easily controlled, and new uses for semiconductors demanded more precise production.

Some newer processes use a gas of the doping material. A process called diffusion passes this gas over the surface of a semiconductor wafer, which has been heated to 2,000°F. The doping elements are slowly absorbed into the wafer. The doping ratios can be carefully controlled during this slow absorption.

Ion implantation uses a 100-kV force to create an arc through the doping gas. The flow of electrons through the gas ionizes it, causing the gas particles to become positively and negatively charged. A semiconductor wafer is bombarded with the ionized gas, and doping elements are deeply implanted in the wafer. This method can be combined with the diffusion method to create a very deep but controlled layer of doped material.

Zener Diode: A junction of semiconductor materials that has been heavily doped so that the junction will allow reverse current flow without damage at any voltage above a specific value.

Breakdown Voltage: The voltage above which a zener diode will allow reverse current flow.

Base: The center layer of semiconductor material in a transistor.

Emitter: The outside layer of semiconductor material in a transistor that conducts current to the base.

Collector: The outside layer of semiconductor material in a transistor that conducts current away from the base.

Figure 3-12. Light-emitting diodes, like these, are used in the digital displays of instruments like clocks and tachometers. Light-emitting diodes light up when current is passed through them.

transfers them to the base. Because this type of transistor uses both holes and electrons to carry current, it is called a **bipolar** transistor.

Transistor Operation

Transistors can be used to control current flow in solid-state electronic systems. In this way, they work like the mechanical relays discussed in Chapter Two, but with no moving parts. The most common automotive uses of transistors are as relays, although they can be used to amplify voltage or current in electronic systems. In the following paragraphs, we will briefly look at how a transistor works as a solid-state relay. These are the basic principles on which many electronic ignition systems and voltage regulators work.

To use a transistor as a simple solid-state relay, the emitter-base junction must be forward biased, and the collector-base junction must be reverse biased. Figure 3-14 shows this arrangement for an NPN transistor.

Input and output circuits

The input circuit for a NPN transistor is the emitter-base circuit, figure 3-15. Because the base is thinner and doped less than the emitter, it has fewer holes than the emitter has free electrons. Therefore, when forward bias is applied, the numerous free electrons from the emitter do not find enough holes to combine with in the base. In this condition, the free electrons accumulate in the base and eventually restrict further current flow.

The output circuit for this NPN transistor is shown in figure 3-16 with reverse bias applied. The base is thinner and doped less than the collector. Therefore, under reverse bias, it has few minority carriers (free electrons) to combine with many minority carriers

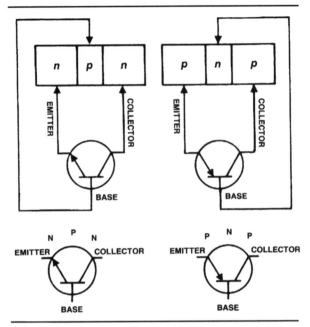

Figure 3-13. Transistor symbols and construction.

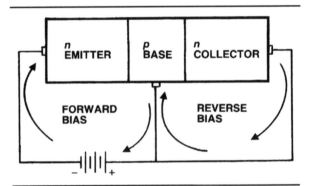

Figure 3-14. Forward and reverse biasing for an NPN transistor.

(holes in the collector). When the collector-base output circuit is reverse biased, very little reverse current will flow. This is similar to the effect of forward biasing the emitter-base input circuit, in which very little forward current will flow.

When the input and output circuits are connected, with the forward and reverse biases maintained, the overall operation of the NPN transistor changes, figure 3-17. Now, the majority of free electrons from the emitter, which could not combine with the base, are attracted through the base to the holes in the collector. The free electrons from the emitter are moved by the negative forward bias toward the base, but most pass through the base to the holes in the collector, where they are attracted by a positive bias. Reverse current flows in the collector-base output circuit, but the overall current flow in the transistor is forward.

Figure 3-15. Free electrons cannot find enough holes to join with in the base. Therefore, electrons accumulate in the base, and little forward current flows.

Figure 3-16. The base does not have enough free electrons to combine with holes in the collector, and little reverse current flows.

A slight change in the emitter-base bias causes a large change in emitter-to-collector current flow. This is similar to a small amount of current flow controlling a large current flow through a relay. As the emitter-base bias changes, either more or fewer free electrons are moved toward the base. This causes the collector current to increase or decrease. If the emitter-base circuit is opened or the bias is removed, no forward current will flow through the transistor because the base-collector junction acts like a PN diode with reverse bias applied.

FIELD-EFFECT TRANSISTORS

The field-effect transistor (FET) is a three-element solid-state device which controls high voltage and large current flow with a small signal voltage. This means that it can be used as an amplifier when installed in the proper circuit. As we have just seen,

INPUT-OUTPUT CIRCUIT INTERACTION

Figure 3-17. Electrons from the emitter pass through the base to the collector, and greater overall forward current flows. Note that greater reverse current flows in the output circuit because more holes in the collector are filled by free electrons.

the bipolar transistor is controlled by altering the current through the emitter-base junction. To control a field-effect transistor, we change the voltage in a capacitive field.

A field-effect transistor consists of three parts:

- The **source,** which is similar to the emitter of a bipolar transistor. It supplies the current-carrying holes or electrons.
- The **drain,** which is similar to the collector. It collects the current carriers.

■ Tran(sfer) + (Re)sistor

The word "transistor" was originally a business trademark used as a name for an electrical part that transferred electric signals across a resistor. The point-contact transistor was invented by two scientists, John Bardeen and Walter H. Brattain, at Bell Telephone Laboratories in 1948. In 1951, the junction transistor was invented by their colleague, William Shockley. As a result of their work, these three men received the 1956 Nobel Prize for physics.

Bipolar: A transistor which uses both holes and electrons as current carriers.

Source: The field-effect transistor (FET) layer which supplies current-carrying holes or electrons (similar to the emitter of a bipolar transistor).

Drain: The field-effect transistor (FET) layer which collects current carriers (similar to the collector of a bipolar transistor).

Figure 3-18. Each small square on the silicon slice or wafer is a complete IC chip. (Chrysler)

- The **gate,** which is similar to the bipolar transistor base. It creates a capacitive field which permits current to flow from source to drain.

Field-effect transistors are generally installed in a circuit to either improve (amplify) the current flow from the source to the drain, or to deplete (shut off) current flow. An easy-to-understand analogy is to compare them to normally open or normally closed switches. Field-effect transistors are used to do much of the switching, processing, and amplifying work required in an electronic circuit.

DISCRETE DEVICES VS. INTEGRATED CIRCUITS

Each of the electronic devices we have seen so far is an individual component with its own leads for installing it in a circuit. Such solid-state components are often called **discrete devices.** Good examples are the rectifying diodes used on older alternators; each diode is an individual unit and is connected into the circuit by itself.

Discrete devices are still in use, but they are being replaced in many cases by the **integrated circuit (IC).** This is a very complex and very small electronic circuit that contains hundreds (or in some cases, thousands) of transistors and other devices on a tiny silicon chip. This has allowed a drastic reduction in the size and cost of electronic components.

An IC is made from a slice or wafer of silicon crystal. Its circuit pattern is reproduced by a photographic and diffusion process to create hundreds of identical circuits, each containing transistors, diodes, conductors, and capacitors within a tiny "chip" on the wafer. Once the ICs have been formed, each chip is cut from the wafer. Figure 3-18 summarizes the major steps in IC manufacture. The individual chip is then incased in

Figure 3-19. The Delco HEI and HEI-EST ignition modules use integrated circuit (IC) chips.

its own packaging device and installed in a larger circuit. Figure 3-19 shows integrated circuit use in ignition control modules.

HYBRID CIRCUITS

A hybrid circuit is one that contains several discrete devices and several ICs. Figure 3-20 shows a hybrid circuit as used in a barometric/manifold absolute pressure (B/MAP) sensor. Like discrete devices, hybrid circuits are being replaced by one or two ICs.

PRINTED CIRCUITS

Printed circuits are often used to connect individual solid-state components. An etched conductor is used on one or both sides of a circuit board to connect the various electronic components. The components are then soldered to the circuit board. Automotive instrument clusters often use a flexible type of circuit board. Figure 3-21 shows both rigid and flexible types of circuit boards.

SUMMARY

Elements with four valence-ring electrons are neither good conductors nor good insulators. They are called semiconductors. Adding small amounts of other elements to semiconductors is called doping. Doping creates either N-material or P-material, depending on whether the doping element has five electrons or three electrons in its valence ring. Doped semiconductor materials behave in unusual but predictable ways when exposed to voltage. A simple PN material

Figure 3-20. A hybrid circuit contains several discrete devices and integrated circuits.

Figure 3-21. Printed circuits may use a rigid or flexible circuit board to connect the components into a complete circuit. (Chrysler)

junction, called a diode, acts as one-way electrical check valve. It allows current flow in one direction but not the other. Applying voltage to a semiconductor device is called biasing.

Transistors are three-part semiconductor devices. They are made of layer of positive-negative-positive (PNP) or negative-positive-negative (NPN) materials. The three parts of a transistor are called the emitter, the base, and the collector. Transistors can be used to amplify current or voltage, but in automobiles, transistors are generally used as solid-state relays.

Other semiconductor devices commonly used in automotive applications are zener diodes, silicon-controlled rectifiers, light-emitting diodes, and integrated circuits. An integrated circuit contains many transistors, diodes, and other discrete devices on a small metallic chip. Hybrid circuits combine discrete devices with IC chips. Printed circuit boards are often used to form a circuit with discrete devices.

Gate: The field-effect transistor (FET) layer which creates a capacitive field that lets current flow from the source to the drain (similar to the base of a bipolar transistor).

Discrete Device: A complete, separately manufactured, individual component with wire leads for connection into a circuit.

Integrated Circuit (IC): A very small, complex electronic circuit that contains hundreds or thousands of transistors and other devices on a tiny silicon chip.

Review Questions

Choose the single most correct answer.
Compare your answers with the correct answers on Page 468.

1. Semiconductors are elements which have _____ electrons in their valence rings.
   a. Two
   b. Four
   c. Six
   d. Eight

2. A diode is a simple device which joins:
   a. P-material and N-material
   b. P-material and P-material
   c. N-material and N-material
   d. P-material and a conductor

3. Which of the following is *not* true of forward bias in a diode?
   a. Free electrons in the N-material and holes in the P-material both move toward the junction
   b. N-material electrons move across the junction to fill the holes in the P-material
   c. Negatively charged holes left behind in the N-material attract electrons from the negative voltage source
   d. The free electrons which moved into the P-material continue to move toward the positive voltage source

4. When reverse bias is applied to a simple diode, which of the following will result?
   a. The free electrons will move toward the junction
   b. The holes of the P-material move toward the junction
   c. No current will flow across the junction
   d. The voltage increases

5. Under normal use, a simple diode acts to:
   a. Allow current to flow in one direction only
   b. Allow current to flow in alternating directions
   c. Block the flow of current from any direction
   d. Allow current to flow from either direction at once

6. "Breakdown voltage" is the voltage at which a Zener diode will:
   a. Allow reverse current to flow
   b. Stop the flow of reverse current
   c. Sustain damage as a result of current overload
   d. Stop the flow of either forward or reverse current

7. Which of the following combinations of materials can exist in the composition of a transistor?
   a. NPN
   b. PNP
   c. Both a and b
   d. Neither a nor b

8. To use a transistor as a simple solid-state relay:
   a. The emitter-base junction must be reverse biased, and the collector-base junction must be forward biased
   b. The emitter-base junction must be forward biased, and the collector-base junction must be reverse biased
   c. The emitter-base junction and the collector-base junction both must be forward biased
   d. The emitter-base junction and the collector-base junction both must be reverse biased

9. Which of the following is *not* commonly used as a doping element?
   a. Arsenic
   b. Antimony
   c. Phosphorus
   d. Silicon

10. The display faces of digital instruments are often made of:
    a. Silicon-controlled rectifiers
    b. Integrated circuits
    c. Light-emitting diodes
    d. Thyristors

11. All of the following are parts of a field-effect transistor (FET), *except* the:
    a. Drain
    b. Source
    c. Base
    d. Gate

12. All of the following are characteristics of an integrated circuit (IC), *except:*
    a. It is extremely small
    b. It contains thousands of individual components
    c. It is manufactured from silicon
    d. It is larger than a hybrid circuit

4

Automotive Computer Control Systems

Revolutionary changes have occurred in automotive technology during the past decade. These changes are the result of the onboard computer, which may control from one to a dozen or more functions that range from fuel metering to suspension leveling. In this chapter, we will look at what an automotive computer is, what it does, and how it performs its functions.

WHAT IS A COMPUTER?

We often use the term "computer" without really understanding what it means. A computer is nothing more than a machine that receives information, which it uses to make a series of decisions, and that acts as a result of the decisions made. A computer cannot think on its own; it does everything according to a detailed set of instructions called a **program.** The old mechanical calculator was a primitive form of computer.

The earliest electronic computers and those in use today all use identical principles. They use voltage to send and receive information. As we have learned, voltage is electrical pressure and does not flow through circuits. It causes current flow, which does the real work in an electrical circuit. However, voltage can be used as a signal. A computer converts input information, or data, into voltage signal combinations that represent number combinations. The number combinations can represent a wide variety of information — temperature, speed, or even words and letters. A computer handles or processes the input voltage signals it receives by computing what they represent and then delivering data in computed or processed form.

Most people are unaware that they are using simple computers every day when they set the cooking time on their microwave oven or set their VCR to tape a favorite program while they are away from home.

Computer Functions

The operation of every computer, regardless of its size or the use to which it is put, can be divided into four basic functions:

- Input
- Processing
- Storage
- Output.

These basic functions are not unique to computers; they can be found in many noncomputer systems. However, we need to know how the functions work in a computer.

Figure 4-1. This is an example of an automotive sensor which provides input to the onboard computer.

Input

The computer receives a voltage signal (input) from an input device. The device can be as simple as a button or switch on an instrument panel. It can also be a **sensor** on an automobile engine, figure 4-1. The keyboard on your personal computer and the programming keyboard of a VCR are other examples of an input device.

Modern automobiles use various mechanical, electrical, and magnetic sensors to measure a variety of things, including vehicle and engine speed, air pressure, oxygen content of exhaust gas, airflow, and temperature. Each sensor transmits its information in the form of voltage signals which the computer can understand. Sensors are described more fully later in this chapter.

Processing

The computer receives input voltage signals and switches them through a series of electronic logic circuits according to its programmed instructions. These processing logic circuits change the input voltage signals, or data, into output voltage signals, or commands.

Storage

The program instructions for a computer are stored in its electronic memory. Some programs may require that certain input data be stored for later reference or future processing. In others, output commands may be delayed or stored before they are transmitted to devices elsewhere in the system. Computers use a number of different memory devices which we will look at later in this chapter.

Figure 4-2. An actuator on a Ford engine that controls air intake.

Output

After the computer has processed the input signals, it sends output voltage signals, or commands, to other devices in the system, such as a solenoid or a display screen. The output devices used on automobiles vary from a display on an instrument panel to a system actuator. An **actuator** is an electrical or mechanical device that performs a desired operation, figure 4-2, whether it is adjusting engine idle speed, changing suspension height, or regulating fuel metering.

To make matters slightly more complicated for the automotive technician, computers can communicate with, and control, each other through their output and input functions. This means that the output signal from one computer system can act as an input signal for another computer system. For instance, on some 1986 and later GM cars, a body computer module (BCM) acts as a master control unit by managing a network containing all sensors, switches, and other vehicle computers, figure 4-3.

As an example, let's suppose the BCM sends an output signal to disengage the air conditioning compressor clutch. That same output signal can become an input signal to the electronic control module (ECM) that controls engine operation. Based on the signal from the BCM, the ECM tells an actuator to adjust engine speed to compensate for the decreased load when the compressor is disengaged.

The four basic functions just described are common to all computers, regardless of size or purpose. They also form an organizational pattern for troubleshooting a malfunctioning system. While most input and output devices may be adjusted or repaired, only the processing and storage functions must be replaced.

Figure 4-3. The body computer module reads data from various input devices, while sending commands to other devices. (GM)

Computer Sizes

The first computers were huge, occupying entire rooms and even buildings with the vacuum tubes and connecting wiring that formed their processing and storage equipment. Since the development of the transistor after World War II, electronics has evolved toward microminiature components. Today, we can identify three major sizes or classes of computers:

- Mainframe computers
- Minicomputers
- Microcomputers.

Mainframe computers, figure 4-4, are used to design automobiles and control automatic factory equipment or robots. These can do several jobs at the same time, receiving and sending thousands of separate inputs and outputs, and often supporting dozens or hundreds of users simultaneously.

Minicomputers also can do several jobs at once using dozens of inputs and outputs, but they do not have the capacity or speed of a mainframe computer. Among other functions, they are used by businesses and schools to maintain records.

Microcomputers, or personal computers, are generally used by one person at a time, although they can

Figure 4-4. A mainframe computer, such as used in a large industrial or commercial operation. (GM)

serve as input terminals for larger computer systems or can be connected together in some applications. Most microcomputers can only do one job at a time, but they can do many different jobs, depending upon the programs used.

Onboard Computers

In Chapter Three, we looked at solid-state silicon chips containing entire circuits. A single chip, or several chips on a single board, may form a computer for a specific function. An example is an engine control computer, figure 4-5. The continuing development of the silicon chip has taken us through various phases from the single transistor to what we now call very large scale integration (VLSI), in which tens of thousands of logic circuits are incorporated on a single silicon chip about one-quarter of an inch (6 mm) square. The end result is what we call a microprocessor, or the central processing unit (CPU) of a microcomputer.

When the microprocessor is enclosed in its circuit package with the necessary leads attached, it is no larger than a couple sticks of chewing gum or a small eraser, figure 4-6. The computer receives the input signals and sends them to the microprocessor, where

Program: The instructions a computer uses to do its job. The program consists of mathematical instructions and may include fixed data and require variable data from vehicle sensors.

Sensor: A device which provides input data in the form of voltage signals to a computer.

Actuator: A device which translates the computer output voltage signal into mechanical energy.

Figure 4-5. This engine control computer is a printed circuit board containing dozens of integrated circuit chips, transistors, diodes, capacitors, and other circuit devices.

Figure 4-6. While this Delco microprocessor is about an inch and a half (40 mm) long, the actual chip inside the packaging is no bigger than a fingernail.

calculation and logic decisions are made, and output commands are sent to the actuators.

ANALOG AND DIGITAL SYSTEMS

A computer has to be told how to do its job. The instructions and data necessary to do this are called a program. Since a computer cannot read words, the information must be translated into a form the computer can understand — voltage signals. This can be done by using an analog or digital system.

Analog Computers

The first automotive computer application was Chrysler's Electronic Lean-Burn (ELB) system used from 1976 through 1978, figure 4-7. Since it received, processed, and sent analog signals, it is called an analog computer. **Analog** means that the voltage signal or processing function varies relative to the field being measured or the adjustment required, position A, figure 4-8.

Figure 4-7. In 1976, Chrysler's Lean-Burn system was the first onboard automotive computer. (Chrysler)

The majority of operating conditions affecting an automobile, such as engine speed, are analog variables. Such operating conditions can be measured by thermistors or potentiometers acting as sensors. For example, engine speed doesn't change abruptly from idle to wide-open throttle; it varies in clearly defined, finite steps — 1,500 rpm, 1,501 rpm, 1,502 rpm, etc. — which can be measured. The same holds true for temperature, fuel metering, airflow, vehicle speed, and other factors.

If a computer is to measure engine speed changes from 0 rpm through 6,500 rpm, it can be programmed to respond to an analog voltage that varies from 0 volts at 0 rpm to 6.5 volts at 6,500 rpm. Any analog signal between 0 and 6.5 volts will represent a proportional engine speed between 0 and 6,500 rpm.

Analog computers have several shortcomings, however. They are affected by temperature changes, supply voltage variations, and signal interference. They also are slower in operation, more expensive to manufacture, and more limited in what they can do than digital computers.

Digital Computers

Digital computers first appeared on automotive applications in 1980. **Digital** means that the voltage signal or processing function is a simple high/low, yes/no, or on/off condition. The digital signal voltage is limited to two voltage levels. One is a positive voltage, the

Figure 4-8. Signal patterns of analog and digital signals. (GM)

Figure 4-9. All information, data, or signals must be converted to an on/off binary system for the computer. (GM)

Figure 4-10. An analog-to-digital converter changes input signals into a binary system the microprocessor can understand. (Chrysler)

other is no voltage. Since there is no stepped range of voltage or current in between, a digital signal is a square wave, position B, figure 4-8.

Using our example dealing with engine speed, suppose that the computer needs to know that engine speed is either above or below a specific level, say 1,800 rpm. Since it doesn't need to know the exact engine speed, but only whether it is above or below 1,800 rpm, the digital signal could be zero volts below 1,800 rpm and one volt above 1,800 rpm. As you can see, a digital signal acts like a simple switch to open and close a circuit.

The signal is called "digital" because the on and off signals are processed by the computer as the digits or numbers 0 and 1. The number system containing only these two digits is called the **binary system.** Any number or letter from any number system or language alphabet can be translated into a combination of binary 0s and 1s for the digital computer, figure 4-9.

A digital computer changes the analog input signals (voltage) to digital **bits** (*bi*nary digi*ts*) of information through an analog-to-digital (AD) converter circuit, figure 4-10. The binary digital number is used by the microprocessor in its calculations or logic networks to come up with the appropriate output signal. Since the output signal is a binary digital number, it often must go through a digital-to-analog (DA) converter circuit to produce a voltage output to operate the actuator device, figure 4-10.

The digital computer can process thousands of digital signals per second because its circuits are able to switch voltage signals on and off in billionths of a second.

Binary Numbers

Digital computer switching circuits are characterized by being either off or on. This state can be represented

by a 0 (off) or a 1 (on). If a digital computer is to understand a command, that command must be stated in binary form, as zeros or ones. A binary number system represents all numbers as sequences of zeros or ones. Therefore, off and on voltage signals can represent the 0 and 1 of the binary number system.

Analog: A voltage signal or processing action that varies relative to the operation being measured or controlled.

Digital: A voltage signal or processing function that has only two levels, on/off or high/low.

Binary System: A mathematical system containing only two digits (0 and 1), which allows a digital computer to read and process input voltage signals.

Bits: A digital input or output signal. One bit roughly equals one computer keystroke, or one discrete piece of information. The word comes from *bi*nary digi*t*.

We call our number system a decimal, or base 10, system; it uses the digits 0 through 9 written in a single column. When numbers above 9 are used, another column is added to the left — the ten's position. Therefore, the number 10 is equal to one ten and zero ones; 18 equals one ten and eight ones. Each additional position to the left multiplies the number by a power of ten:

$$1 = 10^0$$
$$10 = 10^1$$
$$100 = 10^2$$
$$1000 = 10^3$$

Using the binary system, we group whole numbers from right to left, just as in the decimal system. Since the system uses only two digits, the first one must equal either 0 or 1. To indicate the value of 2, we use the second position and write it as 10, since it equals one two and zero ones. Each additional position to the left multiplies the number by a power of two:

$$1 = 2^0 \text{ or decimal } 1$$
$$10 = 2^1 \text{ or decimal } 2$$
$$100 = 2^2 \text{ or decimal } 4$$
$$1000 = 2^3 \text{ or decimal } 8$$

In this way, we can change any decimal number to a binary number:

Decimal	Binary
1	1
2	10
3	11
4	100
5	101
6	110
7	111
8	1000
9	1001

This exercise in translating decimals into their binary equivalents has a very practical application in a digital computer. It allows the computer to understand exactly what we wish it to do. With several thousand circuits arranged in various series and parallel combinations inside the microprocessor, they can switch on and off in combinations that equal any binary number in a microsecond (0.000001 second). You will never have to do this conversion, but understanding it gives you a better insight into how a digital computer works and how it can handle so much information in so little time.

How does the computer know where one binary number (voltage pulse) ends and another one begins? How does it differentiate between a 01 and a 0011? A clock generator inside the computer provides constant pulses. Each pulse is the length of one bit. The computer's memory (or memories) monitors these clock pulses while reading or sending data. In this way, it knows how long each voltage pulse should last.

Analog-to-Digital Conversion

Earlier, we mentioned that most operating conditions affecting an automobile are analog variables. When our computer needs to know whether an operating condition is above or below a specified level or point, a digital sensor can be used as a simple off/on switch. Below the specified point, the switch is open. The computer receives no voltage signal until the condition reaches the specified point, at which time the switch closes. This is an example of a simple digital off/on circuit: off = 0, on = 1.

Let's use engine coolant temperature as an example and specify that the computer needs to know the exact temperature within one degree. This requires analog input signals. Suppose our sensor measures temperature from 0 degrees to 300 degrees and sends an analog signal that varies from 0 to 6 volts. Each 1-volt change in the sensor signal is the equivalent of a 50-degree change in temperature. If 0 volt equals 0 degrees temperature and 6 volts equals 300 degrees:

1.0 volt = 50 degrees
0.5 volt = 25 degrees
0.1 volt = 5 degrees
0.02 volt = 1 degree

In order for the computer to determine temperature within 1 degree, it must react to a sensor voltage change as small as 0.020 volt or 20 millivolts. For example, if the temperature is 125 degrees, the sensor signal will be 2.50 volts. If the temperature rises to 126 degrees, sensor voltage will increase to 2.52 volts. In reality, temperature does not pass directly from one degree to another; it passes through many smaller increments, as does voltage as it changes from 2.50 to 2.52 volts.

Our digital computer, however, processes only signals equaling 1-degree changes in temperature. To do so, the computer sends the signal through analog-to-digital (AD) conversion circuits, where the analog sensor voltage is converted to a series of 0.020-volt changes for each degree. This is called "digitizing" an analog signal.

The analog-to-digital conversion process brings us back to binary numbers. As we have learned, transistors can be designed to switch on and off at different voltage levels or with differing combinations of voltage signals. In the computer we are discussing, transistor groups must switch from off to on at 20-millivolt increments. The input signal is created by varying the transistor combinations that are on or off. In binary numbers, the 125 degree temperature is:

1111101

When the temperature increases to 126 degrees, the binary number also changes:

1111110

Since the computer can read the various voltage signal combinations as binary numbers, it performs its calculations. It does so almost instantly because the current travels through the miniature circuits at the speed of light.

DIGITAL LOGIC

Digital computers all handle data bits with three basic logic circuits called **logic gates:** the NOT, AND, and OR gates. This terminology is used to describe the circuit switching functions only and has nothing to do with their physical construction. They are called "gates" because the circuits act as routes or "gates" for output voltage signals according to different input signal combinations. A voltage signal enters the input terminal of a logic gate where it is processed according to the internal circuit switching pattern and then exits through the logic gate's output terminal.

The thousands of field-effect transistors (FETs) in a microprocessor function as logic gates. Figures 4-11 through 4-15 show the symbols used to represent each type of logic gate. The table contained within each figure is the "truth table", showing the logical or truthful combination of input and output signals for that logic gate.

As we have seen, a digital computer works by switching output voltage on and off according to the input voltage signals. When input voltage enters a logic gate, its transistors change from a cutoff state (no voltage) to full saturation (voltage). This is equivalent to an off, or low, signal and an on, or high, signal (in binary terms, a 0 or a 1). By combining input and output signals in logical combinations, they can be made to equal binary numbers.

The most elementary logic gate inverts the signal. This is called a NOT gate, figure 4-11. When voltage to its single input terminal is high or on (binary 1), output voltage is low or off (binary 0).

The AND gate, figure 4-12, has two inputs and one output. Its output is high (1) only if both inputs are high. If one or both of the inputs are low (0), output is low.

The OR gate also has two inputs and one output, figure 4-13. However, it differs from the AND gate in that output is high (1) when one or both inputs are high. OR gate output is low (0) when both inputs are low (0).

These gates can be combined to produce other logic functions. By placing an invertor or NOT gate after an AND or an OR gate, we can invert the signal and create a NAND (NOT AND) gate, figure 4-14, or a NOR (NOT OR) gate, figure 4-15.

Relay and Switch Logic

You may find it difficult to visualize the computer logic operations just described. You can't watch anything happen because the circuits are so small that they can't be seen with the naked eye and the current moves at literally lightning speed. To help you understand what is happening, let's demonstrate digital logic by using mechanical relays and switches.

Suppose we connect two switches in series to a light bulb and a power source, figure 4-16. The bulb will light only if both switches are closed; if either or both switches are open, the bulb cannot light. We have

■ Other Number Systems

Digital computers require the use of binary digits to perform their processing. However, working with the binary equivalents of decimal numbers can be awkward. For example, 150 in binary is 10010110. That's not bad, but suppose you wish to represent an engine speed of 2179 rpm; its binary equivalent is 100010000011. Binary numbers are usually long and their length introduces the possibility of human error when working with them.

Since any number system can be used to represent any measurable value, computer engineers simplify matters by working with other number systems. Those most often used are the octal system (base 8), the hexadecimal system (base 16) and one called the binary coded decimal (BCD) system.

Using one of these other number systems allows the computer to be loaded with less-complex number combinations. The computer changes the octal, hexadecimal, or BCD numbers into binary numbers for its own use. Octal and hexadecimal systems work quite satisfactorily since they are based on numbers that are whole number powers of 2: $8 = 2^3$, and $16 = 2^4$. A digital computer can make the required conversions between base 8 or base 16 numbers and binary numbers with relative ease.

Converting from decimal (base 10) to binary numbers is not as convenient for a computer, because 10 is not a whole-number power of 2. To make the more complicated calculations, the computer requires additional circuits. Binary coded decimal (BCD) numbers can be used for some operations. In the BCD system, groups of four binary numbers are used to represent each digit of a decimal number.

Logic Gates: Circuit switching functions within a computer which act as routes for output voltage signals according to differing combinations of input signals.

INPUT   OUTPUT

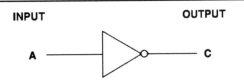

INPUT A	OUTPUT C
1	0
0	1

Figure 4-11. Logic symbol and truth table for a NOT gate.

INPUTS   OUTPUT

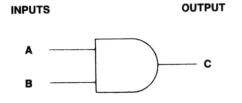

INPUTS		OUTPUT
A	B	C
0	0	0
0	1	0
1	0	0
1	1	1

Figure 4-12. Logic symbol and truth table for an AND gate.

constructed a circuit equal in function to an AND gate. Switch A and switch B are equal to the input (A and B) of the AND gate; the bulb is equal to the output (C) of the AND gate.

Now let's connect the two switches in parallel to the light bulb and power source, figure 4-17. The bulb

INPUTS   OUTPUT

INPUTS		OUTPUT
A	B	C
0	0	0
0	1	1
1	0	1
1	1	1

Figure 4-13. Logic symbol and truth table for an OR gate.

will light if (a) one switch is closed, or (b) both switches are closed. This is a basic OR gate.

What happens when we connect a normally closed relay, a switch, and a light bulb as shown in figure 4-18? When the switch is open, the relay is closed and the bulb lights. The bulb will not light if the switch is closed, since this opens the relay and shuts off current flow to the bulb. This is a basic NOT gate, in which the output is always opposite to the input, or inverted.

Series and parallel connections can be combined in various ways to produce different logic functions. The same thing can be done by arranging thousands of transistors in various combinations to produce thousands of logic gates.

COMPUTER PROGRAMS

Every computer needs instructions to do its job. These instructions are called a computer program. The program for an engine control computer consists of several elements. First are the mathematical instructions that tell the computer how to process, or "compute", the information it receives. Second is information that pertains to *fixed* vehicle values such as the number of cylinders, engine compression ratio, transmission type and gear ratios, firing order, and emission control devices. Finally, there is data that pertains to *variable* vehicle values such as engine speed, car speed,

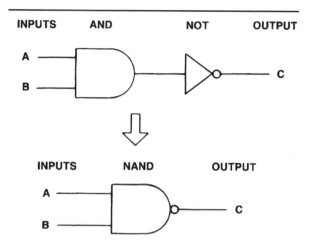

Figure 4-14. Logic symbol and truth table for a NAND gate.

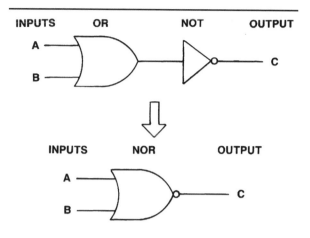

Figure 4-15. Logic symbol and truth table for a NOR gate.

coolant temperature, intake airflow, fuel flow, ignition timing, and others.

Since the mathematic instructions and engine data are constant values, they are fixed and are easily placed into computer memory. To place the variable values into memory, it is necessary to simulate the vehicle and its system in operation. A large mainframe computer at the factory is used to calculate all of the possible variable conditions for any given system. This provides the control program for the individual onboard computers.

This is called system simulation and involves a process called **engine mapping.** By operating a vehicle on a dynamometer and manually adjusting the variable factors such as speed, load, and spark timing, it is possible to determine the optimum output settings for the best driveability, economy, and emission control.

The vehicle information obtained is stored along with the mathematical instructions in a computer memory chip called a **programmable read-only memory (PROM),** figure 4-6, which is installed in the central computer for that particular car model. Since the PROM remembers the information programmed into it, the computer uses the PROM as its memory for comparison with the input from various sensors and then adjusts the systems under its control accordingly.

Engine Mapping: A process of vehicle and engine simulation used to establish variable values for the computer to work with in determining system control.

Programmable Read-Only Memory (PROM): An integrated circuit chip installed in the onboard computer which has been programmed with operating instructions and database information for a particular vehicle.

Figure 4-16. Two switches wired in series, similar to an AND gate. Both must be closed for the bulb to light.

Figure 4-17. Two switches wired in parallel, similar to an OR gate. Either one or both may be closed for the bulb to light.

Figure 4-18. A circuit similar to a NOT gate, in which the output is opposite to the input.

Engine mapping creates a three-dimensional performance graph which applies to a given vehicle and powertrain combination, figure 4-19. Each combination is mapped in this manner to produce a PROM. This allows a manufacturer to use one basic computer for all models; the unique PROM individualizes the computer for a particular model. Also, if a driveability problem can be resolved by a change in the program, the manufacturer can release a revised PROM to supersede the earlier part. Some PROMs are made in such a way that they can be erased by exposure to ultraviolet light and reprogrammed. These are called EPROMs, or erasable PROMs.

Most manufacturers use a single PROM which plugs into the computer, figure 4-20. Some Ford computers use a larger "calibration module" that contains

Figure 4-19. Engine mapping is used to program an automotive computer. (Porsche)

Figure 4-20. An engine computer with a replaceable PROM. (GM)

the system PROM, figure 4-21. If the onboard computer needs to be replaced, the PROM or calibration module must be removed from the defective unit and installed in the replacement computer.

PARTS OF A COMPUTER

We have dealt with the functions, logic, and **software** used by a computer. The software consists of the

Figure 4-21. A Ford calibration module containing the system PROM. (Ford)

Figure 4-22. The basic structure of a microcomputer. (Toyota)

programs and logic functions stored in the computer's circuitry. The **hardware** is the mechanical and electronic parts that physically make up a computer. Figure 4-22 shows the basic structure of a microcomputer.

Central Processing Unit (CPU)

As mentioned earlier, the microprocessor is the **central processing unit (CPU)** of a microcomputer. Since it performs the essential mathematical operations and logic decisions that make up its processing function, the CPU can be considered the brain of a microcomputer. Some microcomputers use more than one microprocessor.

Computer Memory

The computer storage or memory function is provided by other integrated circuit (IC) devices. These simply store the computer operating program, system sensor input data, and system actuator output data for use by the CPU. Computers use two different types of memory for their storage functions, read-only memory (ROM) and random-access memory (RAM).

Read-only memory (ROM)

Permanent memory is called **read-only memory (ROM)** because the central computer can only "read" the contents of the memory, but cannot change the information contained within it. Data stored in ROM is retained even when power to the computer is turned off. The computer control program and specific vehicle data are stored in ROM so they will not be lost if power to the computer is interrupted. Part of the ROM is built into the computer and the remainder is in the PROM described earlier.

Random-access memory (RAM)

Temporary memory is called **random-access memory (RAM)** because the central computer can both "read" information from it and "write" new information into it as dictated by the computer program. However, data contained in RAM is lost whenever power to the computer is shut off. Depending upon the computer design, RAM can provide either short- or long-term memory. Short-term memory is lost every time the ignition switch is turned off; long-term memory is retained until the computer power supply is completely disconnected. System trouble codes and diagnostic test results are usually stored in RAM.

Software: The programs and logic functions that are stored in the computer.

Hardware: The mechanical and electronic components that physically make up a computer.

Central Processing Unit (CPU): The processing and calculating portion of a microcomputer.

Read-Only Memory (ROM): The permanent part of a computer's memory storage function. The ROM can be read but not changed and is retained when power to the computer is shut off.

Random-Access Memory (RAM): Computer memory in which information can be written (stored) and read. Whatever is stored in RAM is lost whenever power to the computer is shut off.

Adaptive memory (computer learning ability)

The control program stored in the central computer unit and PROM is designed to regulate ignition timing, fuel delivery, and other variables on an engine in proper working order. However, production variations, engine wear, variable fuel quality and other factors often combine to make an engine's real needs different from the ideal design values used to establish the initial program.

To compensate for these variables, many late-model engine control systems have an "adaptive memory" that monitors the operation of the engine and related systems. When a controlled value regularly falls outside design limits, the adaptive memory makes a small modification to the control program to reestablish proper operation.

Adaptive memory program modifications are stored in RAM and are lost when power to the computer is disconnected. When this occurs on an older or high-mileage vehicle, the car must be driven long enough to let the adaptive memory again fine-tune the engine operation. This usually requires approximately 20 miles of driving under varied operating conditions.

Input and Output Circuits

A microprocessor is not directly connected to every input or output device. The signals are received and sent by other IC devices, many of which provide the microprocessor with parallel connections. This allows it to receive several input signals while it is sending several output signals.

Converter Circuits

The computer must have circuits to convert input data into a form that the computer can work with. The analog signals which we have discussed must be digitized, or changed to digital signals. This conversion is done by separate IC devices called analog-to-digital (AD) converter circuits.

Similarly, the computer's output signals must be converted into a form which the output device can recognize and act upon. Since some of the output devices are analog, the digital signals to these devices must be changed to analog signals. This conversion is done by digital-to-analog (DA) converter circuits. Because the circuits that perform these functions "interface" the CPU with the input and output devices, they are sometimes called the input/output (I/O) interface, figure 4-22.

Computer Installations

The onboard automotive computer may be called an electronic control unit, module, or assembly, depending

Figure 4-23. A GM onboard computer module.

upon the manufacturer and the computer application. The computer hardware is mounted on one or more circuit boards, figure 4-23, and installed in a metal case to help shield it from electromagnetic interference (EMI). The wiring harnesses that link the computer to sensors and actuators connect to multipin connectors or edge connectors on the circuit boards.

Onboard computers range from single-function units that control a single operation to multifunction units that manage all of the separate but linked electronic systems in the vehicle. They vary in size from a small module to a notebook-sized box. Some Chrysler computers are installed in the engine compartment, figure 4-24. Most computers are installed in the passenger compartment either under the instrument panel or in a side kick panel, figure 4-25, where they can be shielded from possible damage caused by temperature extremes, dirt and vibration, or interference from the high electrical currents and voltages of various underhood systems.

INSTRUMENTATION AND CONTROL SYSTEMS

Automotive computer systems have two purposes, instrumentation and control. An instrumentation system is one which measures variables and displays the output in a form the driver can use. Speedometers, odometers, tachometers, gauges, and warning lamps are examples of instrumentation devices.

Chrysler's Electronic Navigator is a good example of a computerized instrumentation system. The computer receives input data from various sensors as well as an analog input from the fuel gauge. By pressing a series of momentary contact pushbutton switches, the driver selects the processed information to be displayed. This

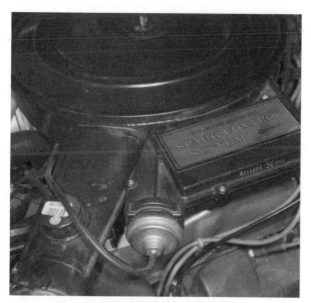

Figure 4-24. This Chrysler engine computer is mounted next to the air cleaner housing.

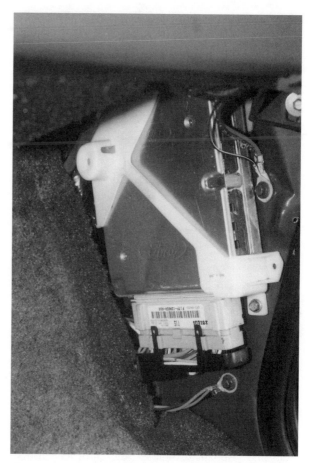

Figure 4-25. A Ford engine computer mounted in the passenger compartment.

can be clock functions, distance to destination, estimated time of arrival, current fuel mileage, and other factors relating to the trip on the instrument panel display.

When a computer is used as a control system, it regulates the operation of another system or systems. While there are several types of computer control systems in use today, the engine control computer is common to virtually all late-model vehicles. This computer receives input data concerning vehicle speed, engine speed and load, ignition timing, exhaust gas composition, fuel metering, and various other factors. After processing the data, the computer sends output signals to various actuators to control ignition timing, fuel metering, and operation of the emission devices.

Computers can perform dual functions by acting as both instrumentation and control systems. A multifunction computer can perform as a trip computer while regulating the speed or cruise control system. An automatic climate control system that regulates heating and air conditioning also can display temperature information. The same basic microprocessor can receive and process an input signal in different systems for different purposes. The output signals it produces can be used for different instrumentation and control purposes.

CONTROL SYSTEM OPERATING MODES

A computer control system can be selective, with different operating modes. It does not have to respond to

data from all of its sensors, nor does it have to respond in the same way each time. It may ignore sensor input under specified conditions. It also may respond in different ways to the same input signal, based on inputs from other sensors. Because of this, control systems are often designed with two operating modes: open loop and closed loop.

Open Loop Control

Open loop control means that the computer functions according to pre-established conditions in its program. It gives the orders and the output actuators carry them out. The computer ignores sensor input (feedback) as long as the pre-established conditions exist.

Open Loop: An operational mode in which the computer adjusts a system to function according to predetermined instructions and does not always respond to feedback signals from its sensors.

Figure 4-26. In open loop control, the computer operates according to preset specifications. (Chrysler)

Figure 4-27. In closed loop control, the computer monitors the oxygen sensor and sends corrections to the carburetor. (Chrysler)

An engine control computer, for example, is programmed to furnish a specified amount of fuel and spark timing when the engine is first started. It will ignore signals (feedback) from the exhaust gas oxygen (EGO) sensor until coolant temperature reaches a predetermined level. Figure 4-26 is a simple diagram of open loop control.

Closed Loop Control

When the system goes into **closed loop,** the computer reads and responds to signals from all of its sensors, figure 4-27. Our engine control computer ignored the EGO sensor when the engine was first started. Once coolant temperature reaches a predetermined level, the computer accepts this sensor input and adjusts the fuel and spark timing accordingly. We say that the computer is responding to a "feedback" signal, that is, the sensor is feeding information back to the computer that there is an error factor in its operation that must be corrected.

INTRODUCTION TO TRANSDUCERS

A **transducer** converts, or transduces, one form of energy into another. All sensors and actuators are transducers. Sensors convert light, temperature, motion, and other types of energy into voltage signals. Actuators convert voltage signals into mechanical energy or work. Sensors and actuators used with modern automotive computer systems often do the same work that mechanical transducers such as vacuum diaphragms did on older vehicles.

Sensors

Engine control system sensors fall into several basic categories including switches, timers, resistors, transformers and generators. With the exception of generators, all automotive sensors are resistive devices. They cannot create a voltage; they can only modify a voltage applied to them. This voltage is controlled by the microprocessor and is called the **reference voltage.**

The computer sends the reference voltage to the sensors, and receives a different voltage back. The returning signal is determined by the changing sensor resistance. The computer interprets the altered return voltage as a sign of specific changes in the engine operating condition and adjusts engine operation accordingly.

Engine control systems use either a 5-volt or a 9-volt reference voltage. In either case, the reference voltage must always be less than minimum battery voltage so it can be maintained at a constant level at all times to prevent faulty input signals from the sensors.

Sensor characteristics and features

Automotive sensors are designed for long-term, reliable operation in a severe environment while providing reliable signals. For a sensor to function properly, it must have certain characteristics or operating features. These not only affect the selection of a particular sensor for a given function, they also set the specifications for troubleshooting and service. These characteristics are:

- Repeatability — the sensor must function consistently. This means that a temperature switch must open and close at the design points thousands of times (repeatedly) without deviation. If the sensor produces a voltage in proportion to the condition being measured, it must do so throughout its operating range.
- Accuracy — the sensor must function within the tolerances or limits designed into it. Our temperature switch may close at 195 degrees ±1 degree, or it may close at 195 degrees ±10

degrees. The tolerances depend upon the use to which the sensor is put, but once established, the sensor must function consistently. These tolerances are used to design sensor test specifications for troubleshooting.

- Operating range — an operating or dynamic range is established for the sensor for it to function within. A digital sensor has only one or two switching points. The operating range of an analog sensor is wider and must be proportional. Signals outside the operating range are ignored by the computer.
- Linearity — this refers to sensor accuracy throughout its dynamic range. Within this range, an analog sensor must be as consistently proportional as possible to the measured value. Sensor linearity is most accurate near the center of its dynamic range, but no sensor has perfect linearity. Therefore, computer programs rely on memory data to compensate for this.

Switches and timers

Switches are the simplest form of sensors; they signal either an on or an off condition. When the switch is closed, full reference voltage is returned to the computer. When the switch is open, no return voltage signal is sent. Not all switches relay reference voltage back to the computer; some send a battery voltage signal directly to the computer when the monitored condition is met.

A common use for switch sensors is to signal the computer when a high-load accessory such as an air-conditioning compressor or rear window defogger is turned on or off. The computer uses the switch signal to adjust the idle speed to compensate for the added load. Coolant temperature switches that close when the engine has reached a certain temperature are also used in some systems.

A timer, when combined with a switch, can delay a signal for a predetermined length of time. Timers prevent the computer from having to compensate for momentary conditions that do not significantly affect engine operation. The timer may be built into the computer, or it can be part of the switch itself.

Potentiometers

A potentiometer is a variable resistance sensor with three terminals, figure 4-28. Reference voltage is applied to one end of the resistor and the other end is grounded. The third terminal is attached to a movable contact that slides across the resistor to vary its resistance. Depending on whether the contact is near the supply or the ground end of the resistor, return voltage will be high or low.

Figure 4-28. A potentiometer is a three-terminal variable resistance sensor.

Throttle position sensors are among the most common potentiometer-type sensors. The computer uses their input to determine the amount of throttle opening and the rate of change. Vane-type intake airflow meters use a potentiometer to signal the amount of air entering the engine. Exhaust gas recirculation (EGR) valve flow sensors use a potentiometer to signal the valve position and thus the amount of flow.

Thermistors

A thermistor is a variable resistor with a **negative temperature coefficient (NTC).** This means that as its temperature *increases,* its resistance *decreases.* In other words, its resistance is high at low temperatures, and low at high temperatures. The computer applies the reference voltage to one sensor terminal and receives the signal voltage from the other. As the thermistor warms up, the signal voltage increases. Coolant and cylinder head temperature sensors are the most common type of NTC thermistor sensors.

Closed Loop: An operational mode in which the computer reads and responds to feedback signals from its sensors, adjusting system operation accordingly.

Transducer: A device that converts (transduces) one form of energy into another. A sensor is such a device, converting light or other energy into a voltage signal.

Reference Voltage: Voltage applied to a sensor to which a microprocessor compares the sensor's output voltage and makes any adjustments.

Negative Temperature Coefficient (NTC): A type of sensor (also called a thermistor) that has *less* resistance as its temperature increases.

Piezoresistive devices

A piezoresistive sensor is one whose signal voltage varies with the amount of pressure or force applied to it. Like a thermistor, a piezoresistive sensor has two terminals, one to receive the reference voltage and the other to return the signal voltage to the computer. Many barometric and manifold pressure sensors are piezoresistive devices, as are engine detonation sensors.

Transformers

A transformer sensor has input and output windings with a movable core in between. The electric coupling between the two cores varies with the core position. Reference voltage is applied to the input winding. The transformer is designed so the signal voltage generated in the output winding is the same as that in the input winding when the core is centered. As the core moves away from the center position, the return signal voltage changes. Transformer sensors are used as one type of manifold pressure sensor.

Generators

Generator-type sensors do not depend upon a reference voltage. They generate a low voltage that is sent to the computer as the signal voltage. There are several types of generator sensors, including magnetic-pulse generators, Hall-effect switches, and galvanic batteries. You will study magnetic-pulse and Hall-effect sensors in detail in *Part Five* of this book.

Magnetic pulse generators are similar to the pick-up coil and reluctor used in many electronic ignition systems. Hall-effect switches are used in some newer applications. These sensors are commonly used to provide an ignition trigger signal, or crankshaft or camshaft position information. They may be located in the distributor or mounted in the block to respond to a tooth or cutout on the harmonic damper or flywheel. Some engines use separate sensors to signal crankshaft and camshaft position.

A galvanic battery is a generator-type sensor that produces a voltage by comparing the oxygen level in the ambient air to that in the engine exhaust. The only galvanic battery on modern cars is the oxygen sensor, figure 4-1, used to help control the air-fuel mixture.

Actuators

Once the central computer has received the inputs and calculated which engine systems must be adjusted to meet the demands of the moment, it sends electrical control signals to the output control devices, or actuators.

Some of the computer's electronic output signals, such as those that regulate ignition timing, provide

Figure 4-29. This feedback solenoid controls vacuum on carburetor diaphragms. (GM)

direct engine control. However, whenever the output must regulate a mechanical device, an actuator is required. Remember that an actuator converts the computer's electrical signal into a mechanical action. Most engine actuators are solenoids, but some are stepper motors.

Solenoids

A solenoid is essentially a digital actuator; it is either on or off. Battery voltage is applied to one terminal on the solenoid and the computer opens and closes the ground circuit attached to the other terminal, figure 4-29. In most applications, the solenoid is energized for varying lengths of time as determined by the computer program. When energized, a solenoid may extend a plunger or an armature to control engine speed. Other types of solenoids regulate vacuum flow to various emission-related systems such as air injection, vapor canister purge, and EGR. Solenoid-controlled hydraulic valves are used in some automatic transmissions to control torque converter lockup.

Pulse width and duty cycle

Solenoids are more precisely controlled on some late-model cars through the use of a procedure called **pulse width modulation (PWM).** In this design, the solenoid is continuously cycled on and off a fixed number of times per second. The solenoid is on (energized) for part of each cycle, and off for the remainder of that cycle. The percentage of the total cycle time that the solenoid is energized is called its **duty cycle.** The duty cycle is determined by a timed voltage pulse from the computer. The computer varies, or modulates, this pulse width to establish the duty cycle and achieve the desired solenoid output.

Pulse width modulation allows a digital output signal to provide varied or analog control of a mechanical device. It is also used to control fuel injectors and carburetor mixture control solenoids.

Figure 4-30. A stepper motor is a digital actuator that moves in fixed increments. (GM)

Stepper motors

A stepper motor, figure 4-30, is also a digital actuator. Stepper motors are dc motors that move in fixed increments from deenergized (no voltage) to fully energized (full voltage). A stepper motor can have as many as 120 discrete steps of motion, allowing it to serve as an analog output operated by a digital signal. The most common uses for stepper motors are as idle speed controls. On carbureted engines, the motor often acts directly on the throttle linkage, but in most fuel injection systems, it controls an idle air bypass built into the throttle body.

SUMMARY

Every computer works on four principal functions: input, processing, storage and output. Computers can operate on analog or digital signals. An analog signal is infinitely variable. A digital signal is an on/off or high/low signal. Most variable measurements on an automobile produce analog signals which must be changed to digital signals for computer processing.

Digital computers use the binary system in which on/off or high/low voltage signals are represented by combinations of 0s and 1s. These voltage signals are switching pulses for thousands of transistor logic gates. The basic NOT, AND, and OR logic gates are the building blocks of all digital computers.

Onboard computers are used in automotive instrumentation and control systems. An instrumentation system measures variable quantities and displays its output to the driver. A control system regulates the operation of a vehicle system. One computer system can perform both functions.

A control system operates in open or closed loop modes. In an open loop mode, the system does not respond to an output feedback signal. In a closed loop mode, the computer responds to the feedback signal and adjusts the output value accordingly.

Computer input is provided by sensors. Sensors can be switches, timers, resistors, transformer, or generators. Computer output is sent to actuators, which transduce or convert the electrical signal to mechanical action. Most actuators are solenoids but some are stepper motors.

Pulse Width Modulation (PWM): The continuous on/off cycling of a solenoid a fixed number of times per second.

Duty Cycle: The percentage of the total time that a solenoid is energized during pulse width modulation as determined by a timed voltage pulse from the computer.

Review Questions

Choose the single most correct answer.
Compare your answers with the correct answers on Page 468.

1. Technician A says an engine computer receives input information from its actuators, processes data, stores data, and sends output information to its sensors.
   Technician B says most late-model computers are based on analog microprocessors.
   Who is correct?
   a. A only
   b. B only
   c. Both A and B
   d. Neither A nor B

2. The operational program for a specific engine and vehicle is stored in the computer's:
   a. Logic module
   b. Programmable read-only memory (PROM)
   c. Random access memory (RAM)
   d. I/O interface

3. An exhaust gas oxygen (EGO) sensor is an example of a:
   a. Resistor
   b. Potentiometer
   c. Generator
   d. Solenoid

4. An engine detonation sensor uses a:
   a. Piezoresistive crystal
   b. Voltage divider pickup
   c. Potentiometer
   d. Thermistor

5. The binary system used by a digital computer consists of:
   a. 5 numbers
   b. 4 numbers
   c. 3 numbers
   d. 2 numbers

6. NOT gates can be added to AND gates and OR gates to create NAND gates and NOR gates because they:
   a. Invert the signal
   b. Have two inputs and one output
   c. Are binary in nature
   d. Convert the signal

7. The result of engine mapping is:
   a. A clean engine compartment
   b. Easy-to-service component locations
   c. A three-dimensional performance graph
   d. Lower design profile of the vehicle hood

8. The computer can read but not change the information stored in:
   a. ROM
   b. RAM
   c. Adaptive memory
   d. Output circuits

9. An onboard computer can act as:
   a. An instrumentation system
   b. A control system
   c. Both a and b
   d. Neither a nor b

10. Technician A says analog input data must be digitized by an AD converter.
    Technician B says output data must be changed to analog signals by a DA converter.
    Who is right?
    a. A only
    b. B only
    c. Both A and B
    d. Neither A nor B

11. A computer control system can do all of the following except:
    a. Ignore sensor input under certain conditions
    b. Respond in different ways to the same input signal
    c. Accept an input signal from another computer
    d. Ignore its program instructions under certain conditions

12. When the engine control computer is in open loop operation, it:
    a. Controls fuel metering to a predetermined value
    b. Ignores the temperature sensor signals
    c. Responds to the EGO sensor signal
    d. All of the above

13. The reference value sent to a sensor by the computer must:
    a. Be above battery voltage
    b. Be exactly the same as battery voltage
    c. Be less than minimum battery voltage
    d. Be + 10 volts of the battery voltage

14. The simplest digital sensor is a:
    a. Solenoid
    b. Switch
    c. Timer
    d. Generator

15. A variable resistance sensor is called a:
    a. Potentiometer
    b. Thermistor
    c. Transformer
    d. Varactor diode

16. The percentage of time a solenoid is energized relative to total cycle time is the:
    a. Pulse width modulation (PWM)
    b. Frequency
    c. Duty cycle
    d. EPROM

17. A stepper motor:
    a. Is either on or off
    b. Is one form of solenoid
    c. Is used to operate the EGR valve
    d. Has discrete steps of movement

18. Most onboard computers work with:
    a. Binary numbers
    b. Voltage signals
    c. Both a. and b.
    d. Neither a. nor b.

19. Technician A says throttle position sensors are analog devices.
    Technician B says manifold absolute pressure (MAP) sensors are digital devices.
    Who is right?
    a. A only
    b. B only
    c. Both A and B
    d. Neither A nor B

20. An engine coolant temperature sensor:
    a. Receives no voltage from the microprocessor
    b. Acts as a thermistor
    c. Is a potentiometer
    d. Provides the microprocessor with a variable frequency signal

PART TWO

Basic Automotive Electrical Systems and Components

5

Automotive Wiring and Basic Circuit Components

WIRING AND HARNESSES

Now that we have discussed current flow, voltage sources, electrical loads, and simple circuits, we can start to build some automotive circuits in this chapter and the next. To build a complete circuit, we must have conductors to carry the current from the voltage source to the electrical loads. The conductors are the thousands of feet of wire and cable used in the complete electrical system. The vehicle chassis is also a conductor for the ground side of the circuits, as we will see later. We will begin our study by looking at the **wiring harnesses,** connectors, and terminals of the system.

An automobile may contain as much as half a mile of wiring, in as many as 50 harnesses, with more than 500 individual connections, figure 5-1. This wiring must perform under very poor working conditions. Engine heat, vibration, water, road dirt, and oil can damage the wiring and its connections. If the wiring or connections break down, the circuits will fail.

To protect the many wires from damage and to keep them from becoming a confusing tangle, the automotive electrical system is organized into wiring harnesses. These are bundles of wires which serve various areas of the automobile. The wires are generally wrapped with tape or plastic covering, or they may be enclosed in insulated tubing. Simple harnesses are designed to connect two components; complex harnesses are collections of simple harnesses bound together, figure 5-2.

Main wiring harnesses are located behind the instrument panel, figure 5-3, in the engine compartment, figures 5-4 and 5-5, and along the body floor. Branch harnesses are routed from the main harness to other parts of the system. The colored insulation used on individual wires makes it easier to trace them through these harnesses, especially where sections of the wire are hidden from view.

A loose or corroded connection, or a replacement wire that is too small for the circuit, will add extra resistance and an additional voltage drop to the circuit. For example, a 10-percent extra drop in voltage to the headlamps will cause a 30-percent voltage loss in candlepower. The same 10-percent voltage loss at the power windows or windshield wiper motor can reduce, or even stop, motor operation.

All automotive electrical circuits, except the secondary circuit of the ignition system (from the coil to the spark plugs), operate on 12 to 14 volts and are called low-voltage systems. (Six-volt systems on

Figure 5-1. The wiring harnesses in this Buick are typical of those in late-model cars. (Buick)

SIMPLE HARNESS   **COMPLEX HARNESS**

Figure 5-2. Wiring harnesses range from the simple to the complex. (Chrysler)

older cars and 24-volt systems on trucks also are considered low-voltage systems.) The low-voltage wiring of a vehicle, with the exception of the battery cables, is called the **primary wiring.** This usually includes all lighting, accessory, and power distribution circuits.

WIRE TYPES AND MATERIALS

Almost all automotive wiring consists of a conductor covered with an insulator. Copper is the most common conductor used. It has excellent conductivity, is flexible enough to be bent easily, solders readily, and is relatively inexpensive.

A conductor must be surrounded with some form of protective covering to prevent it from contacting other conductors. This covering is called insulation. High-resistance plastic compounds have replaced the cloth or paper insulation used on older wiring installations.

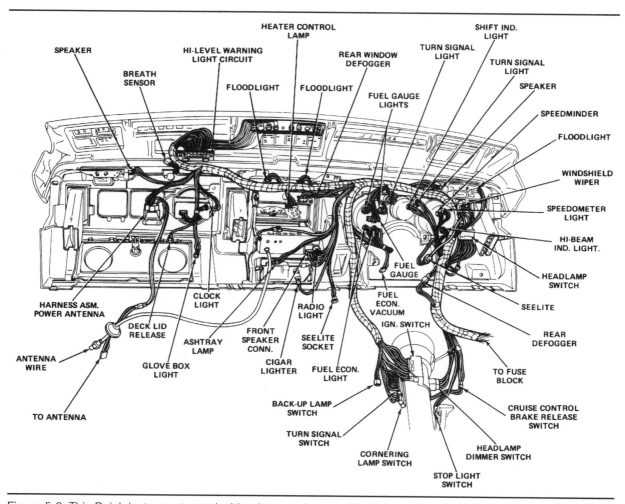

Figure 5-3. This Buick instrument panel wiring harness has 41 different connectors. (Buick)

Figure 5-4. The engine compartment wiring harness on a Ford Escort connects to the headlamps and the engine harness shown in Figure 5-5. (Ford)

Stainless steel is used in some heavy wiring, such as battery cables and some ignition cables.

Some General Motors cars use aluminum wiring in the main body harness. Although less expensive, aluminum is also less conductive and less flexible. For these reasons, aluminum wires must be larger than comparable copper wires and they generally are used in the lower forward part of the vehicle where flexing is not a problem. Aluminum wiring in GM cars can be recognized by its brown plastic wrapping; copper wiring harnesses in the cars have a black wrapping.

Wiring Harness: A bundle of wires enclosed in a plastic cover and routed to various areas of the vehicle. Most harnesses end in plug-in connectors. Harnesses are also called looms.

Primary Wiring: The low-voltage wiring in an automobile electrical system.

Figure 5-5. This Ford Escort engine harness connects the individual engine components to the engine compartment harness in Figure 5-4. (Ford)

Wire Types

Automotive wiring or circuit conductors are used in one of three forms:

- Solid wires (single-strand)
- Stranded wires (multistrand)
- Printed circuitry.

Solid or single-strand wire is used where current is low and flexibility is not required. In automotive electrical systems, it is used inside components such as alternators, motors, relays, and other devices with only a thin coat of enamel or shellac for insulation.

Stranded or multistrand wire is made by braiding or twisting a number of solid wires together into a single conductor insulated with a covering of colored plastic, figure 5-6. Most automotive electrical system wiring uses stranded wire, either as single conductors or grouped together in harnesses or looms.

Printed circuitry is a thin film of copper or other conductor that has been etched or imbedded on a flat insulating plate, figure 5-7. A complete printed circuit consists of conductors, insulating material, and connectors for lamps and other components, and is called a printed circuit (PC) board. It is used in places where space for individual wires or harnesses is limited, such as behind instrument panels.

WIRE SIZE

Automotive electrical systems are very sensitive to changes in resistance. This makes the selection of properly sized wires critical whenever systems are designed or circuits repaired. There are two important factors to consider, wire gauge number and wire length.

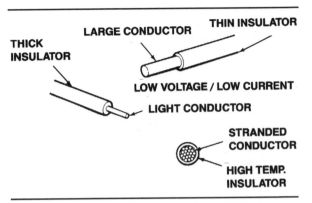

Figure 5-6. Automotive wiring may be a solid wire conductor or a multistrand wire conductor. (Chrysler)

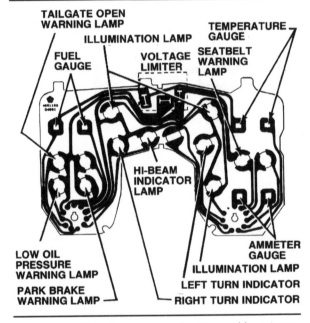

Figure 5-7. Printed circuit boards are used in automotive instrument panels. (Chrysler)

Wire Gauge Number

A **wire gauge** number is an expression of the cross section area of the conductor. The most common system for expressing wire size is the American Wire Gauge (AWG) system. Figure 5-8 is a table of AWG wire sizes commonly used in automotive systems.

Wire cross-section area is measured in circular mils. A mil is one-thousandth of an inch (0.001). A circular mil is the area of a circle 1 mil (0.001) in diameter. A circular mil measurement is obtained by squaring the diameter of a conductor measured in mils. For example, a conductor 1/4-inch in diameter is 0.250 inch, or 250 mils, in diameter. The circular mil cross section area of the wire is 250 squared, or 62,500 circular mils.

American Wire Gauge Sizes

Gauge size	Conductor diameter (inches)	Cross-section area (circular mils)
20	.032	1,020
18	.040	1,620
16	.051	2,580
14	.064	4,110
12	.081	6,530
10	.102	10,400
8	.128	16,500
6	.162	26,300
4	.204	41,700
2	.258	66,400
1	.289	83,700
0	.325	106,000
2/0	.365	133,000
4/0	.460	211,600

Figure 5-8. This table lists the most common wire gauge sizes used in automotive electrical systems.

Gauge numbers are assigned to conductors of various cross section areas. As gauge number increases, area decreases and the conductor becomes smaller, figure 5-9. A 6-gauge conductor is smaller than a 3-gauge conductor, and a 12-gauge conductor is smaller than a 6-gauge conductor. You learned in Chapter One that as the cross section area of a conductor decreases, its resistance increases. As resistance increases, so does the gauge number, figure 5-9. Also, because the current-carrying ability of a conductor decreases as the resistance increases, a conductor with a higher gauge number will carry less current than a conductor with a lower gauge number, figure 5-9.

Remember that the wire gauge number refers to the size of the conductor, not the size of the complete wire (conductor plus insulation). For example, it is possible to have two 16-gauge wires of different outside diameters because one has a thicker insulation than the other.

Twelve-volt automotive electrical systems generally use 14-, 16-, and 18-gauge wire. Main power distribution circuits between the battery and alternator, ignition switch, fuse box, headlamp switch, and larger accessories use 10- and 12-gauge wire. Low-current electronic circuits may use 20-gauge wire. Lighting other than the headlamps, as well as the cigarette lighter, radio, and smaller accessories, use 14-, 16-, and 18-gauge wire. Battery cables, however, generally are listed as 2, 4, or 6 wire, although they may be identified by an AWG wire size.

The gauge sizes used for various circuits in an automobile are generally based on the use of copper wire. A larger gauge size is required when aluminum wiring is used, because aluminum is not as good a conductor as copper. Similarly, 6-volt electrical systems require larger-gauge wires than 12-volt systems for the same current loads. This is because the lower source voltage requires lower resistance in the conductors to deliver the same current. Generally, 6-volt systems use wires two sizes larger than 12-volt systems for equivalent current loads.

While wire sizes are based on current capacity, the voltage of a system has an effect on wire selection. A low source voltage needs less resistance to transmit the same current that a higher source voltage would deliver. For example, a 24-volt electrical system can use smaller gauge wiring than a 12-volt system and still deliver equal current. In the same way, a computer sensor circuit that functions on 5 volts would need heavier wiring than a similar 12-volt circuit if the current flow were the same.

■ Metric Wire Sizes

Look at a wiring diagram or a service manual for an imported car, and you may see wire sizes listed in metric measurements. For example, if you look at a wiring diagram for a Volkswagen Rabbit or Golf, you will see wire sizes listed as 0.5, 1.0, 1.5, 4.0, 6.0, and so on. These numbers are the cross section area of the conductor in square millimeters (mm^2).

These metric measurements are not the same as circular-mil measurements. They are determined by calculating the cross section area of the conductor by the formula:

Area = Radius^2 [x] 3.14

A wire with a 1-mm^2 cross section area actually has a 1.128-mm diameter.

The table below lists AWG sizes and equivalent metric wire sizes.

AWG Size (Gauge)	Metric Size (mm^2)
20	0.5
18	0.8
16	1.0
14	2.0
12	3.0
10	5.0
8	8.0
6	13.0
4	19.0

Wire Gauge: Wire size numbers based on the cross-section area of the conductor. Larger wires have lower gauge numbers.

Figure 5-9. This figure shows the relationship between current capacity and resistance as the cross section of a conductor changes. (Chrysler).

Wire Length

Wire length also must be considered when designing electrical systems or repairing circuits. As conductor length increases, so does resistance. An 18-gauge wire can carry a 10-ampere load for 10 feet without an excessive voltage drop. However, to carry the same 10-ampere load for 15 feet, a 16-gauge wire will be required. Figure 5-10 is a table showing the gauge sizes required for wires of different lengths to carry various current loads. Wire lengths are based on circuits that are grounded to the vehicle chassis.

SPECIAL WIRING

While most of the electrical system is made up of low-voltage primary wiring, special wiring is required for the battery and the spark plugs. Since these wires are larger in size than primary wiring, they are often called cables. Battery cables are low-resistance, low-voltage conductors. Ignition cables are high-resistance, high-voltage conductors.

Battery Cables

The battery is connected to the rest of the electrical system by very large cables. Large cables are necessary to carry the high current required by the starter motor. Figure 5-11 shows several kinds of battery cables. Twelve-volt systems generally use number 4 or number 6 wire cables; 6-volt systems and some 12-volt diesel systems require number 0 or number 1 wire cables. Cables designed for a 6-volt system can be used on a 12-volt system, but the smaller cable intended for a 12-volt system cannot be used on a 6-volt system without causing too much voltage drop.

Total approximate circuit amperes (12 volts)

Wire Gauge Table

Circuit length (feet)

	3	5	7	10	15	20	25	30	40	50	75	100
1	18	18	18	18	18	18	18	18	18	18	18	18
1.5	18	18	18	18	18	18	18	18	18	18	18	18
2	18	18	18	18	18	18	18	18	18	18	16	16
3	18	18	18	18	18	18	18	18	18	16	14	14
4	18	18	18	18	18	18	18	18	16	16	12	12
5	18	18	18	18	18	18	18	18	16	14	12	12
6	18	18	18	18	18	18	16	16	14	14	12	10
7	18	18	18	18	18	18	16	16	14	14	10	10
8	18	18	18	18	18	16	16	16	14	12	10	10
10	18	18	18	18	16	16	14	14	12	12	10	10
11	18	18	18	18	16	16	14	14	12	12	10	8
12	18	18	18	18	16	16	14	14	12	12	10	8
15	18	18	18	18	14	14	12	12	10	10	8	8
18	18	18	18	16	14	14	12	10	10	10	8	8
20	18	18	16	16	14	12	10	10	10	10	8	6
22	18	18	16	16	12	12	10	10	10	8	6	6
24	18	18	16	16	12	12	10	10	10	8	6	6
30	18	16	16	14	10	10	10	10	10	6	4	4
40	18	16	14	12	10	10	8	8	6	6	4	2
50	16	14	12	12	10	10	8	8	6	6	2	2
100	12	12	10	10	6	6	4	4	4	2	1	1/0
150	10	10	8	8	4	4	2	2	2	1	2/0	2/0
200	10	8	8	6	4	4	2	2	1	1/0	4/0	4/0

Figure 5-10. As wire length increases, larger gauge wire must be used to carry the same amount of current.

Battery installations may have an insulated ground cable or one made of braided, uninsulated wire. The braided cables or straps are flat instead of round; however, they have the same resistance and other electrical properties of a round cable of equivalent gauge.

Most battery cables are fitted at one end with a lead terminal clamp to connect to the battery, although many import cars use a spring-clamp terminal. The lead terminal is used to reduce corrosion when attached to the lead battery post. A tinned copper terminal is attached to the other end of the cable to connect to the starter motor or ground, as required.

Ignition Cables

The ignition cables, or spark plug cables, are often called high-tension cables. They carry current at 10,000 to 40,000 volts from the coil to the distributor cap, and then to the spark plugs. Because of the high voltage, these cables must be very well insulated.

Years ago, all ignition cables were made with copper or steel wire conductors. During the past 30 years, however, metallic conductor cables have been replaced by high-resistance, non-metallic cables as original equipment on cars and light trucks. While metallic-conductor ignition cables are still made, they are sold for special high-performance or industrial applications and are not recommended for highway use.

The conductors used in high-resistance, non-metallic ignition cables are made of carbon, or of linen or fiber

Figure 5-11. Assorted battery cables.

glass impregnated with carbon. These cables evolved for two reasons:

- High-voltage ignition pulses emit high-frequency electrical impulses or radio frequency interference (RFI) that interfere with radio and television transmission, as we saw in Chapter Two. The principal method used to limit this interference is the use of high-resistance ignition cables, often referred to as suppression cables.

- The extra resistance in the cable decreases the current flow and thus reduces the burning of spark plug electrodes. The higher resistance also helps take advantage of the high-voltage capabilities of the ignition system, as we will learn in Part Five of this manual.

The high-voltage current carried by ignition cables requires that they have much thicker insulation than low-voltage primary wires. Ignition cables are 7 or 8 millimeters in diameter, but the conductor in the center of the cable is only a small core. The rest of the cable diameter is the heavy insulation used to contain the high voltage and protect the core from oil, dirt, heat, and moisture.

One type of cable insulation material is known by its trade name, "Hypalon", but the type most commonly used today is silicone rubber. Silicone is generally thought to provide greater high-voltage insulation while resisting heat and moisture better than other materials. However, silicone insulation is softer and more pliable than other materials and thus more likely to be torn or damaged by rough handling. Cables often have several layers of insulation over the conductor to provide the best insulating qualities with strength and flexibility.

CONNECTORS AND TERMINALS

Electrical circuits can be broken by the smallest gap between conductors. The gaps can be caused by corrosion, weathering, or mechanical breaks. One of

Figure 5-12. Some common single-wire terminals (connectors).

the most common wear points in an automobile electrical system is where two conductors have been joined. Their insulation coats have been opened and the conductive material exposed. Special connectors are used to provide strong, permanent connections and to protect these points from wear.

These simple connectors are usually called wiring terminals. They are metal pieces that can be crimped or soldered onto the end of a wire. Terminals are made in many shapes and sizes for the many different types of connections required. They can be wrapped with plastic electrical tape or covered with special pieces of insulation. The simplest wire terminals join a single wire to a device, to another single wire, or to a few other wires, figure 5-12. Terminals for connecting to a device often have a lug ring, a spade, or a hook which can be bolted onto the device. Male and female spade terminals or bullet connectors are often used to connect two individual wires, figure 5-13.

Multiple Wire Connectors

While the simple wiring terminals just described are really wire connectors, the term "connector" is normally used to describe multiple-wire connector plugs. This type of plug is used to connect wiring to switches, figure 5-14, or to other components. It also is used to join wiring harnesses.

Multiple wire connectors are sometimes called junction blocks. On older vehicles, a junction block was a stationary plastic connector with terminals set into it, in which individual wires were plugged or screwed in place. Because of the time required to connect this type of junction block on the assembly line, it has been replaced by a modern version that accepts several plugs from different harnesses, figure 5-15.

BULLET CONNECTOR   **SPADE TERMINAL**

Figure 5-13. Male and female bullet connectors and spade terminals are common automotive connectors. (Chrysler)

Figure 5-14. Multiple connectors are used to make complex switch connections. (Ford)

Some multiple connector plugs have as many as 40 separate connections in a single plug. They provide a compact, efficient way to connect wires for individual circuits while still grouping them together in harnesses. Wiring connections can be made quickly and accurately with multiple connectors, an important consideration in assembly line manufacturing.

Such connector plugs generally have hard plastic shells, with one half of the connector containing the male terminals or pins, and the other half containing the female terminals or sockets. Circuit operation can be tested by probing the rear of the individual connections without separating the connector. A locking tab of some type is used to prevent the connector halves from separating. Separation or removal of the plug may require the locking tab to be lifted or depressed, figure 5-16.

Although many hard-shell connector designs allow removal of the individual wires or their terminals for repair, figure 5-17, manufacturers are now using plugs that are serviced as an assembly. If a wire or terminal is defective, the entire plug is cut from the harness.

25-WAY INSTRUMENT PANEL-TO- STEERING COLUMN CONNECTOR

Figure 5-15. This junction block accepts individual wires on one side and connectors on the other. (Chrysler)

The replacement plug is furnished with two or three inches of wires extending from the rear of the plug. These plugs are designed to be replaced by matching and soldering their wire leads to the harness.

Bulkhead Connectors

A special multiple connector, called a bulkhead connector or bulkhead disconnect, is used where a number of wiring circuits must pass through a barrier such as the firewall, figure 5-18. The bulkhead connector is installed in the firewall and multiple connectors are plugged into each side of it to connect wires from the engine and front accessories to wires in the rest of the car.

Weatherproof Connectors

Special weatherproof connectors are used in the engine compartment and body harnesses of late-model GM cars. This type of connector has a rubber seal on the wire ends of the terminals, with secondary sealing covers on the rear of each connector half. Such connectors are particularly useful in electronic systems where moisture or corrosion in the connector can cause a voltage drop. Some Japanese carmakers use a similar design, figure 5-19.

GROUND PATHS

We have spoken as if wiring carried all the current in an automotive electrical system. In fact, wiring is only about half of each circuit. The other half is the automobile engine, frame, and body, which provide a path for current flow. This side of the circuit is called the ground, figure 5-20. Automotive electrical systems are called single-wire, or ground-return systems.

Figure 5-16. Connectors have some form of lock to prevent accidental separation. (Ford)

Figure 5-17. Individual terminals and wires can be removed from some connectors; other connectors are replaced as an entire assembly. (Ford)

ground, figure 5-20. Automotive electrical systems are called single-wire, or ground-return systems.

The cable from one battery post, or terminal, is bolted to the car engine or frame. This is called the **ground cable.** The cable from the other battery terminal provides current for all the car's electrical loads. This is called the **insulated, or hot, cable.** The insulated side of every circuit in the vehicle is the wiring running from the battery to the devices in the circuit. The ground side of every circuit is the vehicle chassis, figure 5-20.

The hot battery cable is always the insulated type of cable described earlier. The ground cable may be an insulated type of cable, or it may be a braided strap. On many vehicles additional grounding straps or cables are connected between the engine block and the vehicle body or frame. The battery ground cable may be connected to either the engine or the chassis, and the additional ground cable ensures a good, low-resistance ground path between the engine and the chassis. This is necessary for proper operation of the circuits on the engine and elsewhere in the vehicle. Late-model vehicles which rely heavily on computerized components often use additional ground straps whose sole purpose is to minimize or eliminate electromagnetic interference (EMI), as we saw in Chapter Two.

The resistances in the insulated sides of all the circuits in the vehicle will vary depending on the number and kinds of loads and the length of the wiring. The resistance on the ground side of all circuits, that is, between each load and its ground connection, must be virtually zero. For this reason, every ground con-

■ Early Wiring Problems

Early automobiles had many problems with their electrical systems. Usually these problems were the result of poor electrical insulation. For example, high-tension cable insulation, made by wrapping cotton or silk around wire and then coating it with rubber, was easily hardened by heat. The insulation often broke off, leaving bare wire exposed.

A common problem in cars that used dry cell batteries was moisture penetration through the batteries' paper insulation. Current would flow to ground, and the batteries would become discharged.

Even washing a car sometimes caused trouble. Water got into the distributor terminals and made the engine hard, if not impossible, to start. Some mechanics poured melted wax into the space between the plug wires and the distributor cap terminals.

For protection from heat, moisture, oil, and grease, wiring was often run through a metal conduit. Armored cable—insulated wire enclosed in a permanent, flexible metal wrapping—was also used, especially in a circuit where any voltage drop was critical.

Ground Cable: The battery cable that provides a ground connection from the vehicle chassis to the battery.

Insulated, or Hot, Cable: The battery cable that conducts battery current to the automotive electrical system.

CAVITY	DESCRIPTION
1	WINDSHIELD WIPER
2	WINDSHIELD WIPER
3	BRAKE WARNING LAMP
4	VACANT
5	WINDSHIELD WIPER
6	WINDSHIELD WIPER
7	BACK-UP LAMP
8	BACK-UP LAMP
9	WINDSHIELD WIPER
10	HAZARD FLASHERS
11	RIGHT TURN SIGNAL
12	HORN
13	LEFT TURN SIGNAL
14	HIGH BEAM
15	LOW BEAM
16	TACHOMETER
17	IGNITION RUN
18	VACANT
19	IGNITION SWITCH
20	AMMETER
21	AMMETER
22	VACANT
23	IGNITION SWITCH
24	VACANT
25	HEADLAMP SWITCH
26	IGNITION SWITCH
27	HEADLAMP SWITCH
28	A/C HIGH BLOWER
29	OIL PRESSURE
30	VACANT
31	A/C CLUTCH
32	TEMPERATURE

Figure 5-18. A bulkhead connector, or disconnect, is mounted on many firewalls. Multiple-wire connectors plug into both sides. (Chrysler)

Figure 5-19. Nissan uses this type of waterproof connector. (Nissan)

Figure 5-20. Half of the automotive electrical system is the ground path through the vehicle chassis.

battery. This is an important point to remember. It may be helpful at this time to review the explanations in Chapter One of voltage drops and current flow in various circuits from the source, through all the loads, and back to the source.

Every electrical load is attached to the chassis so that current can pass through the ground and back to the grounded battery terminal. Grounding connections must be secure for the circuit to be complete. In older cars where plastics were rarely used, most loads had a direct connection to a metal ground. With the increased use of various plastics, designers have had to add a ground wire from some loads to the nearest metal ground. The ground wires in most circuits are black for easy recognition.

MULTIPLEX CIRCUITS

The use of multiplexing, or multiplex circuits, is becoming a necessity in late-model automobiles because of the increasing number of conventional electrical circuits required by the use of electronic control systems. Wiring harnesses used on such vehicles have ballooned in size to 60 or more wires in a single harness, with the use of several harnesses in a vehicle not uncommon. Simply put, there are too many wires and too limited space in which to run them for convenient service. With so many wires in close proximity, they are subject to the problem of electromagnetic interference (EMI), which you learned about in Chapter Two. To meet the almost endless need for electrical circuitry in the growing and complex design of automotive control systems, engineers are gradually reducing the size and number of wire and wiring harnesses by using a **multiplex wiring system.**

The term "multiplexing" means different things to different people, but generally it is defined as a means of sending two or more messages simultaneously over the same channel. Different forms of multiplexing are used in automotive circuits. For example, windshield wiper circuits often use multiplex circuits. The wiper and washer functions in such circuit work though a single input circuit by means of different voltage levels. In this type of application, data is sent in parallel form. However, the most common form of multiplexing in automotive applications is serial data transmission, also known as time-division multiplex. In the time-division type of circuit, information is transmitted between computers through a series of digital pulses in a program sequence that can be read and understood by each computer in the system. The three major approaches to a multiplex wiring system presently in use are:

- Parallel data transmission
- Serial data transmission
- Optical data links.

We will look at each of these types of system, and then we will discuss the advantages of multiplexing over older systems of wiring.

Parallel Data Transmission

The most common parallel data multiplexing circuits use differentiated voltage levels as a means of controlling components. The multiplex wiring circuit used with a Type C General Motors pulse wiper-washer unit is shown in figure 5-21. The circuit diagram shows several major advantages over other types of pulse wiper circuits:

- Eliminating one terminal at the washer pump reduces the wiring required between the wiper and control switch.
- Using a simple grounding-type control switch eliminates a separate 12-volt circuit to the fuse block.
- Eliminating a repeat park cycle when the wash cycle starts with the control switch in the Off position—in standard circuits, the blades begin a wash cycle from the park position and return to park before continuing the cycle—simplifies operation.

An electronic timer controls the park and pulse relays. The timer consists of a capacitor, a variable resistor in the control switch, and electronic switching circuitry. The variable resistor controls the length of time required to charge the capacitor. Once the capacitor reaches a certain level of charge, it energizes the electronic switching circuit, completing the ground circuit to the pulse relay. This energizes the 12-volt circuit to the motor windings and the motor operates. When the driver presses the wash button, it grounds the washer pump ratchet relay coil circuits, starting a wash cycle. The electronic timer circuity uses a high-voltage signal for wiper operation and a low-voltage signal for the wash cycle.

A multiplex circuit that functions with parallel data transmission is a good tool for simple circuit control. However, transmitting data in parallel form is slower and more cumbersome than transmitting in serial form. This is important when the signal is to be used by several different components or circuits at the same time.

Serial Data Transmission

Serial data transmission has become the most frequently used type of multiplex circuit in automotive applications. It is more versatile than parallel transmission but also more complex. A single circuit used to transmit data in both directions also is called a bus data link.

Multiplex Wiring System: An electrical circuit in which several devices share signals on a common conductor. Signals may be transmitted in parallel form by a solid-state switching device or in serial form over a peripheral data bus or fiber-optic cable.

Figure 5-21. Parallel data transmission through differentiated voltage levels reduces the amount of wiring in this multiplex wiper-washer circuit. (GM)

Several different components, or elements within a single component, can be operated by sequencing voltage inputs transmitted in serial form. This allows each component or element to receive input for a specified length of time before the input is transmitted to another component or element. A four-element **light-emitting diode (LED)** display in the instrument cluster is a typical example. By rotating the applied voltage from left to right rapidly enough, each segment of the display is illuminated 25 percent of the time, but the human eye cannot detect that fact. To the eye, the entire display appears to be uniformly illuminated 100 percent of the time.

To prevent interference between the various signals transmitted, a multiplex system using bus data links must have a central transmitter (microprocessor) containing a special encoder. The system also requires a receiver with a corresponding decoder at each electrical load to be controlled. The transmitter and each receiver are connected to battery power and communicate through a two-way data link called a peripheral serial bus. Operational switches for each circuit to be controlled have an individual digital code or signal and are connected to the transmitter. When the transmitter receives a control code, it determines which switch is calling and sends the control signal to the appropriate receiver. The receiver then carries out the command. Suppose a driver operates the headlamp switch. The transmitter will signal the proper receiver to turn the headlights on or off, according to the switch position.

On the Chrysler application shown in figure 5-22, each module has its own microprocessor connected to the data bus through the Chrysler Collision Detection (C2D) integrated circuit which sends and receives

data. The C2D circuit acts like a traffic control officer at a four-way intersection. If the data bus is not in use, it allows unrestricted transmission from a module. However, if one module is transmitting, it blocks the transmission of data from another module until the bus (intersection) is clear. If two or more modules start to transmit at the same time, or almost at the same time, the C2D circuit assigns a priority to the messages according to the identification code at the beginning of the transmission. If a message is blocked by the C2D circuit, the module which originally sent it retransmits the signal until it is successful.

Receivers work in one of two ways: they operate the electrical load directly, or they control a relay in the circuit to operate the load indirectly. They are not capable of making decisions on their own, but only carry out commands from the transmitter. However, they can send a feedback signal informing the transmitter that something is wrong with the system.

Optical Data Links

A variation of the serial data transmission approach to multiplexing substitutes optical data links or fiber-optic cables for the peripheral serial bus. The concept is the same, but light signals are substituted for voltage signals. An optical data link system operates with the transmitter and receivers described above, but a light-emitting diode (LED) in the transmitter sends light signals through the fiber-optic cables to a photo diode in the receiver. The light signals are decoded by the receiver, which then performs the required control function.

This form of multiplexing has been used primarily by Toyota and other foreign manufacturers. Because it

Figure 5-22. The Chrysler EVIC system is an example of a vehicle data communications network which allows separate computers to share data and communicate with each other through serial data transmission. (Chrysler)

uses light instead of voltage to transmit signals, system operation is not affected by EMI, nor does the system create interference that might have an adverse influence on other electrical systems in the vehicle.

Multiplex Advantages

Regardless of the type of multiplex system used, such a circuit offers several advantages over conventional wiring circuits used in the past:

- The size and number of wires required for a given circuit can be greatly reduced. As a result, the complexity and size of wiring harnesses also are reduced.
- The low-current capacity switches used in a multiplex circuit allow the integration of various touch-type switches into the overall vehicle design.
- The master computer or transmitter can be programmed with timing functions for convenience features, such as locking doors above a given speed or unlocking them when the ignition is shut off.

ELECTRICAL SYSTEM POLARITY

We discussed positive (+) and negative (-) electrical charges in Chapter One. We learned that like charges repel each other and unlike charges attract each other.

We also noted that the terminals of a voltage source are identified as positive and negative. In Chapter Two, we defined magnetic polarity in terms of the north and south poles of a magnet and observed that unlike poles of a magnet attract each other, just as unlike charges do. Similarly, like poles repel each other.

■ Connection Protection

It's a well-known fact that salt and calcium used on icy roads take their toll on the underside of vehicles. They can also cause trouble with exposed electrical connections, so the Prestolite Company offers a tip for protecting these connections. When repairing broken wires or adding a splice for an accessory circuit, place a two-inch length of plastic soda straw over one end. Then join the wires, making sure you have a good solder joint. After the soldered splice has cooled, coat it freely with silicone rubber sealant. Slide the plastic straw over the splice, ensuring that the straw is completely filled with the sealing material. After it has cured, the sealed splice will be corrosion-proof.

Light-Emitting Diode (LED): A gallium-arsenide diode that emits energy as light. Often used in automotive indicators.

The polarity of an electrical system refers to the connections of the positive and negative terminals of the voltage source, the battery, to the insulated and ground sides of the system. All domestic cars and trucks manufactured since 1956 have the negative battery terminal connected to ground and the positive terminal connected to the insulated side of the system. These are called negative-ground systems and are said to have positive polarity.

Before 1956, 6-volt Ford and Chrysler vehicles had the positive battery terminal connected to ground and the negative terminal connected to the insulated side of the system. These are called positive-ground systems and are said to have negative polarity. Foreign manufacturers used positive-ground systems as late as 1969. In both kinds of systems, we say that current leaves the hot side of the battery and returns through the ground path to the grounded battery terminal.

In your service work, it is very important to recognize system polarity negative or positive ground before working on the electrical system. Some electrical components and test equipment are sensitive to the system polarity and must be installed with their connections matching those of the battery. Reversing polarity can damage alternators, cause motors to run backwards, ruin electronic modules, and cause relays or solenoids to malfunction. We will learn more about this in later chapters.

COMMON ELECTRICAL PARTS

Many common electrical parts are used in various circuits in an electrical system. All circuits have switches of some kind to control current flow. Most circuits have some form of protective device, such as a fuse or circuit breaker, to protect against too much current flow. Various kinds of solenoids, relays, and motors are used in many circuits, and whatever their purpose, they operate in similar ways wherever they are used.

Before we look at complete circuits and system diagrams in the next chapter, we should learn about some of the common devices used in many circuits. The following paragraphs describe these items.

Switches

Switches are used in automobile electrical systems to start, stop, or redirect current flow. They can be operated manually by the driver or remotely through mechanical linkage. Manual switches, such as the ignition switch and the headlamp switch, allow the driver to control the operation of the engine and accessories. Examples are shown in figure 5-23. A remotely

Figure 5-23. Many different types of switches are used in the complete electrical system of a modern automobile.

TOGGLE   PUSH-PULL   PUSH BUTTON

Figure 5-24. These symbols for normally open switches are used on electrical system diagrams.

operated switch is controlled indirectly by the driver or the passengers. For example, a mechanical switch called a neutral safety switch on automatic transmission gear selectors will not let the engine start if the automobile is in gear. Switches operated by opening and closing the doors control the interior lights.

Switches exist in many forms but have common characteristics. They all depend upon physical movement for operation. A simple switch contains one or more sets of contact points, with half of the points stationary and the other half movable. When the switch is operated, the movable points change position.

Switches can be designed so that the points are normally open and switch operation closes them to allow current flow. Normally closed switches allow the operator to open the points and stop current flow. For example, in an automobile with a seatbelt warning buzzer, the switch points are opened when the seatbelt is buckled. This stops current flow to the buzzer. Figure 5-24 shows the electrical symbols for some simple normally open switches.

A switch may lock in the desired position, or it may be spring-loaded so that a constant pressure is required to keep the points out of their normal position. Switches with more than one set of contact points can control more than one circuit. For example,

Figure 5-25. The instrument panel switch in this two-speed windshield wiper circuit has two sets of contacts linked together as shown by the broken line. The Park switch is operated by mechanical linkage from the wiper motor armature. (Chrysler)

Figure 5-26. This starting and ignition switch has two sets of contacts linked together by the dashed line. Triangular terminals in the Start (ST) position indicate that this position is spring-loaded and that the switch will return to RUN when the key is released. (Chrysler)

a windshield wiper switch might control a low, medium, and high wiper speed, as well as a windshield washer device, figure 5-25.

Switches are shown in simplified form on electrical diagrams so that current flow through them can easily be traced, figure 5-26. Triangular contact points generally indicate a spring-loaded return, with circular contacts indicating a locking-position switch. A dashed line between the movable parts of a switch means that they are mechanically connected and operate in unison, figure 5-26.

Figure 5-27. A coolant temperature switch in its normally open position. (Ford)

In addition to manual switches, automotive electrical circuits use a variety of other switch designs. Switches may be operated by temperature or pressure. Switches designed to sense engine coolant temperature contain a bimetal arm that flexes as it heats and cools, opening or closing the switch contacts, figure 5-27. Oil pressure and vacuum switches respond to changes in pressure.

Mercury and inertia switches are motion detector switches, that is, they open and close circuits automatically when their position is disturbed. A mercury switch uses a capsule containing two electrical contacts at one end. The other end is partially filled with mercury, which is a good conductor, figure 5-28.

Figure 5-28. A mercury switch is activated by motion. (Ford)

Figure 5-29. A relay contains a control circuit and a power circuit. (Ford)

When the capsule moves a specified amount in a given direction, the mercury flows to the opposite end of the capsule and makes a circuit between the contacts. This type of switch often is used to turn on engine compartment or trunk lamps. It can also be used as a rollover switch to open an electric fuel pump or other circuit in an accident.

An inertia switch is generally a normally closed switch with a calibrated amount of spring pressure or friction holding the contacts together. Any sharp physical movement (a sudden change in inertia) sufficient to overcome the spring pressure or friction will open the contacts and break the circuit. This type of switch is used to open the fuel pump circuit in an impact collision. After the switch has opened, it must be reset manually to its normally closed position.

Relays

A relay is a switch that uses electromagnetism to physically move the contacts. It allows a small current to control a much larger one. As you remember from our introduction to relays in Chapter Two, a small amount of current flow through the relay coil moves an armature to open or close a set of contact points. This is called the control circuit because the points control the flow of a much larger amount of current through a separate circuit, called the power circuit, figure 5-29.

A relay with a single control winding is generally used for a short duration, as in a horn circuit, figure 5-30. Relays designed for longer periods or continuous use require two control windings. A heavy winding creates the magnetic field necessary to move the armature; a lighter second winding breaks the circuit on the heavy winding and maintains the magnetic field to hold the armature in place with less current drain.

Figure 5-30. When the horn button is pressed, low current through the relay coil magnetizes the core. This pulls the armature down and closes the contacts to complete the high-current circuit from the battery to the horn.

Solenoids

A solenoid is similar to a relay in the way it operates. The major difference is that the solenoid core moves instead of the armature, as in a relay. This allows a solenoid to change current flow into mechanical movement.

Solenoids consist of a coil winding around a spring-loaded metal plunger, figure 5-31. When the switch is closed and current flows through the windings, the magnetic field of the coil attracts the movable plunger, pulling it against spring pressure into the center of the coil toward the plate. Once current flow stops, the magnetic field collapses and spring pressure moves the plunger out of the coil. This type of solenoid is used to operate remote door locks and to control vacuum valves in emission control and air-conditioning systems.

Figure 5-31. Energizing a solenoid moves its core, converting current flow into mechanical movement. (Ford)

Figure 5-32. A starter solenoid mounted on the starter motor. Solenoid movement engages the starter drive with the engine flywheel gear.

Figure 5-33. A starter solenoid also acts as a relay.

The most common automotive use of a solenoid is in the starter motor circuit. In many systems, the starter solenoid is designed to do two jobs. The movement of the plunger engages the starter motor drive gear with the engine flywheel ring gear so that the motor can crank the engine, figure 5-32. The starter motor requires high current, so the solenoid also acts as a relay. When the plunger moves into the coil, a large contact point on the plunger meets a large stationary contact point, figure 5-33. Current flow across these contact points completes the battery-to-starter motor circuit. The plunger must remain inside the coil for as long as the starter motor needs to run.

A large amount of current is required to draw the plunger into the coil, and the starter motor also requires a large amount of current. To conserve battery energy, starting circuit solenoids have two coil windings, the primary or **pull-in winding** and the secondary or **hold-in winding**, figure 5-34. The pull-in winding is made of very large diameter wire which creates a magnetic field strong enough to pull the plunger into the coil. The hold-in winding is made of much smaller diameter wire. Once the plunger is inside the coil, it is close enough to the hold-in winding that a weak magnetic field will hold it there. The large current flow through the pull-in winding is stopped when the plunger is completely inside the coil, and only the smaller hold-in winding draws current from the battery. The pull-in winding on a starter solenoid may draw from 25 to 45 amperes. The hold-in winding may draw only 7 to 15 amperes.

Some starter motors do not need the solenoid movement to engage gears. Circuits for these motors use a solenoid primarily as a current switch. The physical movement of the plunger brings it into contact with the battery and starter terminals of the

Pull-In Winding: The coil of large-diameter wire in a solenoid that is used to create a magnetic field to pull the solenoid plunger into the coil.

Hold-In Winding: The coil of small-diameter wire in a solenoid that is used to create a magnetic field to hold the solenoid plunger in position inside the coil.

Figure 5-34. A starter solenoid, showing the pull-in and hold-in windings. (Delco-Remy)

Figure 5-35. When the Ford starter relay is energized, the plunger contact disk moves against the battery and starter terminals to complete the circuit. (Ford)

solenoid, figure 5-35, allowing full battery current to flow to the starter motor. This type of solenoid can be designed to provide an alternate path to the ignition coil during starting. This bypasses the resistance wire normally used to lower coil voltage during engine operation and provides a hotter spark during starting.

Buzzers and Chimes

Buzzers are used in some automotive circuits as warning devices. Seatbelt buzzers and door-ajar buzzers are good examples. A buzzer is similar in construction to a relay but its internal connections differ. Current flow through a coil magnetizes a core to move an armature and a set of contact points. However, in a buzzer, the coil is in series with the armature and the contact points are normally closed.

When the switch is closed, current flow through the buzzer coil reaches ground through the normally closed contacts. However, current flow also magnetizes the buzzer core to move the armature and open the contacts. This breaks the circuit, and current flow stops. Armature spring tension then closes the contacts, making the circuit again, figure 5-36. This action is repeated several hundred times a second, and the vibrating armature creates the buzzing sound.

Most simple automotive buzzers are sealed units and simply plug into their circuits. Some buzzers are combined in a single assembly with a relay for another circuit, figure 5-37, such as a horn relay. This application is used on some General Motors cars. While mechanical buzzers are still in use, they are comparatively heavy and draw a relatively high current compared to the lighter solid-state chimes and buzzers provided by electronic technology and tone generators.

Motors

The typical automotive electrical system includes a number of motors which perform various jobs. The most common is the starter motor (also called a cranking motor) which rotates the automobile's crankshaft until the engine starts and can run by itself. Other smaller motors run windshield wipers, power windows, and other accessories. Whatever job they do, all electric motors operate on the same principles of electromagnetism.

We explained the motor principle in terms of magnetic field interaction in Chapter Two. When a current-carrying conductor is placed in an external magnetic field, it tends to move out of a strong field area and into a weak field area, figure 5-38. This motion can be used to rotate an armature. Now we will see how automotive electrical motors are constructed and used.

A simple picture of electric motor operation, figure 5-39, looks much like the operation of a simple generator. Instead of rotating the looped conductor to induce a voltage, however, we are applying a current to force the conductor to rotate. As soon as the conductor has made a half-revolution, the field interaction would tend to force it back in the opposite direction. To keep the conductor rotating in one direction, the current flow through the conductor must be reversed.

Figure 5-36. Armature spring tension is the key to buzzer operation. (Ford)

Figure 5-37. Typical horn relay and buzzer circuits. (Delco-Remy)

This is done by the split-ring commutator, which rotates with the conductor, figure 5-39.

Current is carried to the conductor through carbon brushes. At the point where current direction must be reversed, the commutator has rotated so that the opposite half of the split ring is in contact with the current-feeding brush. Current flow is reversed in the conductor and rotation continues in the original direction. In actual motors, many more conductor loops are mounted on an armature, figure 5-40.

Figure 5-38. The motor principle.

Figure 5-39. A simple motor.

Figure 5-40. An electric motor. (Delco-Remy)

Electric motors can be manufactured with several brushes and varying combinations of series and parallel connections for armature windings and electromagnetic field windings. The design depends upon the use to which the motor will be put.

Electric motors generally use electromagnetic field poles because they can produce a strong field in a

Figure 5-41. The electrical symbol for a motor.

FUSE

Figure 5-42. The electrical symbol for a fuse.

limited space. Field strength in such a motor is determined by the current flow through the field windings. The starter motor is the most common automotive application of this design.

Most small motors used in automotive applications, however, are built with permanent magnet fields. These motors are inexpensive, lightweight, can reverse direction of operation if necessary and be equipped with up to three operating speeds. They are ideal for constant light loads such as a small electric fan.

Regardless of how they are built, all motors work on these principles. Understanding the internal connections of a motor is essential for testing and repair. Figure 5-41 shows the circuit symbol for a motor.

Circuit Protection Devices

Any amount of current flow through a conductor will raise the temperature of the conductor. The amount of heat generated depends upon the gauge of the conductor, its resistance, and the amount of current present. If a wire carries too much current, the heat could damage or destroy the insulation, the conductor, and nearby wires. Similarly, too much current flow can damage other electrical devices. Circuit protection devices are designed to keep circuitry from being overloaded with current. Automotive electrical systems use three types of protectors:

- Fuses
- Circuit breakers
- Fusible links.

A circuit protection device "blows", or opens the circuit, because of a problem somewhere in the circuit. Installing a new device will not solve the problem, as whatever caused the first device to blow will quickly do the same to the replacement. You must always determine and correct the cause of the blown device before the circuit can be restored to working order.

Fuses

A fuse contains a fine piece of metal that can carry a specified current without damage. Any current higher than that rating will melt, or fuse, the metal and open the circuit. Figure 5-42 shows the electrical

symbol for a fuse. Fuses may be cylindrical or blade-type.

Cylindrical fuses

Cylindrical automotive fuses contain a fine strip of zinc, housed either in a glass cylinder or on a ceramic cartridge. Glass fuses are uniform in diameter, but vary in length according to current rating. The narrow section in the middle of the fuse strip is its weak point, and it is this section that will melt if current higher than the rating passes through the fuse. The wide sections at each end of the strip and the end caps of the fuse dissipate the heat of brief current overloads that are not serious enough to harm the circuit.

Fuses are rated by current capacity. It is excessive current, not voltage, that causes a fuse to burn out or blow. As long as the current passing through it is within the limit tolerated by its design, a fuse can operate with varying voltages. For example, a 10-ampere fuse will work in a 10-ampere 6-volt circuit or a 10-ampere 12-volt circuit. Automotive fuse ratings range from 0.5 to 35 amperes, with those in the 4- to 20-ampere range most commonly used. Fuse identification is provided on one or both end caps.

Fuses are made in a range of standard sizes and ampere ratings established by the Society of Fuse Engineers (SFE). All SFE fuses have the same diameter, but the length varies according to the current rating. Figure 5-43 shows several SFE fuses. The Bussman Division of McGraw-Edison makes several types of automotive fuses, known as the AGA, AGW, and AGC series, figure 5-44. These also are made in various current ratings, but the lengths of the fuses in each series are the same. Therefore, an AGC 5-ampere fuse will fit in the same fuse holder as an AGC 20-ampere fuse.

Many European vehicles use ceramic cartridge fuses, figure 5-45. These work exactly like cylindrical glass fuses, but have exposed elements and pointed ends that fit into special fuse holders. Ceramic cartridge fuses are manufactured in a limited number of amperage ratings, and are color-coded accordingly for visual identification. Cylindrical glass fuses designed with pointed ends are available to replace this type of fuse.

Figure 5-43. The lengths of SFE fuses vary with the current ratings.

AGA

AGW

AGC

Figure 5-44. Regardless of the current ratings, all AGA (top) fuses are the same length, as are AGW (center) and AGC (bottom) fuses.

Most of the fuses in an automotive electrical system are located in a fuse box or panel, figure 5-46, located under the instrument panel, behind a side kick panel, or in the engine compartment. Current to the plastic fuse panel comes directly from the battery or through the accessory circuit of the ignition switch. The power leads are attached to **buss bars,** which are solid metal strips to which fuse holders are riveted, figure 5-47.

Figure 5-45. These ceramic cartridge fuses are used in European cars.

Figure 5-46. Front view of a typical fuse panel. (Chrysler)

A circuit which has a frequent heavy current demand, such as for the windshield wipers, the hazard flasher, or the radio, will have its own fuse. Other circuits may have inline fuses installed in plastic fuse holders and spliced into the circuit wiring. Low-current circuits that are used infrequently, such as courtesy lamps, cigarette lighters, and glove box lamps, can be grouped together and protected by a single fuse. Fuse panels generally have some kind of coding used to identify the fuse sizes and circuit connections, figure 5-48.

Buss Bar: A solid metal strip, or bar, used as a conductor in a fuse panel.

- **FEED FROM HEADLAMP SWITCH**
- **PROVIDES CURRENT TO 4-AMP FUSE IDENTIFIED AS PANEL LIGHTS**

- **FEED FROM BATTERY SOURCE**
- **PROVIDES CURRENT TO 9-AMP, 20-AMP, AND 14-AMP FUSES IDENTIFIED AS DOME/ CLOCK, HAZARD SIGNAL/STOP LIGHT, AND PARK/TAIL**

BUSS BARS

- **FEED FROM I-1 TERMINAL OF IGNITION SWITCH**
- **PROVIDES CURRENT TO 4-AMP FUSE IDENTIFIED AS GAUGES**

BUSS BARS

REAR VIEW

- **FEED FROM "A" TERMINAL OF IGNITION SWITCH**
- **PROVIDES CURRENT TO TWO 20-AMP FUSES IDENTIFIED AS TURN SIGNAL ACCESSORY AND HEATER-A/C**

Figure 5-47. Rear of the same fuse panel, showing buss bars and electrical connections. (Chrysler)

Some fuse panels even have a built-in test circuit, figure 5-49. With the ignition and light switches on, the technician moves a slide knob to each detented position and a check light comes on if the fuse is good.

ATO, ATC, and ATM blade-type fuses
The blade-type, or Autofuse, was first introduced in 1977 on General Motors cars and has been adopted by all domestic and most foreign carmakers to reduce the size of the fuse block. The fuse element is similar to that used in cylindrical fuses, but one continuous piece of metal serves both as the element and blade terminals, and is sealed in a flat plastic body. When inserted in a fuse panel, the tops of the terminals are exposed. This allows a technician to check the fuse condition with a test probe without removing the fuse from the fuse block.

Autofuses are color-coded according to current rating (3 to 30 amperes), which also is stamped on the plastic body. Some darker colors, however, make it difficult to visually determine if the fuse is good or bad, while it is sometimes difficult to tell the difference between the pastel colors, especially in bad lighting.

Figure 5-50 shows the Autofuse design and the difference between a good and a bad fuse.

The Minifuse was introduced in 1990 with current ratings of 5 to 30 amperes. This blade-type fuse is identical in design and appearance to the original Autofuse, but only two-thirds its size, figure 5-51. Its smaller size allows more specific circuit fusing for a given size fuse block. As an example, standard Chrysler fuse blocks holding 20 Autofuses would provide enough space for 28 Minifuses.

Circuit breakers
Circuit breakers are mechanical devices that use the different rates of expansion in heated metals to protect circuitry. Unlike fuses, they last through repeated uses. They are used in circuits where temporary overloads are more frequent and where power must be restored rapidly, as in the headlamp circuit.

A circuit breaker consists of a set of contact points, one on a fixed mounting and the other on a bimetallic strip, figure 5-52. As current flows across the bimetallic strip, the metals heat and expand at different rates. If too much current flows, the expansion will be great enough to bend the strip and open the contact points, stopping current flow. The strip cools in a few seconds and the points close. If current flow is still too high, the strip will again heat and open the points. This process will continue until the excessive current is stopped. These are called self-resetting, cycling, or Type I circuit breakers.

Manual resettable or non-cycling, Type II breakers do not reset automatically, but remain open once the current has gone too high. A button pops out of the breaker case to indicate that the circuit has been broken. After correcting the source of the problem, the technician can reset the breaker by simply pressing the button.

A second type of non-cycling circuit breaker is a solid-state device called an Electronic Circuit Breaker (ECB). The device has a positive temperature coefficient. The resistance of the ECB increases greatly whenever it is subjected to excessive current flow. When the resistance reaches a predetermined point, the circuit is effectively open, and the ECB will not reset until voltage is removed from its terminals. When voltage is removed, the ECB will reset within one or two seconds.

Type I circuit breakers are commonly used in the headlamp circuit. If the headlamp circuit receives too much current, the repeated opening and closing of the breaker will flash the headlamps so that the car can be safely stopped. Circuit breakers also can be found inside some electrical devices, to protect the innards,

Cavity	Fuse	Items fused
1	5 amp	Cluster w/wiper and headlamp switch, ashtray lamp, oil gauge, temperature gauge, tailgate lock switch, rear window defogger, heated back-light, stereo tape, radio, clock, heater-A/C control lamps
2	5 amp	Dual brake, oil pressure, door ajar indicator, seatbelt lamps w/lift safety relay, seatbelt time delay relay and buzzer, high-temperature lamp, voltage limiter, radio capacitor, fuel and temperature gauge, oil gauge
3	5 amp	Radio w/tape
4	20 amp	Back-up and left turn signal lamps, turn signal flasher, speed control, rear window defogger, A/C clutch, cornering lamps, power antenna
5	20 amp	Hazard flasher
6	20 amp	Stop, dome, rear dome, trunk, glove box, map, courtesy, headlamp switch, ignition switch, vanity, and visor lamps; time delay relay, key-in and headlamp-on buzzer, clock, cigarette lighter
7	20 amp	Side marker, tail, license, parking, and instrument lamps
8	20 amp	Horn (dual) and horn relay
9	30 amp C/B	Power window, power seat, tailgate window lift, tailgate lock
10	30 amp	A/C blower motor, heater blower motor, heated back-light relay, electric deck lid

Figure 5-48. Fuse panel codes indicate fuse sizes and circuit connections. (Chrysler)

FUSE CHECKER SLIDE KNOB

Figure 5-49. The built-in fuse tester used in some imported vehicles. (Mitsubishi)

GOOD FUSE   BLOWN FUSE

Figure 5-50. A visual inspection will determine the condition of an Autofuse. (GM)

AUTOFUSE   MINIFUSE

Figure 5-51. Autofuse and Minifuse comparison. (GM)

and in other lamp circuits. The electrical symbols for a circuit breaker are shown in figure 5-53.

Fusible links

In addition to fuses and circuit breakers, fusible links can protect circuits. These are short lengths of smaller-gauge wire installed in the circuit they are to protect.

■ Circuit Breakers as Test Aids

Finding a problem in a circuit that keeps blowing fuses as fast as you put them in can be a real problem. You can keep the circuit operating long enough to locate the fault, however, by temporarily substituting a circuit breaker for the fuse. Simply take a 20- to 25-ampere circuit breaker and solder two short leads with alligator clips to the breaker terminals. Then, attach the clips to the fuse clips in the fuse panel. Operate the circuit, and the breaker will pop on and off to keep the circuit working long enough for you to find the trouble spot. After fixing the problem, install a new fuse of the correct current rating.

Figure 5-52. A typical circuit breaker. (Ford)

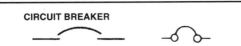

Figure 5-53. The electrical symbols for a circuit breaker.

Figure 5-54. Fusible links in an automotive electrical circuit.

Figure 5-55. Construction of a typical fuse link. (Ford)

Fusible links are used when it would be awkward to run wiring from the voltage source to the fuse panel and back to the load. They also are used in circuits not otherwise protected, and at junction connections or near a circuit splice. Figure 5-54 shows common fusible link locations in a typical circuit.

A current overload will melt the link before it damages the rest of the circuit, figure 5-55. Links are usually four wire-gauge sizes smaller than the rest of the circuit wiring. For example, a circuit using 12-gauge wiring would be protected by a 16-gauge fusible link. The link is covered with a very heavy insulation which will blister and bubble when the conductor melts, showing that the link has fused. However, you cannot always see an open fusible link. Check for battery voltage beyond the fusible link to verify continuity.

Melted links are replaced by soldering or connecting a new one in place after the problem in the circuit has been corrected. Some fusible links are prefabricated and need only be installed. These often are color-coded to indicate current-carrying capacity. Others must be fabricated from a spool of special wire; never use ordinary wire to make a fusible link. When fabricating a fusible link, do not make it longer than nine inches, or it will not provide the required overload protection.

Fuse elements and maxifuses

The Pacific Fuse Element was the first real advance in fusible link design in decades, making its domestic vehicle appearance on the 1988 Lincoln Continental. Often called a fuse link or auto link, this plug-in device looks somewhat like a long, fat blade-type fuse. The fuse link is designed to protect wiring from

a direct short to ground, just as the fusible link does. The housing contains a short link of wire appropriate for the rated current load. The transparent top of the housing allows you to see the link inside, figure 5-56.

Fuse links are available in three configurations. The most commonly used, Series 0 (zero), has a female receptacle at one end, figure 5-56, and plugs into a fuse block containing male terminals. Series 1 has male terminals and plugs into the fuse block like a blade-type fuse. Series 2 has bent terminal legs. Series 1 and 2 can be bolted in place and have a predrilled hole in each terminal leg for this purpose. Like Autofuses, fuse links are color-coded according to amperage value. They are used, however, in high-amperage circuits (30 to 100 amperes), and are easier to inspect or service than a standard fusible link.

The Maxifuse is the latest design to appear as a replacement for fusible links. It looks and acts like a giant Autofuse, figure 5-57, but has a slightly longer average opening time. It was designed as a slower-blowing fuse to prevent nuisance blows. Maxifuses are available in ten-degree increments for circuits from 20 to 80 amperes.

Figure 5-56. The transparent top of the Pacific Fuse Element on the left has been removed to show the element inside. The one on the right shows the legs with the female receptacles that fit over blades in the fuse block or power distribution center.

MAXIFUSE

Figure 5-57. The Maxifuse looks like a large Autofuse. About the same overall size of a Pacific Fuse Element, it is much thinner and requires less space in the fuse block or power distribution center. (GM)

SUMMARY

Many of the conductors in an automobile are grouped together into harnesses to simplify the electrical system. The conductors are usually made of copper, stainless steel, or aluminum covered with an insulator. The conductor can be a solid or single-strand wire, multiple or multistrand wire or printed circuitry.

The wire size or gauge depends on how much current must be carried for what distance. Wire gauge is expressed as a number—the larger the number, the smaller the wire's cross-section.

Cars use some special types of wire, especially in battery cables and ignition cables. Different wires in the car are joined by terminals and connectors. These can join single wires or 40 or more wires.

Part of every automotive circuit is the ground path through the car's frame and body. The battery terminal that is connected to ground determines the electrical system's polarity. Most modern automobiles have a negative-ground system.

Multiplexing simplifies wiring by sending two or more electric signals over a single channel.

Along with conductors, connectors and the ground path, each automotive circuit has controlling or working parts. These include switches, relays, solenoids, buzzers and motors. Most circuits are protected by at least one fuse, circuit breaker, or fusible link.

Review Questions

Choose the single most correct answer.
Compare your answers with the correct answers on Page 468.

1. Which of the following is *not* considered part of the primary wiring system of an automobile?
   a. Spark plug cables
   b. Lighting circuits
   c. Accessory wiring circuits
   d. Power distribution circuits

2. Automotive wiring, or circuit conductors, exist as all of the following, *except:*
   a. Single-strand wire
   b. Multistrand wire
   c. Printed circuitry
   d. Enameled chips

3. Which of the following wires are known as suppression cables?
   a. Turn signal wiring
   b. Cables from the battery to the starter motor
   c. Cables from the distributor cap to the spark plugs
   d. Wiring harnesses from the fuse panel to the accessories

4. High-resistance ignition cables are used to do all of the following, *except:*
   a. Reduce radiofrequency interference
   b. Provide extra resistance to reduce current flow to the spark plugs
   c. Provide more current to the distributor
   d. Boost the voltage being delivered to the spark plugs

5. One of the most common wear points in an automobile electrical system is:
   a. At the ground connecting side
   b. The point where a wire has been bent
   c. Where two connectors have been joined
   d. At a maxifuse connection

6. The symbol below indicates a:

   a. Battery
   b. Capacitor
   c. Diode
   d. Ground

7. Which of the following is *not* a term used to describe an automobile wiring system?
   a. Hot-return system
   b. Single-wire system
   c. Ground-return system
   d. Negative-ground system

8. For easy identification, ground wires on most automotive electrical systems are color-coded:
   a. Red
   b. White
   c. Black
   d. Brown

9. Which of the following is *not* used to switch current flow?
   a. Relay
   b. Solenoid
   c. Transistor
   d. Coil Windings

10. Two separate windings are used in starter solenoids to:
    a. Increase resistance in the circuit
    b. Decrease resistance in the circuit
    c. Increase current being drawn from the battery
    d. Decrease current being drawn from the battery

11. Which of the following reverses the flow of current through the conductor of a motor?
    a. The armature
    b. The terminals
    c. The field coils
    d. The commutator

12. The symbol shown is for a:

    a. Fuse
    b. Relay
    c. Motor
    d. Transistor

13. Which of the following is *not* used to protect a circuit from too much current flow?
    a. Fuse
    b. Buss bar
    c. Fusible link
    d. Circuit breaker

14. What usually causes a fuse to "blow"?
    a. Too much voltage
    b. Too much current
    c. Too little voltage
    d. Too little resistance

15. Fuses are rated by _____ capacity.
    a. Current
    b. Voltage
    c. Resistance
    d. Power

16. Which of the following is true of circuit breakers?
    a. Made of a single metal strip
    b. Must be replaced after excess current flow
    c. Less expensive than fuses are
    d. Used for frequent temporary overloads

6

Introduction to Electrical Diagrams

The preceding chapters used symbols to show some of the components in an automotive electrical system. After studying the basic parts of the system (voltage source, conductors, and loads), it is time to put them together into complete circuits. Figure 6-1 is a diagram showing current flow through a simple circuit consisting of a 12-volt battery for power, a fuse for protection, a switch for control, and a lamp as the load. In this example, each component is labeled and the direction of current is marked.

In real-world cases, diagrams of much greater complexity are used. Technicians must be able to identify each component by its symbol and determine how current travels from the power source to ground. Technicians use electrical circuit diagrams to locate and identify components on the vehicle and trace the wiring in order to make an accurate diagnosis of any malfunctions in the system.

COLOR CODING

Manufacturers use **color coding** to help technicians follow wires in a circuit. Chapter Five explained how most automotive wires are covered with a colored polyvinyl chloride (PVC), or plastic insulation. The color of the insulation helps identify a particular wire in the system. Some drawings of a circuit have letters and numbers printed near each wire, figure 6-2. The code table accompanying the drawing explains what the letters and numbers stand for. This Chrysler diagram contains code information on wire gauge, circuit numbers, and wire color. Circuit numbers are discussed later in this chapter. Figures 6-3, 6-4, and 6-5 show how Chrysler, GM, and Ford may present color code information. Note that the Toyota diagram in figure 6-6 simply has the color name printed on the wires; wire gauge is not identified in this drawing.

THE LANGUAGE OF ELECTRICAL DIAGRAMS

In this Chapter, illustrations from GM, Chrysler, Ford, Toyota, and Nissan show how different manufacturers present electrical information. Note that many component symbols and circuit identification do not look exactly the same among vehicle manufacturers. Once familiar with the diagrams, the differences become less confusing.

Circuit Numbers

If the wire is labeled with a **circuit number,** such as in figures 6-2 and 6-5, those circuits are identified in an accompanying table. The top half of figure 6-3

Figure 6-1. The diagram of a simple circuit.

shows Chrysler's method of identifying circuits with a letter and number. Any two wires with the same circuit number are connected within the same circuit.

General Motors shop manuals contain individual **Valley Forge diagrams,** (named after the company that originally devised them). Electrical circuit diagrams are printed in color so the lines match the color of the wires. The name of the color is printed beside the wire, figure 6-7. The metric wire gauge may also be printed immediately before the color name. Other GM drawings contain a statement that all wires are of a certain gauge, unless otherwise identified. If this is the case, only some wires in the drawing have a gauge number printed on them.

The Ford circuit and table in figure 6-5 are for a heater and air conditioner electrical circuit. The wire numbers are indicated by code numbers, which are also circuit numbers. Again, no wire gauges are identified in this example.

Wire Sizes

Another piece of information found in some electrical diagrams is the wire size. In the past, vehicles built in the United States used wire sizes specified by gauge. Gauge sizes typically vary from two for a starter cable to twenty for a license plate lamp. Note that gauge size numbers are the reverse of physical wire sizes— a lower gauge number for heavy wires and a higher one for light wires. Figure 6-8 shows a typical circuit using 20-gauge wire.

Most vehicles built in recent years specify wire sizes by their diameter in millimeters (mm). In this case, a starter cable might be 32 mm while a typical circuit might be 1 mm or 0.8 mm. The wire size appears next to the color and on the opposite side of

the wire from the circuit number, figure 6-7. Note that the "mm" abbreviation does not appear in the diagram. An advantage to using the metric system is that wire size corresponds directly to thickness.

■ 60 Years of Color-Coding

The sixth edition of the Reo Motor Car Instruction Book shows wiring diagrams for both the left- and right-hand drive models of the 1923-27 E-Roadster. On the left-hand drive model, shown here, the wire from the ignition switch to the generator cutout is identified as 10-gauge wire having a green insulation with a red tracer. The same wire on the right-hand drive model is identified as 10-gauge with yellow insulation.

Color Coding: The use of colored insulation on wire to identify an electrical circuit.

Circuit Number: The number, or number and letter, that manufacturers use to identify a specific electrical circuit in a diagram.

Valley Forge Diagram: A type of system diagram in which current travels from top to bottom and only relevant information is given.

Figure 6-2. A Chrysler diagram showing circuits identified by number and wire color.

CIRCUIT INFORMATION

A   2   18   LB/YL

COLOR OF WIRE
(LIGHT BLUE WITH YELLOW TRACER)

GAUGE OF WIRE
(18 GAUGE)

PART OF MAIN CIRCUIT
(VARIES DEPENDING ON EQUIPMENT)

MAIN CIRCUIT IDENTIFICATION

WIRE COLOR CODE CHART

COLOR CODE	COLOR	STANDARD TRACER COLOR
BL	BLUE	WT
BK	BLACK	WT
BR	BROWN	WT
DB	DARK BLUE	WT
DG	DARK GREEN	WT
GY	GRAY	BK
LB	LIGHT BLUE	BK
LG	LIGHT GREEN	BK
OR	ORANGE	BK
PK	PINK	BK or WT
RD	RED	WT
TN	TAN	WT
VT	VIOLET	WT
WT	WHITE	BK
YL	YELLOW	BK
*	WITH TRACER	

Figure 6-3. Chrysler circuit identification and wire color codes.

WIRE IDENTIFICATION CHART

COLOR	SYMBOL	COLOR	SYMBOL
ALUMINUM	AL	NATURAL	NAT
BLACK	BLK	ORANGE	ORN
BLUE-LIGHT	BLU LT	PINK	PINK
BLUE-DARK	BLU DK	PURPLE	PPL
BROWN	BRN	RED	RED
GLAZED	GLZ	TAN	TAN
GREEN-LIGHT	GRN LT	VIOLET	VLT
GREEN-DARK	GRN DK	WHITE	WHT
GRAY	GRA	YELLOW	YEL
MAROON	MAR		

Figure 6-4. General Motors' diagrams printed in color in the factory manual include this table of color abbreviations.

CIRCUIT NO.	WIRE COLOR
37A	YELLOW
57A	BLACK
181	BROWN W/ORANGE STRIPE
260A	RED W/ORANGE HASH
261A	ORANGE W/BLACK STRIPE
347	BLACK W/YELLOW HASH
348A	LT. GREEN W/PURPLE HASH
687	GRAY W/LT. BLUE STRIPE
752	YELLOW W/RED DOT
754	LT. GREEN W/WHITE HASH

Figure 6-5. This Ford accessory circuit is color coded by circuit number.

Figure 6-6. This Toyota diagram has no color code table; wire color abbreviations are printed directly on the drawing.

Figure 6-7. General Motors Valley Forge schematics are provided in color with the name of the color printed beside the wire.

Component Symbols

It is time to add new symbols to the basic component symbols list, figure 6-9. Figures 6-10a and 6-10b show additional symbols for many of the electrical devices on GM vehicles. Figure 6-11 illustrates symbols used by Chrysler Corporation.

Nissan, as well as other manufacturers, often includes the symbols with its components, connector identification, and switch continuity positions, figure 6-12. Switch continuity diagrams are discussed later in this chapter.

Figure 6-8. In this example from Chrysler, the "X12" in the wire code stands for the #12 part of the main circuit X.

Figure 6-9. These electrical symbols have been discussed up to this point in this *Classroom Manual.*

Logic Symbols

The increasing use of sophisticated electronics in automobiles has caused the appearance of a new type of electrical circuit diagram which contains logic

Figure 6-10a. Some component symbols used by GM.

Figure 6-10b. Some more of GM's component symbols.

Figure 6-11. Some electrical symbols used by Chrysler.

Figure 6-12. This system diagram of a headlight circuit includes a diagram of the headlight switch internal connections.

symbols. It may be a good idea to go back to Chapter Five and review the discussion of various types of logic gates and their functions.

Logic symbols are used to simplify a complex electrical circuit and describe its operation under specified conditions. Figure 6-13 is a basic diagram of a Toyota Celica sunroof control relay which controls the sunroof motor operation. Figure 6-14 shows how the circuit is activated to tilt the sunroof open. The current travels to the motor through relay number one and transistor one when the "up" side of the tilt switch is pressed.

Logic Symbol: A symbol identifying the type of electronic gate in a digital or logic circuit.

Figure 6-13. The advance of computer technology makes logic symbols like these a typical part of an automotive wiring diagram.

Figure 6-14. This circuit uses logic symbols to show how the sunroof motor operates to tilt the mechanism open.

DIAGRAMS

The color codes, circuit numbers, and symbols just illustrated are combined to create a variety of electrical diagrams. Most people tend to refer to any electrical diagram as a "wiring diagram," but there are at least three distinct types with which you should be familiar:

- System diagrams (also called "wiring" diagrams)
- Schematic diagrams (also called "circuit" diagrams)
- Installation diagrams (also called "pictorial" diagrams).

System Diagrams

A **system diagram** is a drawing of the entire automobile electrical system. This may also properly be called a "wiring diagram." System diagrams show the wires, connections to loads, switches, and the type of connectors used, but not how the loads or switches work. Installation diagrams express where and how the loads and wires are installed. This is covered later in this chapter. Figure 6-15 shows the same warning lamp circuit as figure 6-16, but in a different format. System diagrams may cover many pages of a manual

or they may be printed on special oversize, fold-out pages, figure 6-17.

A useful feature provided by some manufacturers on their system diagrams is reference coordinates along the edges. An index is included listing system components alphabetically along with the specific grid coordinates. This system is similar to that found on a road map and is used in the same manner.

Figure 6-18 is a portion of a Toyota system diagram. As previously mentioned, Toyota simply prints the color name on the wire in the drawing without indicating wire gauge. Note that the ground points are identified for all circuits. The diagram is also organized by individual subsystems at the top. This variation on the grid theme is another tool to quickly locate the desired part of the diagram.

A Chrysler Corporation shop manual may not supply an entire system diagram for a vehicle, but instead illustrates all circuits separately, figure 6-19.

■ Wire Size Matters

The drawing shows how a large wire easily conducts a high-amperage current, such as you would find going to a starter motor. The heaviest wires are often called cables, but their purpose is the same. On the other hand, a comparatively light wire tends to restrict current flow, which may generate excess heat if the wire is too small for the job. Too much current running though a light wire may cause the insulation to melt, leading to a short circuit or even a fire.

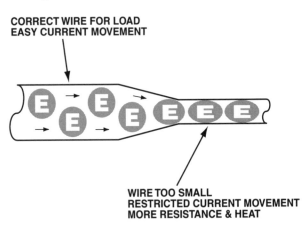

CORRECT WIRE FOR LOAD
EASY CURRENT MOVEMENT

WIRE TOO SMALL
RESTRICTED CURRENT MOVEMENT
MORE RESISTANCE & HEAT

System Diagram: A drawing of a circuit or any part of a circuit that shows circuit numbers, wire size and color coding.

Warning Lamps / Wiring Diagram

Figure 6-15. A system diagram for a warning lamp circuit.

Warning Lamps / Schematic

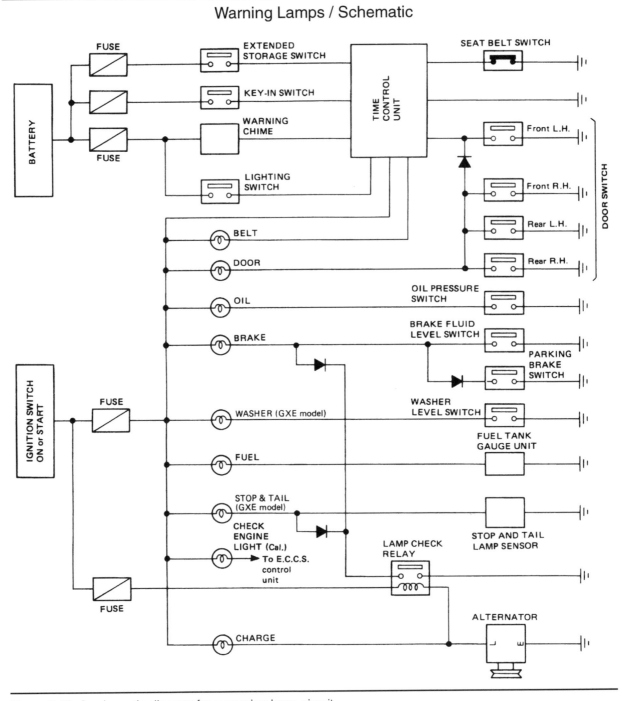

Figure 6-16. A schematic diagram for a warning lamp circuit.

Schematic Diagrams

A **schematic diagram,** also called a "circuit diagram", describes the operation of an individual circuit. Schematics tell you how a circuit works and how the individual components connect to each other, figure 6-16. This type of diagram is commonly used by engineers.

Schematic Diagram: A drawing that shows all of the different circuits in a complete electrical system.

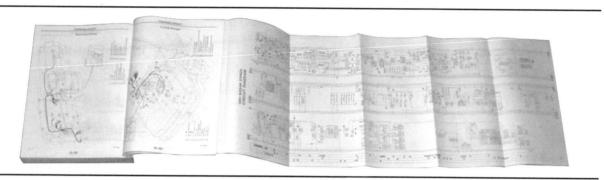

Figure 6-17. Many shop manuals include fold-out pages with a complete set of wiring diagrams for the vehicle.

Figure 6-18. Toyota system diagrams are organized by individual systems and include ground points.

Figure 6-19. A Chrysler radio circuit.

Some schematics are Valley Forge diagrams which present current moving vertically. The power source is at the top and the ground at the bottom of the page, figures 6-7 and 6-20.

Figure 6-19 illustrates the circuit for a Chrysler radio system. Some of the wires are fully identified with two circuit numbers, wire gauge, and wire color. Other wires, such as the two wires connected to the front speaker, are identified only by wire gauge and color. The "20LGN" indicates a 20-gauge, light green wire.

Figure 6-21 is the fuel economy lamp circuit in a GM vehicle. Here, neither wire gauge nor wire color is indicated. The "green" and "amber" refer to the color of the lamp bulbs.

Figure 6-22 shows a Ford side marker lamp circuit. Again, wire size and color are not identified. The numbers on the wires are circuit numbers. Note that the ground wires on the front and rear lamps may not be present depending upon the type of lamp socket used on the automobile.

Switches

Some manufacturers, such as Nissan, extend the system diagram to include major switches, such as the headlight circuit shown in figure 6-12. This illustration shows the current traveling from the fuse block, through the switch, and to the headlights. If a switch does not work properly, it causes a malfunction in the electrical system. Switch diagrams may take extra

Figure 6-20. This diagram shows a backlight, rear window, heater circuit. Power flows from top to bottom. Only components or information that belong to this specific circuit are included.

Figure 6-21. A GM fuel economy lamp circuit.

Figure 6-22. A Ford side marker lamp circuit.

Figure 6-23. A Chrysler installation diagram.

Figure 6-24. A GM installation diagram.

Figure 6-25. A Ford installation diagram.

Figure 6-26. An Acura installation diagram.

time to understand, but they are valuable in testing and diagnosis.

Each connection is shown as two circles joined by a line. The grid diagram shows which individual circuits have power at each switch position. A drawing of the headlight switch is included to explain the meaning of OFF, 1ST, 2ND, A, B, and C. Normally, a drawing of the switch action does not accompany the system diagram. If the switch positions are not clear, find that information elsewhere in the electrical section of the manufacturer's shop manual.

Installation Diagrams

None of the diagrams shown so far have indicated *where* or *how* the wires and loads are installed in the automobile. Many manufacturers provide **installation diagrams,** or pictorial diagrams, which show these locations. Figures 6-23, 6-24, 6-25, and 6-26 show different styles of installation diagrams which help locate the general harness or circuit.

The Chrysler installation diagram in figure 6-23 includes the wiring for radio speakers. The circuit diagram for the speakers was shown in figure 6-19. Compare these two diagrams and notice the installation diagram highlights the location of circuits while the circuit diagram gives more of a detailed picture of the circuit.

Figure 6-24 is a GM installation diagram for the fuel economy indicator switch. The circuit diagram for this accessory was given in figure 6-21. Compare

these two diagrams and note the installation diagram focuses on the harness and circuit location while the schematic diagram shows a specific circuit current reading top to bottom.

This Ford installation diagram for a side lamp assembly, figure 6-25, also details the placement of the bulbs and lenses. Figure 6-22 illustrated the circuit diagram for these lamps. Compare these two diagrams and see if you notice the major differences between the installation diagram and the circuit diagram.

Troubleshooting With Schematic Diagrams

It is quicker and easier to diagnose and isolate an electrical problem using a schematic diagram than by working with a system diagram. This is true because schematic diagrams do not distract or confuse with wiring that is not part of the circuit being tested. A schematic diagram shows the paths that electrical current takes in a properly functioning circuit. It is important to understand how the circuit is supposed to work before determining why it is malfunctioning.

General Motors incorporates a special troubleshooting section in each shop manual for the entire electrical system, broken down by individual circuits, figures 6-7 and 6-20. Each schematic contains all the basic information necessary to trace the circuit it covers: wire size and color, components, connector and ground references, and references to other circuits when necessary. In addition, a quick summary of system operation is provided to explain what should happen when the system is working properly.

Ford provides a similar troubleshooting aid in the form of its Electrical and Vacuum Troubleshooting Guide (EVTG) published for each vehicle in a model year. The Ford circuit schematics contain much of the same information as those used by GM, figure 6-27, but are organized in a more traditional, horizontal manner.

Installation Diagram: A drawing that shows where the wires, switches, loads, attachment hardware, and other parts of an electrical circuit are located.

Figure 6-27. This Ford circuit schematic is read horizontally.

Both GM and Ford include a power distribution diagram as one of the first overall schematics for troubleshooting, figures 6-28 and 6-29. The power distribution diagram represents the "front end" of the overall electrical system. As such, it includes the battery, starter solenoid or relay, alternator, ignition switch, and fuse panel. This diagram is useful in locating short circuits that blow fusible links or fuses, because it follows the power distribution wiring to the first component in each major circuit.

Figure 6-28. A typical GM power distribution schematic.

Figure 6-29. A Ford power distribution schematic.

SUMMARY

There are three types of electrical circuit diagrams: system, schematic, and installation. System diagrams typically present an overall view, while schematic diagrams isolate a single circuit and are more useful for troubleshooting individual problems. Installation diagrams show locations and harness routing. To better understand these diagrams, a variety of electrical symbols are used to represent electrical components. Other tools to aid in successfully reading these diagrams are the color-coding and the circuit numbering of wires which identify the wire and its function. Manufacturers publish diagrams of each vehicle's electrical systems, often using these color codes and circuit numbers. A technician cannot service a circuit without knowing how to read and use these diagrams.

Review Questions

Choose the single most correct answer.
Compare your answers with the correct answers on Page 468.

1. This symbol represents a:

   a. Fixed resistor
   b. Variable resistor
   c. Capacitor
   d. Solenoid

2. This symbol represents which type of switch?

   a. Push-pull
   b. Toggle
   c. Push button
   d. Single-pole, double-throw

3. The following two symbols represent which two devices?

   a. A zener diode and a PNP transistor
   b. A zener diode and a NPN transistor
   c. A one-way diode and a PNP transistor
   d. A one-way diode and a NPN transistor

4. A lamp is indicated by which of the following electrical symbols?

   a.
   b.
   c.
   d.

5. In this section of a Ford Motor Company circuit diagram, what does the number "14" (circled) indicate?

   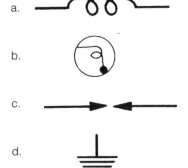

   a. 14 amps
   b. 14 volts
   c. Wire size 14
   d. Circuit number 14

6. The electrical diagram that shows where the wires and loads are physically located on the vehicle is the:
   a. Schematic diagram
   b. Electrical system diagram
   c. Installation diagram
   d. Alternator circuit diagram

7. Automobile manufacturers color-code the wires in the electrical system to:
   a. Help trace a circuit
   b. Identify wire gauge
   c. Speed the manufacturing process
   d. Identify replacement parts

8. A wire in a Valley Forge (system) diagram is identified as ".8 PPL 623". Which of the following accurately describes what this means?
   a. 8-gauge wire, power plant, circuit number 623.
   b. 8-gauge wire, purple, vehicle model 623.
   c. 0.8 mm wire, purple, circuit number 623.
   d. 0.8 points per length, vehicle model 623.

7
Batteries

The automotive battery does not actually store electricity, as is often believed. It converts electrical energy into chemical energy, which is stored until the battery is connected to an external circuit. The stored chemical energy is then converted back to electrical energy, which flows from one battery terminal, through the circuit, and back to the other battery terminal.

We will begin our study of batteries by listing their functions and looking at the chemical action and construction of a battery.

An automotive battery:

- Operates the starter motor.
- Provides current for the ignition system during cranking.
- Supplies power for the lighting systems and electrical accessories when the engine is not operating.
- Acts as a voltage stabilizer for the entire electrical system.
- Provides current when the electrical demand of the vehicle exceeds the output of the charging system.

ELECTROCHEMICAL ACTION

All automotive wet-cell batteries operate because of the chemical action of two dissimilar metals in the presence of a conductive and reactive solution called an **electrolyte**. Because this chemical action produces electricity, it is called electrochemical action. The chemical action of the electrolyte cause electrons to be removed from one metal and added to the other. This loss and gain of electrons causes the metals to be oppositely charged, and a potential difference, or voltage, exists between them.

The metal plate that has lost electrons is positively charged, and is called the positive plate. The plate that has gained electrons is negatively charged, and is called the negative plate. If conductors and a load are connected between the two plates, current will flow through the conductor and the load, figure 7-1. For simplicity, battery current flow is assumed to be conventional current flow (+ to -) through the external circuit connected to the battery.

Primary and Secondary Batteries

There are two general types of batteries: primary and secondary.

The action within a **primary battery** causes one of the metals to be totally destroyed after a period of time. When the battery has delivered all of its voltage to an outside circuit, it is useless and must be replaced. Many small dry-cell batteries, such as those for flashlights and radios, are primary batteries.

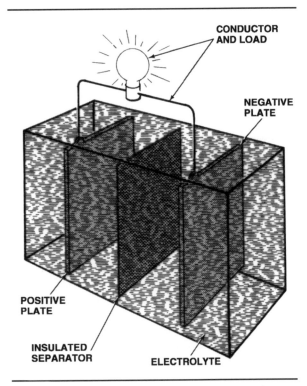

Figure 7-1. The potential difference between the two plates of a battery can cause current to flow in an outside circuit. (Chevrolet)

In **secondary batteries**, both the electrolyte and the metals change their atomic structure as the battery supplies current to an outside circuit. This is called discharging. The action can be reversed, however, by applying an outside current to the battery terminals and forcing current through the battery in the opposite direction. This current causes a chemical action that restores the battery materials to their original condition, and the battery can again supply current. This is called charging the battery. The condition of the battery materials is called the battery's state of charge.

Electrochemical Action in Automotive Batteries

A fully charged automotive battery contains a series of negative plates of chemically active sponge lead (Pb), positive plates of lead dioxide (PbO_2), and an electrolyte of sulfuric acid (H_2SO_4) and water (H_2O), figure 7-2.

As the battery discharges, figure 7-2, the chemical action taking place reduces the acid content in the electrolyte and increases the water content. At the same time, both the negative and the positive plates gradually change to lead sulphate ($PbSO_4$).

A discharged battery, figure 7-2, has a very weak acid solution because most of the electrolyte has changed to water. Both series of plates are mostly lead sulfate. The battery now stops functioning because the plates are basically two similar metals in the presence of water, rather than two dissimilar metals in the presence of an electrolyte.

During charging, figure 7-2, the chemical action is reversed. The lead sulfate on the plates gradually decomposes, changing the negative plates back to sponge lead and the positive plates to lead dioxide. The sulfate is redeposited in the water, which increases the sulfuric acid content and returns the electrolyte to full strength. Now, the battery is again able to supply current.

This electrochemical action and battery operation from fully charged to discharged and back to fully charged is called **cycling**.

A safety note is important here: Hydrogen and oxygen gases are formed during battery charging. Hydrogen gas is explosive. Never strike a spark or bring a flame near a battery, particularly during or after charging. *This could cause the battery to explode.*

Battery Construction

There are four types of automotive batteries currently in use:

- Vent-cap (requires maintenance)
- Low-maintenance (requires limited maintenance)
- Maintenance-free (requires no maintenance)
- Recombinant (requires no maintenance).

The basic physical construction of all types of automotive batteries is similar, but the materials used are not. We will look at traditional vent-cap construction first and then explain how the other battery types differ.

Vent-cap batteries

Battery construction begins with the positive and negative plates. The plates are built on grids of conductive materials, figure 7-3, which act as a framework for the dissimilar metals. These dissimilar metals are called the active materials of the battery. The active materials, sponge lead and lead dioxide, are pasted onto the grids. When dry, the active materials are very porous, so that the electrolyte can easily penetrate and react with them.

A number of similar plates, all positive or all negative, are connected together into a plate group, figure 7-4. The plates are joined to each other by welding them to a plate strap through a process called lead burning. The plate strap has a connector or a terminal post for attaching plate groups to each other.

A positive and a negative plate group are interlaced so that their plates alternate, figure 7-5. The negative

Figure 7-2. Battery electrochemical action from charged, to discharged, and back to charged.

plate group normally has one more plate than the positive group. To reduce the possibility of a short between plates of the two groups, they are separated by chemically inert separators, figure 7-5. Separators are usually made of plastic or fiberglass. The separators have ribs on one side next to the positive plates. These ribs hold electrolyte near the positive plates for efficient chemical action.

A complete assembly of positive plates, negative plates, and separators is called an **element**. It is placed in a cell of a battery case. Because each **cell** provides

approximately 2.1 volts, a 12-volt battery has six cells and actually produces approximately 12.6 volts when fully charged.

The elements are separated from each other by cell partitions, and rest on bridges at the bottom of the case that form chambers where sediment can collect. These bridges prevent accumulated sediment from shorting

Electrolyte: The chemical solution in a battery that conducts electricity and reacts with the plate materials.

Primary Battery: A battery in which chemical processes destroy one of the metals necessary to create electrical energy. Primary batteries cannot be recharged.

Secondary Battery: A battery in which chemical processes can be reversed. A secondary battery can be recharged so that it will continue to supply voltage.

Cycling: Battery electrochemical action and operation from charged to discharged and back. One complete cycle is operation from fully charged to discharged and back to fully charged.

Element: A complete assembly of positive plates, negative plates, and separators making up one cell of a battery.

Cell: A case enclosing one element in an electrolyte. Each cell produces approximately 2.1 to 2.2 volts. Cells are connected in series.

■ Other Secondary Cells

The Edison (nickel-iron alkali) cell and the silver cell are two other types of secondary cells. The positive plate of the Edison cell is made of pencil-shaped, perforated steel tubes that contain nickel hydroxide. These tubes are held in a steel grid. The negative plate has pockets that hold iron oxide. The electrolyte used in this cell is a solution of potassium hydroxide and a small amount of lithium hydroxide.

An Edison cell weighs about one-half as much as a lead-acid cell of the same ampere-hour capacity. This cell has a long life and is not damaged by short circuits or overloads. It is however, more costly than a lead-acid cell.

The silver cell has a positive plate of silver oxide and a negative plate of zinc. The electrolyte is a solution of potassium hydroxide or sodium. For its weight, this cell has a high ampere-hour capacity. It can withstand large overloads and short circuits. It, too, is more expensive than a lead-acid cell.

Figure 7-3. The grid provides a support for the plate active material.

Figure 7-4. A number of plates are connected into a group.

Figure 7-5. Two groups are interlaced to form a battery element.

across the bottoms of the plates. Once installed in the case, the elements (cells) are connected to each other by connecting straps that pass over or through the cell partitions, figure 7-6. The cells are connected alternately in series (positive to negative to positive to negative, and so on), and the battery top is bonded onto the case to form a watertight container.

Vent caps in the battery top provide an opening for adding electrolyte and for the escape of gases that form during charging and discharging. The battery is

connected to the car's electrical system by two external terminals. These terminals are either tapered posts on top of the case or internally threaded connectors on the side. The terminals, which are connected to the ends of the series of elements inside the case, are marked positive (+) or negative (-), according to which end of the series each terminal represents.

Low-maintenance and maintenance-free batteries

Most new batteries today are either partially sealed, low-maintenance or completely sealed, maintenance-free batteries. Low-maintenance batteries provide some method of adding water to the cells, such as:

- Individual slotted vent caps installed flush with the top of the case
- Two vent panel covers, each of which exposes three cells when removed
- A flush-mounted strip cover that is peeled off to reveal the cell openings.

Maintenance-free batteries have only small gas vents that prevent pressure buildup in the case. A low-maintenance battery requires that water be added much less often than with a traditional vent-cap battery, while a maintenance-free battery will never need to have water added during its lifetime.

These batteries differ from vent-cap batteries primarily in the materials used for the plate grids. For decades, automotive batteries used antimony as the strengthening ingredient of the grid alloy. In

POSITIVE POST VENT TEST INDICATOR VENT NEGATIVE POST

PLATES CELL ELECTROLYTE LEVEL

BATTERY CASE

Figure 7-6. A cutaway view of an assembled battery. (Chrysler)

low-maintenance batteries, the amount of antimony is reduced to about three percent. In maintenance-free batteries, the antimony is eliminated and replaced by calcium or strontium.

Reducing the amount of antimony or replacing it with calcium or strontium alloy results in lowering the battery's internal heat and reduces the amount of gassing that occurs during charging. Since heat and gassing are the principal reasons for battery water loss, these changes reduce or eliminate the need to periodically add water. Reduced water loss also minimizes terminal corrosion, since the major cause of this corrosion is condensation from normal battery gassing.

In addition, non-antimony lead alloys have better conductivity, so a maintenance-free battery has about a 20-percent higher cranking performance rating than a traditional vent-cap battery of comparable size.

Sealed maintenance-free batteries

More recently, completely sealed maintenance-free batteries were introduced. These new batteries do not require — and do not have — the small gas vent used on previous maintenance-free batteries. Although these batteries are basically the same kind of lead-acid voltage cells used in automobiles for decades, a slight change in plate and electrolyte chemistry reduces hydrogen generation to almost nothing.

During charging, a vent-cap or maintenance-free battery releases hydrogen at the negative plates and oxygen at the positive plates. Most of the hydrogen is released through electrolysis of the water in the electrolyte near the negative plates as the battery reaches full charge. In the sealed maintenance-free design, the

negative plates never reach a fully charged condition and therefore cause little or no release of hydrogen. Oxygen is released at the positive plates, but it passes through the separators and recombines with the negative plates. The overall effect is virtually no gassing from the battery. Because the oxygen released by the electrolyte recombines with the negative plates, some manufacturers call these batteries "recombination" or **recombinant** electrolyte batteries.

Recombinant batteries

Recombination electrolyte technology and improved grid materials allow some sealed, maintenance-free batteries to develop fully charged, open-circuit voltage of approximately 2.2 volts per cell, or a total of 13.2 volts for a six-cell battery. Microporous fiberglass separators reduce internal resistance and contribute to higher voltage and current ratings.

In addition, the electrolyte in these new batteries is contained within plastic envelope-type separators around the plates, figure 7-7. The entire case is not flooded with electrolyte. This eliminates the possibility of damage due to sloshing or acid leaks from a cracked battery. This design feature reduces battery damage during handling and installation, and allows a more compact case design. Because the battery is not vented, terminal corrosion from battery gassing and electrolyte spills or spray is also eliminated.

The envelope design also catches active material as it flakes off the positive plates during discharge. By holding the material closer to the plates, envelope construction ensures that it will be more completely redeposited during charging.

Although recombinant batteries are examples of advanced technology, test and service requirements are basically the same as for other maintenance-free, lead-acid batteries. Some manufacturers caution, however, that fast charging at high current rates may overheat the battery and can cause damage. Always check the manufacturer's instructions for test specifications and charging rates before servicing one of these batteries.

BATTERY ELECTROLYTE

For the battery to become chemically active, it must be filled with an electrolyte solution. The electrolyte in an automotive battery is a solution of sulfuric acid and water. In a fully charged battery, the solution is

Recombinant: A nongassing battery design in which the oxygen released by the electrolyte recombines with the negative plates.

Figure 7-7. Many maintenance-free batteries have envelope separators that hold active material near the plates.

approximately 35 to 39 percent acid by weight (25 percent by volume) and 61 to 65 percent water by weight. The state of charge of a battery can .be measured by checking the **specific gravity** of the electrolyte.

Specific gravity is the weight of a given volume of liquid divided by the weight of an equal volume of water. Since the acid is heavier than water, and water has a specific gravity of 1.000, the specific gravity of a fully charged battery is approximately 1.260 when weighed in a hydrometer. As the battery discharges, the specific gravity of the electrolyte decreases because the acid is changed into water. The specific gravity of the electrolyte can tell you approximately how discharged the battery has become:

1.265 specific gravity	100% charged
1.225 specific gravity	75% charged
1.190 specific gravity	50% charged
1.155 specific gravity	25% charged
1.120 specific gravity or lower	discharged

These values may vary slightly, according to the design factors of a particular battery.

Specific gravity measurements are based on a standard temperature of 80°F (26.7°C). At higher temperatures, specific gravity is lower. At lower temperatures, specific gravity is higher. For every change of 10°F, specific gravity changes by four points (0.004). That is:

- For every 10°F above 80°F, add 0.004 to the specific gravity reading.
- For every 10°F below 80°F, subtract 0.004 from the specific gravity reading.

When you study battery service in the *Shop Manual*, you will learn to measure specific gravity of a vent-cap battery with a hydrometer.

STATE-OF-CHARGE INDICATORS

Many low-maintenance and maintenance-free batteries have a visual state-of-charge indicator installed in the battery top. The indicator shows whether the electrolyte has fallen below a minimum level, and it also functions as a go/no-go hydrometer.

The indicator, figure 7-8, is a plastic rod inserted in the top of the battery and extending into the electrolyte. In the design used by Delco, a green plastic ball is suspended in a cage from the bottom of the rod. Depending upon the specific gravity of the electrolyte, the ball will float or sink in the cage, changing the appearance of the indicator "eye" from green to dark. When the eye is dark, the battery should be recharged.

Other manufacturers use either the "Delco Eye" under license, or one of several variations of the design. One variation contains a red ball and a blue ball side by side in the cage. When the specific gravity is high, only the blue ball can be seen in the "eye". As the specific gravity falls, the blue ball sinks in the cage, allowing the red ball to take its place. When the battery is recharged, the increasing specific gravity causes the blue ball to move upward, forcing the red ball back into the side of the cage.

Another variation is the use of a small red ball on top of a larger blue ball. When the specific gravity is high, the small ball is seen as a red spot surrounded by blue. As the specific gravity falls, the blue ball sinks, leaving the small ball to be seen as a red spot surrounded by a clear area. The battery then should be recharged.

If the electrolyte drops below the level of the cage in batteries using a state-of-charge indicator, the "eye" will appear clear or light yellow. This means that the battery must be replaced because it has lost too much electrolyte.

WET-CHARGED AND DRY-CHARGED BATTERIES

Batteries may be manufactured and sold as either wet-charged or dry-charged batteries. Before maintenance-free batteries became widely used, dry-charged batteries were very common. A wet-charged battery is

GREEN DOT   "BLACK" DARK   CLEAR

65% OR ABOVE   BELOW 65%   LOW LEVEL
STATE OF CHARGE   STATE OF CHARGE   ELECTROLYTE

Figure 7-8. Delco "Freedom" batteries have this integral hydrometer built into their tops.

completely filled with an electrolyte when it is built. A dry-charged battery is shipped from the factory without electrolyte. During manufacture, the positive and negative plates are charged and then completely washed and dried. The battery is then assembled and sealed to keep out moisture. It will remain charged as long as it is sealed, and it can be stored for a long time in any reasonable environment. A dry-charged battery is put into service by adding electrolyte, checking the battery state of charge, and charging if needed.

Even when a wet-charged battery is not in use, a slow reaction occurs between the plates and the electrolyte. This is a self-discharging reaction, and will eventually discharge the battery almost completely. Because this reaction occurs faster at higher temperatures, wet-charged batteries should be stored in as cool a place as possible when not in use. A fully charged battery stored at a room temperature of 100°F (38°C) will almost completely discharge after 90 days. If the battery is stored at a temperature of 60°F (16°C), very little discharge will take place.

BATTERY-CHARGING VOLTAGE

A battery is charged by forcing current through it in the direction opposite from its discharge current. In an automobile, this charging current is supplied by the generator or alternator. The battery offers some resistance to this charging current, because of the battery's chemical voltage and the resistance of the battery's internal parts. The battery's chemical voltage is another form of counterelectromotive force (CEMF) that you studied in Chapter Two.

When a battery is fully charged, its CEMF is very high. Very little charging current can flow through it. When the battery is discharged, its CEMF is very low,

and charging current flows freely. For charging current to enter the battery, the charging voltage must be higher than the battery's CEMF plus the voltage drop caused by the battery's internal resistance.

Understanding this relationship of CEMF to the battery state of charge is helpful. When the battery is nearly discharged, it needs, and will accept, a lot of charging current. When the battery is fully charged, the high CEMF will resist charging current. Any additional charging current could overheat and damage the battery materials. Charging procedures are explained in Chapter Three of your *Shop Manual*.

The temperature of the battery affects the charging voltage because temperature affects the resistance of the electrolyte. Cold electrolyte has higher resistance than warm electrolyte, so a colder battery is harder to charge. The effects of temperature must be considered when servicing automotive charging systems and batteries, as we shall see later in this chapter and in Part Three.

BATTERY SELECTION AND RATING METHODS

Automotive batteries are available in a variety of sizes, shapes, and current ratings. They are called "starting batteries" and are designed to deliver a large current output for a brief time to start an engine. After starting, the charging system takes over to supply most of the current required to operate the car. The battery acts as a system stabilizer and provides current whenever the electrical loads exceed the charging current output. An automotive battery must provide good cranking power for the car's engine and adequate reserve power for the electrical system in which it is used.

Manufacturers also make 12-volt automotive-type batteries that are not designed for automotive use. These are called "cycling batteries" and are designed to provide a power source for a vehicle or accessory without continual recharging. Cycling batteries provide a constant low current for a long period of time. They are designed for industrial, marine, and recreational vehicle (RV) use. Most of their current capacity is exhausted in each cycle before recharging.

The brief high-current flow required of a starting battery is produced by using relatively thin plates, compared to those used in a cycling battery. The

Specific Gravity: The weight of a volume of liquid divided by the weight of the same volume of water at a given temperature and pressure. Water has a specific gravity of 1.000.

thicker plates of the cycling battery will provide a constant current drain for several hours. Using a starting battery in an application calling for a cycling battery will shorten its life considerably, as we shall see later in the chapter. The use of a cycling battery to start and operate a car will cause excessive internal heat from the brief but high current draw, resulting in a shorter service life.

Test standards and rating methods devised by the Battery Council International (BCI) and the Society of Automotive Engineers (SAE) are designed to measure a battery's ability to meet the requirements of its intended service.

The BCI publishes application charts that list the correct battery for any car. Optional heavy-duty batteries are normally used in cars with air conditioning or several major electrical accessories or in cars operated in cold climates. To ensure adequate cranking power and to meet all other electrical needs, a replacement battery may have a higher rating, but never a lower rating, than the original unit. The battery must also be the correct size for the car, and have the correct type of terminals. BCI standards include a coding system, called the group number. BCI battery rating methods are explained in the following paragraphs.

Ampere-Hour Rating

The oldest battery rating method, no longer used to rate batteries, was the ampere-hour rating. This rating method was the industry standard for decades. It was replaced, however, years ago by the cranking performance and reserve capacity ratings, which provide better indications of a battery's performance.

The ampere-hour method was also called the 20-hour discharge rating method. This rating represented the steady current flow that a battery delivered at a temperature of 80°F (27°C) without cell voltage falling below 1.75 volts (a total of 10.5 volts for a 12-volt battery). For example, a battery that continuously delivered 3 amperes for 20 hours was rated as a 60 ampere-hour battery (3 amperes x 20 hours = 60 ampere-hours).

Cranking Performance Rating

The **cranking performance rating** indicates the power a battery can supply for engine cranking at 0°F (-18°C). The rating figures for car and light-truck batteries range from 165 to 1,050 cold-cranking amperes. These figures represent the current flow a battery can deliver for 30 seconds at 0°F (-18°C) while maintaining at least 1.2 volts per cell, for a minimum terminal voltage of 7.2 volts for a 12-volt battery.

Reserve Capacity Rating

The **reserve capacity rating** indicates the long-term power available from a battery for ignition, lighting, and accessories required in emergencies. Reserve capacity (listed in minutes) is the time a fully charged battery at 80°F (27°C) can deliver 25 amperes and maintain at least 1.75 volts at every cell, or 10.5 volts total for a 12-volt battery. Battery reserve capacity ratings range from 30 to 175 minutes, and correspond approximately to the length of time a vehicle can be driven after the charging system has failed.

Group Number

Manufacturers provide a designated amount of space, usually in the engine compartment, to accommodate the battery. Since battery companies build batteries of various current-capacity ratings in a variety of sizes and shapes, it is useful to have a guide when replacing a battery, because it must fit into the space provided. The BCI size **group number** identifies a battery in terms of its length, width, height, terminal design, and other physical features.

BATTERY INSTALLATIONS

Most automobiles use one six-cell, 12-volt battery installed in the engine compartment. Certain factors influence battery location:

- The distance between the battery and the alternator or starter motor determines the length of the cables used. Cable length is important because of electrical system resistance. The longer the cables, the greater the resistance.
- The battery should be located away from hot engine components in a position where it can be cooled by airflow.
- The battery should be in a location where it can be securely mounted as protection against internal damage from vibration.
- The battery should be positioned where it can be easily serviced.

The decrease in size of late-model vehicles has resulted in lighter, smaller batteries with greater capacity. The use of new plastics and improved grid and plate materials has contributed to the new battery designs.

Some older cars and a few new imported and domestic models have the battery located in the trunk. For example, the battery used with the Ford Escort diesel is mounted in the trunk beneath a trim cover and encased in a protective bag, figure 7-9. The bag will retain battery acid in case of an accident that might damage it. A tube and seal assembly connected to the battery vents allows gassing to the atmosphere.

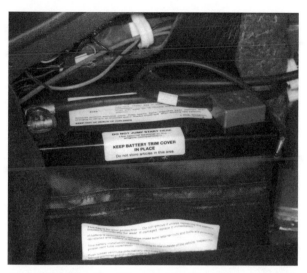

Figure 7-9. This Ford Escort diesel battery is encased in a protective bag and housed in the trunk.

This venting device should be inspected periodically and replaced, if necessary, because proper venting is essential for safety. Such locations require the use of long cables of heavy-gauge wire. The size of such cables offsets their greater length in keeping resistance manageable, but increases cost and weight while reducing convenience.

Late-model GM diesel cars and Ford light trucks use two 12-volt batteries connected in parallel, figure 7-10. Both battery + terminals are connected to each other and to the + battery cable attached to the starter motor (GM) or to the relay (Ford). The battery - terminals are connected to each other in a similar manner, and to the ground cable. The use of a parallel installation doubles the current available for starting the high-compression diesel without increasing system voltage. If the batteries were connected in series, the voltage would double. Both batteries are charged simultaneously by the alternator.

BATTERY INSTALLATION COMPONENTS

Selecting and maintaining properly designed battery installation components are prerequisites for good battery operation and service life.

Connectors, Carriers, and Holddowns

As we saw in Chapter Five, battery cables are very large-diameter multistrand wire, usually no. 0 to no. 6 gauge. Diesel engine vehicles generally use the larger no. 0, while gasoline engine vehicles use no. 6. A new battery cable should always be the same gauge as the one being replaced.

Battery terminals may be tapered posts on the top or internally threaded terminals on the side of the battery. To prevent accidental reversal of battery polarity (incorrectly connecting the cables), the positive terminal is slightly larger than the negative terminal. Three basic styles of connectors are used to attach the battery cables to the battery terminals:

- A bolt-type clamp is used on top-terminal batteries, figure 7-11. The bolt passes through the two halves of the cable end into a nut. When tightened, it squeezes the cable end against the battery post.
- A bolt-through clamp is used on side-terminal batteries. The bolt threads through the cable end and directly into the battery terminal, figure 7-12.
- A spring-type clamp is used on some top-terminal batteries. A built-in spring holds the cable end on the battery post, figure 7-13.

Batteries are usually mounted on a shelf or tray in the engine compartment, although some manufacturers place the battery in the trunk, under the seat, or elsewhere in the vehicle. The shelf or tray that holds the battery is called the carrier, figure 7-14. The battery is mounted on the carrier with brackets called holddowns, figures 7-14 and 7-15. These keep the battery from tipping over and spilling acid. A battery must be held securely in its carrier to protect it from vibration that can damage the plates and internal plate connectors.

■ **Don't Pull The Plugs**

Do you make a practice of removing the vent plugs from a battery before charging it? Prestolite says you shouldn't, at least with many late-model batteries. "A great number of batteries manufactured today will have safety vents," says Prestolite. "If these are removed, the batteries are open to external sources of explosion ignition." Prestolite recommends that, on batteries with safety vents, the vent plugs should be left in place when charging.

Cranking Performance Rating: A battery rating based on the amperes of current that a battery can supply for 30 seconds at 0°F, with no battery cell falling below 1.2 volts.

Reserve Capacity Rating: A battery rating based on the number of minutes a battery at 80°F can supply 25 amperes, with no battery cell falling below 1.75 volts.

Group Number: A battery identification number that indicates battery dimensions, terminal design, holddown location, and other physical features.

Figure 7-11. The most common type of top terminal battery clamp.

Figure 7-10. Diesel vehicles generally have two 12-volt batteries for better cranking with a 12-volt starter. (Ford)

Figure 7-12. The side terminal clamp is attached with a bolt. (Chrysler)

Battery Heat Shields

Many late-model cars use battery heat shields, figure 7-16, to protect batteries from high underhood temperatures. Most heat shields are made of plastic, and some are integral with the battery holddown. Integral shields are usually large plastic plates that sit alongside the battery.

Heat shields do not require removal for routine battery inspection and testing, but must be removed for battery replacement.

BATTERY LIFE AND PERFORMANCE FACTORS

All batteries have a limited life, but certain conditions can shorten that life. The important factors that affect battery life are discussed in the following paragraphs.

Electrolyte Level

As we have seen, the design of maintenance-free batteries has minimized the loss of water from electrolyte so that battery cases can be sealed. Given normal use, the addition of water to such batteries is not required during their service life. However, even maintenance-free batteries will lose some of their water to high temperature, overcharging, deep cycling, and recharging — all factors in battery gassing and resultant water loss.

Figure 7-13. The spring-type clamp generally is found on non-domestic cars.

Figure 7-14. A common type of battery carrier and holddown.

With vent-cap batteries, and to some extent, low-maintenance batteries, water is lost from the electrolyte during charging in the form of hydrogen and oxygen gases. This causes the electrolyte level to drop. If the level drops below the top of the plates, active material will be exposed to the air. The material will harden and resist electrochemical reaction. Also, the remaining electrolyte will have a high concentration of acid, which can cause the plates to deteriorate quickly. Even the addition of water will not restore such hardened plates to a fully active condition.

Figure 7-15. Another common battery holddown.

■ Parasitic Losses

Parasitic losses are small current drains required to operate electrical systems, such as the clock, that continue to work when the car is parked and the ignition is off. The current demand of a clock is small and not likely to cause a problem.

The advent of computer controls, however, has made parasitic losses more serious. Many late-model cars have computers to control such diverse items as engine operation, radio tuning, suspension leveling, climate control, and more. Each of these microprocessors contains random access memory (RAM) that stores information relevant to its job. To "remember", RAM requires a constant voltage supply, and therefore puts a continuous drain on the car's electrical system.

The combined drain of several computer memories can discharge a battery to the point where there is insufficient cranking power after only a few weeks. Vehicles with these systems that are driven infrequently, put into storage, or awaiting parts for repair will require battery charging more often than older cars with lower parasitic voltage losses.

Because of the higher parasitic current drains on late-model cars, the old test of removing a battery cable connection and tapping it against the terminal while looking for a spark is both dangerous and no longer a valid check for excessive current drain. Furthermore, every time the power source to the computer is interrupted, electronically stored information, such as radio station presets, is lost and will have to be reprogrammed when the battery is reconnected.

On engine control systems with learning capability, like GM's Computer Command Control, driveability may also be affected until the computer relearns the engine calibration modifications that were erased from its memory when the battery was disconnected.

Figure 7-16. A molded heat shield that fits over the battery is used by Chrysler and some other manufacturers.

Corrosion

Battery corrosion is caused by spilled electrolyte and by electrolyte condensation from gassing. The sulfuric acid attacks and can destroy not only connectors and terminals, but metal holddowns and carriers as well. Corroded connectors increase resistance at the battery connections. This reduces the applied voltage for the car's electrical system. Corrosion also can cause mechanical failure of the holddowns and carrier, which can damage the battery. Spilled electrolyte and corrosion on the battery top also can create a current leakage path, which can allow the battery to discharge.

Overcharging

Batteries can be overcharged either by the automotive charging system or by a separate battery charger. In either case, there is a violent chemical reaction in the battery. The water in the electrolyte is rapidly broken down into hydrogen and oxygen gases. These gas bubbles can wash active material off the plates, as well as lower the level of the electrolyte. Overcharging can also cause excessive heat, which can oxidize the positive grid material and even buckle the plates.

Undercharging and Sulfation

If an automobile is not charging its battery, either because of stop-and-start driving or a fault in the charging system, the battery will be constantly discharged. As we saw in the explanation of electrochemical action, a discharged plate is covered with lead sulfate. The amount of lead sulfate on the plate will vary according to the state of charge. As the lead sulfate builds up in a constantly undercharged battery, it

can crystallize and not recombine with the electrolyte. This is called battery **sulfation**. The crystals are difficult to break down by normal recharging and the battery becomes useless. Despite the chemical additives sold as "miracle cures" for sulfation, a completely sulfated battery cannot be effectively recharged.

Cycling

As we learned at the beginning of this chapter, the operation of a battery from charged to discharged and back to charged is called cycling. Automotive batteries are not designed for continuous deep-cycle use (although special marine and RV batteries are). If an automotive battery is repeatedly cycled from a fully charged condition to an almost discharged condition, the active material on the positive plates may shed and fall into the bottom of the case. If this happens, the material cannot be restored to the plates. Cycling thus reduces the capacity of the battery and shortens its useful service life.

Temperature

Temperature extremes affect battery service life and performance in a number of ways. High temperature, caused by overcharging or excessive engine heat, increases electrolyte loss and shortens battery life.

Low temperatures in winter can also harm a battery. If the electrolyte freezes, it can expand and break the case, ruining the battery. The freezing point of electrolyte depends upon its specific gravity and thus, on the battery's state of charge. A fully charged battery with a specific gravity of 1.265 to 1.280 will not freeze until its temperature drops below -60°F (-51°C). A discharged battery with electrolyte that is mostly water can freeze at -18°F (-28°C).

As we saw earlier, cold temperatures make it harder to keep the battery fully charged, yet this is when a full charge is most important. Figure 7-17 compares the energy levels available from a fully charged battery at various temperatures. As you can see, the colder a battery is, the less energy it can supply. Yet the colder an engine gets, the more energy it requires for cranking. This is why battery care is especially important in cold weather.

Vibration

As mentioned earlier, a battery must be securely mounted in its carrier to protect it from vibration. Vibration can shake the active materials off the plates and severely shorten a battery's life. Vibration can also loosen the plate connections to the plate strap and damage other internal connections. Some manufacturers now build batteries with plate straps and

**COMPARISON OF CRANKING POWER
AVAILABLE FROM FULLY CHARGED
BATTERY AT VARIOUS TEMPERATURES.**

80°F(26.7°C)	100%
32°F(0°C)	65%
0°F(−17.8°C)	40%

Figure 7-17. Battery power decreases as temperature decreases.

connectors in the center of the plates to reduce the effects of vibration. Severe vibration can even crack a battery case and loosen cable connections.

SUMMARY

Automotive batteries are lead-acid secondary batteries containing a number of electrochemical cells that can be recharged after discharging. Batteries not only store power, they generate voltage and current through the electrochemical action between dissimilar plates in the presence of an electrolyte.

Each lead-acid cell generates about 2.1 volts regardless of the number of positive and negative plates. Cells are connected in series, allowing six cells to produce about 12.6 volts in a fully charged 12-volt battery. Current output of a cell depends upon the total surface area of all the plates. Batteries with higher current or capacity ratings have larger plate areas.

The battery state of charge is determined by electrolyte specific gravity. In a fully charged battery, electrolyte should have a specific gravity of 1.260 to 1.265. Maintenance-free batteries contain calcium-alloy grids to reduce battery heat and water loss. Since such batteries are sealed, their electrolyte cannot be checked and water cannot be added to their cells.

Automotive batteries are designed for starting the engine, not for continual cycling from fully charged to discharged and back to fully charged.

Batteries have cranking performance and reserve capacity ratings, and their size and physical characteristics are indicated by BCI group numbers.

Battery service life is affected by electrolyte level, corrosion, overcharging or undercharging, cycling, vibration, and temperature variations.

■ **How The Battery Got Its Name**

The word "battery" means a group of like things used together. An automobile battery is a group of electro-chemical cells connected and working together. Battery voltage is determined by the number of cells connected in series in the battery.

Early automobile batteries could be taken apart for service. Cases were made of wood, and the tops were sealed with tar or a similar material. The top could be opened and the plate element could be removed from a single cell and replaced with a new one.

■ **Deep-Cycle Service**

Some batteries, like those in golf carts and electric vehicles, are used for deep-cycle service. This means that as they provide electrical current, they go from a fully charged state to an almost fully discharged state, and are then recharged and used again.

Maintenance-free batteries should never be used in deep-cycle service. Deep-cycle service promotes shedding of the active materials from the battery plates. This action drastically reduces the service life of a maintenance-free battery.

Sulfation: The crystallization of lead sulfate on the plates of a constantly discharged battery.

Review Questions
Choose the single most correct answer.
Compare your answers with the correct answers on Page 468.

1. Which of the following occurs within an automobile battery?
   a. The positive plate gains electrons and is positively charged
   b. The negative plate loses electrons and is negatively charged
   c. The positive plate loses electrons and the negative plate gains electrons
   d. The positive plate gains electrons and the negative plate loses electrons

2. Battery electrolyte is a mixture of water and:
   a. Lead peroxide
   b. Sulfuric acid
   c. Lead sulfate
   d. Sulfur crystals

3. The plates of a *discharged* battery are:
   a. Two similar metals in the presence of an electrolyte
   b. Two similar metals in the presence of water
   c. Two dissimilar metals in the presence of an electrolyte
   d. Two dissimilar metals in the presence of water

4. Which of the following is true about a "secondary" battery?
   a. It can be recharged
   b. Neither the electrolyte nor the metals change their atomic structure
   c. One of the metals is totally destroyed by the action of the battery
   d. The action of the battery cannot be reversed

5. Which of the following does *not* occur during battery recharging?
   a. The lead sulfate on the plates gradually decomposes
   b. The sulfate is redeposited in the water
   c. The electrolyte is returned to full strength
   d. The negative plates change back to lead sulfate

6. Each cell of an automobile battery can produce about _____ volts.
   a. 1.2
   b. 2.1
   c. 4.2
   d. 6

7. Which of the following is true of a six-volt automobile battery?
   a. It has six cells connected in series
   b. It has three cells connected in series
   c. It has six cells connected in parallel
   d. It has three cells connected in parallel

8. The correct ratio of water to sulfuric acid in battery electrolyte is *approximately*:
   a. 80 percent water to 20 percent sulfuric acid
   b. 60 percent water to 40 percent sulfuric acid
   c. 40 percent water to 60 percent sulfuric acid
   d. 20 percent water to 80 percent sulfuric acid

9. At 80°F, the correct specific gravity of electrolyte in a fully charged battery is:
   a. 1.200 to 1.225
   b. 1.225 to 1.265
   c. 1.265 to 1.280
   d. 1.280 to 1.300

10. A specific gravity of 1.170 to 1.190 at 80°F indicates that a battery's state of charge is about:
    a. 75 percent
    b. 50 percent
    c. 25 percent
    d. 10 percent

11. Which of the following materials is *not* used for battery separators?
    a. Lead
    b. Wood
    c. Paper
    d. Plastic

12. Batteries are rated in terms of:
    a. Amperes at 65°F
    b. Resistance at 32°F
    c. Voltage level at 80°F
    d. Cranking performance at 0°F

13. Maintenance-free batteries:
    a. Have individual cell caps
    b. Require water infrequently
    c. Have three pressure vents
    d. Use non-antimony lead alloys

14. Which of the following statements is *not* true of a replacement battery?
    a. It may have the same rating as the original battery
    b. It may have a higher rating than the original battery
    c. It may have a lower rating than the original battery
    d. It should be selected according to an application chart

15. An automobile battery with a cranking performance rating of 380 can deliver 380 amps for:
    a. 30 seconds at 0°F
    b. 60 seconds at 0°F
    c. 90 seconds at 32°F
    d. 90 seconds at 0°F

16. The principal cause of battery water loss is:
    a. Spillage from the vent caps
    b. Leakage through the battery case
    c. Conversion of water to sulfuric acid
    d. Evaporation due to heat of the charging current

17. Which of the following is *not* true of a maintenance-free battery?
    a. It will resist overcharging better than a vent-cap battery
    b. It will lose water slower than a vent-cap battery
    c. It will produce a greater voltage than a vent-cap battery
    d. It has a greater electrolyte capacity than a vent-cap battery

18. The electrolyte in a fully charged battery will generally not freeze until the temperature drops to:
    a. 32°F
    b. 0°F
    c. -20°F
    d. -50°F

19. The grid material used in a maintenance-free battery is alloyed with:
    a. Silicon
    b. Antimony
    c. Calcium
    d. Germanium

20. Low-maintenance batteries:
    a. Have no cell caps
    b. Have a higher proportion of sulfuric acid
    c. Have no gas-pressure vents
    d. Require infrequent water addition

21. Recombinant batteries are:
    a. Rebuilt units
    b. Completely sealed
    c. Vented to release gassing
    d. Able to produce a higher cell voltage

PART THREE

The Charging System

Chapter Eight
AC Charging Systems and Alternators

Chapter Nine
Regulators and Indicators

8

AC Charging Systems and Alternators

The charging system converts the engine's mechanical energy into electrical energy. This electrical energy is used to maintain the battery's state of charge and to operate the loads of the automotive electrical system. During our study of the charging system, we will use the conventional theory of current, electrons move from positive to negative (+ to –).

During cranking, all electrical energy for the vehicle is supplied by the battery. After the engine is running, the charging system must produce enough electrical energy to recharge the battery and to supply the demands of other loads in the electrical system.

If the starting system is in poor condition and draws too much current, or if the charging system cannot recharge the battery and supply the additional loads, more energy must be drawn from the battery for short periods of time.

CHARGING SYSTEM DEVELOPMENT

For many years, automotive charging systems used only direct-current (dc) generators to provide electrical energy. Internally, generators produce an alternating current voltage which is mechanically rectified by the commutator into direct current voltage. Systems using dc generators are called dc charging systems. Vehicles with dc generators are very rare today.

Alternators also produce alternating current (ac), but there was no simple way to rectify the current until semiconductor technology finally provided the answer in the form of diodes, or one-way electrical valves. Since the mid-1960s, virtually all new automobiles have a diode-rectified alternator in their charging system. Systems using alternators are commonly called ac charging systems.

Alternators have replaced the generator in the automotive charging system because they have several advantages. They:

- Weigh less per ampere of output
- Can be operated at much higher speed
- Pass less current through the brushes with only a few amperes of field current, reducing brush wear
- Govern their own maximum current output, requiring no external current regulation
- Can produce current when rotated in either direction, although their cooling fans usually are designed for one-way operation.

CHARGING VOLTAGE

Although the automotive electrical system is called a 12-volt system, the alternator must produce more than 12 volts. On a fully charged battery, each cell produces about 2.1 volts. This means the open-circuit voltage of a fully charged 12-volt battery, which has six cells, is approximately 12.6 volts. If the alternator cannot produce more than 12.6 volts, it cannot charge the battery until system voltage drops under 12.6 volts. This would leave nothing extra to serve the other electrical demands put on the system by lights, air conditioning, and power accessories.

Alternating-current charging systems are generally regulated to produce a maximum output of 14.5 volts. Output of more than 16 volts will overheat the battery electrolyte and shorten its life. High voltage also damages components which rely heavily on solid-state electronics, such as fuel injection and engine control systems. On the other hand, low voltage output cause the battery to become sulfated. The charging system must be maintained within the voltage limits specified by the manufacturer if the vehicle is to perform properly.

AC Charging System Components

The automotive charging system, figure 8-1, contains:

- A battery, which provides current to initiate the magnetic field required to operate the alternator and, in turn, is charged and maintained by the alternator.
- An alternator, which is belt driven by the engine and converts mechanical motion into charging voltage and current. A simple alternator, figure 8-2, consists of a magnet rotating inside a fixed-loop stator, or conductor. The alternating current produced in the conductor is rectified by diodes for use by the electrical system.
- A regulator, which limits the field current and thus the alternator output voltage according to the electrical system demand. A regulator can be either an electromechanical or a solid-state device. Some late-model, solid-state regulators are part of the vehicle's onboard computer.
- An ammeter, a voltmeter, or an indicator warning lamp mounted on the instrument panel to give a visual indication of charging system operation.

Charging System Circuits

The charging system consists of two major circuits, figure 8-3:

Figure 8-1. The major components of an automotive charging system. (Chrysler)

Figure 8-2. An alternator is based on the rotation of a magnet inside a fixed-loop conductor. (Chrysler)

- The **field circuit**, which delivers current to the alternator field
- The **output circuit**, which sends voltage and current to the battery and other electrical components.

SINGLE-PHASE CURRENT

Alternators induce voltage by rotating a magnetic field inside a fixed conductor. The greatest current output is produced when the rotor is parallel to the stator with its magnetic field at right angles to the stator, figure 8-2. When the rotor makes one-quarter of a revolution and is at right angles to the stator with its magnetic field parallel to the stator, figure 8-4, there is no current output. Figure 8-5 shows the voltage levels induced across the upper half of the looped conductor during one revolution of the rotor.

The constant change of voltage, first to a positive peak and then to a negative peak, produces a **sine wave voltage**. This name comes from the trigonometric sine function. The wave shape is controlled by the

Figure 8-3. The output circuit and the field circuit make up the automotive charging system. (Prestolite)

Figure 8-4. No current flows when the rotor's magnetic field is parallel to the stator. (Chrysler)

angle between the magnet and the conductor. The sine wave voltage induced across one conductor by one rotor revolution is called a **single-phase voltage.** Positions 1 through 5 of figure 8-5 show complete sine wave single-phase voltage.

This single-phase voltage causes alternating current to flow in a complete circuit because the voltage switches from positive to negative as the rotor turns. The alternating current caused by a single-phase voltage is called **single-phase current.**

DIODE RECTIFICATION

If the single-phase voltage shown in figure 8-5 made current travel through a simple circuit, the current would flow first in one direction and then in the opposite direction. As long as the rotor turned, the current would reverse its flow with every half revolution. The battery cannot be recharged with alternating current. Alternating current must be rectified to direct current to recharge the battery. This is done with diodes.

A diode acts as a one-way electrical valve. If a diode is inserted into a simple circuit, figure 8-6, one-half of the ac voltage is blocked. That is, the diode allows current to flow from "X" to "Y", as shown in position "A". In position "B", the current cannot flow from "Y" to "X" because it is blocked by the diode. The graph in figure 8-6 shows the total current.

The first half of the current, from "X" to "Y", was allowed to pass through the diode. It is shown on the graph as curve "XY". The second half of the current, from "Y" to "X", was not allowed to pass through the

diode. It does not appear on the graph because it never traveled through the circuit. When the voltage reverses at the start of the next rotor revolution, the current is again allowed through the diode from "X" to "Y".

An alternator with only one conductor and one diode would show this current output pattern. However, this output would not be very useful

■ Heat Sinks

The term "heat sink" is commonly used to describe the block of aluminum or other material in which the alternator diodes are mounted. The job of the heat sink is to absorb and carry away the heat in the diodes caused by electrical current through them. This action keeps the diodes cool and prevents damage.

An internal combustion engine is also a heat sink. The engine is designed so that the combustion and friction heat are carried away and dissipated to the atmosphere.

Although they are not thought of as heat sinks, many individual parts of an automobile — such as the brake drums — are also designed to do this important job.

Field Circuit: The charging system circuit that delivers current to the alternator field.

Output Circuit: The charging system circuit that sends voltage and current to the battery and other electrical systems and devices.

Sine Wave Voltage: The constant change, from zero volt to a positive peak, and then to a negative peak, and back to zero, of an induced alternating voltage in a conductor.

Single-Phase Voltage: The sine wave voltage induced within one conductor by one revolution of an alternator rotor.

Single-Phase Current: Alternating current created by a single-phase voltage.

Figure 8-5. These are the voltage levels induced across the upper half of the conductor during one rotor revolution. (Chrysler)

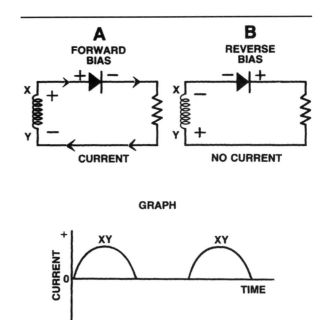

Figure 8-6. A single diode in the circuit results in half-wave rectification. (Delco-Remy)

because half of the time there is no current available. This is called **half-wave rectification**, since only half of the ac voltage produced by the alternator is allowed to flow as dc voltage.

Adding more diodes to the circuit, figure 8-7, allows more of the ac voltage to be rectified to dc. In position "A", current moves from "X" to "Y". It travels from "X", through diode "2", through the load, through diode "3", and back to "Y". In position "B", current moves from "Y" to "X". It travels from "Y", through diode "4", through the load, through diode "1", and back to "X".

Notice that in both cases current traveled through the load in the same direction. This is because the ac has been rectified to dc. The graph in figure 8-7 shows the current output of an alternator with one conductor and four diodes. There is more current available because all of the voltage has been rectified. This is called **full-wave rectification**. However, there are still moments when current is at zero. Most automotive alternators use three conductors and six diodes to produce overlapping current waves so that current output is *never* at zero.

ALTERNATOR CONSTRUCTION

The previous illustrations have shown the principles of alternator operation. To provide enough direct current for an automobile, alternators must have a more complex design. But no matter how the design varies, the principles of operation remain the same.

Figure 8-7. More diodes are needed for full-wave rectification. (Delco-Remy)

The design of an alternator limits its maximum current output. To change this maximum value for

POLE PIECES

BEARING

SLIPRINGS

Figure 8-8. A typical 12-pole rotor. (Chrysler)

different applications, manufacturers change the design of the stator, rotor, and other components. The following paragraphs describe the major parts of an automotive alternator.

Rotor

The rotor carries the magnetic field. Unlike a dc generator, which usually has only two magnetic poles, the alternator rotor has several North (N) and South (S) poles. This increases the number of flux lines within the alternator and increases the voltage output. A typical automotive rotor, figure 8-8, has 12 poles: 6 N and 6 S. The rotor consists of two steel rotor halves, or pole pieces, with fingers that interlace. These fingers are the poles. Each pole piece has either all N or all S poles. The magnetic flux lines travel between adjacent N and S poles, figure 8-9. Keep in mind an alternator is a generator. In some European manufacturers' service manuals, an alternator is referred to as a generator

Along the outside of the rotor, note the flux lines point first in one direction and then in the other. This means as the rotor spins inside the alternator, the fixed conductors are being cut by flux lines which point in alternating directions. The induced voltage alternates, just as in the example of a simple alternator with only two poles. Automotive alternators may have any number of poles, as long as they are placed N-S-N-S. Common alternator designs use eight to fourteen poles.

The rotor poles may retain some magnetism when the alternator is not in operation, but this residual magnetism is not strong enough to induce any voltage across the conductors. The magnetic field of the rotor is produced by current through the rotor winding, which is a coil of wire between the two pole pieces, figure 8-10. This is also called the excitation winding, or the field winding. Varying the amount of field

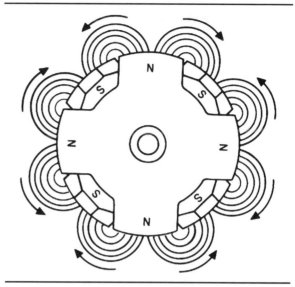

Figure 8-9. The flux lines surrounding an 8-pole rotor. (Prestolite)

POLE PIECE   ROTOR WINDING   POLE PIECE

ROTOR SHAFT

Figure 8-10. The magnetic field of the rotor is created by current through the rotor winding. (Bosch)

current through the rotor winding varies the strength of the magnetic field. This affects the voltage output of the alternator.

A soft iron core is mounted inside the rotor winding, figure 8-11. One pole piece is attached to either end of the core. When field current travels through the

Half-Wave Rectification: A process by which only one-half of an ac sine wave voltage is rectified to dc.

Full-Wave Rectification: A process by which all of an ac sine wave voltage is rectified and allowed to flow as dc.

Figure 8-11. An exploded view of the parts of the complete rotor assembly. (Prestolite)

Figure 8-12. The alternator and drive pulley. (Chrysler)

Figure 8-13. An alternator stator.

Figure 8-14. A stator with only one conductor installed. (Delco-Remy)

winding, the iron core is magnetized. The pole pieces take on the magnetic polarity of the end of the core to which they are attached. Current is supplied to the winding through sliprings and brushes.

The combination of a soft iron rotor core and steel rotor halves provides better localization and permeability of the magnetic field. The rotor pole pieces, winding, core, and sliprings are pressed onto a shaft. The ends of this shaft are supported by bearings in the alternator housing. Outside the housing, a drive pulley is attached to the shaft, figure 8-12 . A belt, driven by the engine crankshaft-pulley, passes around this pulley to turn the alternator shaft and rotor assembly.

Stator

The three alternator conductors are wound onto a cylindrical, laminated core. The lamination prevents unwanted eddy currents from forming in the core. The assembled piece is called a stator, figure 8-13. Each conductor, called a stator winding, is formed into a number of coils spaced evenly around the core. There are as many coils in each conductor as there are pairs of N-S rotor poles. Figure 8-14 shows an incomplete stator with only one of its conductors installed. In this example, there are seven coils in the conductor, so the matching rotor would have seven pairs of N-S poles for a total of fourteen poles. There are two ways to connect the three stator windings. These methods are explained later in this chapter.

Figure 8-15. The alternator housing encloses the rotor and stator.

Figure 8-16. An alternator with exposed stator core.

Housing

The alternator housing, or frame, is made of two pieces of cast aluminum, figure 8-15. Aluminum is lightweight and non-magnetic and conducts heat well. One housing piece holds a bearing for the end of the rotor shaft where the drive pulley is mounted. This is often called the drive-end housing, or front housing, of the alternator. The other end holds the diodes, the brushes, and the electrical terminal connections. It also holds a bearing for the slipring end of the rotor shaft. This is often called the slipring-end housing, or rear housing. Together, the two pieces completely enclose the rotor and the stator windings.

Figure 8-17. An alternator with the stator core enclosed.

The end housings are bolted together. Some stator cores have an extended rim that is held between the two housings, figure 8-16. Other stator cores provide holes for the housing bolts, but do not extend to the outside of the housings, figure 8-17. In both designs, the stator is rigidly bolted in place inside the alternator housing.

The alternator housing is part of the electrical ground path because it is bolted directly to the engine. Anything connected to the housing which is not insulated from the housing is grounded.

Sliprings and Brushes

The sliprings and brushes conduct current to the rotor winding. Most automotive alternators have two sliprings mounted on the rotor shaft. The sliprings are insulated from the shaft and from each other. One end of the rotor winding is connected to each slipring, figure 8-18. One brush rides on each ring to carry current to and from the winding. A brush holder supports each brush and a spring applies force to keep the brush in constant contact with the rotating slipring. The brushes are connected parallel with the alternator output circuit. They draw some of the alternator current output and route it through the rotor winding. Current through the winding must be dc.

Field current in an alternator is usually about 1.5 to 3.0 amperes. Because the brushes carry so little current, they do not require as much maintenance as dc generator brushes, which must conduct all of the current output.

Figure 8-18. The sliprings and brushes carry current to the rotor windings.

Figure 8-19. Each conductor is attached to one positive and one negative diode.

Diode Installation

Automotive alternators which have three stator windings generally use six diodes to rectify the current output. The connections between the conductors and the diodes vary slightly, but each conductor is connected to one positive and one negative diode, figure 8-19.

The three positive diodes are always insulated from the alternator housing. They are connected to the insulated terminal of the battery and to the rest of the automotive electrical system. The battery cannot discharge through this connection because the bias of the diodes blocks any current from the battery. The positive diodes only conduct current traveling from the conductors toward the battery. The positive diodes are mounted together on a conductor called a heat sink, figure 8-20. The heat sink carries heat away from the

Figure 8-20. Positive and negative diodes may be mounted in a heat sink for protection.

Figure 8-21. Negative diodes may be pressed into the rear housing.

diodes, just as the radiator carries heat away from the engine. Too much heat damages the diodes.

The three negative diodes may be pressed or threaded into the alternator rear housing, figure 8-21. On high-output alternators, they may be mounted in a heat sink for added protection. In either case, the connection to the alternator housing is a ground path. The negative diodes conduct only the current traveling from ground into the conductors.

Each group of three or more negative or positive diodes can be called a diode bridge, a diode trio, or a diode plate.

Some manufacturers use complete rectifier assemblies containing all the diodes and connections on a printed circuit board, figure 8-22. This assembly is replaced as a unit if any of the individual components fail.

Figure 8-22. All diodes and connections may be included in a single printed circuit board. (Ford)

Each stator winding connects to its proper negative diode through a circuit in the rectifier. A capacitor generally is installed between the output terminal at the positive diode heat sink to ground at the negative diode heat sink. This capacitor is used to eliminate voltage switching transients at the stator, to smooth out the ac voltage fluctuations, and to reduce Electromagnetic Interference (EMI).

CURRENT PRODUCTION IN AN ALTERNATOR

After studying the principles of alternator operation and the components of an alternator, the total picture of how an automotive alternator produces current becomes clear.

Three-Phase Current

The alternator stator has three windings. Each is formed into a number of coils, which are spaced evenly around the stator core. The voltages induced across each winding by one rotor revolution are shown in the graphs of figure 8-23. The total voltage output of the alternator is three overlapping, evenly spaced, single-phase voltage waves, as shown in the bottom graph of the illustration. If the stator windings are connected into a complete circuit, the three phase voltages cause an ac ouput called **three-phase current**.

Stator Types

When the three conductors are completely wound on the stator core, six loose ends remain. The way in which these ends are connected to the diode rectifier

circuitry determines if the stator is a Y-type or a delta-type, figure 8-24. Both kinds of stators produce three-phase current and the rectification produces dc output. However, the voltage and current levels within the stators differ.

Y-type stator design

In the **Y-type stator** or Y-connected stator, one end of each of the three windings is connected at a **neutral junction**, figure 8-24. The circuit diagram of the Y-type stator, figure 8-25, looks like the letter "Y". This is also sometimes called a wye or a star connection. The free end of each conductor is connected to a positive and a negative diode.

In a Y-type stator, two windings always form a series circuit between a positive and a negative diode. At any given instant, the position of the rotor determines the direction of current through these two windings. Current flows from the negative voltage to

■ **Unrectified Alternators**

Although the battery cannot be recharged with ac, other automotive accessories can be designed to run on unrectified alternator output. Motorola has made alternators with separate terminals for AC output. Ford has offered a front-and-rear-window defroster that heats the windows with three-phase, 120-volt ac. The high-voltage current is supplied by an additional alternator. This second alternator is mounted above the standard 12-volt ac alternator and driven by the same belt.

The Ford high-voltage alternator has a Y-type stator. Field current draw is more than four amps, and there is no regulator in the field circuit. Output is 2,200 watts at high engine speed. All of the wiring between the alternator and the defrosters is special, shielded wiring with warning tags at all connectors. Ford test procedures use only an ohmmeter, because trying to test such high output could be dangerous.

Three-Phase Current: Three overlapping, evenly spaced, single-phase currents that make up the total ac output of an alternator.

Y-Type Stator: An alternator stator design in which one end of each of the three windings in a three-phase alternator is connected at a neutral junction. This design is used in alternators that require high voltage at low alternator speed.

Neutral Junction: The center connection of the three windings in a Y-type stator.

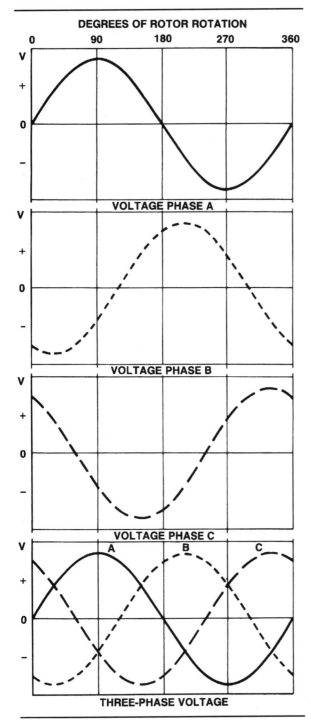

Figure 8-23. The single-phase voltages of the three conductors create a three-phase voltage output. (Bosch)

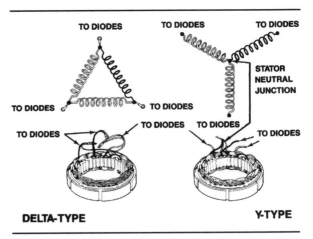

Figure 8-24. The two types of stator windings. (Chrysler)

Figure 8-25. A Y-type stator circuit diagram. (Prestolite)

the output terminal. Y-type stators are used in alternators which require high-voltage output at low alternator speeds. The majority of alternators in use today have Y-type stators.

Some alternators include a center tap lead from the neutral junction to an insulated terminal on the housing, figure 8-26. The center tap may control the field current, to activate an indicator lamp, to control the electric choke on a carburetor, or for other functions.

Delta-type stator design

The **delta-type stator** or delta-connected stator, has the three windings connected end-to-end, figure 8-24. The circuit diagram of a delta-type stator, figure 8-27, looks like the Greek letter Delta (Δ), a triangle. There is no neutral junction in a delta-type stator. The windings always form two parallel circuit paths between one negative and two positive diodes. Current travels through two different circuit paths between the

the positive voltage. A complete circuit from ground, through a negative diode, through two of the windings, and through a positive diode to the alternator output terminal, exists throughout the 360 degree rotation of the rotor. The induced voltages across the two windings added together produce the total voltage at

Figure 8-26. A Y-type stator circuit diagram. The center tap connects to the neutral junction of the Y-type stator of some alternators. (Prestolite)

Figure 8-27. Circuit diagram of a delta-type stator. (Prestolite)

Figure 8-28. A typical current path during rectification in a delta-type stator. (Prestolite)

Figure 8-29. A typical current path during rectification in a Y-type stator. (Prestolite)

diodes, figure 8-28. The current carrying capacity of the stator is double because there are two parallel circuit paths. Delta-type stators are used when a high-current output is needed.

Phase Rectification

The current pattern during rectification is similar in any automotive alternator. The only differences are specific current paths through Y-type and delta-type stators, figures 8-27 and 8-29.

Rectification with Multiple-Pole Rotors

The three-phase voltage output used in the examples, figure 8-30, is the voltage which would result if the alternator rotor had only one N and one S pole. Actual alternator rotors have many N and S poles. Each of these N-S pairs produces one complete voltage sine wave per rotor revolution, across each of the three windings. One complete sine wave begins at zero volt, climbs to a positive, peak, drops past zero to a negative

Delta-Type Stator: An alternator stator design in which the three windings of a three-phase alternator are connected end-to-end. The beginning of one winding is attached to the end of another winding. Delta-type stators are used in alternators that must provide high-current output.

Figure 8-30. The three-phase voltage from one revolution of the rotor. (Bosch)

Figure 8-31. An alternator with six pairs of N-S poles would produce the solid line voltage trace. The dashed line represents an alternator with one pair. (Bosch)

Figure 8-32. This is the total output of a three-winding, multiple-pole alternator.

Figure 8-33. The diodes receive the maximum voltage values.

peak, then returns to zero, or baseline voltage. In figure 8-31, the sine wave voltage caused by a single pole is shown as a dashed line. The actual voltage trace from one winding of a 12-pole alternator is shown as a solid line. The entire stator output is three of these waves, evenly spaced and overlapping, figure 8-32. The maximum voltage value from these waves pushes current through the diodes, figure 8-33.

After rectification, alternator output is dc voltage which is slightly lower than the maximum voltage peaks of the stator output. The positive portion of the ac sine wave greater than the dc output voltage is viewable on an oscilloscope in what is called an alternator ripple pattern, figure 8-34.

Excitation Field Circuit

The magnetic field of the rotor is created by field current through the rotor winding. Field current is drawn from the alternator output circuit once the alternator has begun to produce current. However, there is not

enough residual magnetism in the rotor poles to induce voltage during start up. An alternator cannot start operation independently. Field current must be drawn from another source in order to magnetize the rotor and begin alternator output.

The other source is the vehicle battery connected to the alternator rotor winding through the excitation, or field, circuit. Battery voltage "excites" the rotor magnetic field and begins alternator output. When the engine is off, the battery must be disconnected from the excitation circuit. If not, it could discharge through the rotor windings to ground. Some alternators use a relay to control this circuit. Other systems use the voltage regulator or a part of the ignition switch to control the excitation circuit. Chapter Nine of this *Classroom Manual* covers this circuit in depth.

Once the alternator has started to produce current, field current is drawn from the alternator output. The current may be drawn after it has been rectified by the

Figure 8-34. Alternator ripple is the ac voltage exceeding dc output voltage.

Figure 8-35. Some alternators have additional diodes to rectify field current. (Bosch)

output diodes. Some alternators draw field current from unrectified ac alternator output, which is then rectified by three additional diodes to provide dc to the rotor winding, figure 8-35. These additional diodes are called the exciter diodes or the field diodes.

Circuit Types

Alternators are designed with different types of field circuits. The two most common types are:

- A-circuit
- B-circuit

Circuit types are determined by where the voltage regulator is connected and from where the field current is drawn.

A-circuit

The A-circuit alternator, figure 8-36, is also called an externally grounded field alternator. Both brushes are insulated from the alternator housing. One brush

Figure 8-36. An A-circuit. (Regulator is after the field).

Figure 8-37. A B-circuit. (Regulator is before the field).

connects to the voltage regulator, where it is grounded. The second brush connects to the alternator output circuit within the alternator, where it draws current for the rotor winding. The regulator conects between the rotor field winding and ground. This type of circuit is often used with solid-state regulators, which are small enough to be mounted on the alternator housing.

B-circuit

The B-circuit alternator, figure 8-37, is also called an internally grounded field alternator. One brush is grounded within the alternator housing. The other brush is insulated from the housing and connected through the insulated voltage regulator to the alternator output circuit. The rotor field winding is between the regulator and ground. This type of circuit is most often used with electromagnetic voltage regulators, which are mounted away from the alternator housing.

THE ALTERNATOR IN OPERATION

A Toyota Monolithic Integrated Circuit (MIC) alternator serves as an example of how an alternator operates in the context of the entire charging system. Like most current alternators, this one has an internally mounted regulator, called an Integrated Circuit (IC) Regulator, figures 8-38 through 8-40.

Figure 8-38. With the ignition switch on but the engine not running, the regulator energizes the rotor coil to build a magnetic field in the stator. The regulator turns on the charge light indicating the alternator is not generating a voltage. (Toyota)

Figure 8-39. After the engine is running, the alternator generates a voltage greater than the battery. The charge light goes out indicating normal operation. (Toyota)

Figure 8-40. When alternator voltage is too high, the regulator momentarily cuts off current to the rotor coils, eliminating the magnetic field. The rotor continues to spin, but no voltage is generated. (Toyota)

When the ignition is first switched from off to on, before cranking the engine, a charge lamp comes on. This indicates, of course, that the alternator is not generating a voltage. At the same time, battery voltage is applied to the rotor coil so that when the rotor begins to spin, the magnetic fields cut across the stator windings and produce current, figure 8-38.

After the engine starts, the rotor is spinning fast enough to induce current from the stator. The current travels through the diodes and out to the battery and electrical system, figure 8-39. Once the IC Regulator senses system voltage is greater than battery voltage, it redirects current to switch off the charge lamp.

During normal operation, alternator voltage exceeds the typically specified 14.5 volts at times. To protect the battery and delicate components in the electrical system, the IC Regulator shuts off current to the rotor, cutting alternator output to zero, figure 8-40. Note that even though the alternator is momentarily "turned off," the charge lamp does not come on. Within a split second, the IC Regulator re-energizes the rotor again once output falls below the minimum. The IC Regulator switches battery voltage on and off this way to control alternator output and maintain system voltage at an ideal level. A more detailed

discussion of voltage regulation is found in Chapter Nine of this *Classroom Manual.*

SPECIFIC ALTERNATORS

Manufacturers use various alternator designs for specific applications. It has been noted such factors as maximum current output and field circuit types affect alternator construction. The following paragraphs describe some commonly used automotive alternators.

Delco-Remy

Delco-Remy, a division of General Motors Corporation, supplies most of the electrical devices used on GM vehicles, as well as those of some other manufacturers. The trademark name for Delco-Remy alternators is DelcotronÆ generators. The alternator model number and current output can be found on a plate attached to, or stamped into, the housing.

10-DN series

Internally mounted regulators came into use with Delcotrons beginning in the early 1970s. Before that time, 10-DN series alternators were widely used. Six individual diodes are mounted in the rear housing, figure 8-41, with a capacitor for protection. A 14-pole

Figure 8-41. The Delcotron 10-DN. (Delco-Remy)

Figure 8-42. A 10-SI series alternator. (Delco-Remy)

rotor and Y-type stator provide current output. Field current is drawn from rectified output and travels through a B-circuit.

The terminals on a 10-DN are labeled BAT, GRD, R, and F. If the alternator is used with an electromagnetic regulator:

- BAT connects alternator output to the insulated terminal of the battery
- GRD, if used, is an additional ground path
- R, if used, is connected to a separate field relay controlling the indicator lamp
- F connects the rotor winding to the voltage regulator.

Some 10-DN alternators are used with a remotely mounted solid-state regulator. The voltage control level of this unit is usually adjustable. The terminal connections are the same for electromagnetic and solid-state regulators.

SI series

The most common early-model Delcotron alternators are part of the SI series and include models 10, 12, 15, and 27, figure 8-42. A 14-pole rotor is used in most models. The 10-SI and 12-SI models have Y-type stators, and the 15-SI and 27-SI models have delta-type stators.

Two general SI designs have been used, with major differences appearing in the rear housing diode installation, regulator appearance, field circuitry, and ground path.

Figure 8-43. The rear end housing of the later-model 10-SI Delcotron. (Delco-Remy)

Most SI models have a rectifier bridge which contains all six rectifying diodes, figure 8-43. The regulator is a fully enclosed unit attached by screws to the housing. Field current is drawn from unrectified alternator output and rectified by an additional diode trio.

All SI models have A-circuits. Their terminals are labeled BAT, No. 1, and No. 2:

- The BAT terminal connects alternator output to the insulated terminal of the battery
- The No. 1 terminal conducts battery current to the rotor winding for the excitation circuit and is connected to the indicator lamp
- The No. 2 terminal receives battery voltage so the voltage regulator can react to system operating conditions.

Figure 8-44. The Delco 27-SI alternator has an adjustable voltage regulator. (Delco-Remy)

All SI models have a capacitor installed in the rear housing to protect the diodes from sudden voltage surges and to filter out voltage ripples that could produce EMI.

The 27-SI, which is intended principally for commercial vehicles, has an adjustable voltage regulator, figure 8-44. The voltage is adjusted by removing the adjustment cap, rotating it until the desired setting low, medium, medium-high, or high is opposite the arrow on the alternator housing, and reinstalling it in the new position. Repair or replace a 27-SI alternator only if it fails to pass an output test after the regulator has been adjusted.

CS-series

The smaller Delco-Remy CS series alternators introduced on some 1986 GM cars, figure 8-45, maintain current output similar to larger alternators. This series includes models CS-121, CS-130, and CS-144. The number following the CS designation denotes the outer diameter of the stator lamination in millimeters. All models use a delta-type stator. Field current is taken directly from the stator, eliminating the field diode trio. An integral cooling fan is used on the CS-121 and CS-130.

Electronic connections on a CS alternators include a BAT output terminal and either a one- or two-wire connector for the regulator. Figure 8-46 shows the two basic circuits for CS alternators, but there are a number of variations. Refer to the vehicle service manual for complete and accurate circuit diagrams. The use of the "P", "F", and "S" terminals shown in figure 8-46 is optional:

Figure 8-45. Typical Delco-Remy CS series alternator construction. (Delco-Remy)

- The "P" terminal, connected to the stator, may be connected to a tachometer or other such device.
- The "F" terminal connects internally to field positive and may be used as a fault indicator.
- The "S" terminal is externally connected to battery voltage to sense the voltage to be controlled.
- The "L" terminal connects the regulator to the indicator lamp and battery.

The indicator lamp in a CS charging system works differently than in other Delco-Remy systems. Any defect causes it to light at full brilliance. The lamp also lights if charging voltage is either too low or too high.

If the regulator has an "I" terminal, its wire supplies field current in addition to that applied internally,

Figure 8-46. Two basic circuits for the Delco-Remy CS series alternators. (Delco-Remy)

either directly from the switch or through a resistor. The parallel connections at the top of figure 8-46 are alternate circuits.

Motorcraft

Motorcraft, a division of Ford Motor Company, makes most of the alternators used on domestic Ford vehicles. Model and current rating identifications for later models are stamped on the front housing with a color code. Motorcraft alternators prior to 1985 are used with either an electromechanical voltage regulator or a remotely mounted solid-state regulator. One exception to this is the 55-ampere model of 1969-1971, which has a solid-state regulator mounted on the rear housing, figure 8-47. This model has an A-circuit; all others are B-circuit. The Motorcraft integral alternator/regulator (IAR) model was introduced on some front-wheel drive Ford models in 1985. This alternator has a solid-state regulator mounted on its rear housing, figure 8-48. Some Motorcraft charging systems continue to use an external solid-state regulator with either a rear-terminal, figure 8-49, or side-terminal alternator, figure 8-50. These charging systems are called external voltage regulator (EVR) systems to differentiate them from integral alternator/regulator (IAR) systems.

Integral alternator/regulator models

The Motorcraft IAR alternators, figure 8-48, are rated at 40 to 80 amperes. The sealed rectifier assembly is attached to the slipring-end housing. On early models,

Figure 8-47. The Motorcraft 55-ampere alternator had a solid-state regulator mounted on the rear housing.

the connecting terminals (BAT and STA) protruded from the side of the alternator in a plastic housing. Current models use a single pin stator (STA) connector and separate output stud (BAT). The brushes are attached to, and removed with, the regulator. A Y-type stator is used with a 12-pole rotor. Some applications have an internal cooling fan.

Turning the ignition on sends voltage to the regulator "I" terminal through a resistor in the circuit. System voltage is sensed and field current is drawn through the regulator "A" terminal until the ignition is turned off, which shuts off the control circuit. Figure 8-51 shows the basic IAR alternator circuit.

If the vehicle has a heated windshield, output is switched from the battery to the windshield by an output control relay, figure 8-52. This allows output voltage to increase above the normal regulated voltage and vary with engine speed. The regulator "I" circuit limits the increase to 70 volts, which is controlled by the heated windshield module during the approximate four minute cycle of heated windshield operation. When the cycle times out, the charging system returns to normal operation.

Chrysler

Chrysler Corporation manufactured all of the alternators for its domestic vehicles until the late 1980s, when it phased in Bosch and Nippondenso alternators for use on all vehicles.

Chrysler alternators

Prior to 1972, Chrysler alternators had six individual diodes pressed into a heat sink in the rear housing,

Figure 8-48. The 1985 and later Motorcraft IAR alternator has a rear-mounted regulator.

Figure 8-49. A Motorcraft rear-terminal alternator. (Ford)

figure 8-53. The alternator was used with an electro-mechanical regulator and a B-circuit until 1968. In some 1968 and all 1969 models, the alternator had an A-circuit and used the remotely mounted solid-state regulator.

Chrysler used two alternator designs from 1972 through 1984. The standard-duty alternator, rated from 50 to 65 amperes, is identified by an internal cooling fan and the stator core extension between the

Figure 8-50. The Motorcraft side-terminal alternator. (Ford)

housings, figure 8-54. The heavy-duty 100-ampere alternator has an external fan and a totally enclosed stator core. Identification also is stamped on a color-coded tag on the housing.

Figure 8-51. A circuit diagram of the Motorcraft IAR alternator.

Figure 8-52. A circuit diagram of the Motorcraft IAR alternator used with heated windshields. (Ford)

Figure 8-53. A pre-1972 Chrysler alternator.

Figure 8-55. The terminals on a Chrysler standard-duty alternator. (Chrysler)

Figure 8-54. Chrysler's standard corporate alternator from 1972 to 1984.

All models have a 12-pole rotor and use a remotely mounted solid-state regulator. The brushes can be replaced from outside the housing. Individual diodes are mounted in positive and negative heat sink assemblies, and are protected by a capacitor. The terminals on the standard-duty alternator are labeled "BAT", "GRD", and "FLD", figure 8-55:

- The "BAT" terminal connects alternator output to the insulated terminal of the battery.

- The "GRD" terminal is the ground connection.
- Two "FLD" terminals connect to the insulated brushes. On the 100-ampere model, the "FLD" terminal has two separate prongs that fit into a single connector, figure 8-56. The additional "GRD" terminal is a ground path.

Chrysler standard-duty alternators have a Y-type stator connected to six diodes. Although both brush holders are insulated from the housing, one is indirectly grounded through the negative diode plate, making it a B-circuit.

The 100-ampere alternator has a delta-type stator. Each of the conductors is attached to two positive and two negative diodes. These 12 diodes create additional parallel circuit branches for high-current output.

Chrysler eliminated the use of a separate voltage regulator on most 1985 and later fuel injected and turbocharged engines by incorporating the regulator function into the powertrain control module (PCM), 8-57.

The computer-controlled charging system was introduced with the standard Chrysler alternator on GLH and Shelby turbo models. All other four-cylinder engines used either a new Chrysler 40/90-ampere alternator or a modified Bosch 40/90-ampere or 40/100-ampere model.

The Chrysler-built alternator uses a delta-type stator. The regulator circuit is basically the isolated-field type, but field current is controlled by integrated circuitry in the logic and power modules, figure 8-58, or the logic and power circuits of the single-module engine control computer (SMEC) or single-board engine control computer (SBEC). In addition to

Figure 8-56. The terminals on a Chrysler 100-ampere alternator. (Chrysler)

Figure 8-57. Typical Chrysler computer voltage regulation with Chrysler 40/90-ampere alternator. Circuit connections vary on different models.

sensing system voltage, the logic module or circuit senses battery temperature as indicated by system resistance. The computer then switches field current on and off in a duty cycle that regulates charging voltage as in any other system.

The Chrysler computer-controlled charging system has two important features:

- It varies charging voltage relative to ambient temperature and the system voltage requirements.
- A self-diagnostic program can detect charging system problems and record fault codes in system memory. Some codes will light the POWER LOSS, POWER LIMITED, or

MALFUNCTION INDICATOR lamp on the instrument panel; others will not.

Turning the ignition on causes the logic circuit to check battery temperature to determine the control voltage. A predriver transistor in the logic module or logic circuit signals a driver translator in the power module or power circuit to turn on the alternator field current, figure 8-59. The logic module or logic circuit constantly monitors system voltage and battery temperature and signals the driver in the power module or power circuit when field current adjustment is necessary to keep output voltage within the specified 13.6 to 14.8 volt range.

Bosch alternators

Modified Bosch 40/90-ampere and 40/100-ampere alternators were introduced in 1985 for use with the Chrysler computer-controlled charging system. These Bosch dual-output alternators have a Y-type stator and were modified by removing their internal voltage regulators and changing the external leads. They are fully interchangeable with Chrysler dual-output alternators of the same rating.

Use of dual-output alternators was phased out in favor of a single-output Bosch alternator when

Figure 8-58. The Chrysler charging system with computer-controlled voltage regulation uses integrated circuitry to provide internal field control. (Chrysler)

Figure 8-59. Chrysler computer-regulated charging system internal field control. (Chrysler)

Chrysler ceased manufacture of its own alternators in 1989. Current Chrysler charging systems with a Bosch alternator (84 or 86 amperes) are essentially the same design as those used with the dual-output alternators, figure 8-60. However, an engine controller replaces the separate logic and power modules.

Nippondenso alternators

Some current Chrysler vehicles use Nippondenso alternators with an output range of 68 to 102 amperes. These are virtual clones of the Bosch design, even to the external wiring connections, figure 8-61. Charging system circuitry is the same, as are test procedures.

Figure 8-60. Current Chrysler vehicles equipped with an SBEC or SMEC use the same charging system wiring as earlier models equipped with the logic and power modules. (Chrysler)

Figure 8-61. Nippondenso and Bosch alternators used on Chrysler vehicles have identical wiring connections. (Chrysler)

Import Vehicle Charging Systems

Many European vehicles have Bosch alternators featuring Y-type stators. Bosch models with a remote regulator use six rectifiers and have a threaded battery terminal and two-way spade connector on the rear housing. Those with an integral regulator contain 12 rectifiers and have a threaded battery stud marked B+ and a smaller threaded stud marked D+. This smaller stud is used for voltage from the ignition switch. Models with internal regulators also have a diode trio to supply field current initially and a blocking diode to prevent current from flowing back to the ignition system when the ignition is turned off.

Several manufacturers such as Hitachi, Nippondenso and Mitsubishi provide alternators for Japanese vehicles. While all function on the same principles just studied, the design and construction of some units are unique. For example, figure 8-62 shows a Mitsubishi alternator that uses an integral regulator with double Y-stator and 12 diodes in a pair of

Figure 8-62. A circuit diagram of the Mitsubishi charging system using the double Y-stator alternator.

rectifier assemblies to deliver high current with high voltage at low speeds. A diode trio internally supplies the field, and a 50-ohm resistor in the regulator performs the same function as the Bosch blocking diode.

SUMMARY

The sine wave voltage induced across one alternator conductor generates single-phase current. By connecting the alternator conductor diodes, the ac is fully rectified to dc. In an actual automotive alternator, there are more than two magnetic poles and one conductor. Common alternators have from eight to 14 poles on a rotor, and three conductors wound to create a stator. The rotor and stator are held in a two-piece housing. Two brushes attached to the housings, but often insulated from it, ride on sliprings to carry current to the rotor winding. The diodes are installed in the same end housing as the brushes. Three positive diodes are insulated from the housing; three negative diodes are grounded to the housing.

Stators with three conductors produce three-phase current. The three conductors may be connected to make a Y-type or a delta-type stator. The rectification process is the same for both types, although the current paths through the stators differ. Rectified output from a multiple-pole alternator is a rippling dc voltage.

Because the rotor does not retain enough magnetism to begin induction, an excitation circuit must carry battery current to the rotor winding. The rotor winding is part of an externally grounded field, or A-circuit; or an internally grounded field, or B-circuit. Common alternators used by domestic manufacturers include the Delco-Remy SI and CS series used by GM; the Motorcraft IAR, rear-terminal, and side-terminal models used by Ford; and the Chrysler-built, Bosch, and Nippondenso models used by Chrysler. Most European imports use Bosch alternators, while Asian imports use alternators made by several manufacturers, including Hitachi, Nippondenso, and Mitsubishi.

Review Questions

Choose the single most correct answer.
Compare your answers with the correct answers on Page 468.

1. Alternators induce voltage by rotating:
   a. A magnetic field inside a fixed conductor
   b. A conductor inside a magnetic field
   c. A stator inside a field
   d. A spring past a stator

2. In an alternator, induced voltage is at its maximum value when the angle between the magnetic lines and the looped conductor is:
   a. 0°
   b. 45°
   c. 90°
   d. 180°

3. The sine wave voltage induced across one conductor by one rotor revolution is called:
   a. Single-phase current
   b. Open-circuit voltage
   c. Diode rectification
   d. Half-phase current

4. Alternating current in an alternator is rectified by:
   a. Brushes
   b. Diodes
   c. Slip rings
   d. Transistors

5. An alternator with only one conductor and one diode would show which of the following current output patterns?
   a. Three-phase current
   b. Open-circuit voltage
   c. Half-wave rectification
   d. Full-wave rectification

6. An alternator consists of:
   a. A stator, a rotor, slip rings, brushes, and diodes
   b. A stator, an armature, slip rings, brushes, and diodes
   c. A stator, a rotor, a commutator, brushes, and diodes
   d. A stator, a rotor, a field relay, brushes, and diodes

7. A typical automotive alternator has _____ poles.
   a. 2 to 4
   b. 6 to 8
   c. 8 to 14
   d. 12 to 20

8. The three alternator conductors are wound onto a cylindrical, laminated metal-piece called:
   a. A rotor core
   b. A stator core
   c. An armature core
   d. A field core

9. Automotive alternators that have three conductors generally use _____ diodes to rectify the output current.
   a. Three
   b. Six
   c. Nine
   d. Twelve

10. Which of the following is NOT true of the positive diodes in an alternator?
    a. Connected to the insulated terminal of the battery
    b. Conduct only the current moving from ground into the conductor
    c. Mounted in a heat sink
    d. The bias of the diodes prevents the battery from discharging

11. A group of three or more like diodes may be called:
    a. Diode wing
    b. Diode triplet
    c. Diode dish
    d. Diode bridge

12. Y-type stators are used in alternators that require:
    a. Low voltage output at high alternator speed
    b. High voltage output at low alternator speed
    c. Low voltage at low alternator speed
    d. High voltage at high alternator speed

13. Which of the following is true of a delta-type stator?
    a. There is no neutral junction
    b. There is no ground connection
    c. The windings always form a series circuit
    d. The circuit diagram looks like a parallelogram

14. Delta-type stators are used:
    a. When high-voltage output is needed
    b. When low-voltage output is needed
    c. When high-current output is needed
    d. When low-current output is needed

15. Which of the following is a commonly used type of field circuit in automotive alternators?
    a. X-circuit
    b. Y-circuit
    c. Connected-field circuit
    d. A-circuit

9
Regulators and Indicators

Alternator regulators limit voltage output by controlling field current. The location of the regulator in the field circuit determines whether the alternator is an A-circuit or a B-circuit, as in Chapter Eight of this *Classroom Manual*.

SELF-REGULATION OF CURRENT

The maximum current output of an alternator is limited by the design of the alternator. As induced voltage causes current to travel in a conductor, a countervoltage is also induced in the same conductor. The countervoltage is caused by the expanding magnetic field of the original induced current. The countervoltage tends to oppose any change in the original current.

When induced voltage causes current in the conductors of the stator, a countervoltage also appears. The countervoltage opposes any increased current in the stator windings. The more current the alternator puts out, the greater this countervoltage becomes. At a certain point, the countervoltage is great enough to completely stop any further increase in the alternator's current output. At this point, the alternator has reached its maximum current output. Therefore, because the two voltages continue to increase as alternator speed increases, a method of regulating alternator voltage is required.

VOLTAGE REGULATION

Alternator output voltage is directly related to field strength and rotor speed. An increase in either factor increases voltage output. Similarly, a decrease in either factor decreases voltage output. Rotor speed is controlled by engine speed and cannot be changed simply to control the alternator. Field strength can be changed by controlling the field current in the rotor winding. This is how ac generator voltage regulators work. Figure 9-1 shows how the field current (dashed line) is lowered to keep alternator output (solid line) at a constant maximum, even when the rotor speed increases.

At low rotor speeds, the field current is at full strength for relatively long periods of time, and is reduced only for short periods, figure 9-2A. This causes a high average field current. At high rotor speeds, the field current is reduced for long periods of time and is at full strength only for short periods, figure 9-2B. This causes a low average field current.

On older vehicles, the field circuit was controlled by an electromagnetic regulator. However, in the 1970s, semiconductor technology made solid-state voltage regulators possible. Because they are smaller and have no moving parts, solid-state regulators replaced the older electromagnetic type in ac charging systems. On

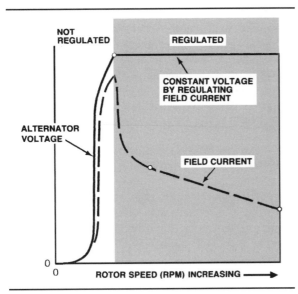

Figure 9-1. Field current is decreased as rotor speed increases to keep alternator output voltage at a constant level.

Figure 9-2. The field current flows for longer periods of time at low speeds (t_1) than at high speeds (t_2). (Bosch)

Figure 9-3. Most regulators use a multiple-plug connector to ensure connections are properly made. (Bosch)

newer vehicles, the solid-state regulator may be a separate component built into the alternator or incorporated into the powertrain control module (PCM).

Some solid-state regulators are mounted on the inside or outside of the alternator housing, as discussed in Chapter Eight of this *Classroom Manual*. Remotely mounted voltage regulators often use a multi-plug connector, figure 9-3, to ensure all connections are properly made. This eliminates exposed wiring and connections which are prone to damage.

ELECTROMAGNETIC REGULATORS

Electromagnetic voltage regulators, sometimes called electromechanical regulators, operate the same whether used with old dc generators or more common ac generators. The electromagnetic coil of the voltage regulator is connected from the ignition switch to ground. This forms a parallel branch receiving system voltage, either from the alternator output circuit or from the battery. The magnetic field of the coil acts upon an armature to open and close contact points controling current to the field.

Double-Contact Voltage Regulator

At high rotor speeds, the alternator may be able to force too much field current through a single-contact regulator and exceed the desired output. This is called **voltage creep**, or **voltage drift**. Single-contact regulators are used only with low-current-output alternators. Almost all electromagnetic voltage regulators used with automotive alternators are double-contact units, figure 9-4. When the first set of contacts

opens at lower rotor speeds, current passes through a resistor wired in series with the field circuit. These contacts are called the **series contacts**. The value of the regulating resistor is kept very low to permit high field current when needed. At higher rotor speeds, the armature is further attracted by the coil and a second set of contacts is closed. This grounds the field circuit, stopping the field current. These contacts are called the **shorting contacts** because they short-circuit the field to ground. The double-contact design offers consistent regulation over a broad range of alternator speeds.

SOLID-STATE REGULATORS

Solid-state regulators completely replaced the older electromagnetic design on late-model vehicles. They are compact, have no moving parts, and are not seriously affected by temperature changes. The early solid-state designs combine transistors with the electromagnetic field relay. The latest and most compact is the integrated-circuit (IC) regulator, figure 9-5. This combines all control circuitry and components on a single silicon chip. Attaching terminals are added, and

Figure 9-4. The circuit diagram of a double-contact regulator. (Delco-Remy)

Figure 9-5. An example of the latest integrated circuit regulator design, a Ford IAR regulator and brush holder.

the chip is sealed in a small plastic module that mounts inside, or on the back of, the alternator. Because of their construction, however, all solid-state regulators are non-serviceable and must be replaced if defective. No adjustments are possible.

Here is a review of most components of a solid-state regulator. They are:

- Diodes
- Transistors
- Zener diodes
- Thermistors
- Capacitors.

Diodes are one-way electrical check valves. Transistors act as relays. A zener diode is specially doped to act as a one-way, electrical check valve until a specific reverse voltage level is reached. At that point, the zener diode allows reverse current to pass through it.

The electrical resistance of a **thermistor**, or **thermal resistor**, changes as temperature changes. Most resistors used in automotive applications are called negative temperature coefficient (NTC) resistors. As discussed in Chapter Four, this is because their resistance decreases as temperature increases. The thermistor in a solid-state regulator reacts to temperature to ensure proper battery charging voltage.

A capacitor is used by some manufacturers to smooth out any abrupt voltage surges and protect the regulator from damage. Diodes may also be used as circuit protection.

General circuit operation

Figure 9-6 is a simplified circuit diagram of a solid-state regulator. This A-circuit regulator is contained within the alternator housing. The "2" terminal on the

alternator is always connected to the battery, but battery discharge is limited by the high resistance of "R2" and "R3". The circuit allows the regulator to sense battery voltage.

When the ignition switch is closed, figure 9-7, current travels from the battery to ground through the base of the "TR1" diode. This causes the diode to conduct current through its emitter-collector circuit from the battery to the low-resistance rotor winding. This energizes the alternator field and turns on the warning lamp.

When the alternator begins to produce current, figure 9-8, field current is drawn from unrectified alternator output and rectified by the diode trio, which is charging voltage. The warning lamp is turned off by equal voltage on both sides of the lamp.

When the alternator has charged the battery to a maximum safe voltage level, figure 9-9, the battery voltage between R2 and R3 is high enough to cause zener diode D2 to conduct in reverse bias. This turns

Voltage Creep: Excessive voltage at high speeds due to excessive field current flow through a single-contact regulator. Also called voltage drift.

Series Contacts: The normally closed set of contacts in a double-contact regulator. When they open, field current must flow through a resistor.

Shorting Contacts: The normally open set of contacts in a double-contact regulator. When closed, they short-circuit the field to ground.

Thermistor: A resistor specially constructed so that its resistance changes as its temperature changes. Also called a thermal resistor.

Figure 9-6. Circuit diagram of a typical solid-state voltage regulator. (Delco-Remy)

Figure 9-7. Field current in a typical solid-state regulator during starting. (Delco-Remy)

on TR2, which shorts the base circuit of TR1 to ground. When TR1 is turned off, the field circuit is turned off at the ground control of TR1.

With "TR1" off, the field current decreases and system voltage drops. When voltage drops low enough, the zener diode switches off and current is no longer applied to diode "TR2". This opens the field circuit ground and energizes the "TR1" diode. TR1 turns back on. The field current and system voltage increase. This cycle repeats many times per second to limit the alternator voltage to a predetermined value.

The other components within the regulator perform various functions. Capacitor "C1" provides stable voltage across resistor "R3". Resistor "R4" prevents excessive current through diode "TR1" at high temperatures. To prevent circuit damage, diode "D3" bypasses high voltages induced in the field windings when diode "TR1" turns off. Resistor "R2" is a thermistor which causes the regulated voltage to vary with temperature. R5 allows the indicator lamp to turn off if the field circuit is open.

Specific Solid-State Regulator Designs

Delco-Remy

The Delco-Remy solid-state automotive regulator was used in figures 9-6 through 9-9 to explain the basic operation of these units. This is the integral regulator unit of the SI series alternators. The "1" and "2" terminals on the alternator housing connect directly to the regulator. The "1" terminal conducts field current from the battery or the alternator and controls the indicator lamp. The "2" terminal receives battery voltage and allows the zener diode to react to it.

Unlike other voltage regulators, the multifunction IC regulator used with Delco-Remy CS-series alternators, figure 9-10, switches the field current on and off at a fixed frequency of 400 Hz. That is four-hundred times per second. The regulator varies the duty cycle, or percentage of on-time to total cycle time, to control the average field current and to regulate voltage. At high speeds, the on-time might be 10 percent with the off-time 90 percent. At low speeds with high electrical loads, this ratio could be reversed: 90 percent on-time

Figure 9-8. Field current drawn from alternator output. (Delco-Remy)

Figure 9-9. When alternator output voltage reaches a maximum safe level, no current is allowed in the rotor winding. (Delco-Remy)

and 10 percent off-time. Unlike the SI series, CS alternators have no test hole to ground the regulator for full-field testing. The regulator cannot be tested with an ohmmeter; a special tester is required.

Motorcraft

At one time, Motorcraft alternators used both remote-mounted and integral solid-state regulators. Motorcraft regulator terminals are designated as follows:

- A+ or A— connects the battery to the field relay contacts
- S— connects the alternator output to the field relay coil
- F— connects the field coil to the regulator transistors
- I— connects the ignition switch to the field relay and regulator contacts, only on vehicles with a warning lamp.

Ford began using a remote-mounted, fully solid-state regulator, figure 9-11, on its intermediate and large models in 1978. The functions of the "I", "A+",

"S", and "F" terminals, figure 9-12, are identical to those of the transistorized regulator shown in figure 9-13. On systems with an ammeter, the regulator is color coded blue or gray, and the "I" terminal is not used. On warning lamp systems, the regulator is black, and all terminals can be used. The two models are not interchangeable, and cannot be substituted for the earlier solid-state unit with a relay or for an electromagnetic regulator. However, Ford does provide red or clear service replacement solid-state regulators which can be used with both systems.

The Motorcraft integral alternator/regulator (IAR) introduced in 1985 uses an IC regulator which is also mounted on the outside of the rear housing. This regulator differs from others because it contains a circuit indicating when the battery is being overcharged, figure 9-14. It turns on the charge indicator lamp if terminal "A" voltage is too high or too low, or if the terminal "S" voltage signal is abnormal.

A-BASIC CIRCUIT USING L TERMINAL   **B-BASIC CIRCUIT USING L AND I TERMINALS**

Figure 9-10. Two basic circuits for the Delco-Remy CS series alternators. (Delco-Remy)

Chrysler

The Chrysler solid-state regulator depends on a remotely mounted field relay to open and close the isolated-field or the A-circuit alternator field. The relay closes the circuit only when the ignition switch is turned on. The voltage regulator, figure 9-15, contains two transistors that are turned on and off by a zener diode. The zener diode reacts to system voltage to start and stop field current. The field current travels through what Chrysler calls a field-suppression diode, which limits current to control alternator output. The regulator also contains a thermistor to control battery-charging voltage at various temperatures. The regulator has two terminals. One is connected to the ignition system; the other is connected to the alternator field.

Computer-Controlled Regulation

Chrysler Corporation eliminated the separate regulator by moving its function to the engine control computer, or PCM, in 1985. When the ignition is turned on, the PCM logic module or logic circuit checks battery temperature to determine the control voltage, figure 9-16. A pre-driver transistor in the logic module or logic circuit then signals the power module or power circuit driver transistor to turn the alternator field current on, figure 9-17. The logic module or logic circuit continually monitors battery temperature and system voltage. At the same time, it transmits output signals to the power module or power circuit driver to adjust the field current as required to maintain 13.6 to 14.8-volt output. Figure 9-18 shows the complete circuitry involved.

General Motors has taken a different approach to regulating CS charging system voltage electronically.

Figure 9-11. The Ford remote solid-state regulator.

Turning the ignition switch on supplies voltage to activate a solid-state digital regulator which uses pulse-width modulation (PWM) to supply rotor current and thus control output voltage. The rotor current is proportional to the PWM pulses from the digital regulator. With the ignition on, narrow width pulses are sent to the rotor, creating a weak magnetic field. As the engine starts, the regulator senses alternator rotation through ac voltage detected on an internal wire. Once the engine is running, the regulator switches the field current on and off at a fixed frequency of about 400 cycles per second (hertz). By changing the pulse width, or on-off time of each cycle, the regulator provides a correct average field current for proper system voltage control.

A lamp driver in the digital regulator controls the indicator warning lamp, turning on the bulb when it detects an under- or over-voltage condition. The warning lamp also illuminates if the alternator is not rotating.

The PCM does not directly control charging system voltage, as in the Chrysler application. However, it does monitor battery and system voltage through an ignition switch circuit. If the PCM reads a voltage above 17 volts, or less than 9 volts for longer than 10 seconds, it sets a code 16 in memory and turns on the malfunction indicator lamp (MIL).

Diagnostic trouble codes

On late-model Chrysler vehicles, the onboard diagnostic capability of the engine control system detects charging system problems and records up to five diagnostic trouble codes (DTC) in the system memory. Some of the codes light a MIL on the instrument panel; others do not. Problems in the General Motors CS charging system cause the PCM to turn on the indicator lamp and set a single code in memory.

INDICATORS

A charging system failure cripples an automobile. Therefore, most manufacturers provide some way for

Figure 9-12. Electrical schematic of Ford's current solid-state regulator (A) and its earlier transistorized model (B).

Figure 9-13. The Ford solid-state voltage regulator with electromagnetic field relay. (Ford)

the driver to monitor the system operation. The indicator may be an ammeter, a voltmeter, or an indicator lamp.

Ammeter

An instrument panel ammeter measures charging system current into and out of the battery and the rest of

Figure 9-14. A circuit diagram of the Motorcraft IAR alternator. (Ford)

Figure 9-15. The Chrysler solid-state regulator.

the electrical system (except the shorter motor), figure 9-19. The ammeter reads the voltage drop of a circuit. When current is traveling from the alternator into the battery, the ammeter needle moves in the positive, or charge, direction. When the battery takes over the

Figure 9-16. Battery temperature circuit of the Chrysler computer regulated charging system. (Chrysler)

Figure 9-17. Chrysler computer-regulated charging-system internal field control. (Chrysler)

electrical system's load, current travels in the opposite direction and the needle moves into the negative, or discharge, zone. The ammeter simply indicates which is doing the most work in the electrical system, the battery or the alternator. Some ammeters are graduated to indicate the approximate current in amperes, such as 5, 10, or 20. Others simply show an approximate rate of charge or discharge, such as high, medium, or low.

Some ammeters have a resistor parallel so the meter does not carry all of the current. These are called shunt ammeters.

While the ammeter tells the driver whether the charging system is functioning normally, it does not give a good picture of the battery condition. Even when the ammeter indicates a charge, the current output may not be high enough to fully charge the battery while supplying other electrical loads. Figure 9-20 shows a typical ammeter circuit, including a shunt resistor.

Voltmeter

The instrument panels of many late-model vehicles contain a voltmeter instead of an ammeter, figure 9-21.

Figure 9-18. Chrysler computer-regulated charging-system voltage control. (Chrysler)

Figure 9-19. A General Motors ammeter installation.

A voltmeter measures electrical pressure and indicates regulated alternator voltage output or battery voltage, whichever is greater. System voltage is applied to the

Figure 9-20. A Ford ammeter installation.

meter through the ignition switch contacts. Figure 9-22 shows a typical voltmeter circuit.

The voltmeter tells a driver more about the condition of the electrical system of a vehicle than an ammeter. When a voltmeter begins to indicate lower-than-normal voltage, it is time to check the battery and the voltage regulator.

Indicator Lamps

Most charging systems use an instrument panel indicator, or warning lamp, to show general charging system operation. Although the lamp usually does not warn the driver of an overcharged battery or high charging voltage, it lights to show an undercharged battery or low voltage from the alternator.

The lamp also lights when the battery supplies field current before the engine starts. The lamp is often connected parallel to a resistor; therefore, field current travels even if the bulb fails. The lamp is wired so it lights when battery current travels through it to the alternator field. When the alternator begins to produce voltage, this voltage is applied to the side of the lamp away from the battery. When the two voltages are equal, no voltage drops are present across the lamp and it goes out.

When indicator lamps are used, the regulator must be able to monitor when the alternator is charging. One

Figure 9-21. An automotive voltmeter for the instrument panel.

method is to use "stator" or neutral voltage. This signal is present only when the alternator is charging, and is 1/2 charging voltage. When stator voltage is about three volts, it energizes a relay to open the indicator lamp ground circuit, figure 9-22. In figure 9-23, stator voltage closes the field relay, which connects battery voltage to the "I" terminal to turn out the indicator lamp.

The indicator lamp will be turned off if the stator voltage is high enough. This may allow a low charging with the indicator lamp off.

The other approach is to measure charging voltage from a diode trio. This provides power to the field circuit, and turns out the light with an equal voltage to both sides of the indicator lamp.

Figure 9-22. The circuit diagram of a typical voltmeter installation.

Figure 9-23. A Ford warning lamp installation.

A signal which measures only when the alternator is charging is needed when an indicator lamp is present. The two approaches used are stator or neutral, which is 1/2 charging voltage, or diode trio which is charging voltage.

Figures 9-14, 9-23, and 9-24 show typical warning lamp circuit installations. In figure 9-14, a 500-ohm resistor is used for warning lamp systems and a 420-ohm resistor for electronic display clusters. In Figure 9-24, a 40-ohm resistor (R5) is installed near the integral regulator. In each case, the grounded path ensures the warning lamp lights if an open occurs in the field circuitry.

As previously discussed, indicator lamps can also be controlled by the field relay.

The indicator lamp for a Delco-Remy CS system works differently than most others. It lights if charging voltage is either too low or too high. Any problem in the charging system causes the lamp to light at full brilliance.

CHARGING SYSTEM PROTECTION

If a charging system component fails or malfunctions, wiring and other units in the system could be damaged by excessive current or heat, voltage surges, and other uncontrolled factors. To protect the system from high current, fusible links are often wired in series at various places in the circuitry. Figures 9-25 and 9-26 show some typical fusible link locations.

Figure 9-24. A General Motors warning lamp installation.

SUMMARY

Because a countervoltage is induced in the stator windings, alternator current output is self-limiting. Voltage regulation is still needed. Electromagnetic voltage regulators have been replaced by those with integrated circuits. Voltage regulators now in use are completely solid-state designs. They replaced the electromagnetic type regulators in ac charging systems. This is because they are smaller and have no moving parts. Because of the construction of solid-state regulators, they are non-serviceable and must be replaced if defective. Their function is the same: to control alternator output by modulating current through the field windings of the alternator.

Indicators allow the driver to monitor the performance of the charging system. These include ammeters, voltmeters, or warning lamps. An ammeter measures the charging system current into and out of the battery and the entire electrical system. A voltmeter measures electrical pressure and indicates regulated alternator voltage output or battery voltage. Indicator lamps illuminate on the instrument panel of the vehicle and indicate to the driver general charging system operation status.

Wiring and other components in the charging system may be damaged if the system fails or malfunctions due to excessive current or heat, voltage surges,

Figure 9-25. A Ford wiring diagram showing fusible link locations.

Figure 9-26. A Buick circuit diagram showing fusible link locations.

and other uncontrolled factors. Fusible links are often wired in series along the circuitry. This protects the system from high current.

■ Motor-Generators

Motors and generators are similar in construction. In fact, it is possible to use the same unit as both a motor and as a generator by changing the external circuitry.

In the early 1900s, motor-generators were built by Delco, Simms-Huff, North East, and others. A Simms-Huff model used on the 1915-1917 Maxwell acted as a 12-volt starter motor and a six-volt generator. The Maxwell had two six-volt batteries. A special switch connected them in series during cranking and in parallel during running and charging. The motor-generator had six pole pieces, with shunt windings on all six and series windings on every other one. The electromagnetic voltage regulator that controlled the field current of the generator had two sets of contact points: One set was for voltage regulation; the other set acted as cutout points.

Review Questions

Choose the single most correct answer.
Compare your answers with the correct answers on Page 468.

1. Alternator output voltage is directly related to:
   a. Field strength
   b. Rotor speed
   c. Both field strength and rotor speed
   d. Neither field strength nor rotor speed

2. Double-contact voltage regulators contain all of the following except:
   a. An armature
   b. An electromagnet
   c. Two sets of contact points
   d. A solenoid

3. The shorting contacts of a double-contact regulator:
   a. Increase voltage creep
   b. Increase field current
   c. React to battery temperature changes
   d. Short the field circuit to the alternator

4. Which of the following can NOT be used in a totally solid-state regulator?
   a. Zener diodes
   b. Thermistors
   c. Capacitors
   d. Circuit breakers

5. Which of the following is used to smooth out any abrupt voltage surges and protect a regulator?
   a. Transistor
   b. Capacitor
   c. Thermistor
   d. Relays

6. Which of the following is used to monitor the charging system?
   a. Ammeter
   b. Ohmmeter
   c. Dynamometer
   d. Fusible link

7. Warning lamps are installed so that they will not light when:
   a. The voltage on the battery side of the lamp is higher
   b. Field current is flowing from the battery to the alternator
   c. The voltage on both sides of the lamp is equal
   d. The voltage on the resistor side of the lamp is higher

8. Maximum current output in an alternator is reached when:
   a. It reaches maximum designed speed
   b. Electrical demands from the system are at the minimum
   c. Induced countervoltage becomes great enough to stop current increase
   d. Induced countervoltage drops low enough to stop voltage increase

9. The regulator is a charging system device which controls _____ circuit opening and closing.
   a. Ignition-to-battery
   b. Alternator-to-thermistor
   c. Battery-to-accessory
   d. Voltage source-to-battery

10. Which of the following methods is used to regulate supply current to the alternator field?
   a. Fault codes
   b. Charge indicator lamp
   c. Pulse-width modulation
   d. Shunt resistor

PART FOUR

The Starting System

Chapter Ten
Starting System Overview

Chapter Eleven
Starter Motors

10

Starting System Overview

The automotive starting system is also called the cranking system. Its only job is to crank the engine fast enough for the engine to fire and run. The ignition and fuel systems must supply the spark and fuel for the engine to start and run, but the starting system cranks the engine to get it going.

SYSTEM OPERATION

The starting system draws a large amount of current from the battery to power the starter motor. The starter circuit on a large gasoline-powered V8 engine must carry as much as 300 amperes under some conditions. Large V8 diesel engines require even more current. To handle this current safely and with a minimum voltage loss from resistance, the cables must be the correct size, and all connections must be clean and tight.

The starting system is controlled by the driver through the ignition switch. If the heavy cables that carry current to the starter were routed to the instrument panel and the switch, they would be so long that the starter would not get enough current to operate properly. To avoid such a voltage drop, the starting system has two circuits, figure 10-1:

- The starter circuit
- The control circuit.

Starter Motor Circuit

The starter circuit, or motor circuit, shown as the solid lines of figure 10-1, consists of:

- The battery
- A magnetic switch
- The starter motor
- Heavy-gauge cables.

The circuit between the battery and the starter motor is controlled by a magnetic switch (a relay or solenoid). Switch design and function vary from system to system.

A gear on the starter motor armature engages with gear teeth on the engine flywheel. When current reaches the starter motor, it begins to turn. This turns the car's engine, which can quickly fire and run by itself. If the starter motor remained engaged to the engine flywheel, the starter motor would be spun by the engine at a very high speed. This would damage the starter motor. To avoid this, there must be a mechanism to disengage the starter motor from the engine. There are several different designs that will do this, as we will see in the next chapter.

Figure 10-1. In this diagram of the starting system, the starter circuit is shown as a solid line and the control circuit is shown as a dashed line. (Delco-Remy)

Control Circuit

The control circuit is shown by the dashed lines in figure 10-1. It allows the driver to use a small amount of battery current, about three to five amperes, to control the flow of a large amount of battery current to the starter motor. Control circuits usually consist of an ignition switch connected through normal-gauge wiring to the battery and the magnetic switch. When the ignition switch is in the start position, a small amount of current flows through the coil of the magnetic switch. This closes a set of large contact points within the magnetic switch and allows battery current to flow directly to the starter motor.

BASIC SYSTEM PARTS

We have already studied the battery, which is an important part of the starting system. The other circuit parts are the:

- Ignition switch
- Starting safety switch (on some systems)
- Relays or solenoids (magnetic switches)
- Starter motor
- Wiring.

Ignition Switch

The ignition switch has jobs other than controlling the starting system. The ignition switch normally has at least four positions:

- Accessories
- Off
- On (Run)
- Start.

Figure 10-2. This ignition switch acts directly on the contact points. (Bosch)

Switches on late-model cars also have a lock position to lock the steering wheel. All positions except start are **detented.** That is, the switch will remain in that position until moved. When the ignition key is turned to start and released, it will return to the on (run) position. The start position is the actual starter switch part of the ignition switch. It applies battery voltage to the magnetic switch.

There are two types of ignition switches in use. On older cars, the switch is mounted on the instrument panel and contains the contact points, figure 10-2. The newer type, used on cars with locking steering columns, is usually mounted on the column. Many column-mounted switches operate remotely mounted contact points through a rod, figure 10-3. Other column-mounted switches operate directly on contact points, figure 10-4. Older domestic and imported cars sometimes used separate push button switches or cable-operated switches that controlled the starting system separately from the ignition switch.

Starting Safety Switch

The **starting safety switch** is also called a neutral start switch. It is a normally open switch that prevents the starting system from operating when the automobile's transmission is in gear. If the car has no starting safety switch, it is possible to spin the engine with the transmission in gear. This makes the car lurch forward or backward, which could be dangerous. Safety switches or interlock devices are now required by law with all automatic and manual transmissions.

Starting safety switches can be connected in two places within the starting system control circuit. The safety switch can be placed between the ignition switch and the magnetic switch, figure 10-5, so that the safety switch must be closed before current can flow to the magnetic switch. The safety switch also can be connected between the magnetic switch and ground, figure 10-6, so that the switch must be closed before current can flow from the magnetic switch to ground.

Figure 10-3. Many column-mounted ignition switches act on the contact points through the movement of a rod. (Ford)

Figure 10-4. This column-mounted ignition switch acts directly on the contact points.

Where the starting safety switch is installed depends upon the type of transmission used and whether the gearshift lever is column-mounted or floor-mounted.

Automatic transmissions

The safety switch used with an automatic transmission can be either an electrical switch or a mechanical device. Electrical switches have contact points that are closed only when the gear lever is in Park or Neutral, as shown in figure 10-5. The switch can be mounted near the gearshift lever, figures 10-7 and 10-8, or on the transmission housing, figure 10-9. The contacts are in series with the control circuit, so that no current can flow through the magnetic switch unless the transmission is out of gear.

Mechanical interlock devices physically block the movement of the ignition key when the transmission is in gear, figures 10-10 and 10-11. The key can be turned only when the gear shift lever is in Park or Neutral.

Some manufacturers use an additional circuit in the neutral start switch to light the backup lamps when the transmission is placed in Reverse, figures 10-8 and 10-9.

The Beginning

The automobile became common in America in the early 1900s. The first automobiles had no electric starting systems. The driver had to insert a crank into the front of the engine and turn it by hand until the engine fired and ran. This required both skill and physical strength. Without a self-starting system, engines were limited in displacement and compression ratios. Operating an automobile was very inconvenient for those who could not crank the engine themselves.

In 1910, Charles F. Kettering began work on a practical automotive self-starter. The system first appeared on the 1912 Cadillac, and was quickly adopted by other manufacturers.

Detented: Positions in a switch that allow the switch to stay in that position. In an ignition switch, the On, Off, Lock, and Accessory positions are detented.

Starting Safety Switch: A neutral start switch. It keeps the starting system from operating when a car's transmission is in gear.

Figure 10-5. This starting safety switch must be closed before battery current can reach the magnetic switch. (Ford).

Figure 10-6. The clutch switch must be closed before battery current can flow from the magnetic switch to ground. (Chrysler)

Ford vehicles equipped with an electronic automatic transmission or transaxle use an additional circuit in the neutral safety switch to inform the microprocessor of the position of the manual lever shaft. This signal is used to determine the desired gear and electronic pressure control. The switch is now called a manual lever position sensor or switch (MLPS).

General Motors has done essentially the same as Ford, renaming the Park/Neutral switch used on its THM 4T60-E transaxle. It now is called either a PRNDL switch or a Park/Neutral position switch and provides input to the PCM regarding torque converter clutch slip. This input allows the PCM to make the necessary calculations to control clutch apply and release feel.

Manual transmissions

The starting safety switch used with a manual transmission on older vehicles is usually an electrical switch similar to those shown in figures 10-7 and 10-8. A **clutch start switch** (also called an interlock switch) is commonly used with manual transmissions

Figure 10-7. An electrical safety switch installed near the floor-mounted gear shift lever. (Chevrolet)

and transaxles on late-model vehicles. This is an electric switch mounted on the floor or firewall near the clutch pedal. Its contacts are normally open and close only when the clutch pedal is fully depressed, figure 10-12.

Relays and Solenoids

A magnetic switch in the starting system allows the control circuit to open and close the starter circuit. The switch can be a:

- Relay, which uses the electromagnetic field of a coil to attract an armature and close the contact points
- Solenoid, which uses the electromagnetic field of a coil to pull a plunger into the coil and close the contact points.

Figure 10-8. An electrical safety switch installed near the column-mounted gear shift lever. (Chevrolet)

Figure 10-9. An electrical safety switch mounted on the transmission housing. (Chrysler)

In addition to closing the contact points, solenoid-equipped circuits often use the movement of the solenoid to engage the starter motor with the engine flywheel. We will explain this in the next chapter.

The terminology used with relays and solenoids is often confusing. Technically, a relay operates with a hinged armature and does only an electrical job. A solenoid operates with a movable plunger and usually does a mechanical job. Sometimes, a solenoid is used only to open and close an electric circuit. The movement of the plunger is not used for any mechanical work. Manufacturers sometimes call these solenoids "starter relays". Figure 10-13 shows a commonly used Ford starter relay. We will continue to use the general term "magnetic switch", and will tell you if the manufacturer uses a different name for the device.

Starter Motor

The starter motors used by various manufacturers are explained in detail in Chapter Eleven.

■ Crank Lost?

In 1935, if a car's electric starter wouldn't work, and if the starting crank had been misplaced, motorists were advised that they could jack up a rear wheel, put the clutch in, place the transmission gears in "high", let the clutch out, and start the engine by turning the rear wheel.

Clutch Start Switch: A starting safety switch that is operated by the clutch pedal.

Figure 10-10. A mechanical device within the steering column blocks the movement of the ignition switch actuator rod when the transmission is in gear. (Buick)

Figure 10-11. A lever on the steering wheel blocks the movement of the ignition key when the transmission is in gear.

Wiring

The starter motor circuit uses heavy-gauge wiring to carry current to the starter motor. The control circuit carries less current and thus uses lighter-gauge wires.

SPECIFIC STARTING SYSTEMS

Various manufacturers use different starting system components. The following paragraphs briefly describe the circuits used by major manufacturers. We will study the starter motors used by each manufacturer in the next chapter.

Delco-Remy and Bosch

Delco-Remy and Bosch starter motors are used by General Motors. The most commonly used Delco-Remy and Bosch automotive starter motor depends

Figure 10-12. The clutch pedal must be fully depressed to close the clutch switch and complete the control circuit. (Buick)

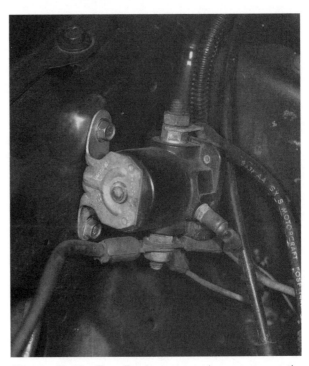

Figure 10-13. The Ford starter relay or magnetic switch.

upon the movement of a solenoid both to control current flow in the starter circuit and to engage the starter motor with the engine flywheel. This is called a **solenoid-actuated starter.** The solenoid is mounted on, or enclosed with, the motor housing, figure 10-14.

The type and location of starting safety switches vary within the GM divisions and car lines. Larger-size GM cars use a mechanical blocking device in the

Figure 10-14. A typical GM starting circuit. (Delco-Remy)

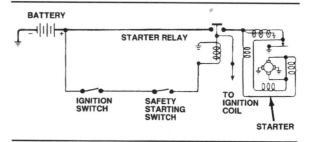

Figure 10-16. The Ford starting system with the positive engagement starter. (Ford)

Figure 10-17. The Ford solenoid-actuated system uses the starter-mounted solenoid only for a mechanical job, not for an electrical job. (Ford)

steering column, figure 10-10. The intermediate and smaller cars with automatic transmissions have electrical switches mounted near the shift lever. These are either on the column, figure 10-8, or on the floor, figure 10-7. On front-wheel-drive (FWD) cars with automatic transmissions, the Park/Neutral or PRNDL switch is an electrical switch mounted on the transaxle case manual lever shaft, figure 10-15. GM cars with floor-shift manual transmissions use a clutch pedal-operated safety switch. With column-shift manual transmissions, an electric switch is mounted on the column.

Figure 10-15. Location of the park/neutral or PRNDL switch on GM THM transaxles. (Oldsmobile)

Solenoid-Actuated Starter: A starter that uses a solenoid both to control current flow in the starter circuit and to engage the starter motor with the engine flywheel.

Figure 10-18. The Ford PMGR starter circuit may use only a solenoid instead of a solenoid and a relay. (Ford)

Motorcraft

Ford has used three types of starter motors, and therefore has several different starting system circuits.

The Motorcraft positive engagement starter has a movable pole shoe that uses electromagnetism to engage the starter motor with the engine. This motor does not use a solenoid to *move* anything, but it uses a solenoid to open and close the starter circuit as a magnetic switch, figure 10-16. Ford calls this solenoid a starter relay, figure 10-13.

The Motorcraft solenoid-actuated starter is very similar to the Delco-Remy and depends upon the movement of a solenoid to engage the starter motor with the engine, figure 10-17. The solenoid is mounted within the motor housing and receives battery current through the same type of starter relay used in the positive engagement system. Although the motor-mounted solenoid could do the job of this additional starter relay, the second relay is installed on many Ford automobiles to make the cars easier to build. Motorcraft solenoid-actuated starters were used on Ford cars and trucks with large V8 engines.

The Motorcraft permanent magnet gear-reduction (PMGR) starter is a solenoid-actuated design that operates much like the Motorcraft solenoid-actuated

starter described above. However, the starter circuit may or may not use a starter relay, depending on the car model, figure 10-18.

Rear-wheel-drive (RWD) Ford automobiles with manual transmissions have no starting safety switch. Front-wheel-drive (FWD) models with manual transaxles have a clutch interlock switch. If a Ford car with an automatic transmission has a column-mounted shift lever, a blocking interlock device prevents the ignition key from turning when the transmission is in gear. If the automatic transmission shift lever is mounted on the floor, an electrical switch prevents current from flowing to the starter relay when the transmission is in gear. The switch may be mounted on the transmission case or near the gearshift lever.

Chrysler

Chrysler uses a solenoid-actuated starter motor. The solenoid is mounted inside the motor housing and receives battery current through a starter relay, figure 10-19.

Chrysler starter relays used prior to 1977 have four terminals, as shown in figure 10-20A. In 1977, a second set of contacts and two terminals were added, figure 10-20B. The extra contacts and terminals allow

Figure 10-19. A typical Chrysler starting system. (Chrysler)

Figure 10-20. Comparison of the terminals on a pre-1977 Chrysler starter relay (A) and a 1977 or later relay. (Chrysler)

■ Vacuum Control Switches

Magnetic switches are not the only control devices that have been used in the starting system's control circuit. Before the 1950s, some GM cars had a vacuum control switch that was mounted in the carburetor. To start the car, the driver turned on the ignition switch and depressed the accelerator pedal. The pedal movement was transmitted through a linkage to the vacuum control switch, closing its contacts. Current flowed from the battery, through the vacuum switch contacts, to the starter motor.

When the engine started and ran, carburetor vacuum opened the vacuum switch contacts to stop cranking. If the carburetor vacuum was not great enough to do this, a secondary system would stop the cranking. Generator voltage was applied to the ground side of the motor. When generator voltage equalled battery voltage, there would be no voltage drop across the motor and the motor would not crank.

Figure 10-21. The Chrysler starting system with a five-terminal Bosch relay. (Chrysler)

Figure 10-22. Only four of the five relay terminals are used when the Bosch relay is installed in the Chrysler starting system. (Chrysler)

Figure 10-23. The Chrysler clutch switch. (Chrysler)

Figure 10-24. When the automatic transmission is in park or neutral, a transmission lever touches the contact and completes the control circuit to ground. (Chrysler)

more current to flow through the relay to the ignition system and to the exhaust gas recirculation (EGR) timer. This has no effect on the operation of the relay within the starting system. These starter relays generally were mounted on the firewall.

Current Chrysler starting systems use a standard five-terminal Bosch relay, figure 10-21, but only four terminals are used in the circuit, figure 10-22. The relay is located at the front of the driver's side strut tower in a power distribution center or cluster.

Chrysler automobiles with manual transmissions have a clutch interlock switch, figure 10-23. Current from the starter relay can flow to ground only when the clutch pedal is fully depressed. Cars with automatic transmission have an electrical neutral start switch mounted on the transmission housing, figure 10-24. When the transmission is out of gear, the switch provides a ground connection for the starter control circuit.

Figure 10-25. A typical Nissan starting system used on gasoline engines.

Toyota and Nissan

Toyota and Nissan use a variety of solenoid-actuated direct drive and reduction gear starter designs manufactured primarily by Hitachi and Nippondenso, figures 10-25 and 10-26. The neutral start switch (called an inhibitor switch by the Japanese) incorporates a relay in its circuit.

Figure 10-26. A typical Nissan diesel starting system.

SUMMARY

Electric starting systems consist of a high-current starter circuit controlled by a low-current control circuit. The ignition switch includes contacts that conduct battery current to the magnetic switch. The magnetic switch may be a relay or a solenoid and may have other jobs besides controlling the starter circuit current flow. The starter motor and connecting wires are also included in the system. Variations are common among the starting systems used by the various manufacturers.

Review Questions

Choose the single most correct answer.
Compare your answers with the correct answers on Page 468.

1. The first practical automotive self-starter was introduced in:
   a. 1895
   b. 1902
   c. 1912
   d. 1916

2. The starting system has _____ circuits to avoid excessive voltage drop.
   a. Two
   b. Three
   c. Four
   d. Six

3. The starter circuit consists of which of the following?
   a. Battery, ignition switch, starter motor, large cables
   b. Battery, ignition switch, relays or solenoids, large cables
   c. Battery, magnetic switch, starter motor, primary wiring
   d. Battery, magnetic switch, starter motor, large cables

4. Which of the following is *not* part of the starter control circuit?
   a. The ignition switch
   b. The starting safety switch
   c. The starter relay
   d. The starter motor

5. The ignition switch will *not* remain in which of the following positions?
   a. Accessories
   b. Off
   c. On (run)
   d. Start

6. The starting safety switch is also called a:
   a. Remote-operated switch
   b. Manual-override switch
   c. Neutral-start switch
   d. Single-pole, double-throw switch

7. Safety switches are most commonly used with:
   a. Automatic transmissions
   b. Imported automobiles
   c. Domestic automobiles
   d. Manual transmissions

8. Starting safety switches used with manual transmissions are usually:
   a. Electrical
   b. Mechanical
   c. Floor-mounted
   d. Column-mounted

9. Which of the following is not true of solenoids?
   a. They use the electromagnetic field of a coil to pull a plunger into the coil
   b. They are generally used to engage the starter motor with the engine flywheel
   c. They operate with a movable plunger and usually do a mechanical job
   d. They send electronic signals to the control module and have no moving parts

11

Starter Motors

Chapter Two explained how the interaction of magnetic fields can be used to convert electrical energy to mechanical energy. Positions A and B of figure 11-1 show that a current-carrying conductor placed in a magnetic field tends to move from the stronger field area to the weaker field area. Position C shows that two conductors carrying current in opposite directions tend to move in opposite directions. The simple motor in position D uses this movement to rotate an armature.

Automotive starter motors are constructed to put this motor principle to work.

FRAME AND FIELD ASSEMBLY

The frame, or housing, of a starter motor, figure 11-2, encloses all of the moving motor parts. It supports the parts and protects them from dirt, oil, and other contamination. The part of the frame that encloses the pole shoes and field windings is made of iron to provide a path for magnetic flux lines, figure 11-3. To reduce weight, other parts of the frame may be made of cast aluminum.

One end of the housing holds one of the two bearings or bushings in which the armature shaft turns. On most motors, it also contains the brushes that conduct current to the armature, figure 11-4. This is called the brush, or commutator, end housing. The other end housing holds the second bearing or bushing in which the armature shaft turns. It also encloses the gear that meshes with the engine flywheel. This is called the drive end housing. The drive end housing often provides the engine-to-motor mounting points. These end pieces may be made of aluminum because they do not have to conduct magnetic flux.

The magnetic field of the starter motor is provided by two or more pole shoes and field windings. The pole shoes are made of iron and are attached to the frame with large screws, figure 11-5. Figure 11-6 shows the paths of magnetic flux lines within a four-pole motor. The field windings are usually made of a heavy copper ribbon, figure 11-7, to increase their current-carrying capacity and electromagnetic field strength. Automotive starter motors usually have four pole shoes and two to four field windings to provide a strong magnetic field within the motor. Pole shoes that do not have field windings are magnetized by flux lines from the wound poles.

Torque is the force of a starter motor, a force applied in a rotary, or circular, direction. The torque, speed, and current draw of a motor are related. As speed increases in most automotive starter motors,

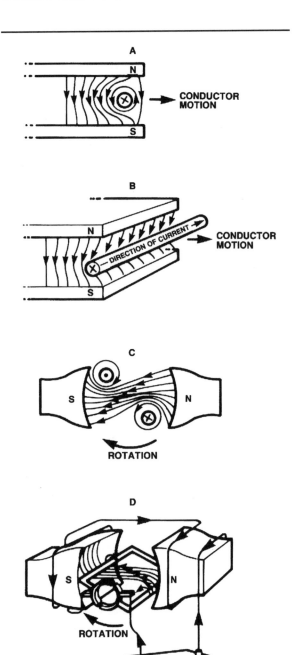

Figure 11-1. The motor principle.

Figure 11-2. The starter motor housing.

Figure 11-3. The motor frame is a path for flux lines.

torque and current draw decrease. These motors develop maximum torque just before the engine begins to turn. Once the engine begins to turn, the motor speed increases and torque decreases. The maximum amount of torque produced by a motor depends upon the strength of its magnetic fields. As field strength increases, torque increases.

Because field current and armature current flow to the motor through one terminal on the housing, the field and armature windings must be connected in a single complete circuit. The internal circuitry of the motor (the way in which the field and armature windings are connected) gives the motor some general operating characteristics. Figure 11-8 shows the three general types of motor internal circuitry:

Figure 11-4. The brush end and drive end housings.

Figure 11-6. Flux line paths in a four-pole motor.

Figure 11-5. Pole shoes and field windings are installed in the housing.

Figure 11-7. A pole shoe and field winding.

- Series
- Shunt (parallel)
- Compound (series-parallel).

All automotive starter motors in use today are the series type or the compound type. The **series motor**, figure 11-8A, has only one path for current. As the armature rotates, its conductors cut magnetic flux lines. A countervoltage is induced in the armature windings, opposing the original current through them. The countervoltage decreases the total current through both the field and the armature windings, because they are connected in series. This reduction of current also reduces the magnetic field strength and motor torque. Series motors produce a great amount of torque when they first begin to operate, but torque decreases as the

Torque: Twisting or rotating force; usually expressed in foot-pounds, inch-pounds, or Newton-meters.

Series Motor: A motor that has only one path for current flow through the field and armature windings. Commonly used for starter motors.

Figure 11-8. Basic motor circuitry.

Figure 11-9. The torque output characteristics of series, shunt, and compound motors.

engine begins to turn, figure 11-9. Series motors work well as automotive starters because cranking an engine requires a great amount of torque at first, and less torque as cranking continues.

The **shunt motor**, figure 11-8B, does not follow the increasing-speed/decreasing-torque relationship just described. The countervoltage within the armature does not affect field current, because field current travels through a separate circuit path. A shunt motor, in effect, adjusts its torque output to the imposed load and operates at a constant speed. Shunt motors are not used as automotive starters because of their low initial torque, figure 11-9, but are used to power other automotive accessories.

The **compound motor**, position C of figure 11-8, has both series and shunt field windings. It combines both the good starting torque of the series-type and the relatively constant operating speed of the shunt-type motor, figure 11-9. A compound motor is often used as an automotive starter.

Figure 11-10 shows the actual relationships of field and armature windings in different types of motors.

ARMATURE AND COMMUTATOR ASSEMBLY

The motor armature, figure 11-11, has a laminated core. Insulation between the laminations helps to reduce eddy currents in the core. For reduced resistance, the armature conductors are made of a thick copper wire. Motor armatures are connected to the commutator in one of two ways. In a **lap winding**, the

Figure 11-10. Actual motor circuit connections.

two ends of each conductor are attached to two adjacent commutator bars, figure 11-12. In a **wave winding**, the two ends of a conductor are attached to commutator bars that are 180 degrees apart (on opposite sides of the commutator), figure 11-13. A lap-wound armature is more commonly used because it offers less resistance.

The commutator is made of copper bars insulated from each other by mica or some other insulating material. The armature core, windings, and commutator are assembled on a long armature shaft. This shaft

Figure 11-11. The motor armature.

LAP WINDING

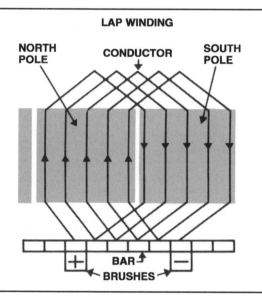

Figure 11-12. Armature lap winding.

Shunt Motor: A motor that has its field windings wired in parallel with its armature. Not used as a starter motor, but often used to power vehicle accessories.

Compound Motor: A motor that has both series and shunt field windings. Often used as a starter motor.

Lap Winding: A method of wiring a motor armature. The two ends of a conductor are attached to two commutator bars that are next to each other.

■ **The Compressed Air Starter**

This early starting system used fresh air stored in a tank to supply the power to crank the engine. The starting "motor" was an airtight chamber mounted on the front of the chassis. A rod from the starter was attached to the crankshaft. When the driver operated a foot pedal mounted on the floorboard, air rushed from the supply tank to the starter. A revolving vane inside the starter was turned by the air, turning the crankshaft at the same time.

Wave Winding: A method of wiring a motor armature. The two ends of a conductor are attached to two commutator bars that are opposite each other.

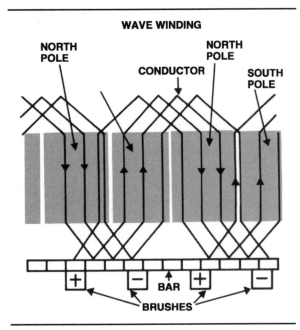

Figure 11-13. Armature wave winding. (Delco-Remy)

Figure 11-14. The pinion gear meshes with the flywheel ring gear.

also carries the pinion gear that meshes with the engine flywheel ring gear, figure 11-14. The shaft is supported by bearings or bushings in the end housings.

To supply the proper current to the armature, a 4-pole motor must have four brushes riding on the

Figure 11-15. A four-brush motor.

commutator, figure 11-15. Most automotive starters have two grounded and two insulated brushes. The brushes are held against the commutator by spring force.

PERMANENT-MAGNET FIELDS

The permanent-magnet, planetary-drive starter motor is the first significant advance in starter design in decades. It was first introduced on some 1986 Chrysler and GM models, and in 1989 by Ford on Continental and some Thunderbird models. Permanent magnets are used in place of the electromagnetic field coils and pole shoes. This eliminates the motor field circuit, which in turn eliminates the potential for field wire-to-frame shorts, field coil welding, and other electrical problems. The motor has only an armature circuit. Because the smaller armature in permanent magnet starters uses reinforcement bands, it has a longer life than the armature in wound-field starter motors.

Figure 11-16. A cutaway view of a typical starter motor.

The magnetic field of the starter motor is provided by four or six small permanent magnets. These magnets are made from an alloy of iron and rare-earth materials that produces a magnetic field strong enough to operate the motor without relying on traditional current-carrying field coil windings around iron pole pieces. Removing the field circuit not only minimizes potential electrical problems, the use of permanent-magnet fields allows engineers to design a gear reduction motor half the size and weight of a conventional wound-field motor without compromising cranking performance.

STARTER MOTOR AND DRIVE TYPES

Starter motors, figure 11-16, are direct-current (dc) motors that use a great amount of current for a short time. As explained in Chapter Ten, the starter motor circuit is a simple one containing just the starter motor and a solenoid or relay. This circuit is a direct path for delivering the momentary high current required by the starter motor from the battery.

Figure 11-17. The Chrysler reduction gear starter motor.

The starter motor cranks the engine through a pinion gear that engages a ring gear on the engine flywheel. The pinion gear is driven directly off the starter armature, figure 11-16, or through a set of reduction gears, figure 11-17, that provide greater starting torque, although at a lower rpm.

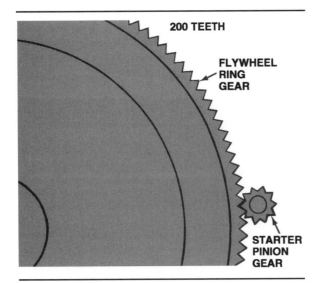

Figure 11-18. The ring gear to pinion gear ratio is about 20 to 1.

Figure 11-19. A typical solenoid-actuated drive.

For the starter motor to be able to turn the engine quickly enough, the number of teeth on the flywheel ring gear, relative to the number of teeth on the motor pinion gear, must be between 15 and 20 to 1, figure 11-18.

When the engine starts and runs, its speed increases. If the starter motor were permanently engaged to the engine, the motor would be spun at a very high speed. This would throw armature windings off the core. Thus, the motor must be disengaged from the engine as soon as the engine turns more rapidly than the starter motor has cranked it. This job is done by the starter motor drive.

Four general kinds of starter motors are used in late-model automobiles:

- Solenoid-actuated, direct drive
- Solenoid-actuated, reduction drive
- Movable pole shoe
- Permanent-magnet, planetary drive.

Solenoid-Actuated, Direct Drive

The main parts of a solenoid-actuated, direct-drive starter, figure 11-19, are the solenoid, the shift lever, the overrunning clutch, and the starter pinion gear.

The solenoid used to actuate a starter drive has two coils: the pull-in winding and the hold-in, or holding, winding, figure 11-20. The pull-in winding consists of few turns of a heavy wire. The winding is grounded through the motor armature and grounded brushes. The hold-in winding consists of many turns of a fine wire and is grounded through the solenoid case.

Figure 11-20. The solenoid has a heavy-gauge pull-in winding and a lighter-gauge hold-in winding. (Delco-Remy)

When the ignition switch is turned to the start position, current flows through both windings. The solenoid plunger is pulled in, and the contacts are closed. This applies battery voltage to both ends of the pull-in winding, and current through it stops. The magnetic field of the hold-in winding is enough to keep the plunger in place. This circuitry reduces the solenoid current draw during cranking, when both the starter motor and the ignition system are drawing current from the battery.

PINION AND GEAR ENGAGED

Figure 11-21. The movement of the solenoid plunger meshes the pinion gear and the flywheel ring gear.

The solenoid plunger action, transferred through the shift lever, pushes the pinion gear into mesh with the flywheel ring gear, figure 11-21. When the starter motor receives current, its armature begins to turn. This motion is transferred through the overrunning clutch and pinion gear to the engine flywheel.

The teeth on the pinion gear may not immediately mesh with the flywheel ring gear. If this happens, a spring behind the pinion compresses so that the solenoid plunger can complete its stroke. When the motor armature begins to turn, the pinion teeth line up with the flywheel, and spring force pushes the pinion to mesh.

Figure 11-22. The Delco-Remy solenoid-actuated drive motor. (Delco-Remy)

The Delco-Remy MT series, figure 11-22, is the most common example of this type of starter motor and has been used for decades on almost all GM cars and light trucks. While this motor is manufactured in different sizes for different engines, figure 11-23, the most common application is a four-pole, four-brush design. The solenoid plunger action, in addition to engaging the pinion gear, closes contact points to complete the starter circuit. To avoid closing the contacts before the pinion gear is fully engaged, the

■ Bendix Drive

Bendix drive starter motors were very common before the 1960s, but have been almost completely replaced by the three other types of drives. Some import models use a Bendix drive starter manufactured in England by Lucas. Delco-Remy and Autolite also built Bendix drive units.

The Bendix drive relies on inertia to engage and disengage the pinion and ring gear. The Bendix drive pinion gear rides loosely on threads in the armature shaft. The inside of the pinion has matching threads.

When the motor armature begins to rotate, the pinion does not pick up speed as quickly as the armature. The pinion moves along the shaft threads and meshes with the ring gear. As the pinion hits the pinion stop, it begins to rotate with the armature to crank the engine.

When the engine fires and runs, the flywheel begins to turn the pinion faster than the armature. This makes the pinion move back along the shaft threads, disengaging it from the flywheel ring gear. A drive spring attached to the pinion helps this disengagement.

STARTER MOTOR — INLINE-6 AND V6 ENGINE

STARTER MOTOR — 455 CID ENGINE

STARTER MOTOR — 260 AND 350 CID ENGINE

Figure 11-23. Delco-Remy provides differently connected starter motors for use with various engines. (Oldsmobile)

Figure 11-24. The Delco-Remy solenoid plunger is in two pieces. (Delco-Remy)

Figure 11-25. The Ford solenoid-actuated drive starter. (Ford)

solenoid plunger is in two pieces, figure 11-24. When the solenoid windings are magnetized, the first plunger moves the shift lever. When the pinion gear reaches the flywheel, the first plunger has moved far enough to touch the second plunger. The first plunger continues to move into the solenoid, pushing the second plunger against the contact points.

A similar starter design, figure 11-25, has been used by Ford on diesel engines and older large displacement V8 gasoline engines. It operates in the same way as the starter just described. The solenoid action closes a set of contact points, figure 11-26.

Because Ford installs a remotely mounted magnetic switch in all of its starting circuits, the solenoid contact points are not required to control the circuit. The solenoid contact points are physically linked, so that they are always "closed".

In the early 1970s, Chrysler also manufactured a fully enclosed direct-drive starter motor, figure 11-23. It works in the same way as the solenoid-actuated starters described above. The solenoid plunger closes contact points to complete the motor circuitry, but the system also has a remotely mounted starter relay. Reduction drive starters are usually compound motors.

Figure 11-26. Ford solenoid-actuated starter circuitry. (Ford)

Most Bosch and virtually all Japanese starter motors operate on the same principles.

Solenoid-Actuated, Reduction Drive

The Chrysler solenoid-actuated, reduction-drive starter uses a solenoid to engage the pinion with the flywheel and close the motor circuit. The motor armature does not drive the pinion directly, however. It drives a small gear that is permanently meshed with a larger gear, figure 11-17. The armature gear to reduction gear ratio is from 2 to 3.5:1, depending upon the engine application. This allows a small, high-speed motor to deliver increased torque at a satisfactory cranking rpm. Solenoid and starter drive operation is basically the same as a solenoid-actuated, direct drive starter.

Movable Pole Shoe Drive

Manufactured by the Motorcraft Division of Ford, the movable pole shoe starter motor is used on most Ford automobiles. One of the motor pole shoes pivots at the drive end housing, figure 11-27. The field winding of this shoe also contains a holding coil, wired in parallel and independently grounded, figure 11-28. When the starter relay is closed, battery current flows through the field windings and the holding coil of the pole shoe to ground. This creates a strong magnetic field, and the pole shoe is pulled down into operating position. The motion is transferred through a shift lever, or drive yoke, to mesh the pinion gear with the ring gear.

When the pole shoe is in position, it opens a set of contacts. These contacts break the ground connection of the field windings. Battery current is allowed to flow through the motor's internal circuitry, and the

Figure 11-27. The Ford movable-pole-shoe starter.

engine is cranked. During cranking, a small amount of current flows through the holding coil directly to ground to keep the shoe and lever assembly engaged.

An overrunning clutch prevents the starter motor from being turned by the engine. When the ignition switch moves out of the start position, current no longer flows through the windings of the movable pole shoe or the rest of the motor. Spring force pulls the shoe up, and the shift lever disengages the pinion from the flywheel.

Permanent-Magnet Planetary Drive

This high-speed, low-torque motor operates the drive mechanism through gear reduction provided by a

---

■ **Starter Drive Lubrication**

The 1936 Hudson Terraplane factory shop manual recommends that once a year, before cold weather, the starter be removed and the starter drive cleaned and lubricated. This will make sure that the drive will engage the flywheel all through the winter months.

The factory shop manual cautions that only kerosene should be used as a cleaner. Gasoline will remove all of the lubricant. If Gredag No. 31-1/4 is not available, use a few drops of SAE 10 engine oil for relubrication. Do not try to clean or lubricate the screw threads of the starter drive.

Figure 11-28. Circuit diagram of a system using a movable-pole-shoe starter.

Figure 11-29. Bosch permanent-magnet, gear-reduction starter components. (Chrysler)

Figure 11-30. Delco-Remy permanent-magnet, gear-reduction starter components.

simple planetary gearset. Figure 11-29 shows the Bosch gear reduction design , which is similar to that used in Chrysler starters. Figure 11-30 shows the gear reduction design used in the Delco-Remy permanent-magnet, gear-reduction (PMGR) starter. Figure 11-31 shows the PMGR design used by Ford, and compares permanent magnet starters to those of a typical wound-field starter.

All PMGR starter designs use a solenoid to operate the starter drive and close the motor armature circuit. The drive mechanism is identical to that used on other solenoid-actuated starters already described. Some models, however, use lightweight plastic shift levers.

The planetary gearset between the motor armature and the starter drive reduces the speed and increases the torque at the drive pinion. The compact gearset is only 1/2 to 3/4 inch (13 to 19 mm) deep and is mounted inline with the armature and drive pinion. An

internal ring gear is keyed to the field frame and held stationary in the motor. The armature shaft drives the sun gear for the planetary gearset. The sun gear meshes with three planetary pinions, which drive the pinion carrier in reduction as they rotate around the ring gear. The starter driveshaft is mounted on the carrier and driven at reduced speed and increased torque. This application of internal gear reduction through planetary gears delivers armature speeds in the 7,000 rpm range. The armature and driveshaft ride on roller or ball bearings rather than bushings.

Permanent-magnet, planetary-drive starters differ mechanically in how they do their job, but their

Figure 11-31. Comparison of the Ford PMGR starter motor components with those of a typical wound-field starter motor. (Ford)

Figure 11-32. Field coils and permanent-magnet starters use the same electrical wiring. (Chrysler)

electrical wiring is the same as that used with field-coil designs, figure 11-32. Field circuit testing and service are not required, but brush, commutator, and armature testing and service are basically the same as for any other motor.

■ Kick Starter

Solenoid-operated and movable-pole shoe starters have been standard equipment for so long that a lot of people have forgotten that engines didn't always start at the turn of a key. The standard starter motor on Chevrolets from the 1930s through the 1940s was a "kick starter".

The motor and drive pinion were quite similar to the Delco-Remy starters used by GM today. In place of a solenoid, however, a large lever moved the pinion into mesh with the flywheel and closed the motor switch contacts. The lever pivoted on the engine bellhousing and had a large "button" that projected through the floorboard to the right of the accelerator. The driver turned the ignition key to Run and kicked the starter with his or her right foot. Because the starter "button" was close to the accelerator, the driver could operate the throttle and the starter at the same time.

The Chevrolet kick starter was simple and direct, but motorists demanded more convenience on modern vehicles. The kick starter disappeared from cars in 1948 and from trucks in the mid-1950s.

Figure 11-33. A cutaway view of an overrunning clutch.

Figure 11-34. The operation of an overrunning clutch.

Although PMGR motors are lighter in weight and simpler to service than traditional designs, they do require special handling precautions. The material used for the permanent magnet fields is quite brittle. A sharp impact caused by hitting or dropping the starter can destroy the fields.

Overrunning Clutch

Regardless of the type of starter motor used, when the engine starts and runs, its speed increases. The motor must be disengaged from the engine as soon as the engine is turning more rapidly than the starter motor that has cranked it. With a movable-pole-shoe or solenoid-actuated drive, however, the pinion remains engaged until power stops flowing to the starter. In these applications, the starter is protected by an overrunning clutch, figure 11-33.

The overrunning clutch consists of rollers that ride between a collar on the pinion gear and an outer shell. The outer shell has tapered slots for the rollers so that the rollers either ride freely or wedge tightly between the collar and the shell. Figure 11-34 shows the operation of an overrunning clutch. In figure 11-34A, the armature is turning, cranking the engine. The rollers are wedged against spring force into their slots. In figure 11-34B, the engine has started and is turning faster than the motor armature. Spring force pushes the rollers so that they float freely. The engine's motion is not transferred to the motor armature. These devices are sometimes called one-way clutches, because they transmit motion in one direction only.

Once the engine starts, the ignition switch is to be released from the start position. The solenoid hold-in winding is demagnetized, and a return spring moves the plunger out of the solenoid. This moves the shift lever back so that the overrunning clutch and pinion gear slide away from the flywheel.

SUMMARY

Traditional starter motors have pole pieces wound with heavy copper field windings attached to the housing. A new design, the permanent-magnet planetary drive, uses small permanent magnets to create a magnetic field instead of pole pieces and field windings.

One end housing holds the brushes; the other end housing shields the pinion gear. The motor armature windings are installed on a laminated core and mounted on a shaft. The commutator bars are mounted on, but insulated from, the shaft.

The solenoid-actuated drive uses the movement of a solenoid to engage the pinion gear with the ring gear. Delco-Remy, Chrysler, Motorcraft, and many foreign manufacturers use this type of starter drive. The movable pole-shoe drive, used by Ford, has a pivoting pole piece that is moved by electromagnetism to engage the pinion gear with the ring gear. In the planetary gear drive used by Chrysler, Ford, and GM, an armature shaft sun gear meshes with the planetary pinions, which drive the pinion carrier in reduction as they rotate around the ring gear. The starter driveshaft is mounted on the carrier and driven at reduced speed and increased torque. An overrunning clutch is used with all starter designs to prevent the engine from spinning the motor and damaging it.

Review Questions

Choose the single most correct answer.
Compare your answers with the correct answers on Page 468.

1. Starter motors usually have
   _____ pole shoes.
   a. Two
   b. Four
   c. Six
   d. Eight

2. The rotational force of a starter
   motor is:
   a. Polarized
   b. Rectified
   c. Torque
   d. Current

3. Which of the following is true of
   a shunt motor?
   a. It has high initial torque
   b. It operates at variable
      speeds
   c. It has only one path for cur-
      rent flow
   d. It is not often used as a
      starting motor

4. Which of the following is true of
   a compound motor?
   a. It has low initial torque
   b. It operates at variable
      speeds
   c. It has only one path for cur-
      rent flow
   d. It is often used as a starting
      motor

5. In a lap-wound motor armature,
   the two ends of each conductor
   are attached to commutator
   segments that are:
   a. Adjacent
   b. 45° apart
   c. 90° apart
   d. 180° apart

6. Most automotive starters have
   _____ grounded and _____
   insulated brushes.
   a. 2,2
   b. 2,4
   c. 4,4
   d. 4,8

7. The ratio between the number
   of teeth on the flywheel and the
   motor pinion gear is about:
   a. 1:1
   b. 5:1
   c. 20:1
   d. 50:1

8. The overrunning clutch accom-
   plishes which of the following?
   a. Separates the starter motor
      from the starter solenoid
   b. Brings the starter motor into
      contact with the ignition
      circuit
   c. Lets the starter motor rotate
      in either direction
   d. Protects the starter motor
      from spinning too rapidly

9. A starting motor must have
   _____ brushes as poles.
   a. The same number of
   b. Twice as many
   c. One-half as many
   d. Three times as many

10. The illustration below shows a:
    a. Permanent magnet planetary
       gear starter
    b. Movable pole shoe starter
    c. Direct drive, solenoid-
       actuated starter
    d. Reduction gear drive,
       solenoid-actuated starter

11. Which type of starter drive is
    not used on late-model cars?
    a. Direct drive
    b. Bendix drive
    c. Reduction drive
    d. Planetary drive

12. A solenoid uses two coils. Their
    windings are called:
    a. Push-in and pull-out
    b. Pull-in and push-out
    c. Push-in and hold-out
    d. Pull-in and hold-in

13. Which of the following is true of
    a reduction drive?
    a. The motor armature drives
       the pinion directly
    b. The sun gear is mounted on
       the armature shaft
    c. The overrunning clutch
       reduces battery current
    d. The small gear driven by the
       armature is permanently
       meshed with a larger gear

14. The planetary drive starter
    uses:
    a. Permanent magnets
    b. Field coils
    c. Both a and b
    d. Neither a nor b

15. Which of the following is *not*
    required of a permanent mag-
    net starter?
    a. Brush testing
    b. Commutator testing
    c. Field circuit testing
    d. Armature testing

PART FIVE

The Ignition System and Electronic Engine Controls

12

The Ignition System and Engine Operation

Automobile engines commonly used today burn a mixture of air and gasoline to produce power. The air-fuel mixture must be ignited by a spark before it can burn. This is the job of the ignition system. It must provide a high-voltage spark in the correct cylinder at the correct time for the most efficient combustion. This chapter explains the relationship between the engine and the ignition system. Chapters Thirteen and Fourteen cover the primary and secondary ignition circuits. Chapter Fifteen explains ignition timing. Chapter Sixteen covers the solid-state electronic ignition systems, and Chapter Seventeen deals with electronic engine control systems.

ENGINE OPERATION

Modern automotive engines are called internal combustion engines because fuel burns inside the engine. The engine converts the burning fuel's thermal energy to mechanical energy.

Reciprocating Engine

Except for the Wankel rotary engine, all production automotive engines are the reciprocating, or piston, design. Reciprocating means "up and down" or "back and forth". It is this up-and-down action of a piston in a cylinder that gives the **reciprocating engine** its name. Almost all engines of this type are built upon a cylinder block, or engine block, figure 12-1. The block is an iron or aluminum casting that contains the engine cylinders. The top of the block is covered with the cylinder head, figure 12-2, which forms the combustion chambers.

Power is produced by the reciprocating motion of a piston in a cylinder, but this power must be changed to rotating power to turn the wheels of a car. The piston is attached to the top of a connecting rod by a pin, called a wristpin, figure 12-3. The bottom of the connecting rod is attached to the crankshaft. The connecting rod transmits the up-and-down motion of the piston to the crankshaft, which changes it to rotating motion.

Most automotive engines are fueled by gasoline. The gasoline is mixed with air and is drawn into the combustion chambers through valves. The mixture is compressed and then ignited by the spark plug. Force from the burning, expanding gases drives the piston down and makes the crankshaft turn.

One complete top-to-bottom or bottom-to-top movement of the piston is called a **stroke**, figure 12-4. One stroke of a piston causes the crankshaft to rotate 180 degrees. Two strokes of the piston cause the crankshaft to make a complete 360-degree revolution. In previous chapters, we have used the terms "engine

Figure 12-1. The automobile engine block.

Figure 12-2. The cylinder head forms combustion chambers above the pistons.

revolution" and "revolutions per minute" (rpm). These terms refer to the complete 360-degree revolution of the crankshaft caused by two piston strokes.

Most automobile engines are a four-stroke, spark-ignition, reciprocating design. Other types of engines include two-stroke and compression-ignition (diesel) engines. Two-stroke engines are used mainly in motorcycles, lawnmowers, outboards, and other types of equipment. They are rarely used in automobiles and so are not covered in this text. Compression-ignition engines do not need a spark to ignite the air-fuel mixture; their high compression causes extreme heat that ignites the fuel. We will not discuss them here, because they do not have an electric ignition system.

FOUR-STROKE CYCLE

In the **four-stroke cycle**, four strokes of the piston, figure 12-5, are required to complete one operating cycle:

1. Intake stroke: As the piston moves downward, the air-fuel mixture is drawn into the cylinder through an open intake valve.
2. Compression stroke: The intake valve closes and the upward stroke of the piston compresses the mixture, which is ignited by a spark.
3. Power stroke: With both valves closed, the expanding gases of combustion force the piston downward.
4. Exhaust stroke: The piston moves upward and pushes the burned gases out an open exhaust valve. The next stroke will be another intake stroke, and the cycle will repeat.

Ignition Interval

Every two strokes of a piston cause the crankshaft to rotate 360 degrees. Therefore, every four strokes of a piston cause the crankshaft to rotate 720 degrees (360 + 360 = 720). Since four strokes of a piston equal one engine operating cycle, that cycle equals 720 degrees of crankshaft rotation.

During the four strokes of the operating cycle, the spark plug fires only once, at the beginning of the power stroke. In a one-cylinder engine, there would be only one ignition spark every 720 degrees of crankshaft rotation. These 720 degrees are called the **ignition interval**, or **firing interval**, of the engine. It is the number of degrees of crankshaft rotation that occurs between ignition sparks.

MULTIPLE-CYLINDER ENGINES

Up to this point, we have been talking about a single piston in a single cylinder. However, most car engines have four, six, or eight cylinders, although engines with one, two, three, five, ten, twelve, and sixteen cylinders

Figure 12-3. The reciprocating motion of the piston is converted to rotary motion of the crankshaft.

Figure 12-4. One top-to-bottom or bottom-to-top movement of the piston is called a stroke. One piston stroke equals 180 degrees of crankshaft rotation; two strokes equal 360 degrees of crankshaft rotation.

have been built and used. In automotive engines, all pistons are connected to a single crankshaft, figure 12-1.

The more cylinders an engine has, the more power strokes are produced per crankshaft revolution. A four-cylinder engine produces a power stroke four times as often as a one-cylinder engine. The four-cylinder engine has power strokes that are closer together in terms of time and degrees of crankshaft rotation.

A one-cylinder engine has one power stroke during each engine operation cycle, that is, one power stroke for every two crankshaft revolutions. In a four-cylinder engine, the operating cycles of each cylinder mean that there are four power strokes for every two crankshaft revolutions.

Common Ignition Intervals

If four power strokes occur during 720 degrees of crankshaft rotation, then each power stroke must occur every 180 degrees (720 ÷ 4 = 180). The ignition must produce a spark for every power stroke, so it produces a spark every 180 degrees of crankshaft rotation. This means that a four-cylinder engine has an ignition interval of 180 degrees.

An inline six-cylinder engine has six power strokes during every 720 degrees of crankshaft rotation,

resulting in an ignition interval of 120 degrees (720 ÷ 6 = 120). An eight-cylinder engine has an ignition interval of 90 degrees (720 ÷ 8 = 90).

Unusual Ignition Intervals

Most automotive engines have four, six, or eight cylinders, but some unusual engines are still being used today. Manufacturers such as Jaguar and Ferrari produce twelve-cylinder engines with a 60-degree firing interval. Audi of Germany has a five-cylinder engine with a 144-degree firing interval. Suzuki uses a three-cylinder engine with a 240-degree firing interval.

Other unusual firing intervals result from particular engine designs. General Motors has produced two

Reciprocating Engine: Also called a piston engine. An engine in which the pistons move up and down or back and forth, as a result of combustion on the top of the cylinder.

Stroke: One complete top-to-bottom or bottom-to-top movement of an engine piston.

Four-Stroke Cycle: One complete operating cycle of a piston in a four-stroke engine. The four strokes of the cycle are: intake, compression, power, and exhaust.

Ignition Interval (Firing Interval): The number of degrees of crankshaft rotation between ignition sparks.

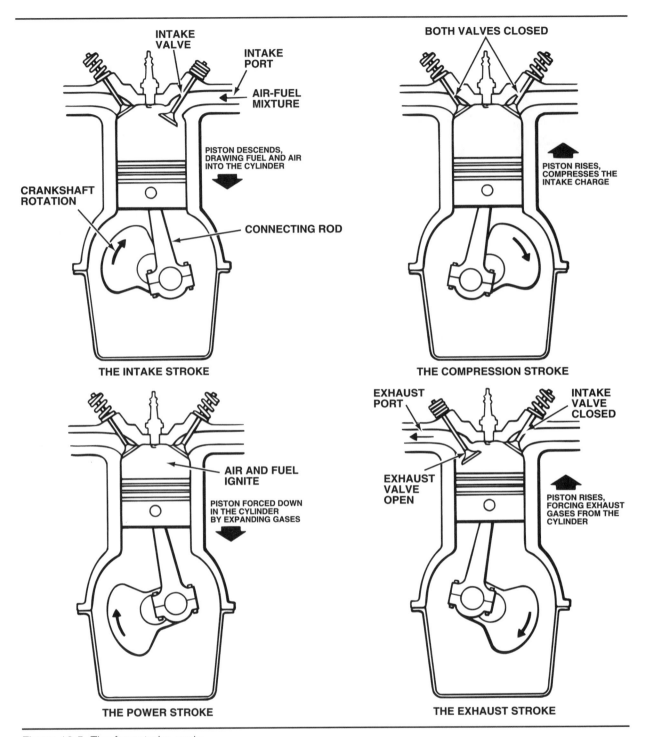

Figure 12-5. The four-stroke cycle.

different V6 engines from eight-cylinder blocks. A Buick engine developed in the early 1960s has alternating 90- and 150-degree firing intervals, figure 12-6. The uneven firing intervals resulted from building a V6 with a 90-degree crankshaft and block. This engine was modified in mid-1977 by redesigning the crankshaft to provide uniform 120-degree firing intervals, as in an inline six. Chevrolet introduced a V6 engine in 1978 that fires at alternating 108- and 132-degree intervals.

Figure 12-6. The uneven firing intervals of Buick's early V6 engine. (Buick)

| 4-CYLINDER FIRING ORDER 1-3-4-2 OR 1-2-4-3 | 5-CYLINDER FIRING ORDER 1-2-4-5-3 | 6-CYLINDER FIRING ORDER 1-5-3-6-2-4 |

Figure 12-7. Cylinder numbering of an inline engine.

Spark Frequency

Each power stroke in a spark-ignition engine is caused by a spark igniting the air-fuel mixture, and each power stroke needs an individual spark. For example, an eight-cylinder engine requires four sparks per engine revolution (remember that there are two 360-degree engine revolutions in each 720-degree operating cycle). When a V8 engine is running at about 1,000 rpm, its ignition system must deliver 4,000 sparks per minute. At an engine speed of about 4,000 rpm, the ignition system must deliver 16,000 sparks per minute. Precise ignition system performance is required to meet such demands.

FIRING ORDER

To cause each cylinder in an engine to fire once within 720 degrees of crankshaft rotation and at regular intervals, the pistons and connecting rods are arranged on the crankshaft in a specific order. This is called the **firing order** and it varies with different engine designs. Firing orders also are designed to reduce the vibration and imbalance created by the power strokes of the pistons.

Engine cylinders are numbered for easy identification. However, the cylinders do not usually fire in the order in which they are numbered. Straight, or inline, engines are generally numbered from front to rear, figure 12-7. In front-wheel-drive (FWD) cars with transverse-mounted engines, the front is the accessory (drive belt) end; the rear is the flywheel end.

A typical four-cylinder engine firing order is 1-3-4-2. That is, the number 1 cylinder power stroke is

followed by the number 3 cylinder power stroke, then the number 4 power stroke and finally the number 2 power stroke. Then, the next number 1 power stroke occurs. A few four-cylinder engines have different firing orders. For example, the English Ford and Pinto 1,600-cc engines fire 1-2-4-3. The Suzuki three-cylinder firing order is 1-3-2.

The cylinders of inline five- and six-cylinder engines also are numbered from front to rear, but do not fire in that order. The firing order for inline five-cylinder engines is 1-2-4-5-3, and the firing order for inline six-cylinder engines is 1-5-3-6-2-4, figure 12-7.

The cylinders of 90° V-type engines in domestic cars and in some Japanese imports are numbered the same, figure 12-8. The front cylinders are numbered 1 (driver's side) and 2 (passenger's side). Behind number 1 is number 3; behind number 2 is number 4, and so on. The firing order for most domestic 90° V6 engines numbered this way is 1-6-5-4-3-2. For Japanese versions, the firing order is 1-2-3-4-5-6.

The cylinders in 60° V6 engines in GM cars and in some Japanese models are numbered with 1 on the passenger's side and 2 on the driver's side, figure 12-8. Number 3 comes behind number 1; number 4 behind number 2; and so on. The firing order for these engines is 1-2-3-4-5-6. Finally, Ford and Acura V6 cylinders, figure 12-8, are numbered with number 1

Firing Order: The order in which combustion occurs in the cylinders of an engine.

Figure 12-8. V6 engines are numbered in this way.

Figure 12-9. V8s have these firing orders.

on the passenger's side, with numbers 2 and 3 behind it. Number 4 is on the driver's side, with numbers 5 and 6 behind it. The firing order is 1-4-2-5-3-6.

V8 engine cylinders are numbered back and forth or straight back, depending on the manufacturer, figure 12-9. In GM, Chrysler, Lexus, and Infiniti engines, the number 1 cylinder is on the driver's side, and number 2 is on the passenger's side. Number 3 comes behind number 1; number 4 behind number 2; and so on. The firing order for the domestics and for Lexus is 1-8-4-3-6-5-7-2. The Infiniti firing order is 1-8-7-3-6-5-4-2. In Ford, Audi, and Mercedes-Benz V8s, the number 1 cylinder is on the passenger's side, and numbers 2, 3, and 4 come behind it. The number 5 cylinder is on the driver's side, and numbers 6, 7, and 8 are behind it. Ford has two possible firing orders: 1-3-7-2-6-5-4-8 or 1-5-4-2-6-3-7-8. The German V8 firing order is 1-5-4-8-6-3-7-2.

Whenever a V-type engine (or a horizontally opposed engine) is numbered from front to rear, the number one bank is located slightly forward of the other. When looking at the engine from the side, you will see that one valve cover is closer to the front than the other.

The distributor rotor must deliver ignition voltage to the correct cylinder at the correct time. To maintain the firing order, the spark plug cables must be attached to the distributor cap in the proper order, figure 12-10.

ENGINE-IGNITION SYNCHRONIZATION

During the engine operating cycle, the intake and exhaust valves open and close at specific times. The ignition system delivers a spark when the piston is near the top of the compression stroke and both valves are closed. These actions must all be coordinated, or engine damage could occur.

Figure 12-10. The spark plug cables must be connected to the distributor in the proper firing order.

Figure 12-11. Valve mechanism for an overhead-valve engine.

Valve Timing

The intake and exhaust valves are operated by the engine camshaft, figure 12-11. As the camshaft turns, its lobes cause the valves to open. The valves are closed by the valve springs. Each valve opens and closes once per camshaft revolution, which equals one engine operating cycle. The engine crankshaft makes two complete revolutions during one engine operating cycle. Therefore, the camshaft must turn at one-half the speed of the engine crankshaft. The two shafts are connected by a chain, by a toothed belt, or by gears, figure 12-12. The gear on the end of the camshaft has twice as many teeth as does the gear on the end of the crankshaft, creating a 1:2 gear ratio.

To coordinate valve action with piston action, the camshaft's rotation must be synchronized with the rotation of the crankshaft. This is called **valve timing**.

■ The Rotary Engine

The constant repetition of the reciprocating engine's two-way motion (up and down or back and forth) makes a piston engine the eventual instrument of its own destruction. Since the reciprocating engine must change the linear movement of its pistons into rotating power, engineers like Dr. Felix Wankel have long reasoned that there must be a more efficient approach. Dr. Wankel did more than reason; he developed the Wankel rotary engine, once used for automotive applications by NSU in Germany and by Curtiss-Wright aircraft in the U.S. Even General Motors once had plans to develop Wankel-powered vehicles. However, Dr. Wankel's rotary engine is best known for its use in Mazda RX-7 automobiles.

A rotary engine uses the same sequence of intake, compression, power, and exhaust as the reciprocating engine, but the power cycle takes place as separate stages in a single revolution of a three-sided or triangular rotor. The rotor revolves around, and turns an eccentric shaft (equivalent to the reciprocating engine's crankshaft). The rotors ride on eccentric journals on the shaft, with shaft motion turning a flywheel.

Intake, compression, power, and exhaust phases of the rotor's revolution take place as the rotor passes and uncovers the intake port. The side of the rotor then turns to face the top of the housing, enlarging the combustion chamber and creating a vacuum that draws in the air-fuel mixture. As the rotor continues its movement, the air-fuel mixture is compressed and placed next to the spark plugs. One or both of the spark plugs fire, depending upon engine speed, load, and temperature. The expanding gases turn the rotor until its tip passes the exhaust port. As the rotor continues turning, the size of the combustion chamber is reduced. The exhaust gases are then forced out and the cycle begins again.

A single rotor revolution results in a power phase for each face of the rotor, or a total of three per revolution. Since each rotor face acts as a piston, the ignition intervals of a single rotor engine are approximately equal to those of a three-cylinder reciprocating engine.

Rotary engines can be built with more than one rotor. By properly positioning multiple rotors and combining their power phases, it is possible to build a smooth, powerful engine that is considerably smaller than a comparable reciprocating design. The output of a two-rotor engine can equal that of a six-cylinder reciprocating engine. There are no valves, connecting rods, or pistons to self-destruct.

The rotary engine, however, does have its own design limitations and disadvantages. Mazda's initial engines had very poor sealing of the rotor tips, which led to major problems that temporarily gave the rotary engine a bad name. This problem has been solved, but rotary engines are still not as fuel-efficient as a comparable piston engine, although fuel injection and turbocharging have lessened the gap.

Valve Timing: A method of coordinating camshaft rotation and crankshaft rotation so that the valves open and close at the right times during each of the piston strokes.

Figure 12-12. The camshaft is driven by the crankshaft at one-half crankshaft speed.

The gears on the ends of the two shafts are marked by the manufacturer, figure 12-13, and must be aligned during installation.

Distributor Drive

The distributor must supply one spark to each cylinder during each cylinder's operating cycle. The distributor cam has as many lobes as the engine has cylinders, or in a solid-state system, the trigger wheel has as many teeth as the engine has cylinders. One revolution of the distributor shaft will deliver one spark to each cylinder. Each cylinder needs only one spark for each two crankshaft revolutions. The distributor shaft must turn at one-half engine crankshaft speed. On most engines, therefore, the distributor is driven by the camshaft, which also turns at one-half crankshaft speed.

Distributorless Ignition

Many late-model engines have eliminated the distributor by using a multiple coil pack and the **waste spark** theory of ignition. In a distributorless ignition system, sensors indicate crankshaft position and speed information to the engine control computer, which signals the ignition module when to fire a specific coil in the coil pack. Each coil fires two spark plugs at the same time. The plugs are connected to the coil so that when one fires during the compression stroke to ignite the air-fuel mixture, the other fires during the exhaust stroke when the spark is useless or wasted. Thus, a power stroke occurs on each cylinder event, with a wasted spark fired in an exhausting cylinder. The key

Figure 12-13. Timing marks on the timing gears synchronize valve action with piston movement.

to this method of engine-ignition synchronization is the ignition module, which determines coil turn-on and firing time through crankshaft position and cylinder identification sensors.

Many manufacturers are taking advantage of faster, more sophisticated engine computers by designing ignition systems that use an individual, unitized ignition coil and module for each spark plug. The ignition coils are mounted directly to the spark plug in most vehicles. These systems are usually referred to as coil-on-plug or direct ignition systems. The engine computer uses the same crankshaft position and speed information to identify cylinder number one and determine the optimum timing advance for each cylinder in the correct firing order. The computer then signals each ignition module to trigger its ignition coil and fire the spark plug. Tighter control of each cylinders timing advance results in increased engine power, better fuel mileage and lower exhaust emissions.

CRANKSHAFT POSITION

The bottom of the piston stroke is called **bottom dead center (BDC)**, figure 12-14. The top of the piston stroke is called **top dead center (TDC)**. The ignition spark occurs near top dead center, as the compression stroke is ending. As the piston approaches the top of

BTDC   TDC   ATDC

ADVANCED   RETARDED
SPARK   SPARK

Figure 12-14. Piston position is identified in terms of crankshaft rotation.

its stroke, it is said to be **before top dead center (BTDC)**. A spark that occurs before top dead center is called an advanced spark. As the piston passes top dead center and starts down, it is said to be **after top dead center (ATDC)**. A spark that occurs after top dead center is called a retarded spark.

Burn Time

Approximately three milliseconds (0.003 second) elapse from the instant the air-fuel mixture ignites until its combustion is complete. Remember that this burn time is a function of time and not of piston travel or degrees of crankshaft rotation. The ignition spark must occur early enough so that the combustion pressure reaches its maximum just after top dead center, when the piston is beginning its downward power stroke. Combustion should be completed by about 10° ATDC.

If the spark occurs too soon before top dead center, the rising piston will be opposed by combustion pressure. If the spark occurs too late, the force on the piston will be reduced. In either case, power will be lost. In extreme cases, the engine could be damaged. Ignition must start at the proper instant for maximum power and efficiency.

Engine Speed

As engine speed increases, piston speed increases. If the air-fuel ratio remains relatively constant, the fuel burning time will remain constant. However, at greater engine speed, the piston will travel farther during this burning time. Ignition timing must be advanced to ensure that maximum combustion pressure occurs at the proper piston position.

For example, consider an engine, figure 12-15, that requires 0.003 second for the fuel charge to burn and that achieves maximum power if the burning is completed at 10° ATDC.

- At an idle speed of 625 rpm, figure 12-15A, the crankshaft rotates about 11 degrees in 0.003 second. Therefore, timing must be set at 1° BTDC to allow ample burning time.
- At 1,000 rpm, figure 12-15B, the crankshaft rotates 18° in 0.003 second. Ignition should begin at 8° BTDC.

■ The Rarest Firing Order of All

The booming economy of the 1920s encouraged Cadillac to design one of the grandest cars ever to hit the road, the Sixteen. Engines with sixteen cylinders have always been uncommon and this overhead-valve, 452 cubic-inch, V16 powerplant has one of the rarest of all firing orders: 1-8-9-14-3-6-11-2-15-10-7-4-13-12-5-16. Odd-numbered cylinders are on the left bank; even-numbered cylinders are on the right.

Unfortunately, Cadillac announced its new 16-cylinder machine just prior to the stock market crash of 1929 and the beginning of the Great Depression. Even with a large amount of the Sixteen's projected market gone, General Motors' vast financial strength kept the Sixteen alive for nine model years. Such expensive cars were difficult to sell and by 1938, fewer than 300 customers drove home in new Sixteens.

For 1939, Cadillac presented a new design that, though still a V16, was less expensive to produce. Based on the company's successful V8, the new engine was a 431-cubic-inch flat-head design. This engine's wide, 135-degree cylinder block required a new ignition interval, producing a unique firing order: 1-4-12-3-16-11-8-15-14-7-6-13-2-9-5-10.

Throughout the 1930s, technical advances improved Cadillac's V8 to the point that a V16 had no clear-cut advantages. Management prudently decided to concentrate on V8 engines, a policy they have broken only once in the last 50 years. The flat-head V16 lasted only one more year, until 1940, making it the very last production 16-cylinder automotive powerplant.

Waste Spark: An ignition system without a distributor in which one coil in a coil pack fires two spark plugs at the same time. The spark in the cylinder on compression ignites the air-fuel mixture, while the spark in the cylinder on its exhaust stroke is wasted.

Bottom Dead Center (BDC): The exact bottom of a piston stroke.

Top Dead Center (TDC): The exact top of a piston stroke. Also, a specification used when tuning an engine.

Before Top Dead Center (BTDC): The position of a piston as it nears top dead center. Usually expressed in degrees, such as 5° BTDC.

After Top Dead Center (ATDC): The position of a piston after it has passed top dead center. Usually expressed in degrees, such as 5° ATDC.

Figure 12-15. As engine speed increases, ignition timing must be advanced.

- At 2,000 rpm, figure 12-15C, the crankshaft rotates 36° in 0.003 second. Spark timing must be advanced to 26° BTDC.

This change in timing is called spark advance, or ignition advance, and is explained in more detail in Chapter Fifteen.

INITIAL TIMING

As we have seen, ignition timing must be set correctly for the engine to run at all. This is called the engine's initial, base, or basic timing. Initial timing is the correct setting at a specified engine speed. In figure 12-15, initial timing was 1° BTDC. Initial timing is normally within a few degrees of top dead center. For many years, most engines were timed at the specified slow-idle speed for the engine. However, since about 1974, many Ford, Oldsmobile, and Cadillac engines require timing at speeds either above or below the slow-idle speed.

Initial timing can be adjusted to compensate for mechanical wear, slippage, and other factors. We will learn more about setting the ignition timing in the *Shop Manual*. The following paragraphs describe the basics of initial timing.

Timing Marks

We have seen that initial timing is related to crankshaft position. To properly time the engine, we must be able to determine crankshaft position. The crankshaft is completely enclosed in the engine block, but most cars have a pulley and vibration damper or harmonic balancer bolted to the front of the crankshaft, figure 12-16. This pulley rotates with the crankshaft and can be considered an extension of the shaft.

Figure 12-16. Most engines have a pulley bolted to the front end of the crankshaft.

Marks on the pulley show crankshaft position. For example, when a mark on the pulley is aligned with a mark on the engine block, the number 1 piston is at top dead center.

Timing marks vary widely, even within a manufacturer's product line. There are two common types of timing marks:

- A mark on the crankshaft pulley and marks on the engine block that represent degrees of crankshaft position, figure 12-17A
- Marks representing degrees of crankshaft position on the pulley and a pointer on the engine block, figure 12-17B.

Some cars have timing marks on the engine flywheel. The flywheel is attached to the end of the crankshaft

Figure 12-17. Typical timing marks.

Figure 12-18. A diagram of the timing light connections.

opposite the pulley. Hondas, some Opels, Dodge Omnis and Plymouth Horizons, Renaults, Saabs, and water-cooled Volkswagens, Audis, and Porsches have this type of timing mark. Some older domestic engines also used a flywheel timing mark.

Ignition Timing Light

A timing light is used with pulley and flywheel timing marks. It usually contains a transistor installed so that a surge of secondary current will make the transistor conduct. The timing light is connected to the automobile battery terminals and the number 1 spark plug circuit, figure 12-18. When the number 1 spark plug receives a surge of ignition voltage, the transistor conducts and the timing bulb is lit by battery current.

When the engine is running, the timing light flashes very rapidly. This is a **stroboscopic effect**, so timing lights are called stroboscopic lights. When the timing light is aimed at the moving timing marks, figure 12-19, the marks appear to stand still with each flash of light. Since the light flashes as the number 1 spark plug fires, the position of the timing mark will show crankshaft position at the instant of ignition. The distributor can be rotated to change this, if necessary, until the correct degree mark appears opposite the pointer when the timing light flashes.

Electromagnetic Timing

Electromagnetic timing was introduced by major manufacturers as a more accurate timing method. Because special equipment for this newer method is required, timing marks are still put on most engines.

The system uses a timing pickup socket on the engine, figure 12-20, and a magnetic probe that is inserted into the socket. The timing socket may be located at the front of the engine, in the side of the engine block, or in the bellhousing. The magnetic probe is inserted into the socket. A tab, notch, or

magnetic particle on the crankshaft, crankshaft damper, harmonic balancer, or on the flywheel alters the magnetic reluctance around the pickup coil as it rotates past the probe. Solid-state electronic circuitry translates the electromagnetic impulses from the crankshaft into a readout of ignition timing on a digital or analog meter.

Electromagnetic timing is more accurate because:

- It eliminates the viewing angle error (parallax) on the part of the technician.
- The crankshaft position signal comes directly from the crankshaft instead of the distributor.

Manufacturers use this method to time engines when they are assembled at the factory. Technicians can use the method if they have the correct equipment.

■ In Place Of A Spark Plug

In the early "make-and-break" ignition system, a movable electrode and a stationary electrode were mounted close to each other and protruded into the side of an engine cylinder. The movable electrode, similar to a lever mounted on a rod, was operated by an outside pushrod that contacted a camshaft. The stationary electrode was insulated from the cylinder wall with mica. Battery current passed through a coil and a switch to reach the stationary electrode. The movable electrode was grounded to complete the electrical circuit.

As the camshaft rotated, it forced the movable electrode to open and close contact with the stationary electrode, "making and breaking" the circuit. Each time the circuit was opened, a spark occurred, igniting the air-fuel mixture in the cylinder.

Stroboscopic Effect: The effect caused by a rapidly flashing light as it makes moving objects appear stationary.

Figure 12-19. Using a timing light.

Computer-Controlled Timing

Electromagnetic timing was an interim step between fully adjustable and completely nonadjustable ignition timing. Late-model engines increasingly allow the engine control computer to determine the correct time for ignition. Base ignition timing on such engines is fixed at the factory when the engine is assembled and installed in the vehicle. This eliminates the need for initial timing adjustments. However, as you have learned, constant spark timing adjustment is required for the best engine performance.

Various engine sensors provide the computer with constantly changing data about engine speed, coolant temperature, EGR flow rate, intake air temperature and volume, manifold absolute or barometric pressure, throttle position, and engine knock. Once these inputs are received by the computer, it compares them

MAGNETIC TIMING PROBE RECEPTACLE

Figure 12-20. The socket for an electromagnetic timing test probe often is near the pulley timing marks. (Chrysler)

to its strategy, calibration, and adaptive learning data stored in memory. After processing this data, the computer signals the ignition module to fire the spark plugs at precisely the right moment.

Computer-controlled timing first eliminated the vacuum and centrifugal advance functions of the distributor. By reassigning these functions to the engine control computer, no distributor calibration was required and adjusting base ignition timing was necessary only if the distributor was physically removed from the engine. With the advent of distributorless ignitions, base ignition timing is referenced to the position of the crankshaft position sensor relative to the crankshaft. During engine startup, the computer provides a fixed amount of fuel at the system's base timing until it picks up the reference signal that allows it to identify crankshaft position. In just a few milliseconds, it can correctly time or sequence fuel injection while sending five-volt, high-low pulses to the ignition module. The high-to-low transition signal is used by the module to fire the proper coil before or after the base timing pulse. In this way, the computer advances or retards timing according to engine requirements.

SUMMARY

The ignition system must be mechanically synchronized with engine operation to deliver an ignition spark to each cylinder at the correct time. Most automobile engines are reciprocating four-stroke engines. The four strokes of the four-stroke cycle are: intake, compression, power and exhaust. Ignition occurs at the beginning of the power stroke.

One complete four-stroke cycle equals 720 degrees of crankshaft rotation. The sequence in which the cylinders of an engine fire is called the firing order. Firing intervals depend on the number of cylinders in an engine. A three-cylinder engine fires every 240 degrees; a four-cylinder engine fires every 180 degrees; an eight-cylinder engine fires every 90 degrees. Inline six-cylinder engines and even-firing V6 engines fire every 120 degrees. Some V6 engines fire at uneven intervals. The ignition distributor rotates at one-half engine speed to deliver an ignition spark at the right time to each cylinder.

Synchronizing ignition and engine operation is called ignition timing. Engine timing marks are used to set the initial ignition timing near top dead center on the engine's power stroke. The air-fuel mixture requires approximately three milliseconds to burn and deliver full power with the piston and crankshaft in the right position. As engine speed increases, spark timing must be advanced to allow enough burn time for combustion to be complete at the correct position of the piston and crankshaft.

Review Questions

Choose the single most correct answer.
Compare your answers with the correct answers on Page 468.

1. How many strokes of a piston are required to turn the crankshaft through 360°?
   a. One
   b. Two
   c. Four
   d. Six

2. Most automobile engines are *not*:
   a. Four-stroke types
   b. Spark ignition types
   c. Reciprocating types
   d. Wankel types

3. One engine cycle equals _____ degrees of crankshaft rotation.
   a. 90°
   b. 180°
   c. 360°
   d. 720°

4. The firing interval of an engine is the number of degrees of crankshaft rotation that:
   a. Takes place in a four-stroke engine
   b. Is required to complete one full stroke
   c. Occurs between ignition sparks
   d. Takes place in a compression ignition engine

5. The sequence in which combustion occurs in an engine's cylinders is called the:
   a. Firing order
   b. Ignition interval
   c. Firing interval
   d. Four-stroke cycle

6. The intake and exhaust valves of each cylinder are operated by:
   a. Reduction gears
   b. Engine camshaft
   c. Firing relays
   d. Engine crankshaft

7. Valve timing is accomplished:
   a. By adjusting setscrews
   b. During camshaft installation
   c. By advancing or retarding spark timing
   d. None of the above

8. The distributor is driven by the:
   a. Crankshaft
   b. Rocker arms
   c. Connecting rods
   d. Camshaft

9. A "retarded spark" is one that occurs:
   a. At top dead center
   b. Before top dead center
   c. After top dead center
   d. At bottom dead center

10. Approximately _____ milliseconds elapse from the instant the air-fuel mixture ignites until its combustion is complete.
    a. 3
    b. 10
    c. 20
    d. 30

11. As engine speed increases, ignition timing:
    a. Must be advanced
    b. Must remain constant
    c. Must be retarded
    d. Varies inversely with the speed

12. Which of the following is *not* true of initial timing?
    a. It is the correct setting for a specified low speed
    b. It is normally within a few degrees of bottom dead center
    c. It can be adjusted to compensate for mechanical wear
    d. All of the above

13. Timing lights are also called _____ lights.
    a. Self-powered
    b. 12-volt test
    c. Power-seeking
    d. Stroboscopic

13

The Ignition Primary Circuit and Components

The primary ignition circuit is considered to be the heart of the ignition system. The secondary ignition circuit cannot function efficiently if the primary ignition circuit is damaged. This chapter explains components of the low-voltage primary ignition circuit and how the circuit operates. Breaker points opened and closed the low-voltage primary circuit until the 1970s when solid-state electronic switching devices took their place. Whether breaker points or electronic switches are used, the principles of producing high voltage by electromagnetic induction remain the same.

NEED FOR HIGH VOLTAGE

Energy is supplied to the automotive electrical system by the battery. The battery supplies about twelve volts, but the voltage required to ignite the air-fuel mixture ranges from about 5,000 to more than 25,000 volts, depending upon engine operating conditions.

High voltage is required to create an arc across the spark plug air gap. The required voltage level increases when the:

- Spark plug air gap increases
- Engine operating temperature increases
- Air-fuel mixture is lean
- Air-fuel mixture is at a greater pressure

Battery voltage must be greatly increased to meet the needs of the ignition system. Engine operating temperature increases the required voltage because resistance increases with greater temperature. A lean air-fuel mixture contains fewer volatile fuel particles, so resistance increases. More voltage is needed when the air-fuel mixture is at a greater pressure because resistance increases with an increase in pressure. The ignition system boosts voltage using electromagnetic induction, as explained in Chapter Two of this *Classroom Manual*.

HIGH VOLTAGE THROUGH INDUCTION

Any current-carrying conductor or coil is surrounded by a magnetic field. As current in the coil increases or decreases, the magnetic field expands or contracts. If a second coiled conductor is placed within this magnetic field, figure 13-1, the expanding or contracting magnetic flux lines will cut the second coil, causing a voltage to be induced into the second coil. This transfer of energy between two unconnected conductors is called mutual induction, as explained in Chapter Two of this *Classroom Manual*.

Figure 13-1. Mutual induction in the ignition coil supplies voltage to the spark plugs. (Prestolite)

Induction in the Ignition Coil

The ignition coil uses the principle of mutual induction to step up or transform low battery voltage to high ignition voltage. The ignition coil, figure 13-2, contains two windings of copper wire wrapped around a soft iron core. The primary winding is made of a hundred or so turns of heavy wire. It connects to the battery and carries current. The secondary winding is made of many thousand turns of fine wire. When current in the primary winding increases or decreases, a voltage is induced into the secondary winding, figure 13-2.

The ratio of the number of turns in the secondary winding to the number of turns in the primary winding is generally between 100:1 and 200:1. This ratio is the voltage multiplier. That is, any voltage induced in the secondary winding is 100 to 200 times the voltage present in the primary winding.

Several factors govern the induction of voltage. Only two of these factors are easily controllable in an ignition system. Induced voltage increases with:

- More magnetic flux lines
- More rapid movement of flux lines.

More magnetic flux lines produce a stronger magnetic field because there is a greater current. The rapid movement of flux lines results in a faster collapse of

the field because of the abrupt end to the current.

Voltage applied to the coil primary winding with breaker points is about nine to ten volts. However, at high speeds, voltage may rise to twelve volts or more. This voltage pushes from one to four amperes of current through the primary winding. Primary current causes a magnetic field buildup around the windings. Building up a complete magnetic field is called **magnetic saturation**, or coil saturation. When this current stops, the primary winding magnetic field collapses. A greater voltage is self-induced in the primary winding by the collapse of its own magnetic field. This **self-induction** creates from 250 to 400 volts in the primary winding. For example, in a typical electronic ignition system, when the switching device turns ON, the current in the primary ignition circuit increases to approximately 5.5 amps. As the magnetic field builds in the primary circuit, the magnetic flux lines cross over into the secondary windings of the coil and induce an even greater voltage charge. The amount of voltage in the primary circuit builds up to 240 volts. The secondary windings meanwhile are building 200 times the primary voltage, or 48,000 volts. This is enough voltage to ignite the air-fuel mixture under most operating conditions.

Figure 13-2. The ignition coil produces high-voltage current in the secondary winding when current is cut off in the primary winding.

This collapsing magnetic field can be observed on an oscilloscope as a primary waveform pattern and is often referred to as the **firing line**. The voltage fluctuations vary by manufacturer, but most ignition systems range in amplitude between 250 to 400 volts. The secondary windings within the ignition coil are much thinner and have between 100 to 200 times the amount of windings. The voltage induced by the collapsing magnetic field is in the kilovolt (1000 X) range.

This kind of ignition system, based on the induction of a high voltage in a coil, is called an **inductive-discharge ignition system**. An inductive-discharge system, using a battery as the source of low-voltage current, has been the standard automotive ignition system for about eighty years.

Most ignition systems work on the inductive discharge principle except for one type, the **capacitive-discharge ignition system**. This high-performance

Magnetic Saturation: The condition when a magnetic field reaches full strength and maximum flux density.

Self-induction: A self-induced voltage potential formed by the building or induction of current through a conductor, such as the primary windings in a coil.

Firing line: The section of the ignition waveform trace reflecting the collapsing magnetic field. The primary firing line is usually between 250 to 400 volts.

Inductive-Discharge Ignition: A method of igniting the air-fuel mixture in an engine cylinder through the induction of a high voltage in the secondary winding of a coil.

Capacitive-Discharge Ignition: A method of igniting the air-fuel mixture in an engine cylinder through the storage of a voltage potential within a capacitor.

Figure 13-3. The ignition system is divided into the primary circuit and the secondary circuit. (Prestolite)

electronic ignition system is explained in detail later in this chapter. Basically, in the capacitive discharge system, the primary current voltage charges a capacitor inside the ignition module. The current does not travel through the coil during this period but instead, charges the storage capacitor. The stored voltage is released by the switching device at the proper time.

The ignition system transforms low battery voltage into high ignition voltage through induction. A look at the ignition system circuitry reveals how the system works.

BASIC CIRCUITS AND CURRENT

The ignition system, figure 13-3, consists of two interconnected circuits:

- The low-voltage primary circuit
- The high-voltage secondary circuit.

When the ignition switch is turned on, battery current travels:

- Through the ignition switch or the primary resistor if present
- To and through the coil primary winding
- Through a switching device
- To ground at the negative and the grounded terminal of the battery.

Low-voltage current in the coil primary winding creates a magnetic field. When the switching device interrupts this current:

- A high-voltage surge is induced in the coil secondary winding
- Secondary current is routed from the coil to the distributor
- Secondary current passes through the distributor cap, rotor, across the rotor air gap, and through another ignition cable to the spark plug.

- Secondary current creates an arc across the spark plug gap, as it travels to ground.

The Kettering inductive-discharge battery ignition system was invented by Charles F. Kettering in 1908. He used a set of contact points as a mechanical switch to open and close the circuit to the primary winding of the ignition coil. These contacts are opened by the rotation of a cam on the distributor shaft. They are called **breaker points** because they continually break the primary circuit.

The Kettering ignition system was quickly adopted as the standard for the automotive industry and used virtually unchanged for over sixty years. By the early 1970s, solid-state electronic components began to replace breaker points as switching devices for the primary circuit. The electronic or breakerless ignitions on late-model vehicles still use the inductive-discharge principles to produce a high-voltage spark. However, the primary circuits are controlled by electronic, rather than mechanical, switching devices.

PRIMARY CIRCUIT COMPONENTS

The primary circuit, figure 13-3, contains the:

- Battery
- Ignition switch
- Pickup coil in the distributor
- Coil primary winding
- Ignition Control Module.

Battery

The battery supplies low-voltage current to the ignition primary circuit. Battery current is available to the system when the ignition switch is in the START or the RUN position.

Ignition Switch

The ignition switch controls low-voltage current through the primary circuit. The switch allows current to the coil when it is in the START or the RUN position. Other switch positions route current to accessory circuits and lock the steering wheel in position.

Manufacturers use differing ignition switch circuitry. The differences lie in how battery current is routed to the switch. Regardless of variations, full system voltage is always present at the switch because it is connected directly to the battery.

General Motors automobiles draw ignition current from a terminal on the starter motor solenoid, figure 13-4. Ford Motor Company systems draw ignition

current from a terminal on the starter relay, figure 13-5. In Chrysler Corporation vehicles, ignition current comes through a wiring splice installed between the battery and the alternator, figure 13-6. Imported and domestic automobiles may use different connections. Ignition current is drawn through a wiring splice between the battery and the starter relay to simplify the circuitry on some systems, figure 13-7.

■ Charles Franklin Kettering (1876-1958)

Charles F. Kettering was a leading inventor and automotive engineer. After graduating from Ohio State University, he became chief of the inventions department at the National Cash Register Company. While there he designed a motor used in the first electrically operated cash register.

In 1909, he helped form a company called Dayton Engineering Laboratories Company, later to be known as Delco. In 1917, he became the president and general manager of the General Motors Research Corporation.

Kettering invented both the automobile self-starter and the inductive-discharge battery ignition system. The accompanying illustration is an early sketch by Kettering of his design for an ignition system. He was involved in the invention and perfection of high-octane gasoline; improvements for engines, especially diesel engines; electric refrigeration; and much more. He also helped establish the Sloan-Kettering Institute For Cancer Research in New York City.

Breaker Points: The metal contact points that act as an electrical switch in a distributor to open and close the ignition primary circuit.

Figure 13-4. General Motors products draw current from a terminal on the starter solenoid. (Buick)

Figure 13-5. Ford products draw ignition current from a terminal on the starter relay.

Ballast Resistor

For an ignition coil to have uniform secondary voltage capabilities over a wide range of engine speeds, complete saturation of its magnetic field must develop at varying speeds. The amount of time available for the coil to become saturated contributes to the uniform voltage. Magnetic saturation depends on the amount of voltage applied to the coil, the resistance of the circuit, and the amount of current in the windings. It also depends on the amount of time current is available.

If the resistance is high, or the voltage applied is low, a longer amount of time must be allowed for the coil to become saturated.

Ignition systems which have the primary circuit turned on when the ignition is on, have an additional resistor in the circuit to limit current through the coil. Systems with breaker points, and early electronic ignition, allow current through the primary windings with the ignition on and the engine not running. An additional resistor is added to these circuits to protect

Figure 13-6. Chrysler products draw ignition current from a wiring splice between the battery and the alternator.

Figure 13-7. The ignition current is drawn from a wiring splice between the battery and the starter relay.

the coil and breaker points from too much current. These systems also have a longer dwell time to allow enough time for the coil to become saturated.

This resistance wire or **ballast resistor** limits the voltage to the coil. It normally drops the voltage to about 7.5 volts with the key on, engine off (KOEO), and about 9.5-11 volts with the key on, engine running (KOER). As the current in the coil increases, the voltage drop across the ballast resistor increases.

At low speeds, current travels the circuit for relatively long periods of time. As the current heats the resistor, its resistance increases. The increased resistance reduces the applied voltage at the coil. At higher speeds, the breaker points open more often and current travels for shorter periods of time. As the ballast resistor cools, its resistance drops. Higher voltage is applied to the coil, but the shorter current duration results in about the same magnetic saturation of the coil.

When the engine is cranking, the system voltage drops because of the starter load. The ballast resistor is bypassed to allow full system voltage to the coil, figure 13-8. When the engine starts, the bypass circuit opens and primary current travels through the resistor. Ignition primary voltage is reduced to the desired level.

There are many different variations of size and location of the ballast resistor depending upon manufacturer. Some are mounted on the firewall while some are on the ignition coil, figure 13-9. Ford uses a length of resistance wire in the ignition switch circuit as a ballast resistor on some early electronic ignition systems.

Ballast Resistor: A resistor in the primary circuit that stabilizes ignition system voltage and current. Also known as a primary resistor.

Mechanical Ignition system: Any type of ignition system that uses a mechanical set of points to switch the primary current on and off.

Electronic Ignition system: Any type of ignition system that uses electronic components to switch the primary current on and off.

Distributor Ignition system: An ignition system, either mechanical or electronic, that incorporates a distributor in the design.

Figure 13-8. A ballast resistor protects the primary circuit from excessive voltage.

Figure 13-9. A Chrysler dual ballast resistor protects both the primary circuit and the solid-state ignition circuitry.

Types of Ignition Systems

Technology has advanced over the years producing a variety of primary ignition circuit switching devices. Although different in design, they all function to control the primary circuit current.

The magnetic field of the coil primary winding must completely collapse in order to induce a high voltage in the secondary winding. For the field to collapse, current through the primary winding must rapidly stop. Current must then start and stop again to induce the next high-voltage discharge. The primary circuit needs a switching device that rapidly breaks and completes the circuit. For more than sixty years, **Mechanical ignition systems** used breaker points as a switching device. Solid-state electronic devices have replaced breaker points on modern ignition systems. All non-points type ignition systems are referred to as **Electronic ignition systems**. Updated terminology lists a new category called the **Distributor ignition system**. Any ignition system which incorporates a distributor, whether the system is mechanical or electronic, falls into this category. It is easier to remember the design of the switching device and then place the ignition system into the proper sub-category. Ignition system categories include the distributorless and the distributor types while sub-categories include the mechanical and the electronic ignition systems. After closer examination, ignition systems are often referred to by their manufacturer-specific name: DuraSpark I,

II or II, HEI, TFI, EDIS, etc. Refer to Chapter Sixteen for more information on ignition systems.

Electronic ignition systems are more efficient than the breaker points ignition systems because there are no points to wear, become damaged, or deteriorate by heat and corrosion. A hotter secondary spark is produced by electronic ignition systems, which in turn results in more complete and precise burning of the air/fuel mixture. Electronic ignition systems also help engine designers meet the tougher emission control regulations.

There are several different types of electronic ignition systems depending upon the methods used to trigger the coil and to direct the high voltage to the correct spark plug at the correct time.

The capacitive discharge (CD) ignition system works similar to the inductive discharge system. In the capacitive discharge system, the primary current charges a capacitor inside the ignition module. The dwell, or charge time, for the inductive discharge systems corresponds to the capacitor charge time in the CD ignition system. In the CD system, the current does not travel through the coil during this period but, instead, travels to the storage capacitor. A charging circuit within the module powers a transformer that increases battery voltage to charge the capacitor to approximately 300 to 400 volts. The module is equipped with a silicon-controlled rectifier (SCR) that prevents capacitor discharge. When the switching device sends the trigger signal to the gate of the SCR,

Figure 13-10. A schematic of a typical capacitive discharge ignition system.

it closes the capacitor discharge circuit and discharges the voltage to the coil primary windings, figure 13-10. The abrupt change in coil primary voltage and current induces the secondary voltage in the coil.

In an inductive discharge system, primary current travels through the coil during the dwell period and is turned off to induce the high secondary voltage. In a capacitive discharge system, the primary voltage and current charge the capacitor. The capacitor is switched on to induce the high secondary voltage. These CD ignition systems charge the capacitor and discharge the coil faster than inductive discharge systems. The CD ignition system produces a higher and faster firing voltage. The CD ignition system also starts better in cold and wet weather and improves high-speed performance.

Current limiting devices and systems
To prevent damage to ignition components, a current limiting system is built into the primary circuit. Ballast resistors work well in points ignition systems to limit current. With the arrival of modern electronic ignition systems, specialized electronic components were designed to control excess primary circuit current. The key to achieving precise primary coil saturation is by controlling the charge time, or dwell, of the coil by limiting the current in the primary ignition circuit. After saturation is achieved, excess current in the

■ Dwell and engine speed

As engine speed increases, the distributor cam rotates faster. Dwell angle is unchanged, but the time it takes the cam to rotate through this angle is decreased. That is, the amount of time that the points are closed is reduced as engine speed increases.

It takes a specific amount of time, about 0.010 second, for the primary current to reach full strength. At a 625-rpm idle speed, the 33-degree dwell angle of an 8-cylinder engine lasts about 0.0165 second. Primary current easily reaches full strength before the points open to interrupt it.

As engine speed increases to 1,000 rpm, the 33-degree dwell period decreases to 0.0099 second. Primary current is interrupted just before it reaches its maximum strength; therefore, available secondary voltage is decreased slightly.

At 2,000 rpm, the dwell period is reduced to 0.0045 second. Primary current is interrupted well before it reaches its maximum strength. Available secondary voltage is reduced considerably. If the engine and ignition system are not in excellent condition, the required voltage level may be greater than the available voltage level. If this occurs, the engine misfires.

The electronic ignition systems reduced the resistance in the primary circuit to allow faster coil saturation. It can now be done in about 0.004 second. Together with a 6-cylinder engine being more common, this has allowed a higher available voltage at higher engine rpm because of the higher coil saturation.

If a waste spark system, or one coil for two cylinders, is used the effective frequency of each coil firing is reduced by 1/3 of engine rpm, with the 6-cylinder engine. At 5000 rpm, the time interval between each coil firing is 0.012 second. If each cylinder has an individual coil, the time interval doubles.

Fixed dwell: The ignition dwell period begins when the switching device turns on and remains constant, specified in distributor degrees, through all speeds.

Variable dwell: The ignition dwell period varies in distributor degrees at different engine speeds, but remains relatively constant in duration.

primary windings of the ignition coil results in damage to the coil and points or ignition module.

The current limiting functions of modern electronic ignitions are accomplished by several different designs. One type of current limiting system incorporates resistive coil windings and specialized transistors which switch to resistor mode after excess current is detected, figure 13-11. Another type of current limiting system is equipped with an ignition module that monitors the maximum current during the previous coil saturation. If the proper coil saturation time is achieved, the module trims the dwell to limit current, thereby reducing the amount of electrical energy used by the ignition system. If maximum current is not achieved during the coil saturation time, the module increases the dwell time.

In order to understand current limiting systems, it is important to understand dwell and the ability of the ignition system to control the amount of current in the primary circuit. Dwell is the period of time when the switching device is closed and the current is traveling in the primary winding of the coil. Solid state or electronic ignition systems require a dwell period for the same purpose, the charge time is controlled by an ignition module or computer. There are two basic designs for controlling dwell in the primary circuit: **Fixed dwell** and **variable dwell**.

All points systems operate on fixed dwell. As the distributor rotates and the points close, the amount of time closed is determined by the degree settings. The time period the points open and close is identical for each cylinder and each rotation, providing the lobes on the distributor shaft are not worn. **Dwell** measured in distributor degrees remains constant at all speeds but the **dwell time** shortens at high speed and lengthens at slow speeds. Remember how the ballast resistor works in the points system. At low speeds, current travels through the circuit for relatively long periods of time. As the current heats the resistor, its resistance increases, dropping the applied voltage at the coil. At higher speeds, the breaker points open more often and current travels for shorter periods of time. As the ballast resistor cools, its resistance drops. Higher voltage is applied to the coil but the shorter current duration results in about the same magnetic saturation of the coil. Dwell is fixed, but dwell time varies with engine speed. Because points are a mechanical component and could only be designed with fixed dwell, ballast resistors protect the primary circuit during engine rpm variations. Figure 13-12 shows the primary circuit oscilloscope pattern of a typical fixed dwell electronic

Figure 13-11. Some early electronic ignitions are equipped with a current limiting transistor.

ignition. All fixed dwell systems use a ballast resistor to limit current and voltage. Some early electronic ignition systems also incorporate the fixed dwell system and ballast resistor.

Variable dwell ignition systems do not use ballast resistors so the ignition coil and module receive full battery voltage. These systems do not conduct through the primary system until they get a signal to turn on. A module circuit senses primary current to the coil and limits the current when the magnetic field is saturated. The dwell time in milliseconds is relatively constant, but dwell in degrees increases with engine RPM.

Figure 13-12. Dwell measured in degrees of distributor rotation remains relatively constant at all engine speeds in a fixed-dwell system.

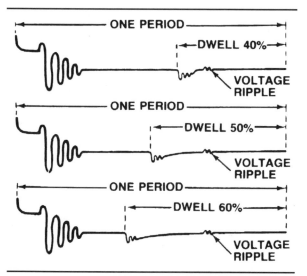

Figure 13-13. The dwell period increases with engine speed in the variable-dwell Delco HEI and some Motorcraft ignition systems.

The other method of limiting current through the coil is to limit the "on-time". This method can be used when the PCM controls all dwell and ignition timing. Although the dwell increases with RPM, the dwell time in milliseconds stays constant. Variable dwell ignition systems have a higher available voltage capacity, lower primary resistance, and a hotter spark to burn leaner air-fuel mixtures designed for low emissions automobiles. Figure 13-13 shows the oscilloscope pattern of a typical variable dwell electronic ignition system. Refer to Chapter Sixteen of this *Classroom Manual* for more information on ignition systems.

Dual trace digital and analog oscilloscopes are useful tools for diagnosing primary circuit malfunctions. Because the primary circuit operates on relatively small voltages, more accurate analysis of the primary

circuit can be achieved over the standard automotive oscilloscopes. Current limiting can be monitored on the scope on all types of ignition systems. The rule to follow is: When viewing voltage on a circuit that is ground controlled, as voltage goes down, current increases and as voltage goes up, current decreases. Figure 13-14 show the exact point in the dwell when

■ Dual-Point, Dual-Coil, Dual-Plug Ignition

Some early Nash automobiles used a "Twin Ignition" system. This system had two ignition coils, two sets of spark plugs and cables, a distributor with 16-plug terminals and two coil wire terminals, a rotor with offset tips, two sets of breaker points, and two condensers.

The inline engines were designed with spark plugs on both sides of the cylinders. The overhead valves were located directly over each cylinder in a vertical position.

The breaker points were synchronized by using a dual-bulb test lamp. With the ignition switch on, the distributor cam was turned to just break a stationary set of points, thereby lighting one bulb. A movable set of points was then adjusted to break contact, and light the second bulb, at the same instant. This adjustment assured that both sparks would occur in a cylinder at the same time. The dual-coil, dual-plug system has also been used to reduce exhaust emissions on some Nissan engines.

Dwell: Period of time when the ignition switching device is closed. During dwell, the primary circuit is complete so there is current in the primary winding of the coil.

Dwell time: The duration or actual time the dwell period, in distributor degrees, cycles.

Figure 13-14. Abrupt voltage changes from the current limiting device cause a current limiting hump in the trace on electronic ignition systems.

the current limiting device in the ignition system switches ON and voltage increases. This portion of the waveform on an electronic ignition system is called the current limiting hump. The **current limiting hump** appears at different locations for different ignition systems. Some early electronic ignition systems are not equipped with sophisticated circuitry and therefore do not display the hump in the primary ignition trace. By learning the typical waveform patterns of properly operating ignition systems, ignition system degradation can be easily detected. Once the control of the ignition timing has been taken away from the ignition system, the primary turn-off point is stable and does not vary. At this point, any variation between the cylinders indicates an engine mechanical failure such as worn distributor bushings, distributor drive gears, loose timing chains, etc.

Solid-state switching devices

Breaker-point ignitions make it difficult for an engine to meet modern exhaust emission control standards. Such standards not only require maximum system performance, they also require consistent performance. Because breaker points wear during normal operation, ignition system settings and performance change.

Since solid-state switching devices do not wear, ignition system performance remains consistent and exhaust emissions are effectively maintained. All manufacturers now use solid-state ignition systems.

The most basic electronic ignition is the transistor-switching device. Early electronic ignition systems use breaker points as the trigger device and a power transistor as the switching device. Although the points trigger the primary circuit, it is the transistor that actually opens and closes the primary circuit. The transistor acts as a load-carrying switch. A small amount of current is used to control a large amount of current, similar to a relay. Therefore, this type of ignition is

Figure 13-15. Schematic of a typical transistorized ignition system.

considered electronic. The points enjoy extended life because only a small amount of current is applied to them, see Figure 13-15. This system is much more efficient than mechanical ignition systems and the trigger device does require periodic replacement.

Electronic ignition systems quickly progressed to more sophisticated designs. Points were no longer used to trigger the transistor. Instead, a solid-state control module is responsible for switching the primary current on and off. A big design change with electronic ignition systems is that no primary current passes through the distributor. All primary current passes through the module by way of the transistors, resistors, and capacitors. The ignition coil positive terminal (+) is connected to the ignition switch, same as breaker point systems, but the negative (-) side of the coil is connected to the ignition module and then to ground. The transistors switch the primary current from the ground side.

The module must be signaled when to turn the current off. Of the four devices commonly used to do this, magnetic pulse generators and Hall-effect switches are the most common. Chrysler and some Japanese manufacturers, such as Isuzu, use optical signal generators.

A simple and very common ignition electronic switching device is the magnetic pulse generator. The

Figure 13-16. A typical magnetic pulse generator.

Figure 13-17. The pick-up coil generates an ac voltage signal as the reluctor moves closer and then away from the magnetic field.

magnetic pulse generator is installed in the distributor housing where the breaker points used to be. The pulse generator, figure 13-16, consists of a trigger wheel (reluctor) and a pick-up coil. The pick-up coil consists of an iron core wrapped with fine wire in a coil at one end and attached to a permanent magnet at the other end. The center of the coil is called the pole-piece.

The trigger wheel is made of steel with a low reluctance which cannot be permanently magnetized. Therefore, it provides a low-resistance path for magnetic flux lines. The trigger wheel has as many teeth as the engine has cylinders.

As the trigger wheel rotates, its teeth come near the pole piece. Flux lines from the pole piece concentrate in the low-reluctance trigger wheel, increasing the magnetic field strength and inducing a positive voltage signal in the pickup coil. When the teeth and the pole piece are aligned, the magnetic lines of force from the permanent magnet are concentrated and the voltage drops to zero. The reluctor continues and passes the pole piece, but now the voltage induced is negative, creating an ac voltage signal, figure 13-17. The pickup coil is connected to the electronic control module, which senses this ac voltage, converts the signal to dc voltage and switches the primary current off, figure 13-18. Each time a trigger wheel tooth comes

Current Limiting Hump: The portion of the waveform that indicates the exact point in the dwell when the current limiting device switches on. The device decreases current, so voltage level increases.

Magnetic Pulse Generator: A signal generating switch that creates a voltage pulse as magnetic flux changes around a pickup coil. The device transmits an analog ac signal voltage that varies in frequency and amplitude.

Figure 13-18. Schematic of a typical magnetic pulse generator ignition system.

near the pole piece, the control module is signaled to switch off the primary current. Solid-state circuitry in the module determines when the primary current is turned on again. Figure 13-19 shows the typical construction of a pulse generator for an eight-cylinder engine. These generators produce an ac signal voltage whose frequency and amplitude vary in direct proportion to rotational speed.

The terms "trigger wheel" and "pickup coil" describe the magnetic pulse generator. Various manufacturers have different names for these components. Other terms for the pick-up coil are pole piece, magnetic pick-up, or stator. The trigger wheel is often called the reluctor, armature, timer core, or signal rotor.

A **Hall-effect switch** also uses a stationary sensor and rotating trigger wheel, figure 13-20. Unlike the magnetic pulse generator, it requires a small input voltage in order to generate an output or signal voltage. Hall effect is the ability to generate a small voltage signal in semiconductor material by passing current through it in one direction and applying a magnetic field to it at a right angle to its surface. If the input current is held steady and magnetic field fluctuates, the output voltage changes in proportion to field strength.

Most Hall-effect switches in distributors have a Hall element or device, a permanent magnet, and a ring of metal blades similar to a trigger wheel. Some blades are designed to hang down. These are typically found in Bosch and Chrysler systems, figure 13-21, while others may be on a separate ring on the distributor shaft, typically found in GM and Ford distributors. When the shutter blade enters the gap between the magnet and the Hall element, it creates a magnetic shunt that changes the field strength through the Hall

Figure 13-19. A magnetic pulse generator installed in the distributor housing. (Ford)

Figure 13-20. Hall-effect ignition systems use a reference voltage to power the hall device.

element, thereby creating an analog voltage signal. The Hall element contains a logic gate that converts the analog signal into a digital voltage signal. This digital signal triggers the switching transistor. The transistor transmits a digital square waveform at varying frequency to the powertrain control module (PCM).

Figure 13-21. Shutter blades rotating through the Hall-effect switch air gap bypass the magnetic field around the pickup and drops the output voltage to zero.

The Hall-effect switch requires an extra connection for input voltage; however, its output voltage does not depend on the speed of the rotating trigger wheel. Therefore, its main advantage over the magnetic pulse generator is that it generates a full strength output voltage signal even at slow cranking speeds. This allows precise switching signals to the ignition primary circuit and accurate and fine adjustments of the air-fuel mixture.

The **optical signal generator** uses the principle of light beam interruption to generate voltage signals. Many optical signal distributors contain a pair of light-emitting diodes (LED) and photo diodes installed opposite each other, figure 13-22. A disc containing two sets of chemically etched slots is installed between the LEDs and photo diodes. Driven by the camshaft, the disc acts as a timing member and revolves at half engine speed. As each slot interrupts the light beam, an alternating voltage is created in each photo diode. A hybrid integrated circuit converts the alternating voltage into on-off pulses sent to the PCM.

The high-data-rate slots, or outer set, are spaced at intervals of two degrees of crankshaft rotation, figure 13-23. This row of slots is used for timing engine speeds up to 1,200 rpm. Certain slots in this set are missing, indicating the crankshaft position of the

■ Dual Breaker Points

In the early days of the automobile, short dwell time was an obstacle to increasing the rpm limit and power of high-performance street engines. Racing engines used magnetos which, by design, increase spark strength with rpm. Street engines, because of cost and starting requirements, were stuck with point-coil ignitions. At high engine speeds, above 4,500 or 5,000 rpm, a typical 33-degree dwell angle on a V8 engine did not allow enough coil saturation time. The result was insufficient voltage, making high-speed misfires a familiar problem. Reducing the point gap to increase dwell time drastically cut point life because the narrow gap caused point arcing and burning at low speeds.

By approximately the 1930s, manufacturers built the first production dual-point distributors that eliminated this problem. The two point sets had staggered openings and closings. The dwell on each set of points might be only 27 to 31 degrees; however, the combined dwell could be 36 to 40 degrees, which provided adequate coil saturation time and voltage for strong ignition at high speeds.

The point sets were connected parallel, so the primary circuit was complete, or closed, whenever either or both point sets were closed. However, both sets of points had to be open to break the primary circuit and fire the spark plug. The first set of points to open did not break the circuit because the other set still provided a current path through the primary circuit. The second set to open was the "opening" set, since both sets were then open simultaneously for a short period. Because the first set to open was also the first to close, it was the "closing" set, and vital coil saturation time could begin. Dual-point distributors survived into the 1970s, but were not needed with the universal adoption solid-state switching devices and electronic ignition.

Hall-Effect Switch: A signal-generating switch that develops a transverse voltage across a current-carrying semiconductor when subjected to a magnetic field. A Hall-device transmits a digital, dc signal that varies in frequency.

Figure 13-22. This Nissan optical signal generator works by interrupting a beam of light passing from the LEDs to photodiodes.

Figure 13-23. Each row of slots in this Chrysler optical distributor disc acts as a separate sensor, creating signals used to control fuel injection, ignition timing, and idle speed.

number one cylinder to the PCM. The low-data-rate slots, or inner set, consist of six slots correlated to the crankshaft top-dead-center angle of each cylinder. The PCM uses this signal for triggering the fuel injection system and for ignition timing at speeds above 1,200 rpm. This way, the optical signal generator acts both as the crankshaft position (CKP) sensor and engine speed (RPM) sensor, as well as a switching device.

MONITORING IGNITION PRIMARY CIRCUIT VOLTAGES

An ignition system voltage trace, both primary and secondary, is divided into three sections: firing, intermediate, and dwell. Deviations from a normal pattern indicate a problem. In addition, most scopes display ignition traces in three different patterns. Each

pattern is best used to isolate and identify particular kinds of malfunctions. The three basic patterns are superimposed pattern, parade pattern, and stacked, or raster, pattern.

In a superimposed pattern, voltage traces for all cylinders are displayed one on top of another to form a single pattern. This display provides a quick overall view of ignition system operation and also reveals certain major problems. The parade pattern displays voltage traces for all cylinders one after another across the screen from left to right in firing order sequence. A parade display is useful for diagnosing problems in the secondary circuit. A raster pattern shows the voltage traces for all cylinders stacked one above another in firing order sequence. This display allows you to compare the time periods of the three sections of a voltage trace.

All ignition waveforms contain a vast amount of information about circuit activity, mechanical condition, combustion efficiency, and fuel mixture. Electronic ignition system waveform patterns vary with manufacturer and ignition types; therefore, it is important to be able to recognize the normal waveform patterns and know how they relate to the particular system. The differences between the scope trace of breaker point and electronic ignition systems occur in the intermediate and the dwell sections, figure 13-24. The most noticeable difference is that no condenser oscillations are present in the intermediate section of the waveform trace on electronic ignition systems. Also, the beginning of the dwell section in the breaker point system is the points closing, while on electronic ignition systems it is the current on signal from the switching device. Another difference is that the current limiting devices on electronic ignition systems often display an abrupt rise in dwell voltage called a current limiting hump. These and other waveform characteristics are used to diagnose many primary circuit malfunctions.

With ignition scope experience and knowledge of waveform data, primary ignition traces are categorized according to the particular features of the ignition system. The GM HEI ignition system is capable of producing 30,000 volts of secondary voltage at the spark plug. The primary firing line measures approximately 250 volts, figure 13-25. As the secondary firing voltage goes up or down, it performs the same in the primary firing voltage. Ford TFI systems display a dwell line with 4.25 milliseconds between the primary turn-on and the current limiting hump, figure 13-26. The low resistance coil of a TFI system produces current acceleration to about 6 amps before the

Figure 13-24. The primary superimposed pattern traces all the cylinders, one upon the other.

Figure 13-26. Ford Thick Film Integrated (TFI) ignition systems use low-resistance coils that allow current acceleration and produce a distinct current limiting hump in the dwell trace.

Figure 13-25. The firing line on Ford Electronic Distributorless Ignition System (EDIS) should be approximately 342 volts for the primary circuit.

current limiting restricts the current. Early electronic ignition systems display features not particular to the newer, more efficient ignition systems.

Observing Switching Devices and Their Waveforms

The ignition scope has its place in diagnosing many primary ignition system malfunctions. Because the primary circuit deals with low voltage values, the lab scope is the best tool for diagnosing primary ignition system problems. A lab scope has greater resolution, which provides more clarity than an ignition scope. Many digital scopes are capable of storing waveform patterns for future review and comparison. Lab scopes are convenient because they observe other activity on the ignition primary circuit. The various primary circuit-switching devices also display voltage

fluctuations during their prescribed trigger cycle that can be observed and diagnosed.

Magnetic pulse generators provide an ac voltage signal easily observed using a lab scope. The GM HEI ignition system magnetic pick-up coil applies this ac symmetrical sine wave signal voltage to the "P" and "N" terminals on the HEI module, figure 13-27. The solid state circuitry inside the ignition module converts the ac signal to a dc square wave that peaks at 5.0 volts. These ac and dc voltage fluctuations are observed separately. While the engine is cranking, the ac voltage signal from the pick-up coil is accessed from terminal "P", figure 13-28. The square-wave signal HEI reference signal, is accessed from terminal "R". A dual-trace scope simultaneously displays the primary circuit voltage and the reference signal voltage, figure 13-29.

A Hall-effect switching device requires a three-wire circuit: power input, signal output, and ground. The Hall element receives an input voltage from the ignition switch or PCM, figure 13-30. As the shutter blade opens and closes, so does the input signal ground circuit. This opening and closing transmits a digital square-wave signal to the PCM. Many ignition systems are designed with the Hall effect square waves peaking at 5.0 volts. Others may use 7.0, 9.0, or some other voltage.

More complex Hall-effect ignition systems require more details. The Hall-effect TFI ignition system on many Ford vehicles uses a camshaft position (CMP) sensor which is a Hall-effect device inside the

DEFINITIONS:

1. 5 VOLT REGULATOR
2. SIGNAL CONVERTER, ALSO CONTAINS BIAS
3 COUNTER / MULITPLEXER
4. CLOCK OSCILLATOR, KEEPS DATA SYNCHRONIZED
5. CPU (CENTRAL PROCESSING UNIT)
6. PROM
7. SOLID STATE BYPASS RELAY
8. CURRENT LIMITING MONITOR

TERMINAL VOLTAGE VALUES:

C	PRIMARY IGNITION PATTERN	G	LESS THAN 100 Mv (DC VOLTAGE)
+	BATTERY VOLTAGE	R	5 VOLT OR 12 VOLT SQUARE WAVE
N	GROUND SIDE OF PICK-UP COIL	B	APPROPRIATE GROUND
C	PICK-UP COIL WAVEFORM	E	LESS THAN .5 VOLT SQUARE WAVE

Figure 13-27. Schematic of the GM HEI magnetic pulse generator ignition system.

distributor. The CMP sensor produces a digital profile ignition pick-up (PIP) signal. The shutter blade passes over a smaller vane, which identifies the number one cylinder for fuel injector firing. This signal is called the Signature PIP. The PIP signal is sent from the CMP sensor to the PCM and the ignition control module (ICM). The computer uses this signal to calculate the spark angle data for the ignition control module to control ignition coil firing. The ICM acts as a switch to ground in the primary circuit. The falling edge of the SPOUT signal controls the battery voltage applied to the primary circuit. The rising edge of the SPOUT signal controls the actual switch opening, figure 13-31. The PCM uses the inductive voltage spike when the primary field collapses and converts it into

an ignition diagnostic monitor signal (IDM), figure 13-32. This diagnostic monitor signal is used by the computer to observe the primary circuit. Because the ICM mounts on the exterior of the distributor, the various voltage waveforms are observed on a scope.

Optical ignition systems create distinct voltage signals. The Chrysler Optical ignition system on the 3.0L engine uses two photocells and two LEDs with solid-state circuitry to create two 5.0-volt signals. The inner set, or low data, of slots signals TDC for each cylinder while the outer slots (high data) monitor every two degrees of crankshaft rotation, figure 13-33. When observing the waveforms, if the low data rate or the high data rate signals fail on the high section, then the LED is most likely malfunctioning. If

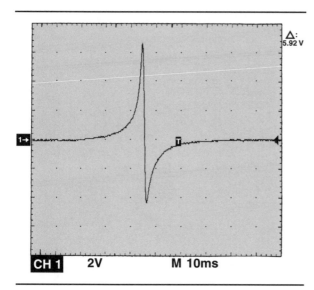

Figure 13-28. A lab scope displays an ac sine wave during cranking on HEI Terminal "P".

Figure 13-29. The HEI primary circuit voltage trace is displayed on the top and the square-wave, reference signal is displayed on the bottom of the scope screen.

the signals fail on the low section, then the PCM is most likely not delivering the 5.0-volt reference signal. If the low data signal is lost, the engine normally starts. If the high data signal is lost, the engine starts, but on default settings from the PCM, figure 13-34.

Figure 13-30. The lab scope displays the Hall-effect output signal transmitted to the PCM.

■ Useful Distributor Tool

When timing an engine and rotating the distributor to advance or retard the spark, sometimes the distributor does not want to budge. This may occur even after the holddown bolt has been loosened. If it does, try using an oil filter wrench around the distributor. It may give the grip and leverage needed to free the distributor.

DISTRIBUTOR IGNITION SCHEMATIC EXAMPLE

REMOTE IGNITION CONTROL MODULE

Figure 13-31. Schematic of the Ford TFI CCD ignition system on late-model trucks.

SUMMARY

Through electromagnetic induction, the ignition system transforms the low voltage of the battery into the high voltage required to fire the spark plugs. Induction occurs in the ignition coil where current travels through the primary winding to build up a magnetic field. When the field rapidly collapses, high voltage is induced in the coil secondary winding. All domestic original-equipment ignitions are the battery-powered, inductive-discharge type.

The ignition system is divided into two circuits: primary and secondary. The primary circuit contains the battery, the ignition switch, the coil primary winding, a switching device, and signal devices to determine crankshaft position.

ICM WAVEFORM EXAMPLES (DISTRUBUTOR IGNITION)

Figure 13-32. The IDM, SPOUT, and PIP signals are monitored to check power input, power output, and ground.

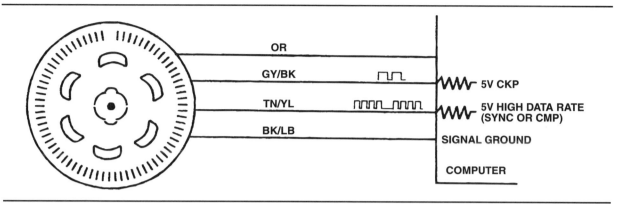

Figure 13-33. In a Chrysler Optical Ignition system, the low data rate square wave looks different than the high data rate square wave.

Figure 13-34. The primary circuit voltage trace of a Chrysler Photo Optical Ignition system is displayed on the top while the CKP square wave is displayed on the bottom of the scope screen.

For over sixty years, mechanical breaker points were used as the primary circuit-switching device. Solid-state electronic components replaced breaker points as the switching device in the 1970s. The two most common solid-state switching devices are the magnetic pulse generator and the Hall-effect switch.

The breaker points are a mechanical switch that opens and closes the primary circuit. The time period when the points are closed is called the dwell angle. The dwell angle varies inversely with the gap between the points when they are open. As the gap decreases, the dwell increases. The ignition condenser is a capacitor that absorbs primary voltage when the points open. This prevents arcing across the points and premature burning.

Three types of common ignition electronic signal devices are the magnetic pulse generator, the Hall-effect switch, and the optical signal generator. The magnetic pulse generator creates an ac voltage signal as the reluctor continually passes the pole piece, changing the induced voltage to negative. The Hall-effect switch uses a stationary sensor and rotating trigger wheel just like the magnetic pulse generator. Its main advantage over the magnetic pulse generator is that it can generate a full strength output voltage signal even at slow speeds. The optical signal generator acts both as the crankshaft position CKP sensor and TDC sensor, as well as a switching device. It uses light beam interruption to generate voltage signals.

Review Questions
Choose the single most correct answer.
Compare your answers with the correct answers on Page 468.

1. The voltage required to ignite the air-fuel mixture ranges from:
   a. 5 to 25 volts
   b 50 to 250 volts
   c. 500 to 2,500 volts
   d. 5,000 to 25,000 volts

2. Which of the following does NOT require higher voltage levels to cause an arc across the spark plug gap?
   a. Increased spark plug gap
   b. Increased engine operating temperature
   c. Increased fuel in air-fuel mixture
   d. Increased pressure of air-fuel mixture

3. In an Inductive Discharge ignition, the coil transforms low voltage from the primary circuit to high voltage for the secondary circuit through:
   a. Magnetic induction
   b. Capacitive discharge
   c. Series resistance
   d. Parallel capacitance

4. Voltage induced in the secondary winding of the ignition coil is how many times greater than the self-induced primary voltage?
   a. 1 to 2
   b. 10 to 20
   c. 100 to 200
   d. 1,000 to 2,000

5. The two circuits of the ignition system are:
   a. The "Start" and "Run" circuits
   b. The point circuit and the coil circuit
   c. The primary circuit and the secondary circuit
   d. The insulated circuit and the ground circuit

6. Which of the following components is part of both the primary and the secondary circuits?
   a. Ignition switch
   b. Distributor rotor
   c. Switching device
   d. Coil

7. Which of the of the following is NOT contained in the primary circuit of an ignition system?
   a. Battery
   b. Spark plugs
   c. Ignition switch
   d. Coil primary winding

8. Which of the following is true of the coil primary windings?
   a. They consist of 100 to 150 turns of very fine wire
   b. The turns are insulated by a coat of enamel
   c. The negative terminal is connected directly to the battery
   d. The positive terminal is connected to the switching device and to ground

9. In order to collapse the magnetic field of the coil, the primary circuit requires a:
   a. Ballast resistor
   b. Switching device
   c. Condenser
   d. Starting bypass circuit

10. In a solid-state ignition system, the distributor cam are replaced by:
    a. RFI filter capacitors
    b. Auxiliary ballast resistors
    c. Magnetic pickup triggering devices
    d. Integrated coil and distributor cap assemblies

11. All of the following are electronic ignition switching devices EXCEPT:
    a. Pick-up coil
    b. Photo Optical LED
    c. Capacitor
    d. Hall-effect switch

12. A Hall-effect switch requires _____ to generate an output voltage signal.
    a. A reference voltage
    b. A crankshaft position sensor
    c. Pick-up coil
    d. A shunt transistor

13. Dwell is measured in distributor degrees while dwell time is measured in:
    a. Kilovolts
    b. Milliseconds
    c. Millimeters
    d. Ohms

14. The distributer rotates at _____ the speed of the crankshaft.
    a. One-half
    b. The same speed as
    c. Twice
    d. One-quarter

15. A current limiting hump displays:
    a. Voltage changes
    b. Time increments
    c. Firing line
    d. Current changes

16. As voltage increases, current _____.
    a. Induces
    b. Decreases
    c. Lowers
    d. Stays the same

14

The Ignition Secondary Circuit and Components

The general operation of the ignition primary circuit and some of the system components have already been covered. This chapter examines the secondary circuit and its components.

The secondary circuit must conduct surges of high voltage. To do this, it has large conductors and terminals, and heavy-duty insulation. The secondary circuit in a Distributor Ignition system, figure 14-1, consists of the:

- Coil secondary winding
- Distributor cap and rotor
- Ignition cables
- Spark plugs.

The secondary circuit in a Distributorless Ignition system (DIS), figure 14-2, consists of the:

- Coil packs
- Ignition cables, where applicable
- Spark plugs.

The secondary circuit in a Coil Over Plug DIS consists of the same components as a DIS system except that each cylinder has its own separate coil and there are usually no ignition wires to the spark plugs, figure 14-3. Also, the coil over plug system fires each cylinder sequentially rather than using the waste spark method. Refer to Chapter Sixteen of this *Classroom Manual* for additional information.

IGNITION COILS

The ignition coil steps up voltage in the same way as a transformer. When the magnetic field of the coil primary winding collapses, it induces a high voltage in the secondary winding.

Coil Secondary Winding and Primary-to-Secondary Connections

Two windings of copper wire compose the ignition coil. The primary winding of heavy wires consists of 100 to 150 turns; the secondary winding is 15,000 to 30,000 turns of a fine wire. The ratio of secondary turns to primary turns is usually between 100 and 200. To increase the strength of the magnetic field, the windings are wrapped around a laminated core of soft iron, figure 14-4.

The coil must be protected from the underhood environment to maintain its efficiency. Four coil designs are used:

- Oil-filled coil
- Laminated E-core coil
- DIS coil packs
- Coil over plug assemblies.

Figure 14-1. Typical early Chrysler electronic ignition system with a distributor, cap, and rotor.

Oil-filled coil

In the oil-filled coil, the primary winding is wrapped around the secondary winding, which is wrapped around the iron core. The coil windings are insulated by layers of paper and the entire case is filled with oil for greater insulation. The top of the coil is molded from an insulating material such as Bakelite. Metal inserts for the winding terminals are installed in the cap. Primary and secondary terminals are generally marked with a + and -, figure 14-5. Leads are attached with nuts and washers on some coils; others use push-on connectors. The entire unit is sealed to keep out dirt and moisture.

Laminated E-core coil

Unlike the oil-filled coil, the E-core coil uses an iron core laminated around the windings and potted in plastic, much like a small transformer, figure 14-6. The coil is so named because of the "E" shape of the laminations making up its core. Because the laminations provide a closed magnetic path, the E-core coil has a higher energy transfer. The secondary connection looks much like a spark plug terminal. Primary leads are housed in a single snap-on connector that attaches to the coil's blade-type terminals. The E-core coil has very low primary resistance and is used without a ballast resistor in Ford TFI and some GM HEI ignitions.

DIS coil packs

Distributorless ignitions use two or more coils in a single housing called a coil pack, figure 14-7. Figure 14-8 compares the internal windings of a typical coil pack with those of the oil-filled and E-core coils. Because the E-core coil has a primary and secondary winding on the same core, it uses a common terminal. Both ends of the E-core coil's primary winding connect to the primary ignition circuit; the open end of its secondary winding connects to the center tower of the coil, where the distributor high-tension lead connects.

Coil packs are significantly different, using a closed magnetic core with one primary winding for each two high-voltage outputs. The secondary circuit of the coil pack is wired in series. Each coil in the coil pack directly provides secondary voltage for two of the spark plugs, which are in series with the coil secondary winding. Coil pack current is limited by transistors called output drivers, which are located in the ignition module attached to the bottom of the pack. The output drivers open and close the ground path of the coil primary circuit. Other module internal circuits control timing and sequencing of the output drivers.

Coil over plug coil assemblies

Each cylinder has its own separate coil and there are no ignition wires to the spark plugs on all coil over plug ignition systems. Each cylinder is fired only on its compression stroke.

Figure 14-2. Typical Ford EDIS ignition system with a coil pack and separate spark plug wires for the secondary system.

Coil Voltage

A coil must supply the correct amount of voltage for any system. Since this amount of voltage varies, depending on engine and operating conditions, the voltage available at the coil is generally greater than what is required by the system. If it is less, the engine may not run.

Available voltage

The ignition coil supplies much more secondary voltage than the average engine requires. The peak voltage that a coil produces is called its **available voltage**.

Available Voltage: The peak voltage that a coil can produce.

COP IGNITION SCHEMATIC

Figure 14-3. Typical Coil Over Plug ignition system on a V8 with a separate coil/spark plug assembly for each cylinder.

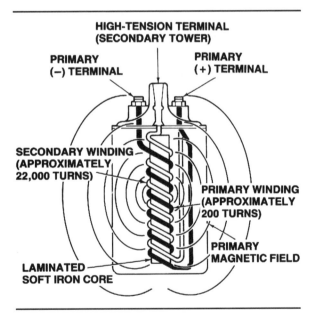

Figure 14-4. The laminated iron core within the coil strengthens the coil's magnetic field.

Three important coil design factors determine available voltage level:

- Secondary-to-primary turns ratio
- Primary voltage level
- Primary circuit resistance.

Figure 14-5. The Ford coil used with breakerless ignitions has a polarized slide-on primary terminal connector with a tachometer connection. (Ford)

The turns ratio is a multiplier that creates high secondary voltage output. The primary voltage level that is applied to a coil is determined by the ignition circuit design and condition. Anything affecting circuit resistance such as incorrect parts or loose or corroded connections, affects this voltage level. Generally, a primary circuit voltage loss of one volt may decrease available voltage by 10,000 volts.

Figure 14-6. The E-core coil is used without a ballast resistor.

Figure 14-7. Typical DIS coil packs used on four-cylinder engines.

If there were no spark plug in the secondary circuit, the coil secondary voltage would have no place to discharge quickly. That is, the circuit would remain open so there is no path to ground for the current to follow. As a result, the voltage oscillates in the secondary circuit and dissipates as heat. The voltage is completely gone in just a few milliseconds. Figure 14-9 shows the trace of this no-load, open-circuit voltage. This is called secondary voltage **no-load oscillation**. The first peak of the voltage trace represents the maximum available voltage from that particular coil. Available voltage is usually between 20,000 and 50,000 volts.

Required voltage

When there is a spark plug in the secondary circuit, the coil voltage creates an arc across the plug air gap to complete the circuit. Figure 14-10 compares a typical no-load oscillation to a typical secondary firing voltage oscillation. At about 15,000 volts, the spark plug air gap ionizes and becomes conductive. This is the ionization voltage level, also called the **firing voltage**, or **required voltage**.

As soon as a spark has formed, less voltage is required to maintain the arc across the air gap. This reduces the energy demands of the spark causing the secondary voltage to drop to the much lower spark voltage level. This is the inductive portion of the spark. **Spark voltage** is usually about one-fourth of the firing voltage level.

Figure 14-11 shows the entire trace of the spark. The spark duration or **burn time** of the trace indicates the amount of resistance and efficiency of the spark voltage. Burn time on most ignition systems is between 1.6 and 1.8 milliseconds. The traces shown are similar to the secondary circuit traces seen on an oscilloscope screen. High secondary resistance causes the spark voltage to increase and a quick burn time, or short spark duration. This occurs as the secondary system overcomes the resistance by reducing current and increasing voltage. This section of the waveform trace indicates secondary efficiency. When the secondary voltage falls below the inductive air-gap voltage level, the spark can no longer be maintained. The spark gap becomes nonconductive. The remaining secondary voltage oscillates in the secondary circuit, dissipating as heat. This is called secondary **voltage decay**. At this time, the primary circuit closes and the cycle repeats, figure 14-12.

No-Load Oscillation: The rapid, back-and-forth, peak-to-peak oscillation of voltage in the ignition secondary circuit when the circuit is open.

Firing Voltage (Required Voltage): The voltage level that must be reached to ionize and create a spark in the air gap between the spark plug electrodes.

Spark Voltage: The inductive portion of a spark that maintains the spark in the air gap between the electrodes, usually about one-quarter of the firing voltage level.

Burn time: The duration of spark voltage, usually indicated in milliseconds, necessary to overcome secondary ignition resistance

Voltage Decay: The rapid oscillation and dissipation of secondary voltage after the spark in a spark plug air gap has stopped.

Figure 14-8. Coil Wiring Comparison (Ford Motor Company).

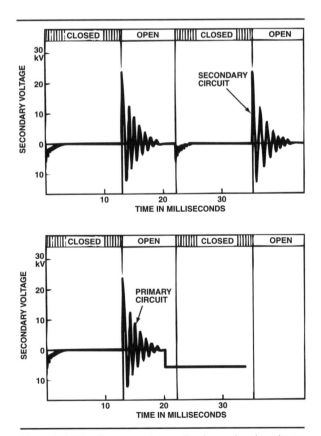

Figure 14-9. A secondary circuit no-load voltage trace. (Bosch)

Figure 14-10. The dashed line shows no-load voltage; the solid line shows the voltage trace of firing voltage and spark voltage. (Bosch)

Figure 14-11. The voltage trace of an entire secondary ignition pulse. (Bosch)

Figure 14-12. As the primary circuit opens and closes, the ignition cycle repeats. (Bosch)

SECONDARY WAVEFORM

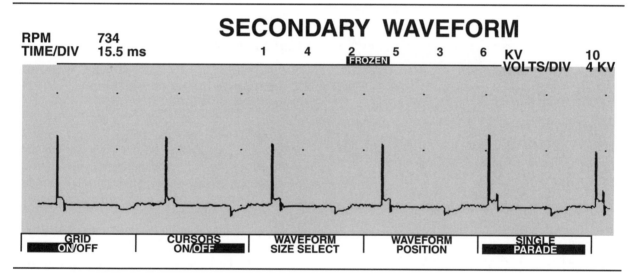

Figure 14-13. Normal secondary firing voltages for the secondary system with an 0.045-inch air gap.

It is a good idea to memorize the three most typical firing voltages and their respective air gap settings. The firing voltage on the spark plug of 0.035 inch is about 6 to 8 kV; 0.045 inch air gap is 8 to 10 kV; and 0.060 air gap is 10 to 12 kV. There are many more plug air gap settings but it is important to know the three most popular spark plug gap settings and their kilovolt requirements to compare to other systems. The scope pattern for the secondary circuit quickly shows the firing voltage, figure 14-13.

Secondary ignition component failure due to wear is a common problem that results in high circuit resistance. Whether caused by a damaged plug wire, worn distributor cap, or excessive spark plug gap, this additional resistance disrupts current and alters the scope trace. Higher voltage, which is required to overcome this type of resistance, reduces current. The energy in

the coil dissipates more rapidly than normal. As a result, high circuit resistance produces a high firing spike followed by high, short spark line.

Firing voltage for the DIS exhibits a slightly different waveform pattern than Distributor Ignition systems because of the design of the "waste spark" secondary system. Distributorless ignition systems pair two cylinders, called companion cylinders, and fire both spark plugs at the same time. One cylinder fires on the compression stroke while the other cylinder fires on the exhaust stroke. The spark plugs are wired in series. One fires in the conventional method, from center electrode to ground electrode, while the other fires from ground electrode to center electrode. Every other cylinder has reverse polarity, figure 14-14. The cylinder on the compression stroke requires more voltage to fire the air-fuel mixture than

Figure 14-14. Although the current in the secondary windings of the DIS coil does not reverse, one spark plug fires with normal polarity while the other spark plug fires with reverse polarity.

the other cylinder. The exhaust waste spark, or stroke pattern, shows less voltage because there is much less resistance across the spark plug gap of the waste spark, figure 14-15. Also, the DIS fires once per engine revolution as opposed to every other revolution in a distributor engine. As a result, DIS plugs wear twice as fast as distributor ignition plugs.

Secondary waveform patterns should be viewed first to gather the most complete list of ignition and engine driveability problems. The secondary system clearly indicates the operating resistance – or the systems that are expending too much resistance. The secondary waveform patterns include data for resistance in three areas: the electrical resistance (air gaps and secondary circuit), the cylinder compression resistance (mechanical), and the combustion resistance (air-fuel ratio performance). The resistance expended by faulty secondary ignition wires, excessive spark plug and rotor air gaps, weak compression, incorrect valve timing, or poor air-fuel mixing may be detected on the secondary waveform pattern.

Some other conditions of high resistance that cause required voltage levels to increase are:

- Eroded electrodes in the distributor cap, rotor, or spark plug
- Damaged ignition cables
- Reversed plug polarity

- High compression pressures
- Lean air-fuel mixture that is more difficult to ionize.

Voltage reserve

The physical condition of the automotive engine and ignition system affects both available and required voltage levels. Figure 14-18 shows available and required voltage levels in a particular ignition system under various operating conditions. **Voltage reserve** is the amount of coil voltage available in excess of the voltage required.

Under certain poor circuit conditions, there may be no voltage reserve. At these times, some spark plugs do not fire and the engine runs poorly or not at all. Ignition systems must be properly maintained to ensure that there is always some voltage reserve. Typically, an ignition system should have a voltage reserve of about 60 percent of available voltage under most operating conditions.

Coil Installations

Ignition coils are usually mounted with a bracket on a fender panel in the engine compartment or on the engine, figure 14-17.

Some ignition coils have an unusual design and location. The Delco-Remy High Energy Ignition (HEI) solid-state ignition system has a coil mounted in the distributor. The coil output terminal is connected directly to the center electrode of the distributor cap. The connections to the primary winding are made through a multi-plug connector.

Many ignition systems manufactured in Asia have the coil inside the distributor along with the pick-up coil, rotor, and module. Toyota mounts the ignition coil inside the distributor, figure 14-18, but positions the module (igniter) on the bulkhead or shock tower for cooling purposes.

Distributorless ignitions use an assembly containing one or more separate ignition coils and an electronic ignition module, figure 14-19. Control circuits in the module discharge each coil separately in sequence, with each coil serving two cylinders 360 degrees apart in the firing order. Chapter Sixteen of this *Classroom Manual* covers this type of system in more detail.

In any system, the connections to the primary winding must be made correctly. If spark plug polarity is reversed, greater voltage is required to fire the plug. Plug polarity is established by the ignition coil connections.

One end of the coil secondary winding is connected to the primary winding, figure 14-20, so the secondary circuit is grounded through the ignition

Figure 14-15. The cylinder with the greatest resistance (compression) exhibits high firing voltage while the cylinder with the least resistance (waste) exhibits the lower firing voltage.

Figure 14-16. Available and required voltage levels under different system conditions.

Figure 14-17. Typical coil pack mounting on a Ford V6 Distributorless Ignition system.

primary circuit. When the coil terminals are properly connected to the battery, the grounded end of the secondary circuit is electrically positive. The other end of the secondary circuit, which is the center electrode of the spark plug, is electrically negative. Whether the secondary winding is grounded to the primary + or [-] terminal depends on whether the windings are wound clockwise or counterclockwise.

The secondary circuit must have negative polarity, or positive ground, for two main reasons. First, electrons flow more easily from negative to positive than they do in the opposite direction. Second, high

temperatures of the spark plug center electrode increase the rate of electron movement, or current. The center electrode is much hotter than the side electrode because it cannot transfer heat to the cylinder head as easily. The electrons move quickly and easily to the side electrode when the air-fuel mixture is ignited. Although the secondary operates with negative polarity, it is a positive ground circuit.

If the coil connections are reversed, figure 14-21, spark plug polarity is reversed. The grounded end of

Voltage Reserve: The amount of coil voltage available in excess of the voltage required to fire the spark plugs.

Figure 14-18. Toyota mounts the ignition coil inside the distributor.

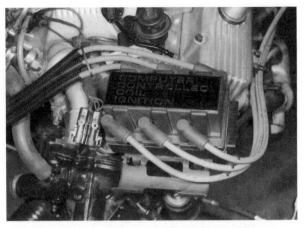

Figure 14-19. The Buick C3I distributorless ignition uses a single coil pack with three coils, each of which serves two cylinders 360 degrees apart in the firing order.

Figure 14-20. When coil connections are made properly, the spark plug center electrode is electrically negative.

the secondary circuit is electrically negative. The plug center electrode is electrically positive, and the side electrode is negative. When plug polarity is reversed, 20 to 40 percent more secondary voltage is required to fire the spark plug.

Coil terminals are usually marked BAT or +, and DIST or [-]. To establish the correct plug polarity with a negative-ground electrical system, the + terminal must be connected to the positive terminal of the battery through the ignition switch, starter relay, and other circuitry. The [-] coil terminal must be connected to the ignition control module.

DISTRIBUTOR CAP AND ROTOR

The distributor cap and rotor, figure 14-22, receive high-voltage current from the coil secondary winding. Current enters the distributor cap through the central terminal called the coil tower. The rotor carries the current from the coil tower to the spark plug electrodes in the rim of the cap. The rotor mounts on the distributor shaft and rotates with the shaft so the rotor electrode moves from one spark plug electrode to another in the cap to follow the designated firing order.

Figure 14-21. When coil connections are reversed, spark plug polarity is reversed.

Distributor Rotor

A rotor is made of silicone plastic, **Bakelite**, or a similar synthetic material that is a very good insulator. A metal electrode on top of the rotor conducts current from the carbon terminal of the coil tower.

The rotor is keyed to the distributor shaft to maintain its correct relationship with the shaft and the spark plug electrodes in the cap. The key may be a flat section or a slot in the top of the shaft. Delco-Remy V6 and V8, shown at the left in figure 14-23, are keyed in place by two locators and secured by two screws. On the right is shown a plug-on or push-on distributor rotor. Most other rotors are pressed onto the shaft by hand. The rotor in a Chrysler optically triggered distributor is retained by a horizontal capscrew.

The Ford Electronic Engine Control (EEC) I, II, and III ignitions have rotors with two pickup arms and two electrodes, figure 14-24. The electrodes are on different levels that correspond to two levels of distributor cap electrodes. This minimizes high-voltage **crossfiring** in the distributor. When the rotor is removed or replaced on 1978 EEC-I systems, figure 14-24, left, it requires alignment. A modification of this design is used on 1979 and later distributors, figure 14-24, right, and alignment is not normally required when replacing this rotor.

Older fuel distributors use a blade-type rotor tip. This was changed to a multiwire or "cat-whisker", rotor tip, figure 14-25, in some 1983-85 systems. This was an attempt to further reduce Radio Frequency Interference (RFI) from the secondary circuit without using silicone grease on the rotor tip. However, arcing

Figure 14-22. A distributor rotor and a cutaway view of the distributor cap.

from the multiwire tip formed ozone and nitrogen oxides from the air inside the distributor. Over a period of time, these combined to form nitric acid that reacted with the distributor cap to create a short-circuit path for secondary voltage.

Ford released replacement caps of a different material in 1985 to counteract the crossfiring problem and discontinued the cat-whisker rotors in 1986. Replacement rotors for 1983-85 models are the blade-type design.

Except for the multiwire-tip rotors, Ford and Chrysler breakerless distributor rotors are coated at the factory with a silicone grease. As the silicone ages, it may look like contamination, but it is not. Do not remove or reapply any coating on a used Ford rotor. Chrysler recommends removing any excess on the tip of the rotor.

Bakelite: A synthetic plastic material that is a good insulator. Distributor caps are often made of Bakelite.

Crossfiring: Ignition voltage jumping from the distributor rotor to the wrong spark plug electrode inside the distributor cap. Also, ignition voltage jumping from one spark plug cable to another due to worn insulation.

Figure 14-23. Typical distributor rotors.

Figure 14-24. Ford bilevel rotor used with the 1978 EEC-I distributor (left) requires alignment when installed; the style used with 1979 and later EEC-I, -II, and -III distributors (right) normally does not. (Ford)

Rotors used with Hall-effect switches often have the shutter blades attached, figure 14-26, serving a dual purpose: In addition to distributing the secondary current, the rotor blades bypass the Hall-effect magnetic field and create the signal for the primary circuit to fire.

Rotor air gap

An air gap of a few thousandths of an inch, or a few hundredths of a millimeter, exists between the tip of the rotor electrode and the spark plug electrode of the cap. If they actually touch, both would wear very quickly. Because the gap cannot be measured when the distributor is assembled, it is usually described in terms of the voltage required to create an arc across the electrodes. Only about 3,000 volts are required to create an arc across some air gaps, but others require as much as 9,000 volts. As the rotor completes the secondary circuit and the plug fires, the rotor air gap adds resistance to the circuit. This raises the plug firing voltage, suppresses secondary current, and reduces RFI.

Figure 14-25. Typical Ford multiwire or "cat-whisker" rotors used in some 1983-86 systems. (Ford)

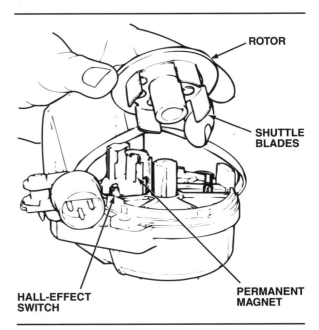

Figure 14-26. A Hall-effect triggering device attached to the rotor. (Chrysler)

Distributor Cap

The distributor cap is also made of silicone plastic, Bakelite, or a similar material that resists chemical attack and protects other distributor parts. Metal electrodes in the spark plug towers and a carbon insert in the coil tower provide electrical connections with the ignition cables and the rotor electrode, figure 14-27. The cap is keyed to the distributor housing and is held on by two or four spring-loaded clips or by screws.

Delco-Remy HEI distributor caps with an integral coil, figure 14-28, are secured by four spring-loaded clips. When removing this cap, ensure that all four clips are disengaged and clear of the housing. Then lift the cap straight up to avoid bending the carbon button in the cap and the spring that connects it to the coil. If the button and spring are distorted, arcing can occur that will burn the cap and rotor.

Positive-engagement spark plug cables are used with some Chrysler and Ford four-cylinder ignition systems. There are no electrodes in distributor caps used with these cables. A terminal electrode attached to the distributor-cap end of the cable locks inside the cap to form the distributor contact terminal. The secondary terminal of the cable is pressed into the cap, figure 14-29.

Ford distributors used with some electronic engine control (EEC) systems have caps and rotors with the terminals on two levels to prevent secondary voltage arcing. Spark plug cables are not connected to the caps in firing order sequence, but the caps are numbered with the engine cylinder numbers, figure 14-30. The caps have two sets of numbers, one set for 5.0-liter standard engines, and the other for 5.7-liter and 302-cid high-performance engines. Cylinder

■ Dual Plug DIS

In 1989, Ford introduced the Dual Plug Distributorless Ignition system (DP-DIS) on the 2.3L Ranger. This system was added to the 2.3L EFI Mustang engine in 1991. The Dual Plug system is made up of a crankshaft position sensor mounted near the crankshaft, two 4-tower DIS coil packs, and a DIS ignition module. Each coil fires two spark plugs at the same time. This system is also a typical waste spark system. The dual plug DIS features simultaneous firing voltages to the same cylinder to provide more efficient combustion and cleaner emissions. The coil pack and plugs on the right side operate continuously while the coil pack and plugs on the left side are controlled by the computer and are switched on or off according to engine temperatures, engine load, and air-fuel mixture demands.

2.3. RANGER DP-DIS SCHEMATIC

Figure 14-27. The distributor cap and rotor assembled with the distributor housing.

numbers must be carefully checked when changing spark plug cables.

Distributor caps used on some late-model Ford and Chrysler vehicles have a vent to prevent the buildup of moisture and reduce the accumulation of ozone inside the cap.

IGNITION CABLES

Secondary ignition cables carry high-voltage current from the coil to the distributor and from the distributor to the spark plugs. They use heavy insulation to prevent the high-voltage current from jumping to ground before it reaches the spark plugs. Ford, GM, and some other electronic ignitions use an 8-mm cable; all others use a 7-mm cable.

Conductor Types

Spark plug cables originally used a solid steel or copper wire conductor. Cables manufactured with these conductors were found to cause radio and television interference. While this type of cable is still made for special applications such as racing, most spark plug cables have been made of high-resistance, nonmetallic conductors for the past 30 years. Several nonmetallic conductors may be used, such as carbon, and linen or fiberglass strands impregnated with graphite. The nonmetallic conductor acts as a resistor in the secondary circuit and reduces RFI and spark plug wear due to high current. Such cables are often called **television-radio-suppression (TVRS) cables**, or just suppression cables.

When replacing spark plug cables on vehicles with computer-controlled systems, ensure that the resistance of the new cables is within the original equipment specifications to avoid possible electromagnetic interference with the operation of the computer.

Terminals and Boots

Secondary ignition cable terminals are designed to make a strong contact with the coil and distributor electrodes. They are, however, subject to corrosion and arcing if not firmly seated and protected from the elements.

Positive-engagement spark plug cable terminals, figure 14-31, lock in place inside the distributor cap and cannot accidentally come loose. They can only be removed when the cap is off the distributor. The terminal electrode is then compressed with pliers and the wire is pushed out of the cap.

The ignition cables must have special connectors, often called spark plug boots, figure 14-32. The boots provide a tight and well-insulated contact between the cable and the spark plug.

SPARK PLUGS

Spark plugs allow the high-voltage secondary current to arc across a small air gap. The three basic parts of a spark plug, figure 14-33, are:

- A ceramic core, or insulator, that insulates the center electrode and acts as a heat conductor
- Two electrodes, one insulated in the core and the other grounded on the shell
- A metal shell that holds the insulator and electrodes in a gas-tight assembly and has threads to hold the plug in the engine.

The metal shell grounds the side electrode against the engine. The other electrode is encased in the ceramic insulator. A spark plug boot and cable are attached to the top of the plug. High-voltage current travels through the center of the plug and arcs from the tip of the insulated electrode to the side electrode and ground. This spark ignites the air-fuel mixture in the combustion chamber to produce power.

Figure 14-28. Many Delco-Remy HEI solid-state ignition systems used on V6 and V8 engines have a coil mounted in the distributor cap.

Figure 14-29. Chrysler four-cylinder distributors have used positive locking terminal electrodes as part of the ignition cable since 1980. (Chrysler)

The burning gases in the engine can corrode and wear the spark plug electrodes. Electrodes are made of metals that resist this attack. Most electrodes are made of high-nickel alloy steel, but platinum and silver alloys are also used.

Spark Plug Firing Action

The arc of current across a spark plug air gap provides two types of discharge:

Figure 14-30. Spark plug cable installation order for Ford V8 EEC systems.

- Capacitive
- Inductive.

When a high-voltage surge is first delivered to the spark plug center electrode, the air-fuel mixture in the air gap cannot conduct an arc. The spark plug acts as

Television-Radio-Suppression (TVRS) Cables: High-resistance, carbon-conductor ignition cables that suppress electromagnetic interference (RFI).

4-CYLINDER

Figure 14-31. Positive locking terminal electrodes are removed by compressing the wire clips with pliers and removing the wire from the cap.

a capacitor, with the center electrode storing a negative charge and the grounded side electrode storing a positive charge. The air gap between the electrodes acts as a dielectric insulator. This is the opposite of the normal negative-ground polarity, and results from the polarity of the coil secondary winding.

Secondary voltage increases, and the charges in the spark plug strengthen until the difference in potential between the electrodes is great enough to **ionize** the spark plug air gap. That is, the air-fuel mixture in the gap is changed from a nonconductor to a conductor by the positive and negative charges of the two electrodes. The dielectric resistance of the air gap breaks down and current travels between the electrodes. The voltage level at this instant is called ionization voltage. The current across the spark plug air gap at the instant of ionization is the capacitive portion of the spark. It flows from negative to positive and uses the energy stored in the plug itself when the plug was acting as a capacitor, before ionization. This is the portion of the spark that starts the combustion process within the engine.

The ionization voltage level is usually less than the total voltage produced in the coil secondary winding. The remainder of the secondary voltage (voltage not needed to force ionization) is dissipated as current across the spark plug air gap. This is the inductive portion of the spark discharge, which causes the visible flash or arc at the plug. It contributes nothing to the combustion of the air-fuel mixture, but is the cause of electrical interference and severe electrode erosion. High-resistance cables and spark plugs suppress this inductive portion of the spark discharge and reduce wear.

SPARK PLUG CONSTRUCTION
Spark Plug Design Features

Spark plugs are made in a variety of sizes and types to fit different engines. The most important differences among plugs are:

Figure 14-32. Ignition cables, terminals, and boots work together to carry the high-voltage secondary current.

Figure 14-33. A cutaway view of the spark plug.

- Reach
- Heat range
- Thread and seat
- Air gap.

These are illustrated in figure 14-34.

Reach
The **reach** of a spark plug is the length of the shell from the seat to the bottom of the shell, including both threaded and unthreaded portions. If an incorrect plug is installed and the reach is too short, the electrode will be in a pocket and the spark will not ignite the air-fuel mixture very well, figure 14-35.

If the spark plug reach is too long, the exposed plug threads could get hot enough to ignite the air-fuel mixture at the wrong time. It may be difficult to remove the plug due to carbon deposits on the plug threads. Engine damage can also result from interference between moving parts and the exposed plug threads.

Heat range

The **heat range** of a spark plug determines its ability to dissipate heat from the firing end. The length of the lower insulator and conductivity of the center electrode are design features that primarily control the rate of heat transfer, figure 14-36. A "cold" spark plug has a short insulator tip that provides a short path for heat to travel, and permits the heat to rapidly dissipate to maintain a lower firing tip temperature. A "hot" spark plug has a long insulator tip that creates a longer path for heat to travel. This slower heat transfer maintains a higher firing tip temperature.

Engine manufacturers choose a spark plug with the appropriate heat range required for the normal or expected service for which the engine was designed.

Proper heat range is an extremely important factor because the firing end of the spark plug must run hot enough to burn away fouling deposits at idle, but must also remain cool enough at highway speeds to avoid preignition. It is also an important factor in the amount of emissions an engine will produce.

Current spark plug designations use an alphanumeric system that identifies, among other factors, the heat range of a particular plug. Spark plug

Ionize: To break up molecules into two or more oppositely charged ions. The air gap between the spark plug electrodes is ionized when the air-fuel mixture is changed from a non-conductor to a conductor.

Reach: The length of the spark plug shell from the seat to the bottom of the shell.

Heat Range: The measure of a spark plug's ability to dissipate heat from its firing end.

■ Making Tracks

You often read instructions to inspect ignition parts for carbon tracks. Although you may have heard about or seen carbon tracks, have you ever thought about what they are and what causes them?

Carbon tracks are deposits or defects on distributor rotors, caps, spark plugs, and cables that create a short-circuit path to ground for secondary high voltage. They also cause crossfiring, in which the high voltage jumps from the distributor rotor to the wrong terminal in the cap.

The problems caused by carbon tracks are all pretty similar, but the causes for these defects are rather complex. A distributor cap or rotor may develop a hairline crack because of rough handling, a manufacturing defect, or some other problem. Under certain conditions, moisture collects in the crack and creates a lower-resistance path for high voltage. High-voltage arcing to ground in a distributor ionizes molecules and forms air-conductive deposits along its path. If any dirt or grease is in the short-circuit path, the combination of high voltage and its accompanying current causes carbon deposits to form around the crack. Thus, a carbon track develops.

Carbon tracks also form without a crack in a cap or rotor. High voltage ionizes air and oil molecules in the distributor and causes deposits to form. The deposits have high resistance, but if they are the least bit conductive, secondary voltage can arc to them. Over a period of time, the deposits build up and create a short circuit.

Outside a distributor, similar carbon tracks form on spark plug insulators and ignition cables due to grease deposits and weak points in damaged cable insulation.

Carbon tracks inside a distributor cap are often tricky to diagnose. Sometimes an engine runs

smoothly at idle but misfires at high speed. As the distributor advance mechanisms operate, the rotor moves farther away from the cap terminals as the coil discharges. The high-voltage current must cross an increasing air gap. If a nearby carbon track provides lower resistance, the voltage will jump to ground and the engine misfires.

A typical carbon track has about the same, or a little less, resistance as a TVRS ignition cable. That is quite conductive enough to cause a misfire or a no-start problem. The accompanying photo shows a classic set of carbon tracks inside a distributor cap.

Figure 14-34. The design features of a spark plug.

Figure 14-35. Spark plug reach.

Figure 14-36. Spark plug heat range.

manufacturers are gradually redesigning and redesignating their plugs. For example, a typical AC-Delco spark plug carries the alphanumeric designation R45LTS6; the new all-numeric code for a similar AC spark plug of the same length and gap is 41-600. This makes it more difficult for those who attempt to correct driveability problems by installing a hotter or colder spark plug than the manufacturer specifies. Eventually, it no longer will be possible for vehicle owners to affect emissions by their choice of spark plugs.

Thread and seat

Most automotive spark plugs are made with one of two thread diameters: 14 or 18 millimeters, figure 14-37. All 18-mm plugs have tapered seats that match similar tapered seats in the cylinder head. The taper seals the plug to the engine without the use of a gasket. The 14-mm plugs are made either with a flat seat that requires a gasket or with a tapered seat that does not. The gasket-type, 14-mm plugs are still quite common, but the 14-mm tapered-seat plugs are now used in most late-model engines. A third thread size is 10 millimeters; 10-mm spark plugs are generally used on motorcycles, but some automotive engines also use them; specifically, Jaguar's V12 uses them as well.

The steel shell of a spark plug is hex-shaped so a wrench fits it. The 14-mm, tapered-seat plugs have shells with a 5/8-inch hex; 14-mm gasketed and 18-mm tapered-seat plugs have shells with a 13/16-inch hex. A 14-mm gasket plug with a 5/8-inch hex is used for special applications, such as a deep recessed with a small diameter opening.

Air gap

The correct spark plug air gap is important to engine performance and plug life. A gap that is too narrow causes a rough idle and a change in the exhaust emissions. A gap that is too wide requires higher voltage to jump it; if the required voltage is greater than the available ignition voltage, misfiring results.

Special-Purpose Spark Plugs

Specifications for all spark plugs include the design characteristics just described. In addition, many plugs have other special features to fit particular requirements.

Resistor-type spark plugs

This type of plug contains a resistor in the center electrode, figure 14-38. The resistor generally has a value

Figure 14-37. Spark plug thread and seat types.

Figure 14-38. A resistor-type spark plug.

of 7,500 to 15,000 ohms and is used to reduce RFI. **Resistor-type spark plugs** can be used in place of nonresistor plugs of the same size, heat range, and gap without affecting engine performance.

Extended-tip spark plugs

Sometimes called an **extended-core spark plug**, this design uses a center electrode and insulator that extend farther into the combustion chamber, figure 14-39. The extended-tip operates hotter under slow-speed driving conditions to burn off combustion deposits and cooler at high speed to prevent spark plug overheating.

Wide-gap spark plugs

The electronic ignition systems on some late-model engines require spark plug gaps in the 0.045- to 0.080-inch (1.0- to 2.0-mm) range. Plugs for such systems are made with a wider gap than other plugs. This wide gap is indicated in the plug part number. Do not try to open the gap of a narrow-gap plug to create the wide gap required by such ignitions.

■ Spark Plug Design

Many people have tried to redesign the spark plug. Not all of the "new" designs have worked out. For example, a plug manufactured before World War I had an insulated handle at the top. By pulling this handle up, an auxiliary gap was opened, presumably to create a hotter spark and stop oil fouling. A window in the side of the plug showed whether the gap was open or closed.

Another "revolutionary" type of plug had a screw connector that allowed the inner core assembly to be removed and cleaned quickly.

Still another design had threads and electrodes at each end of the plug. The plug could be removed, the terminal cap installed on the other end, and then reinstalled upside down. All of the photos were provided by Champion Spark Plug Company.

Resistor-Type Spark Plug: A plug that has a resistor in the center electrode to reduce the inductive portion of the spark discharge.

Extended-Core Spark Plug: The insulator core and the electrodes in this type of spark plug extend farther into the combustion chamber than they do on other types. Also called power tip.

STANDARD CORE **EXTENDED CORE**

Figure 14-39. A comparison of a standard and an extended-core spark plug.

Copper-core spark plugs

Many plug manufacturers are making plugs with a copper segment inside the center electrode. The copper provides faster heat transfer from the electrode to the insulator and then to the cylinder head and engine coolant. Copper-core plugs are also extended-tip plugs. This combination results in a more stable heat range over a greater range of engine temperatures and greater resistance to fouling and misfire.

Platinum-tip spark plugs

Platinum-tip plugs are used in some late-model engines to increase firing efficiency. The platinum center electrode increases electrical conductivity which helps prevent misfiring with lean mixtures and high temperatures. Since platinum is very resistant to corrosion and wear from combustion chamber gases and heat, recommended plug life is twice that of other plugs.

Long-reach, short-thread spark plugs

Some late-model GM engines, Ford four-cylinder engines, and Ford 5.0-liter V8 engines use 14-mm, tapered-seat plugs with a 3/4-inch reach but which have threads only for a little over half of their length, figure 14-40. The plug part number includes a suffix that indicates the special thread design, although a fully threaded plug can be substituted if necessary.

Advanced combustion igniters

This extended-tip, copper-core, platinum-tipped spark plug was introduced by GM in 1991. It combines all the attributes of the individual plug designs described earlier and uses a nickel-plated shell for corrosion protection. This combination delivers a plug life in excess of 100,000 miles (160,000 km). No

Figure 14-40. A long-reach, short-thread spark plug.

longer called a spark plug, the GM advanced combustion igniter (ACI) has a smooth ceramic insulator with no cooling ribs. The insulator is coated with a baked-on boot release compound that prevents the spark plug wire boot from sticking and causing wire damage during removal.

IGNITION POLARITY

If the ignition coil is correctly connected, figure 14-41, voltage is delivered to the spark plug so the center electrode is negatively charged and the grounded electrode is positively charged. Electrons move from the hotter center electrode to the cooler side electrode at a relatively lower voltage. This is called **negative polarity**. If the coil is incorrectly connected, figure 14-42, electrons are forced to move from the cooler side electrode to the hotter center electrode. This is called **positive polarity**, or reverse polarity. Figure 14-43 shows how much more voltage is required to fire a spark plug with positive polarity than one with negative polarity.

Figure 14-41. Negative, or ground, ignition polarity.

Figure 14-42. Reverse, or positive, ignition polarity.

SUMMARY

The ignition secondary circuit generates the high voltage and distributes it to the engine to ignite the combustion charge. This circuit contains the coil secondary winding, the distributor cap and rotor, the ignition cables, and the spark plugs.

The ignition coil produces the high voltage necessary to ionize the spark plug gap through electromagnetic induction. Low-voltage current in the primary

Figure 14-43. More voltage is required to fire a spark plug that has reverse polarity. (Prestolite)

winding induces high voltage in the secondary winding. A coil must be installed with the same primary polarity as the battery to maintain proper secondary polarity at the spark plugs.

Available voltage is the amount of voltage the coil is capable of producing. Required voltage is the voltage necessary to ionize and fire the spark plugs under any given operating condition. Voltage reserve is the difference between available voltage and required voltage. A well-tuned ignition system should have a 60-percent voltage reserve.

The spark plugs allow the high voltage to arc across an air gap and ignite the air-fuel mixture in the combustion chamber. Important design features of a spark plug are its reach, heat range, thread and seat size, and the air gap. Other special features of spark plugs are the use of resistors, extended tips, wide gaps, and copper cores. For efficient spark plug firing, ignition polarity must be established so that the center electrode of the plug is negative and the ground electrode is positive.

Negative Polarity: A correct polarity of the ignition coil connections. Coil voltage is delivered to the spark plugs so that the center electrode (tip) of the plug is negatively charged and the grounded electrode (cylinder head) is positively charged. Also called ground polarity.

Positive Polarity: An incorrect polarity of the ignition coil connections. Coil voltage is delivered to the spark plug so that the center electrode (tip) of the plug is positively charged and the grounded electrode (cylinder head) is negatively charged. Also called reverse polarity.

Review Questions

Choose the single most correct answer.
Compare your answers with the correct answers on Page 468.

1. Which of the following is used as insulation to protect the windings of coils?
   a. Steel
   b. Wood
   c. Iron
   d. Plastic

2. Which of the following statements is true about ignition coils?
   a. Easily repaired
   b. Adjustments made by setscrews
   c. Requires periodic adjustment
   d. Can be replaced

3. When the coil terminals are properly connected to the battery, the grounded end of the secondary circuit is electrically:
   a. Positive
   b. Negative
   c. Neutral
   d. Ionized

4. A loss of one volt in the primary circuit may decrease available secondary voltage by.
   a. 10 volts
   b. 100 volts
   c. 1,000 volts
   d. 10,000 volts

5. Firing voltage is usually about _____ as high as spark voltage.
   a. One-fourth
   b. One-half
   c. Four times
   d. Two times

6. The voltage delivered by the coil is:
   a. Its full voltage capacity under all operating conditions
   b. Approximately half of its full voltage capacity at all times
   c. Only the voltage necessary to fire the plugs under any given operating condition
   d. Its full voltage capacity only while starting

7. The voltage reserve is the:
   a. Voltage required from the coil to fire a plug
   b. Maximum secondary voltage capacity of the coil
   c. Primary circuit voltage at the battery side of the ballast resistor
   d. Difference between the required voltage and the available voltage of the secondary circuit

8. A well-tuned ignition system should have a voltage reserve of about _____ of available voltage, under most operating conditions.
   a. 30 percent
   b. 60 percent
   c. 100 percent
   d. 150 percent

9. Bakelite is a synthetic material used in distributors because of its good:
   a. Permeability
   b. Conductance
   c. Insulation
   d. Capacitance

10. Which of the following are basic parts of a spark plug?
    a. Plastic core
    b. Paper insulator
    c. Fiberglass shell
    d. Two electrodes

11. Which of the following is NOT an important design feature among types of spark plugs?
    a. Reach
    b. Heat range
    c. Polarity
    d. Air gap

12. In the illustration below, the dimension arrows indicate the:

    a. Heat range
    b. Resistor portion of the electrode
    c. Extended core length
    d. Reach

13. All spark plugs have:
    a. A resistor
    b. An extended core
    c. A ceramic insulator
    d. A series gap

15

Ignition Timing and Spark Advance Control

Chapter Twelve covered ignition intervals and how the ignition must be synchronized with crankshaft rotation and cylinder firing order. The initial ignition timing is set for the best engine operation at a specific engine speed, usually at or near slow-idle speed. When engine speed changes, ignition timing must also change.

This chapter covers how ignition timing changes as engine speed and load change and how timing changes are made. This chapter also covers some centrifugal and vacuum advance units and the emission control systems used to modify the vacuum advance operation. With the latest generation of electronic ignition systems, the computer has taken the place of mechanical and vacuum advance devices. Early electronic spark timing controls are discussed at the end of the chapter.

REVIEWING BASIC TIMING AND BURN TIME

Engine speed and load changes require the ignition timing to advance or to retard. The burn time of an air-fuel mixture is about three milliseconds. Maximum combustion pressure should occur with the piston, connecting rod, and crankshaft in position to produce the most power. At low engine speeds, relatively little spark advance is required. However, as engine speed increases, the process of combustion must be started earlier to provide enough burn time.

Combustion is not an instantaneous explosion, but rather a process of controlled burning. The spark duration or **burn time** of an oscilloscope trace indicates the amount of resistance and efficiency of the spark voltage. Burn time is strictly a function of time, not of piston position. Ignition must occur early enough so maximum combustion pressure develops when the piston is starting down on its power stroke. Combustion should be finished about 10 degrees after top dead center (TDC). If combustion occurs to early, while the piston is still approaching TDC, then the rising piston is opposed by the combustion pressure. If ignition occurs too late after TDC, then the combustion force is considerably reduced as the piston is already going down on the power stroke. In both cases, the combustion process does not develop full power.

Burn time does not vary as the engine speed and load changes. As the engine speed increases, the piston and the crankshaft rotate more degrees in a set amount of time. Burn time is relatively constant due to the built-in design of the ignition and the fuel system. Therefore, ignition timing must vary (advance and retard) with engine speed so the most efficient combustion process occurs at the correct piston position.

SPARK ADVANCE

Ignition must be synchronized with the piston and crankshaft position at the end of the compression stroke and the start of the power stroke. The point where ignition occurs is called ignition timing or spark timing, and is measured in terms of crankshaft degrees before top dead center (BTDC) or after top dead center (ATDC). The ignition timing of an engine at idle speed is called basic or **initial timing.** On engines equipped with non-adjustable computerized ignition systems, this setting is called **base timing.** As engine speed increases, the ignition must occur sooner before top dead center, and this is called **spark advance** or advanced timing. As engine speed decreases from high rpm, timing must retard from its advanced position.

Some engines, because of strict emission standards, require timing to be set ATDC. But, most often, ignition timing at idle is set at a few degrees BTDC. For example, an engine requiring a 2 millisecond burn time with peak combustion efficiency ending at 10 degrees ATDC rotates the crankshaft 12 degrees in 2 milliseconds. Therefore, ignition must occur 2 degrees BTDC for proper burn time to occur. At 1200 rpm the crankshaft rotates 20 degrees in 2 milliseconds. Therefore, ignition must occur at 10 degrees BTDC for combustion to end at 10 degrees ATDC. At 2400 rpm, the crankshaft rotates 40 degrees in 2 milliseconds. Therefore ignition must occur at 30 degrees BTDC for combustion to occur at 10 degrees ATDC. Ignition must occur well in advance of the piston position to compensate for the faster rotation of the crankshaft and piston. It is also important to remember spark propagation (complete combustion) always finishes at 10 degrees ATDC.

Prior to computer control of ignition timing, two basic factors were used—engine speed and engine load. All changes were related to only these two factors:

- Timing must increase, or advance, as engine speed increases, and it must decrease, or retard, as engine speed decreases.
- Timing must decrease, or retard, as load

increases, and it must increase, or advance, as load decreases.

Optimum ignition timing under any given combination of these basic factors results in maximum cylinder pressure. In turn, this delivers maximum power with a minimum of exhaust emissions and the best possible fuel economy.

When ignition takes place too early, the combustion pressure slows down the piston. If timing is too far advanced, the increased combustion pressure causes engine knock. When ignition takes place too late, the piston is too far down on its power stroke to benefit from the combustion pressure, resulting in a power loss.

Before the introduction of computer-controlled timing, most automotive distributors had two spark advance mechanisms reacting to engine operating changes and altering ignition timing:

- The centrifugal advance changed ignition timing to match engine speed by altering the position of the distributor cam or trigger wheel on the distributor shaft.
- The vacuum advance changed ignition timing to match engine load by altering the position of the breaker points or the magnetic pickup coil (electronic sensor).

These changes in position altered the time, relative to crankshaft position, at which the primary circuit opened.

Compression has a direct affect on the secondary firing voltages, which affect the spark advance. As the piston approaches TDC, compression peaks and more molecules of air compress into a smaller space. When spark advance occurs, the spark appears before the base timing specification. If the spark occurred at 30 BTDC, the kilovolt (KV) demand would decrease because of less compression at an earlier stage.

Centrifugal Advance — Speed

The **centrifugal advance**, or **mechanical advance**, mechanism in the older non-computer-controlled distributor consists of two weights connected to the distributor driveshaft by two springs, figure 15-1. The distributor cam, or electronic trigger wheel, and the distributor rotor are mounted on another shaft. The second shaft fits over the driveshaft like a sleeve. Driveshaft motion is transmitted to the second shaft through the centrifugal advance weights. When the weights move, the relative position of the driveshaft and the second shaft changes.

CAM

DISTRIBUTOR DRIVESHAFT

CENTRIFUGAL ADVANCE WEIGHTS

Figure 15-1. The centrifugal advance weights transfer the rotation of the distributor driveshaft to the cam, or trigger wheel, and the rotor.

CAM   WEIGHTS   SPARK ADVANCE

SPRINGS

Figure 15-2. When the centrifugal advance weights move, the position of the cam, or trigger wheel, and the rotor changes.

As engine speed increases, distributor shaft rotation speed increases. The advance weights move outward because of **centrifugal force.** The outward movement of the weights shifts the second shaft and the cam or the trigger wheel, figure 15-2. The primary circuit opens earlier in the compression stroke, and the spark occurs earlier.

Each advance weight is connected to the distributor driveshaft by a control spring. These springs are selected to allow the correct amount of weight movement and ignition advance for a particular engine.

At low engine speeds, spring force holds the weights in so initial timing is maintained. As engine speed increases, centrifugal force overcomes spring force and the weights move outward. The advance is not a large, rapid change, but rather a slow, gradual shift. Figure 15-3 shows a typical centrifugal advance curve. The advance curve can change by adjusting the tension of the control springs. Remember, centrifugal advance responds to engine speed.

In most distributors, the centrifugal advance mechanism is mounted below the cam and breaker points, figure 15-1, or below the trigger wheel and pickup coil. Delco-Remy V6 and V8 distributors, as well as

some distributors made in Japan, have the advance mechanism above the cam or trigger wheel, just below the rotor, figure 15-4.

Vacuum Advance — Load

The **vacuum advance** mechanism allows efficient engine performance within a range of air-fuel ratios. These ratios are important since limits exist as to how rich or how lean they can be and still remain fully

Initial Timing: The ignition timing of an engine at idle speed.

Base Timing: The ignition timing of an engine at idle speed with a non-adjustable computerized ignition system.

Spark Advance: Moving ignition timing earlier for maximum efficiency as engine requirements change.

Centrifugal (Mechanical) Advance: A method of advancing the ignition spark using weights in the distributor that react to centrifugal force.

Centrifugal Force: The natural tendency of objects, when rotated, to move away from the center of rotation.

Vacuum Advance: The use of engine vacuum to advance ignition spark timing by moving the distributor breaker plate.

Figure 15-3. A typical distributor advance curve.

Figure 15-4. Delco-Remy V6 and V8 distributors have the centrifugal advance mechanism above the cam and rotor, or above the pickup coil and trigger wheel.

combustible. The **air-fuel ratio** for maximum engine efficiency ranges from 8 to 1 to 18.5 to 1 by weight, figure 15-5.

These ratios are generally stated as eight parts of air combined with one part of gasoline (8 to 1), which is the richest mixture an engine can tolerate and still fire regularly. A ratio of 18.5 parts of air mixed with one part of gasoline (18.5 to 1) is the leanest mixture an engine can tolerate without misfiring.

An average air-fuel ratio is about 14.7 to 1. This mixture takes about three milliseconds to burn. A lean mixture (one with more air and less fuel) requires more time to burn. The ignition timing must be advanced to provide maximum combustion pressure at the correct piston position. A rich mixture (one with more fuel and less air) burns more quickly and emits more exhaust pollutants. Ignition timing must be retarded for complete combustion and emission control.

Engine Vacuum

The reciprocating engine can be considered an air pump. As a piston moves downward, air pressure in the cylinder decreases. Air from the atmosphere rushes in to fill the void.

The fuel delivery system uses this air movement to carry fuel to the cylinders. On older engines, the air must travel through a carburetor, figure 15-6, to reach the cylinders. Under several operating conditions, air movement caused by the downstroke of a piston is not great enough to draw fuel into the cylinder. The carburetor forces the air to flow through a restriction called a **venturi.** This increases the speed of the air-flow and creates a low-pressure (vacuum) area. The

Figure 15-5. Air-fuel ratio limits for a 4-stroke gasoline engine. (Chevrolet)

vacuum draws fuel into the airflow and the resulting air-fuel mixture enters the cylinder combustion chambers. The air-fuel ratio changes as the **vacuum** in the carburetor changes.

The ignition timing must be changed as the air-fuel ratio changes so the mixture has enough time to burn. The vacuum advance mechanism is connected to a small hole or port in the carburetor, figure 15-7, just above the throttle plate. This is called **ported vacuum.** When vacuum exists at the port, timing is advanced. When no vacuum exists at the port, the timing remains

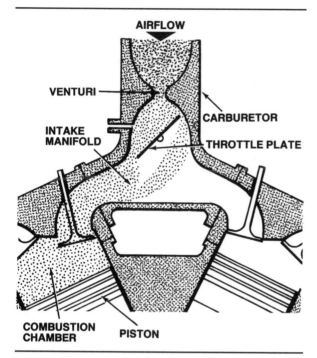

Figure 15-6. Air flows through the carburetor and intake manifold to reach the combustion chamber.

at a basic setting or is effected only by the centrifugal advance. The vacuum advance mechanism is explained in more detail later. The following paragraphs explain the relationship between carburetor vacuum and the need for advanced timing.

The driver of a carburetor-equipped automobile controls engine load and carburetor vacuum through the action of the throttle plate, which is a variable restriction in the carburetor airflow. When the engine is at idle, figure 15-8, the throttle plate is almost closed. Very little air flows through the carburetor to mix with the fuel. With this rich air-fuel mixture, no spark advance is necessary. High vacuum exists in the intake manifold, but there is no vacuum at the port because it is above the closed throttle plate. There is no vacuum-controlled spark advance with a closed throttle. A large amount of vacuum *below* the throttle plate exists because of the small amount of air entering the engine. This is called **manifold vacuum.**

When the throttle plate is partially open, figure 15-9, more air flows through the carburetor. The air-fuel mixture becomes lean and requires an advanced spark. Since the port is now exposed to vacuum, ignition timing advances.

At medium cruising speeds, the engine operates with a partly open throttle and an air-fuel ratio of

Figure 15-7. The vacuum advance assembly is connected to a port in the carburetor.

■ Air Pressure High and Low

You can think of an internal combustion engine as a big air pump. As the pistons move up and down in the cylinders, they pump in air and pump out the burned exhaust. They do this by creating a difference in air pressure. The air outside an engine has weight and exerts pressure. So does the air inside an engine.

As a piston moves down on an intake stroke with the intake valve open, it creates a larger area inside the cylinder for the air to fill. This lowers the air pressure inside the engine. Because the pressure inside the engine is lower than the pressure outside, air flows in through the carburetor to try to fill the low-pressure area and equalize the pressure.

We call the low pressure in the engine "vacuum". You can think of vacuum as pulling air into the engine, but it is really the higher pressure on the outside that forces air into the low-pressure area inside. The difference in pressure between two areas is called a "pressure differential". The pressure differential principle has many applications in an automobile engine.

Air-Fuel Ratio: The ratio of air to gasoline by weight in the air-fuel mixture drawn into an engine.

Venturi: A restriction in an airflow, such as in a carburetor, that increases the airflow speed and creates a reduction in pressure.

Vacuum: A pressure less than atmospheric pressure.

Ported Vacuum: Vacuum immediately above the throttle plate in a carburetor.

Manifold Vacuum: Low pressure in an engine's intake manifold, below the carburetor throttle.

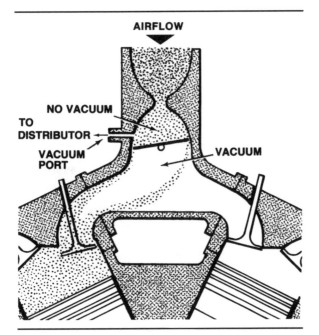

Figure 15-8. When the throttle is closed during idle or deceleration, there is no vacuum at the port.

Figure 15-9. When the throttle is partially open, the port is exposed to manifold vacuum.

approximately 15:1. Airflow velocity is high, and the vacuum signal at the carburetor port is strong enough to provide vacuum advance for this relatively lean air-fuel mixture.

A lean mixture is not the only factor affecting ignition timing requirements. During part-throttle operation, the cylinders are only partially filled with the air-fuel mixture. Because there is less to compress, the compression pressure is low. A less highly compressed mixture takes longer to burn.

At wide-open throttle, figure 15-10, the power circuit in the carburetor provides a richer mixture than at part-throttle cruising. Also, the cylinders are more completely filled because airflow volume increases. These factors cause a faster burn requiring the ignition timing to retard or decrease slightly for proper efficiency. Manifold vacuum and ported vacuum drop at wide-open throttle and become approximately equal. Vacuum may drop to as little as 2.5 inches of mercury (8.4 kPa), and typically 3.5 inches (11.8 kPa) of vacuum are required to operate a vacuum advance mechanism.

Vacuum advance also decreases when the throttle is opened quickly from idle or a part-throttle position. This occurs because airflow velocity lags behind throttle opening. This reduced vacuum does not draw enough fuel through the main metering circuit of the carburetor. This causes the accelerator pump to supply extra fuel. This momentarily rich mixture does not

need as much spark advance for complete combustion. Because ported vacuum is low when the throttle is opened quickly, the vacuum advance decreases or retards to meet the needs of the momentarily rich mixture. Remember, vacuum advance responds to engine load.

Vacuum advance mechanism

The vacuum advance mechanism at the distributor, figure 15-7, consists of the:

- Movable breaker plate on which the points or electronic pickup coil are mounted
- Vacuum assembly, a housing with a flexible diaphragm and a spring
- Actuating link connecting the vacuum diaphragm to the breaker plate
- Tubing to connect the vacuum unit to the vacuum source.

When the **diaphragm** is pulled toward a vacuum, it pulls the actuating link, figure 15-11. This rotates the breaker plate to change the position of the point rubbing block in relation to the cam. Ignition timing increases or advances. In an electronic system, the pickup is shifted relative to the trigger wheel to advance timing.

Some older vacuum advance units can be adjusted by changing spring tension against the diaphragm.

Some distributors used by Ford and Volkswagen

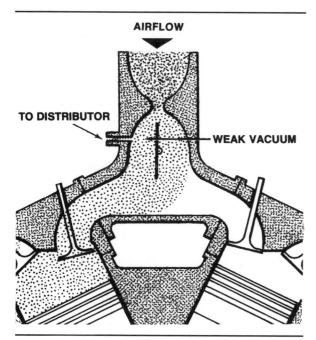

Figure 15-10. When the throttle is fully open, the vacuum at the port is too weak to create any vacuum advance.

Figure 15-11. Vacuum at the carburetor port causes the position of the breaker plate to shift.

had a dual-diaphragm vacuum unit. This design was also common on Japanese vehicles. A dual-diaphragm vacuum advance unit retards timing during certain engine operating conditions. In these systems, figure 15-12, one diaphragm acts as described above to advance ignition timing. The second diaphragm is exposed to intake manifold vacuum (between the throttle plate and the combustion chamber), which is high during idle and closed-throttle deceleration. This vacuum acts upon the second diaphragm to shift the breaker plate in the retard direction.

The dual-diaphragm was used to retard ignition prior to the oxidation catalytic converter. Retarded timing was used to reduce HC and CO. After the catalytic converter appeared the dual diaphragm could be used for two purposes. The secondary diaphragm is used to control ignition timing when the engine is cold. Control of the vacuum was through a thermal vacuum valve (TVV).

The ignition timing is retarded to warm up the engine and exhaust gases faster. The increased exhaust temperature improves the efficiency of the catalytic converter and secondary air injection. The timing can be advanced for better driveability, while the engine relies on the air injection and converter to control HC and CO. Although advancing the timing

tends to increase NOx, this is not a problem on a cold engine because NOx forms at high temperatures.

Both systems are used. It is important that the correct vacuum hose is connected to the correct port on the dual-diaphragm unit. The amount of advance for each diaphragm is different.

Total Ignition Advance

The two types of advance mechanisms previously described work on different parts of the distributor to advance timing. Therefore, their effects are cumulative: The **total ignition advance** is the sum of the centrifugal advance and the vacuum advance, *plus* the initial ignition timing. This formula determines actual ignition timing under all conditions. Figure 15-13 shows the advance curves of a typical ignition system.

Diaphragm: A thin flexible wall, separating two cavities, such as the diaphragm in a vacuum advance unit.

Total Ignition Advance: The sum of centrifugal advance, vacuum advance, and initial timing; expressed in crankshaft degrees.

Figure 15-12. Operation of a typical dual-diaphragm vacuum advance assembly. (Ford)

SPARK-TIMING EMISSION CONTROLS

Spark-timing control systems were introduced in the 1960s to reduce exhaust emissions. Certain types of pollutants are produced under specific engine operating conditions. Spark timing control systems help reduce **hydrocarbons (HC)** and, to some extent, **oxides of nitrogen (NOx)** emissions. Retarded timing reduces combustion temperature to help reduce NOx formation. At the same time, higher temperatures are created toward the end of combustion. This results in higher exhaust temperatures, which reduce the amount of HC in the exhaust.

These systems were designed primarily to delay vacuum advance at low and intermediate speeds and allow it during high-speed cruising. The most common types of control systems are:

- Distributor solenoids
- Vacuum delay valves
- Speed- and transmission-controlled timing.

Figure 15-13. This typical advance curve shows the total advance is the total of vacuum plus centrifugal advances.

Many spark-timing control systems were discontinued when catalytic converters were introduced in 1975. Converters reduce HC and CO emissions, and exhaust gas recirculation (EGR) provides more effective control of NOx emissions.

■ Does a Vacuum Pull Air In?

As you study automotive service, you see many applications for vacuum devices. The engine is a large air pump and the source of vacuum used to operate a variety of accessories. Vacuum diaphragms control ignition advance, EGR operation, carburetor chokes and power valves, air-conditioning doors and vents, heater water valves, concealed headlamp mechanisms, power brake boosters, cruise control servos, and many other devices.

It's very easy — and practical for day-to-day use — to think of vacuum as an independent force. But it isn't. Vacuum is simply air pressure that is lower than atmospheric pressure. Vacuum doesn't actually pull air in; air pressure pushes. We talk about connecting a diaphragm to a "vacuum source," but what actually moves the diaphragm? Low pressure (vacuum) on one side allows higher atmospheric pressure on the other to move the diaphragm.

Similarly, we often talk about finding and fixing a "vacuum leak." That concept works just fine for on-the-job troubleshooting, but ask yourself, "Can vacuum actually *leak*?" Not really. What you are actually fixing is an air leak. An unwanted opening allows air to leak *into* the low-pressure area that we call a vacuum.

Emission standards continued to tighten during the mid-1970s. During this period, fuel mileage requirements also became important. Meeting the challenge of more stringent emission standards and better fuel economy required far more accurate ignition system performance than mechanical devices could deliver. Centrifugal and vacuum advance mechanisms simply could not respond quickly enough to changes in engine operating conditions to provide the necessary accuracy, so major manufacturers turned to computer-controlled ignition systems.

ELECTRONICALLY CONTROLLED TIMING

In a computer-controlled ignition system, an electronic control module receives signals from various system sensors. These signals may include information on coolant temperature, atmospheric pressure and temperature, throttle position and rate of change of position, and crankshaft position. The central processing unit in the powertrain control module (PCM) is programmed to interpret this information and calculate the proper ignition timing for each individual spark.

Early systems worked with the existing solid-state ignition system. Some changes were made to these ignition systems because they no longer had to control spark timing, but many components remained the same.

Some early electronically controlled ignition systems also have vacuum advance mechanisms to change timing in response to engine load. The vacuum advance plate is attached to the pick-up coil or photo optic sensor plate. High vacuum at light load rotates the "baseplate" opposite to distributor rotation. This causes the sensor or pick-up coil to align with the trigger wheel slightly sooner, thereby advancing the ignition timing.

Two types of early computer-controlled ignition systems were used by domestic manufacturers. In one type, rotation of the distributor shaft sends a crankshaft position signal to the control module. The other type receives crankshaft position information from a sensor mounted near the crankshaft. The sensor reacts to a trigger attached to the crankshaft itself.

Signals taken directly from the crankshaft are more accurate than those taken from the distributor shaft. The gears or chain driving the camshaft and the gears driving the distributor shaft are manufactured within tolerances. Although the actual measurements are small, these tolerances can combine to cause a significant difference between crankshaft position and ignition timing.

■ Starting the Locomobile

If you owned a 1927 or 1928 Locomobile, you had to know how to adjust the spark advance lever when you started the engine. The spark lever allowed you to advance or retard spark timing for all conditions. Here are the owner's manual instructions for positioning the lever when starting your Locomobile:

1. Be sure gear shift lever is in neutral position and the hand brake is applied.
2. Retard the spark lever, which is at right center of steering wheel, about one-half way down from the full advance position.
3. The throttle control lever is to the left of center of the steering wheel. Move lever up an inch or more from the closed position.
4. Turn ignition switch arm to the "on" position.
5. Pull choke button as far as it will go, then place the right foot on the starting switch button and press down. On pushing down on the starting switch button, the starter gear will engage itself in the teeth of the flywheel and the motor will start to turn over. As soon as the motor starts, release the starting button and push the choke button part-way in. As the motor warms up a little, push the choke button all the way in. Do this as soon as possible to avoid excessive choking, as any excess gasoline thrown into the cylinders will pass by the rings into the oil in the crankcase, thus diluting and partly destroying its lubricating value.
6. Advance spark by pushing lever up as far as it will go and bring the throttle lever toward the closed position to slow the motor down.

Hydrocarbon: A chemical compound of hydrogen and carbon. A major pollutant from an internal combustion engine. Gasoline itself is a hydrocarbon compound.

Oxides of Nitrogen: Chemical compounds of nitrogen and oxygen. Major pollutants produced by an internal combustion engine which combine with hydrocarbons to produce smog.

Early systems used by Chrysler, GM, and Ford were called:

- Chrysler Electronic Lean-Burn (ELB)
- GM Microprocessed Sensing and Automatic Regulation (MISAR)
- Ford Electronic Engine Control (EEC).

These early electronic timing control systems were partial-function engine control systems. They controlled ignition timing only. They were not fully integrated systems that controlled fuel metering with feedback signals from various engine sensors. Nevertheless, these early systems were the ancestors of the late-model engine control systems that are detailed in Chapter Seventeen.

The electronic timing-regulation function of all three systems is similar, but the electronics are fundamentally different. The Lean-Burn system uses an analog computer, while MISAR and EEC use digital microprocessors.

The practical difference between analog and digital electronics in this kind of application is that a digital computer can instantly alter timing from one degree to 65 degrees. An analog computer must calculate through all the points on a theoretical curve to make such an adjustment. Since an electronic spark advance adjustment takes only a few milliseconds, this fact is not really significant to the driver or service technician. However, a digital system is more flexible and more economical to build than an analog system.

■ Vacuum Measurement

When working with vacuum devices on late-model vehicles, you will encounter several different units of measurement used to gauge vacuum. The auto industry customarily has measured air pressure in pounds per square inch (psi) or kilopascals (kPa), and vacuum in inches of mercury (in-Hg) or millimeters of mercury (mm-Hg). This is confusing right away, because we're using two different kinds of units to measure essentially the same thing — air pressure. The reason we use both is based on scientific tradition.

Air pressure and vacuum are measured in a laboratory with a device called a manometer. This is a U-shaped glass tube with each end connected to different pressure sources. One end can be opened to the atmosphere, and the other can be connected to a pump or another source of low pressure. The tube is filled with liquid that moves up and down the two columns formed by the two legs of the U. Using two columns joined in a "U" eliminates the effects of gravity and the weight of the liquid. Displacement caused by changes in pressure is read in marks graduated on the columns.

Laboratory manometers ordinarily are filled with mercury because it is stable and flows freely when exposed to pressure differentials. When low pressure on one side drops enough to move the mercury column one inch, vacuum (low pressure) equals 1 in-Hg. When atmospheric pressure is removed completely from one side of the manometer, the mercury column

is displaced 29.291 inches at 32°F (0°C). Thus, 29.921 inches of mercury equals one atmosphere of negative pressure, or 14.696 psi. When the manometer column is graduated in millimeters instead of inches, one atmosphere of displacement equals 760 mm-Hg.

Another unit you will encounter is the "bar". A bar equals one unit of atmospheric pressure. This is barometric pressure, and that is where we get the term "bar". A standard bar equals one kilogram of force applied to one square centimeter. This equals 750 mm-Hg or 14.5 psi. These values are close to the customary atmospheric pressure values of 14.7 psi and 760 mm Hg. All standard pressures are calculated at 32°F (0°C) because pressure drops as temperature rises, and vice versa.

In automobile service, we work with psi and kPa to measure positive pressure. The most common units of vacuum measurement are in-Hg, mm-Hg, and bar. Here are some handy conversion factors you can use to switch from one unit to another:

1 psi = 6.895 kPa
1 psi = 2.036 in-Hg = 51.72 mm-Hg
1 in-Hg = 0.4912 psi
1 bar = 14.5 psi = 29.9 in. Hg = 760 mm-Hg

All these equivalent measurements are at a standard temperature of 32°F (0°C), but the conversions are quite close enough for car service work.

SUMMARY

Ignition distributors have used two devices to advance or retard spark timing in response to changing conditions of engine operation. The two primary factors that determine spark advance are engine speed and load. The centrifugal advance alters the position of the distributor cam or trigger wheel on the distributor shaft and changes engine timing as engine speed changes. The vacuum advance alters the position of the breaker points or magnetic pickup coil with respect to the cam or trigger wheel. It changes timing as engine load changes. Many different spark timing emission control systems have been used. Regardless of their design and operation, these systems all regulate distributor vacuum advance. Vacuum advance is generally allowed only at cold startup, during high gear operation, or if the engine overheats. Development of the exhaust gas recirculation (EGR) systems and catalytic converters, and the expanded use of air injection systems, eliminated the use of transmission-controlled spark and speed-controlled spark systems. Electronic spark timing systems appeared because more accurate control was required. They regulate ignition timing for the best combination of emission control, fuel economy, and driveability. Early electronic spark timing systems were the forerunners of late-model, fully integrated electronic engine control systems that we will study in Chapter Seventeen.

Review Questions

Choose the single most correct answer.
Compare your answers with the correct answers on Page 468.

1. Burn time remains constant but as engine speed increases, engine rotation varies in relationship to burn time measured by
   a. Dwell
   b. Voltage
   c. Degrees
   d. Time

2. Secondary firing voltages are reduced at advanced ignition timing settings because:
   a. Ignition primary voltage is reduced
   b. Air/fuel ratio is reduced
   c. Computer alters the compression ratio
   d. Air-fuel mixture is less compressed

3. Distributors commonly have two automatic spark advance mechanisms, which are:
   a. Initial advance and mechanical advance
   b. Initial advance and dynamic advance
   c. Dynamic advance and static advance
   d. Centrifugal advance and vacuum advance

4. Centrifugal advance responds directly to engine:
   a. Load
   b. Horsepower
   c. Speed
   d. Torque

5. The purpose of the venturi in the carburetor is to:
   a. Mix the air and fuel mixture
   b. Speed the airflow and create a low-pressure area
   c. Carry fuel to mix with air
   d. Raise the air pressure sufficiently

6. Vacuum advance responds directly to engine:
   a. Load
   b. Horsepower
   c. Speed
   d. Torque

7. The richest air-fuel ratio at which an engine can operate efficiently is:
   a. 4:1
   b. 6:1
   c. 8:1
   d. 16:1

8. At medium cruising speeds, the engine operates with a partially open throttle and an air-fuel ratio of about:
   a. 8:1
   b. 12:1
   c. 15:1
   d. 18.5:1

9. Which of the following is NOT a component of the vacuum advance mechanism?
   a. Movable breaker plate
   b. Throttle valve
   c. Diaphragm
   d. Actuating link

10. Automotive emission control equipment is designed to reduce exhaust emissions of which pollutants?
    a. Hydrogens
    b. Nitrogens
    c. Carbons
    d. Hydrocarbons

11. Almost all spark timing emission control systems work with the vacuum advance units to:
    a. Increase vacuum advance at low and intermediate vehicle speeds
    b. Cut off vacuum advance during high-speed acceleration
    c. Retard the timing during high-speed deceleration
    d. Cut off vacuum advance at low and intermediate vehicle speeds

12. The dual-diaphragm vacuum unit provides:
    a. Twice as much vacuum advance as a single-diaphragm unit
    b. Faster vacuum retard than does a single-diaphragm unit
    c. Both vacuum advance and vacuum retard
    d. Neither vacuum advance nor vacuum retard

16

Solid-State Electronic Ignition Systems

During the 1960s, solid-state ignition systems were used only on a few high-performance engines. Solid-state systems were not standard on domestic automobiles until the early 1970s; foreign manufacturers followed a few years later with their versions. Within less than one decade, solid-state systems completely replaced breaker-point ignitions. Breaker-point and electronic ignition systems do the same thing, except that a breaker-point system switches the primary circuit mechanically while an electronic system does this by means of a transistor. The major driving force behind the rapid transition to electronic systems was their ability to help meet stringent emission-control standards.

Although solid-state systems are more expensive to produce than breaker-point systems, their advantages greatly outweigh the drawback of increased cost:

- Greater available voltage, especially at high engine speeds
- Reliable system performance at all engine speeds
- Potential for more responsive and variable advance curves
- Decreased maintenance
- Engine operation and exhaust emissions are more accurately controlled by solid-state circuitry.

BASIC SOLID-STATE SYSTEMS

Solid-state systems differ from breaker-point systems in the devices used to control primary circuit current. Breaker-point systems use mechanical breaker points to open and close the primary circuit. The points are operated by a cam on the distributor shaft. Most solid-state systems use an electronic switch in the form of a sealed module to control primary circuit current. This module contains one or more transistors, integrated circuits, or other solid-state control components. A triggering device in the distributor functions with the control module.

As we learned in Chapter Thirteen, this triggering device is usually a magnetic pulse generator or a Hall-effect switch. Solid-state ignitions also can be triggered by a set of breaker points, as will be explained later in this chapter.

Solid-state ignitions can be classified in terms of their primary circuit operation. There are two general types:

- Inductive discharge
- Capacitive discharge.

The difference between these types lies in how they use primary current to produce a high-voltage secondary current.

Inductive Discharge

The inductive discharge system uses battery voltage to create current through the coil primary winding. When a signal is sent by the triggering device, primary current is interrupted. This sudden *decrease* in primary current collapses the coil's magnetic field and induces a high-voltage surge in the secondary circuit.

In an electronic ignition, primary current passes through the ignition control **module**, not through the distributor breaker points. Most modules contain one or more large power transistors that switch the primary current. A power or a switching transistor can transmit as much as 10 amperes of current—far more than a set of breaker points can. The power transistor is controlled by a driver transistor that receives voltage signals from the distributor signal generator.

Original equipment solid-state ignitions use inductive discharge to provide about 30,000 volts of available voltage and sustain a spark for about 1.8 milliseconds (a millisecond is one-thousandth of a second, or 0.001 second).

Breaker points

Inductive discharge is used in both electronic and breaker point systems; only the device used to open the circuit differs. The earliest transistorized ignitions used breaker points as a mechanical switch to control voltage applied to a power transistor. Battery voltage causes current to travel through the control module to the breaker points, figure 16-1. This current biases the transistor base so that current can also travel through the coil primary winding. When the points open, current stops. The power transistor no longer conducts current to the coil primary winding, and an ignition spark is produced.

While full primary current travels through the transistor, the points carry less than one ampere of current. This minimized the pitting and burning problems encountered with breaker points. However, they were still subject to mechanical wear and bounced at high speeds. Electronic ignitions replaced the points with a solid-state signal generator containing no moving parts.

Figure 16-1. A typical breaker-point-triggered electronic ignition system.

Capacitive Discharge

The capacitive discharge system uses battery voltage to charge a large capacitor in the control module. The capacitor charging time, while the module is on, corresponds to dwell in the inductive discharge system. Current travels to the storage capacitor instead of to the coil during this period. The module charging circuit uses a transformer to increase the voltage in the capacitor to as high as 400 volts. The module also contains a silicon-controlled rectifier (SCR), which functions as an open switch to prevent the capacitor from discharging as it charges, figure 16-2.

When the triggering device signals the module, the SCR closes the capacitor discharge circuit, figure 16-3, allowing the capacitor to discharge through the coil primary winding. This sudden *increase* in primary current expands the coil's magnetic field and induces a high-voltage surge in the secondary circuit.

In an inductive discharge system, primary current travels through the coil during the dwell period and then is turned off to induce the high secondary voltage. In a capacitive discharge system, the primary voltage and current charge the capacitor. The capacitor is then switched on, to induce the high secondary voltage. CD ignition systems charge the capacitor and discharge the coil faster than inductive discharge systems. The CD ignition system can produce a higher (more kilovolts) and faster firing voltage. The CD ignition system also starts better in cold and wet weather and improves high-speed performance.

Figure 16-2. When the SCR blocks current, the capacitor is charged. (Bosch)

Figure 16-3. When a signal voltage makes the SCR conduct current, the capacitor discharges through the coil primary winding. (Bosch)

Capacitive discharge systems are available in the automotive aftermarket, but no major domestic manufacturer installs them as original equipment. A few imported cars such as Audi and Mercedes-Benz have used these ignition systems in the past. They provide a greater available voltage than inductive discharge systems, but can sustain a spark for only about 200 microseconds. The spark is much more intense than that produced by an inductive discharge system and fires plugs that are in very poor condition. Under certain engine operating conditions, however, a longer spark time is required or the air-fuel mixture does not burn completely.

Figure 16-4 shows the time and voltage characteristics of a breaker-point ignition system, a capacitive discharge system, and a solid-state inductive system.

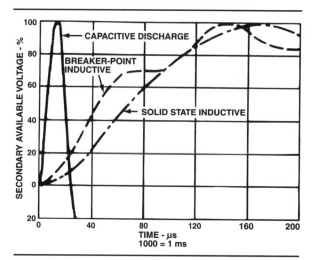

Figure 16-4. A major difference in ignition system performance is the time at which maximum secondary voltage is developed. (Bosch)

CONTROL MODULES AND PRIMARY CIRCUITRY

Although various manufacturers use different circuitry within their ignition system control modules, the basic function of all modules is the same. The following paragraphs explain how these electronic ignition modules work. Because the electronic components within the module are delicate and complex, the modules are sealed during assembly. If any individual component within the module fails, the entire unit is replaced rather than repaired. Our explanation of module circuitry and operation is brief, because the technician never needs to service module components.

Inductive-Discharge System

Figure 16-5 is a simple inductive-discharge ignition control module circuit. The various triggering devices that can be used in this system all produce a pulsating voltage signal. In the illustration, the signal comes from the pickup coil of a magnetic pulse generator. This pulsating voltage is applied to the control module's switching transistor and signals the module to turn primary current off.

Module: A self-contained, sealed unit that houses the solid-state circuits that control certain electrical or mechanical functions.

Figure 16-5. A simplified inductive discharge control module. (Chevrolet)

Primary Circuit Control

Technology has advanced over the years, producing a variety of primary ignition circuit triggering devices and increasingly sophisticated ignition modules to switch primary ignition current on and off. Although different in design, all triggering devices function to control the timing of primary current switching. There are several types of electronic ignition systems in use today. They are loosely defined by the triggering devices they use. Photoelectric ignitions use a light emitting diode (LED) and a photoelectric cell to produce a dc square wave as the triggering signal. Magnetic pulse generators use an induction coil and a rotating reluctor to produce an ac signal that is sent to the ignition module. Hall-effect ignitions produce a dc triggering signal through use of a Hall-effect device and a rotating shutter wheel.

Primary circuit control is made possible in an electronic ignition by the ability of transistors to control a high current in response to a very small current. The transistor, as covered in Chapter Three, is like a solid-state relay. It has a base of one type of semiconductor material and an emitter and collector of the other type of material, figure 16-6. A certain amount of current must travel through the base-to-emitter or base-to-collector circuit before any current travels through the emitter-to-collector circuit. In this way, a small

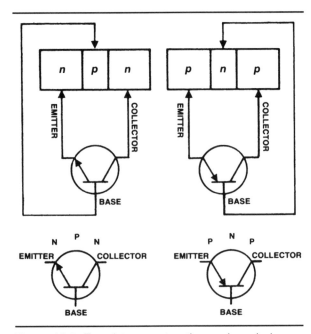

Figure 16-6. Transistor construction and symbols.

amount of current controls the travel of a large amount of current.

Ignition Transistor Operation

The module can be either in the dwell mode (when primary current travels) or in the firing mode (when primary current stops), figure 16-5.

During the dwell mode, TR1 and TR3 are conducting. TR2 is nonconducting. A signal from the pickup coil turns TR3 off, charges C1, and turns TR4 on. This results in the firing mode, as reduced primary current travel causes a high-voltage secondary surge.

TR4 stays on until C1 is discharged. When C1 is discharged, TR3 turns on and the module returns to the dwell mode. At higher engine speeds, C1 is charged less and less. This results in reduced firing times and longer dwell periods. C2 is a capacitor in the distributor for radio noise suppression.

Actual electronic ignition modules take various forms, but all work on these principles. Some modules are large units, figure 16-7. Others are relatively small integrated circuit (IC) units mounted in the distributor, figure 16-8.

TRIGGERING DEVICES AND IGNITION TIMING

All triggering devices produce a pulsating voltage that signals the generation of an ignition spark. Three

Figure 16-7. Typical external ignition modules from Ford.

Figure 16-8. The ignition module may be installed inside the distributor, as in the HEI system.

triggering devices are commonly used in a solid-state ignition:

- Magnetic pulse generator
- Hall-effect switch
- Optical (light detection) signal generator.

Magnetic Pulse Generator

A simple and very common ignition electronic switching device is the magnetic pulse generator system. Most manufacturers use the rotation of the distributor shaft to time the voltage pulses. The **magnetic pulse generator** is installed in the distributor housing where the breaker points used to be. The pulse generator, figure 16-9, consists of a trigger wheel (reluctor) and a pickup coil. The pickup coil consists of an iron core wrapped with fine wire, in a coil at one end and attached to a permanent magnet at the other end. The center of the coil is called the pole piece.

Magnetic Pulse Generator: A signal-generating switch that creates a voltage pulse as magnetic flux changes around a pickup coil.

Figure 16-9. This Delco-Remy magnetic pulse generator has a pole piece for each cylinder (arrows), but operates in the same manner as single pole piece units.

Figure 16-10. The pick-up coil generates an ac voltage signal as the trigger wheel moves close to the pole piece.

The trigger wheel is made of steel with a low reluctance that cannot be permanently magnetized. Therefore, it provides a low-resistance path for magnetic flux lines. The trigger wheel usually has as many teeth as the engine has cylinders.

As the trigger wheel rotates, its teeth come near the pole piece. Flux lines from the pole piece concentrate in the low-reluctance trigger wheel, increasing the magnetic field strength and inducing a positive voltage signal in the pickup coil. When the teeth and the pole piece are aligned, the magnetic lines of force from the permanent magnet are concentrated and the voltage drops to zero. The point at which the trigger

wheel tooth aligns with the pole piece is the ignition timing point for one cylinder and corresponds to the point where breaker points open in the older breaker points systems. The reluctor continues and passes the pole piece but now the voltage induced is negative, creating an alternating current (ac) voltage signal, figure 16-10. The pickup coil is connected to the electronic control module, which senses this ac voltage, converts the signal to a direct current (dc) voltage and switches the primary current on and off. Each time a trigger wheel tooth comes near the pole piece, the control module is signaled to switch off the primary current. Solid-state circuitry in the module determines when the primary current will be turned on again.

Figure 16-11. The ac sine wave can be observed while the engine is cranking (GM HEI ignition system shown).

We have used the terms "trigger wheel" and "pick-up coil" in describing the magnetic pulse generator. Various manufacturers have different names for these components. Other terms for the pick-up coil are pole piece, magnetic pick-up, or stator. The trigger wheel is often called the reluctor, armature, timer core or signal rotor.

The magnetic pulse generator produces an ac voltage signal that can be observed using a lab scope. Although the ignition module converts the ac signal to dc, the ignition system can be disabled (coil wire grounded) and the ac voltage signal can be observed. Typically, most magnetic pulse generator ignition systems produce between 4 to 5 volts peak-to-peak

voltage signals while cranking, figure 16-11. This GM high energy ignition (HEI) system displays approximately 2.24 volts positive peak, which gives approximately 4.48 volts peak-to-peak volts. An ac voltage that fluctuates less than 1 volt peak-to-peak causes stalling and driveability problems. Severe HEI problems such as weak or cracked pick-up coil magnets, incorrect air gaps, and so on. may cause engine performance problems during all ranges. Figure 16-12 shows an ac voltage signal from a defective HEI system with a peak-to-peak voltage value of only 776 millivolts (mV). With the engine running and a dual trace lab scope installed, the converted ac to dc voltage signal can be observed in

Δ: 776mV

2 V   M   10ms

Figure 16-12. A defective pick-up coil will often display a low peak-to-peak voltage range – this example shows a limited 776 millivolt range peak-to-peak value (GM HEI ignition system shown).

conjunction with the firing voltages. Figure 16-13 shows that the rising edge of the converted ac signal (D/REF) lines up directly with the primary switching on point, while the falling edge lines up directly with the primary switching off point where the coil fires the plug. This perfect alignment of voltage signals happens only at idle because as the rpm increases, the HEI internal dwell circuit varies the turn-on signal sooner to compensate for advance timing changes. The HEI magnetic pulse generator can be observed at many different stages to decisively conclude the working condition of the ignition system.

As mentioned in Chapter Fifteen, GM, Ford, and other manufacturers have used magnetic pulse generators that rely on engine crankshaft rotation (instead of distributor shaft rotation) to produce a signal voltage. In the 1977 GM microprocessed sensing and automatic regulation (MISAR) system, the pickup coil, pole piece, and permanent magnet are mounted near a disc mounted on the end of the crankshaft, figure 16-14. Teeth on the disc act like the teeth on a distributor-mounted trigger wheel to induce a single

voltage in the pickup coil. In the 1978 MISAR system, the pickup coil and trigger wheel were installed in the distributor.

Ford's EEC-I system takes its crankshaft rotation signal from the flywheel end of the crankshaft. As we will see later in this chapter, Buick's C3-I system uses a Hall-effect crankshaft sensor.

Hall-Effect Switch

The Hall-effect switch is the most recent switching technology in electronic ignitions. A **Hall-effect switch** also uses a stationary sensor and rotating trigger wheel (shutter), figure 16-15. Unlike the magnetic pulse generator, the Hall-effect switch requires a small input voltage in order to generate an output or signal voltage. **Hall effect** is the ability to generate a voltage signal in semiconductor material (gallium arsenate crystal) by passing current through it in one direction and applying a magnetic field to it at a right angle to its surface. If the input current is held steady and magnetic field fluctuates, an output voltage is produced that changes in proportion to field strength, figure 16-16.

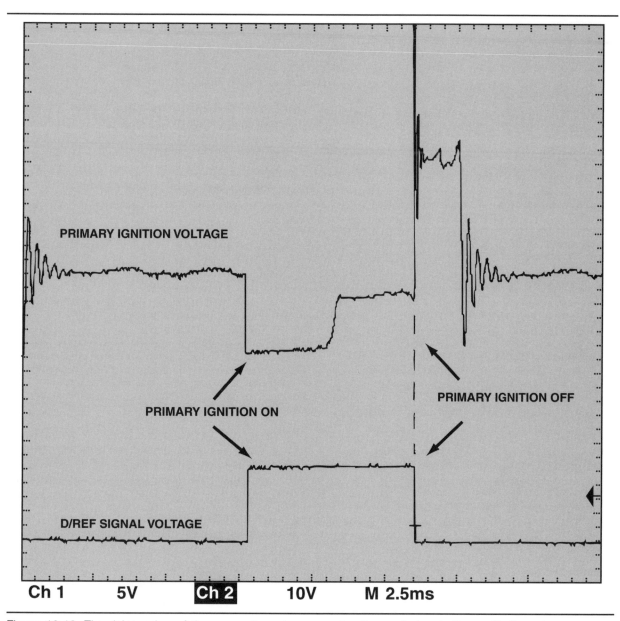

PRIMARY IGNITION VOLTAGE

PRIMARY IGNITION ON

PRIMARY IGNITION OFF

D/REF SIGNAL VOLTAGE

| Ch 1 | 5V | Ch 2 | 10V | M 2.5ms |

Figure 16-13. The rising edge of the magnetic pulse generator (turn-on) signal aligns with the primary current switching (turn-on) signal.

Most Hall-effect switches in distributors have a Hall element or device, a permanent magnet, and a rotating ring of metal blades (shutters) similar to a trigger wheel (another method uses a stationary sensor with a rotating magnet). Some blades are designed to hang down, typically found in Bosch and Chrysler systems, while others may be on a separate ring on the distributor shaft, typically found in GM and Ford Hall-effect distributors. When the shutter blade enters the gap between the magnet and the Hall element, it creates a magnetic shunt that changes the field strength through the Hall element, thereby creating an analog voltage signal. The Hall element contains a logic gate that converts the analog signal into a digital voltage signal, which triggers the switching transistor. The transistor transmits a digital square waveform at varying frequency to the ignition module or onboard computer.

Hall-Effect Switch: A signal-generating switch that develops a transverse voltage across a current-carrying semiconductor when subjected to a magnetic field.

Figure 16-14. This magnetic pulse generator reacts to the movement of a disc mounted on the crankshaft. (Oldsmobile)

Figure 16-15. A Hall-effect triggering device.

A Hall-effect switch is a complex electronic circuit. Figure 16-17 shows the relationship of the Hall-effect switch and ignition operation. An important point to understand is that ignition occurs when the Hall shutter *leaves* the gap between the Hall semiconductor element and the magnet. Also, notice that primary current "builds up" during the coil saturation period after primary voltage is switched on. This waveform is referred to as **current ramping.** The pattern will often display itself in the shape of a ramp.

Hall-effect switches require extra connections for input voltage; however, their output voltage does not depend on the speed of the rotating trigger wheel. Magnetic pulse generators depend upon induction to

U_H = **HALL VOLTAGE**
B = **MAGNETIC FIELD (FLUX DENSITY)**
I_V = **CONSTANT SUPPLY CURRENT**
A_1, A_2 = **HALL LAYER**

Figure 16-16. The magnetic field generates a voltage signal as the electrons from the supply current move (generate) toward the Hall negative layer.

create the signal voltage. The strength of an induced voltage varies if the magnetic lines move more quickly or slowly. The Hall effect is not induction, and the speed of the magnetic lines has no effect on the signal voltage. This constant-strength signal voltage offers more reliable ignition system performance throughout a wide range of engine speeds. Moreover, a Hall-effect switch provides a uniform digital voltage pulse regardless of rotation speed. This makes a Hall-effect switch ideal as a digital engine sensor for fuel injection timing and other functions besides ignition control. Therefore, its main advantage over the magnetic pulse generators is that it can generate a full-strength output voltage signal even at slow cranking speeds. This allows precise switching signals to the ignition primary circuit and accurate adjustments of the air-fuel mixture.

Lab scopes easily display the digital voltage signals from the Hall-effect switching devices. Hall-effect switches typically display square waves with a rising edge (leading edge), a flat top, the falling edge, and finally the flat bottom, figure 16-18. Square wave amplitude is the distance between the high level and the low level. Square waves with time durations on the top and bottom portion of the waveform are symmetrical. Most electronic ignition Hall-effect switching devices are 3-wire; ground (−), operating voltage (reference), and output signal. The output signal is the

Vane	Magnetic field (B)	Hall voltage	Generator Output Signal Voltage To Module	Ignition Module Transistors
Not in the air gap	Permeates the Hall layer	Maximum	Minimum	Switched off
Enters the air gap	Is deflected away from the Hall layer	Drops	Increases abruptly	Switched on
In the air gap	Very weak at the Hall layer	Minimum	Maximum	Switched on (energy storage)
Leaves the air gap	Permeates the Hall layer	Increases	Drops abruptly	Switched off (ignition point)

Figure 16-17. The relationship of Hall-effect signal voltage and ignition discharge. (Bosch)

Figure 16-18. A typical Hall-effect square wave output signal.

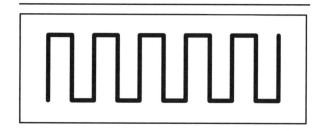

Figure 16-19. A schematic of a typical 3-wire Hall-effect sensor.

Figure 16-20. A schematic of a typical 4-wire Hall-effect sensor.

systems are equipped with 4-wire Hall-effect switching devices that are designed with two output signal voltage wires: signal HI and signal LO, figure 16-20. Signal HI is used for the lab scope hookup and the display of the square waveform for the circuit. Signal LO is a bias voltage signal of approximately 0.7 volt for the signal processing circuit.

Chrysler 2.2L and 2.5L engines equipped with the TBI system use 3-wire Hall-effect switching devices.

Current Ramping: The shape of the current waveform on a primary ignition circuit as coil saturation builds and then releases.

square wave digital signal that has been processed by the signal processing circuit and converted from ac to a dc digital signal, figure 16-19. Some ignition

Figure 16-21. The converted ac sine wave can be observed on the GY wire as a square wave switching (toggle) signal.

Early Chrysler ignition systems require two separate signals from the distributor, one for the sync signal for TDC number 1 and the other for the primary ignition turn-on signal. Later systems required only the primary ignition turn-on signal from the Hall-effect sensor, figure 16-21. This uniform 5-volt square wave toggles from the GY wire.

Optical (Light Detection) Signal Generator

The **optical signal generator,** often called a photo optical signal generator, uses the principle of light beam interruption to generate voltage signals. Many optical signal distributors contain a pair of light-emitting diodes (LED) and photo diodes installed

OPTICAL SENSOR AND
INTEGRATED CIRCUIT

TIMING DISK

HIGH-DATA-RATE SLOTS

LOW-DATA-RATE SLOTS

PROTECTIVE INNER COVER

Figure 16-22. Components of the Chrysler optical distributor. The slotted timing disc interrupts the light beam in the optical sensor to produce on-off signals used to control fuel injection, idle speed, and ignition timing. (Chrysler)

opposite each other, figure 16-22. A disc containing two sets of chemically etched slots is installed between the LEDs and photo diodes. Driven by the camshaft, the disc acts as a timing member and revolves at half engine speed. As each slot aligns with the light beam, an alternating voltage is created in each photo diode. A hybrid integrated circuit converts the alternating voltage into on-off pulses sent to the engine controller. Because the sensors are self-contained within the distributor, a protective inner cover is used to separate them from the high-tension distribution part of the distributor housing. The cover prevents actuation errors caused by electrical noise.

The high-data-rate slots, or outer set, are spaced at intervals of two degrees of crankshaft rotation, figure 16-23. This row of slots is used for timing engine

Optical Signal Generator: A switching device that uses the principle of light-beam interruption to generate voltage signals.

Figure 16-23. The high-data-rate slots coincide with ignition timing while the low-data-rate slots coincide with the TDC mark for each cylinder (3.0L V6 engine shown).

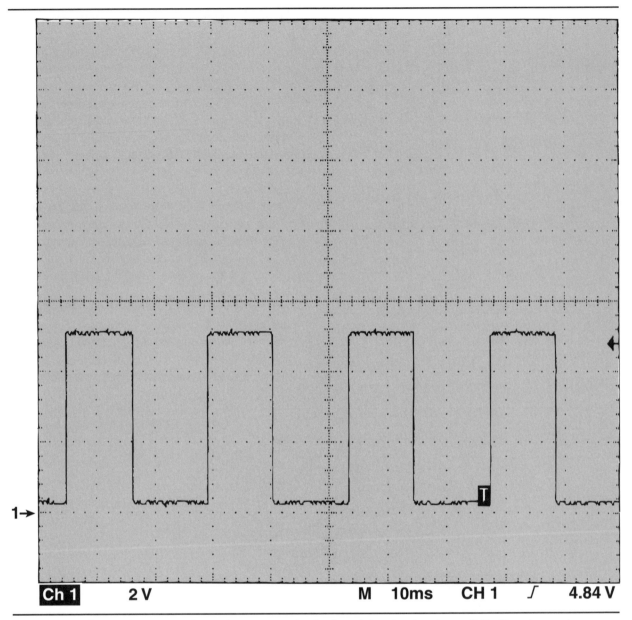

Figure 16-24. Typical known good waveform pattern for the low-data-rate signal on a 3.0L Chrysler engine.

speeds up to 1,200 rpm. Certain slots in this set are missing, indicating the crankshaft position of Number 1 cylinder to the engine controller. For sequential fuel injection (SFI), the low-data-rate slots, or inner set, consists of six slots correlated to the crankshaft top-dead-center angle of each cylinder. The engine computer uses this signal for triggering the fuel injectors and for ignition timing at speeds above 1,200 rpm. In this way, the optical signal generator acts both as the crankshaft position sensor and TDC sensor, as well as a triggering device.

Until Chrysler introduced one on some 1987 models, no domestic manufacturer had used an optical

signal generator as original equipment. The Isuzu I-TEK and other Japanese ignition systems, however, rely on optical signal generators, which operate in essentially the same way as the Chrysler version.

The optical signal generator provides a more reliable signal voltage at much lower engine speeds than a magnetic pulse unit. However, periodic LED and photocell cleaning may be required. Several aftermarket, or add-on, ignition systems have been produced using this switching device.

Optical ignition systems create distinct voltage signals that can be observed using a lab scope. The Chrysler optical ignition system on the 3.0L engine

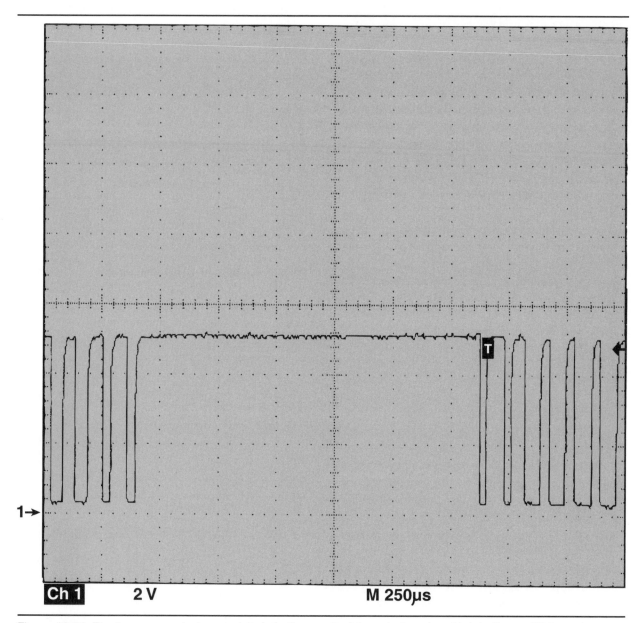

Figure 16-25. The long pause between signals is the result of the missing slot which indicates TDC number 1 to the computer (high-data-rate signal on a 3.0L Chrysler engine).

uses two photocells and two LEDs with solid state circuitry to create two 5.0-volt signals. The inner sets of slots (low data) signal TDC for each cylinder while the outer slots (high data) monitor every 2 degrees of crankshaft rotation. Observing the waveforms, if the low-data-rate or the high-data-rate signals fail on the high section, then the LED is most likely malfunctioning. If the signals fail on the low section, then the computer is most likely not delivering the 5.0-volt reference signal. If the low-data signal is lost, the engine will not start. If the high-data signal is lost, the engine will run, but only on default settings from the computer, figures 16-24 and 16-25.

ELECTRONIC IGNITION DWELL, TIMING, AND ADVANCE

Dwell is the period of time when the breaker points are closed and current is traveling in the primary winding of the coil. Although solid-state ignitions require a dwell period for the same purpose, it is controlled by a timing or current sensing circuit in the ignition module, rather than by a signal from the distributor.

The initial timing adjustment for most basic electronic ignitions is similar to that for breaker-point ignition systems. Timing is set by rotating the distributor housing with the engine idling at normal operating temperature.

The first generation of electronic ignitions used the same centrifugal and vacuum advance mechanisms to advance timing as those used by breaker-point ignitions. As manufacturers began to equip their engines with computer-controlled systems in the late 1970s, however, timing advance became a function of the computer. Since a computer can receive, process, and send information very rapidly, it can change ignition timing with far more efficiency and accuracy than any mechanical device.

The distributor in an electronic ignition used with a computer engine control system contains a triggering device for basic timing. Because the computer actually controls ignition timing, however, the distributor's primary function is to distribute secondary voltage.

Fixed and Variable Dwell

Although dwell is not adjustable in electronic distributors, electronic ignitions may have one of two kinds of dwell control:

• Fixed dwell
• Variable dwell.

Fixed dwell

A ballast resistor is placed in the primary circuit of a **fixed dwell** electronic ignition to limit current and voltage. Dwell is the length of time the switching transistor sends current to the primary coil windings. It begins once the secondary voltage and current have fallen below predetermined levels. The ballast resistor functions just as it does in a breaker-point system to control primary voltage and current. Dwell, measured in distributor degrees of rotation, remains constant at all engine speeds.

All points systems operate on fixed dwell. As the distributor rotates and the points close, the amount of time they remain closed is determined by the dwell settings. Each time period the points open and close is identical for each cylinder and each rotation, provided the lobes on the distributor shaft are not worn. **Dwell**, measured in distributor degrees of rotation remains constant at all speeds, but the **dwell time** shortens at high speed and lengthens at slow speeds. Remember how the ballast resistor works in the points system. At low speeds, current travels through the circuit for relatively long periods of time. As the current heats the resistor, its resistance increases, dropping the applied

Figure 16-26. Dwell, measured in degrees of distributor rotation, remains relatively constant at all engine speeds in a fixed-dwell system.

voltage at the coil. At higher speeds, the breaker points open more often and current travels for shorter periods of time. As the ballast resistor cools, its resistance drops. Higher voltage is applied to the coil but the shorter current travel duration results in about the same magnetic saturation of the coil. Dwell is fixed, but dwell time varies with engine speed. Because points are a mechanical component and they can be designed only with fixed dwell, ballast resistors protect the primary circuit during engine rpm variations. Figure 16-26, shows the primary circuit oscilloscope pattern of a typical fixed dwell electronic ignition. All fixed dwell systems use a ballast resistor to limit current and voltage. Some early electronic ignition systems also incorporate the fixed dwell system.

Chrysler's original electronic ignition is a good example of a fixed dwell system. The original Ford solid-state ignition (SSI) and Dura-Spark II are other examples of fixed dwell systems with ballast resistors, as are some Bosch and Japanese electronic ignitions.

Variable dwell

Variable dwell ignition systems do not use ballast resistors and the ignition coil and module receive full battery voltage. A module circuit senses primary current to the coil and reduces the current when the magnetic field is saturated. Unlike the fixed dwell system, dwell varies, but the dwell *time* remains relatively constant. Dwell time in variable dwell ignition systems is often referred to as **coil charge time.** In general, variable dwell ignition systems have a higher available voltage capacity, lower primary resistance and a hotter spark to burn leaner air-fuel mixtures designed for low-emissions automobiles. Figure 16-27 shows the primary circuit oscilloscope pattern of a typical variable dwell electronic ignition.

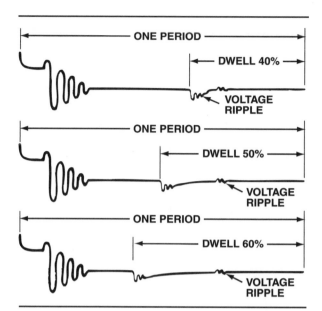

Figure 16-27. The dwell period increases with engine speed in the variable-dwell Delco HEI and some Motorcraft systems.

In order to diagnose primary circuit malfunctions, it is important to understand how the ignition system controls dwell while simutaneously limiting current. The current limiting functions of modern electronic ignitions are accomplished by several different designs. Each design incorporates specialized transistor circuitry that switches to resistor mode after excess current is detected. These sophisticated modules and/or computers are able to set coil charge times and limit current. If the proper coil saturation time (dwell) was achieved, the module trims the dwell to limit current, thereby reducing the amount of electrical energy used by the ignition system. If maximum current was not achieved during the coil saturation time, the module increases the dwell time.

Dual trace digital and analog oscilloscopes are useful tools for diagnosing primary circuit malfunctions. Because the primary circuit operates on relatively small voltages, more accurate analysis of the primary circuit can be achieved over the standard automotive oscilloscopes. Current limiting can be monitored on the scope on all types of ignition systems. The basic rule here is—when viewing voltage on a circuit that is ground controlled, as voltage goes down, current increases, and as voltage goes up, current decreases. A waveform pattern can show the exact point in the dwell when the current limiting device in the ignition module switches on and voltage

increases. Figure 16-28 displays a typical primary ignition firing sequence. Primary current is switched on (step 3) and then the ignition module detects that the coil is saturating (step 4) and limits current travel just before turning off primary circuit voltage (number 5). This portion of the waveform on electronic ignition systems is called the **current limiting hump.** The current limiting hump will appear at different locations for different manufacturers' ignition systems. By learning the typical waveform patterns of properly operating ignition systems, ignition system degradation can be easily monitored. Once the control of the ignition timing has been taken away from the ignition system (distributor vacuum, computer timing disconnects, and so on), the primary turn-off point will be stable and will not vary. At this point, any variation between the cylinders may indicate an engine mechanical failure (worn distributor bushings, distributor drive gears, loose timing chains, and so on).

Technicians frequently use voltage waveform patterns to diagnose problems in modern electronic circuits. In addition to the latest digital oscilloscopes and computer programs, technicians are using current waveform patterns to test modern ignition systems for circuit operation and component performance.

Fixed Dwell: The ignition dwell period begins when the switching device (points or transistor) turns on and remains constant, specified in distributor degrees of rotation, through all speeds.

Dwell: Degrees of distributor rotation when the ignition switching device (points or transistor) is closed and primary current is traveling in the primary winding of the coil.

Dwell Time: The duration or actual time of the dwell period, measured in milliseconds (MS).

Variable Dwell: The ignition dwell period varies in distributor degrees at different engine speeds but remains relatively constant in duration.

Coil Charge Time: Dwell time (duration) in variable dwell ignition systems.

Current Limiting Hump: The portion of the waveform that indicates the exact point in the dwell when the current limiting device switches ON thereby changing voltage levels (increase) and decreasing current.

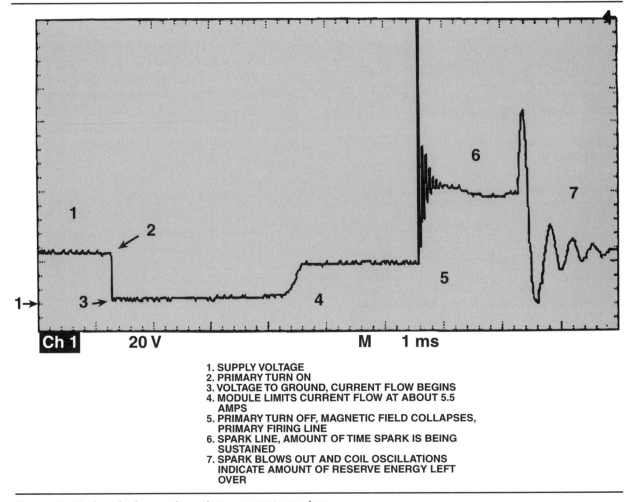

1. SUPPLY VOLTAGE
2. PRIMARY TURN ON
3. VOLTAGE TO GROUND, CURRENT FLOW BEGINS
4. MODULE LIMITS CURRENT FLOW AT ABOUT 5.5 AMPS
5. PRIMARY TURN OFF, MAGNETIC FIELD COLLAPSES, PRIMARY FIRING LINE
6. SPARK LINE, AMOUNT OF TIME SPARK IS BEING SUSTAINED
7. SPARK BLOWS OUT AND COIL OSCILLATIONS INDICATE AMOUNT OF RESERVE ENERGY LEFT OVER

Figure 16-28. A typical operating primary current waveform.

Voltage is electrical "pressure" and current is electrical "volume". When testing modern fuel systems with electrical fuel pumps, the fuel system often exhibits proper fuel pressure but falls short of fuel volume. The fuel pump, under load, cannot supply enough fuel! In electrical systems, voltage specifications will frequently read properly, but once the system is under load, current fluctuations will quickly pinpoint defective circuit and component operations.

The primary current waveform, after it is recorded by a digital storage oscilloscope, will slope upward much like a ramp, figure 16-29. This type of waveform diagnostics is commonly called current ramping. Once the coil primary circuit switches on, the coil charge time or primary charge time slopes upward as current builds. The current ramp will flatten at the top during primary coil saturation. Quickly, the coil primary current is switched off (falling edge) and the dwell period ends. The secondary system fires the

plug (not indicated in the illustration) and the primary current remains off, indicated by a flat bottom line. The coil primary will then be switched back on and the cycle repeats. The sloped current waveforms resemble ramps.

The two most important specifications that must be observed on a typical primary current ramp is the coil charge time, specified in milliseconds, and the amount of current in the circuit at the limiting hump (peak amperage rating). Most electronic distributor ignition systems will limit the current between 6.0 and 6.5 amps. Distributorless ignition systems limit the current slightly higher, between 8.0 and 10 amps, because of the different saturation times of the hot coil (forward polarity) and cold coil (reverse polarity) in the waste spark system. The following list is a general guideline for the coil charge times on most domestic electronic ignition systems.

IGNITION COIL CONTROL

IMAGE				VEHICLE INFORMATION	

H 100mV DC 1:1   **E** 100mV DC 1:1   **HOLD**

CURSOR 1			CURSOR 2
A: 136 mV	⇥ 252 mV ⇤		A: 338 mV
	⇥ 9.20ms ⇤		

a⌠

5ms/DIV

SCOPE

REMOTE

INPUT A	INPUT B	SINGLE SHOT	TRIGGER	RANGE A MOVE A

VEHICLE INFORMATION

TEST_PT.	DI Ignition Power lead
COMMENT:	Contact point Distributor (GM V-8)
YEAR:	1967
MAKE:	Chevrolet
MODEL:	Malibu SS 396
ENGINE:	6.5L
FUELSYS:	carburetor
VIN:	rfjldatacenter

COMMENTS

GM-V-8 Distributor (contact Points)
Current waveform taken at idle.

Note long (by todays standard) coil buildup of 9.20 ms and current peak of 3.88 amperes.

Figure 16-29. Current ramp for the primary ignition on a points distributor.

Ford electronic distributor ignition systems
3.6 milliseconds

GM electronic distributor ignition systems
3.6 milliseconds

GM electronic distributor ignition systems w/OBD II
2.5 milliseconds

GM electronic distributorless ignition systems
2.6 milliseconds

Chrysler electronic distributor ignition systems w/external module
8.6 milliseconds

Chrysler electronic distributor ignition systems w/computer
3.8 milliseconds

Figure 16-29 displays the primary ignition current ramp for a Chevrolet V8 with points ignition. Notice that the coil charge time is 9.20 milliseconds and the peak amperage is only 3.88 amps. Points ignition systems became obsolete because of the long coil charge times and the inability to switch primary currents above 4 amps. Figure 16-30 shows a normally operating TFI ignition on a 1992 Ford Taurus with a coil charge time of 3.6 milliseconds and a current limit at 6.16 amps. Figure 16-31 shows this same ignition system with a defective relay. The coil charge

time is only 3.92 milliseconds while the current limits at 4.88 amps. Low supply voltage to the ignition coil resulted in high resistance and less current.

In general, ignition coils used with variable dwell systems have a higher available voltage capability, lower primary resistance, and a higher turns ratio than the coils used with fixed dwell systems.

All variations of the GM Delco-Remy High Energy Ignition (HEI) are variable dwell systems, as well as Ford Dura-Spark I and thick-film integrated (TFI) ignition systems. Other examples are most Chrysler Hall-effect ignitions, some Bosch, Marelli, and several Japanese electronic ignitions.

Basic Timing and Advance Control

We learned in Chapter Fifteen that ignition takes place at a point just before or just after top dead center is reached during the compression stroke. This time is measured in degrees of crankshaft rotation and is established in distributor-type ignitions by the mechanical coupling between the crankshaft and distributor. Basic or initial ignition timing is usually set at idle speed.

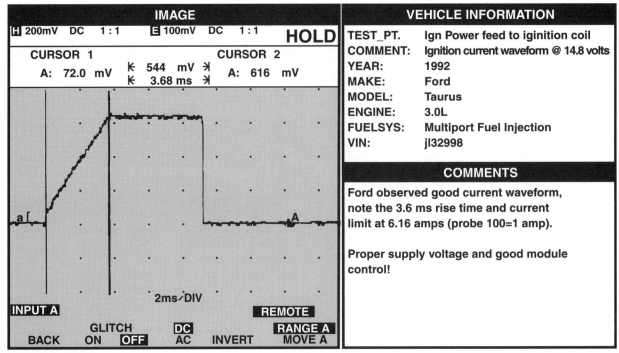

FORD TFI

Figure 16-30. Current ramp for the primary ignition on a Ford distributor ignition (TFI). Coil charge time is 3.6 milliseconds with the current limited at 6.16 amps.

Figure 16-31. Abnormal current ramp for the primary ignition on a Ford TFI ignition system. Coil charge time is 3.92 milliseconds with a 4.88 amps output.

Figure 16-32. As rpm increases, the spark must be advanced to deliver the maximum spark for the best torque. (Ford)

As engine speed increases, however, ignition must take place earlier. This is necessary to ensure that maximum compression pressure from combustion develops as the piston starts downward on its power stoke, figure 16-32. This change in ignition timing is called spark advance and is controlled in basic electronic ignitions (those not integrated with electronic engine controls) by the same mechanical devices used with a breaker-point ignition:

- Centrifugal advance weights
- Vacuum advance diaphragm.

The centrifugal advance mechanism responds to changes in engine speed and moves the position of the trigger wheel relative to the distributor shaft. The vacuum advance mechanism responds to changes in engine load and moves the position of the pickup coil. These changes in position alter the time, relative to crankshaft position, at which the primary circuit is opened.

When electronic ignitions are integrated with electronic control systems, the computer monitors engine speed and load changes, engine temperature, manifold pressure (vacuum), air travel, exhaust oxygen content, and other factors. The computer then changes ignition timing to produce the most efficient combustion. Electronic engine controls are used on late-model vehicles as will be discussed in the next chapter.

ORIGINAL-EQUIPMENT ELECTRONIC DISTRIBUTOR-TYPE IGNITIONS

This section contains brief descriptions of the major distributor-type electronic ignitions used by domestic and foreign manufacturers. All are inductive-discharge systems, but their triggering devices and module circuits vary somewhat from manufacturer to manufacturer.

Because these systems have been under constant development, they have been modified from year to year and model to model. The descriptions given in this section summarize the basic changes resulting from this ongoing development. Whenever an electronic ignition requires service, you should always refer to the manufacturer's shop manual or an appropriate repair manual to determine the exact specifications and whether the system has any unique features you should know about.

Figure 16-33. A basic HEI distributor.

Figure 16-34. The HEI distributor used with some inline and V6 GM engines.

Delco-Remy

High-energy ignition (HEI)

The Delco-Remy High Energy Ignition (HEI) system, figure 16-33, was introduced on some 1974 GM V8 engines and became standard equipment on all GM engines in 1975. The HEI system was developed from an earlier Delco-Remy Unitized ignition used on a limited number of 1972-74 engines. The HEI and Unitized ignitions have all of the ignition components built into the distributor.

The HEI system was the first domestic original-equipment manufacturer (OEM) electronic ignition to use a variable dwell primary circuit and no ballast resistor. The control module lengthens the dwell period as engine rpm increases to maintain uniform primary current and coil saturation throughout all engine speed ranges. The HEI module is installed on

the breaker plate inside the distributor, and the basic ignition module has four terminals: two connected to the primary circuit and two attached to the pickup coil of a magnetic pulse ignition pickup. The back of the HEI module is coated with a silicone dielectric compound before installation.

The HEI pickup looks different from those of other manufacturers, but it operates in the same basic manner. The rotating trigger wheel of the HEI distributor is called the "timer core", while the coil is attached to a fixed ring-shaped magnet called the "pole piece". The pole piece and trigger wheel have as many equally spaced teeth as the engine has cylinders, except on uneven-firing V6 engines, which have three teeth on the trigger wheel and six unevenly spaced teeth on the pole pieces.

The most common early HEI system has an integral (built-in) coil mounted in the distributor cap, figure 16-33. Some four- and six-cylinder engines have HEI systems with a separate coil, figure 16-34, that provides additional distributor clearance on the engine. Both designs operate in the same way and have similar wiring connections. All early HEI systems use 8-mm spark plug cables with silicone insulation to minimize crossfiring caused by the high secondary voltage capability of the HEI coil. Some engines use wide-gap spark plugs to take advantage of the system's high-voltage capability.

In addition to distributing the spark to the appropriate cylinder, the HEI rotor serves as a fuse to protect the module. If an open circuit occurs in the ignition secondary and voltage rises above a certain level, the center of the rotor will burn through and allow the spark to travel to ground rather than arcing through and destroying the module. Early black rotors have a dielectric strength of approximately 70,000 volts; later white ones are designed to ground the secondary circuit at around 100,000 volts.

The newer design rotor may be used in place of the earlier one, but the cap and rotor must be replaced as a matched set. The air gap between the rotor tip and cap electrodes was 0.090 inch (2.29 mm) on the earlier parts, but the later design has an air gap of 0.125 inch (3.18 mm) to better suppress radiofrequency interference (RFI) that could interfere with the engine control computers of the systems discussed in Chapter Seventeen. Caps and rotors from the early and late designs should never be mixed.

In addition to this basic HEI system, GM has used six other HEI versions with electronic engine controls and for certain spark timing requirements. The six systems are HEI with:

- Electronic spark selection (ESS)
- Electronic spark control (ESC)
- Electronic module retard (EMR)
- Electronic spark timing (EST)
- EST and ESC
- EST and a Hall-effect switch.

The HEI system with electronic spark selection (ESS) uses a five-terminal HEI module and was introduced by Cadillac on the Seville in 1978. The system has an electronic decoder that receives inputs from the:

- EGR solenoid that signals engine temperature
- Ignition switch that signals cranking
- The fuel economy switch that signals engine vacuum level.

The decoder uses these signals to determine the appropriate timing alterations. Timing is retarded by a fixed amount during cranking and during cold-engine operation on California models. Timing is advanced, again by a fixed number of degrees, during cruise.

The HEI system with electronic spark control (ESC) is a detonation-control system used on 1980

and later turbocharged and high-compression engines. The system consists of a knock sensor, a controller unit, and a special five-terminal HEI module.

When detonation occurs, the knock sensor sends a signal to the controller, which then instructs the module to retard the ignition timing by a small amount. If the knock sensor continues to detect detonation, the controller instructs the module to further retard timing by another small increment. This sensor-controller-module cycle goes on continuously, and the controller's instructions to the module are updated many times a second until the detonation is eliminated. As soon as that happens, the process reverses itself and timing is advanced in small steps as long as detonation does not reoccur. Once the detonation-producing conditions have been eliminated, the timing will return to normal within 20 seconds.

The HEI system with electronic module retard (EMR) is a simple 10-degree timing retard system used for cold starts and was also introduced in 1980. The retard circuitry is contained within the special five-terminal HEI module and is activated by a simple vacuum switch on most models. On cars with the computer-controlled catalytic converter (C-4) system, the module is controlled by the C-4 computer.

The HEI system with electronic spark timing (EST) was introduced on 1981 engines with computer command control (CCC), except those with minimum-function CCC systems (Chevette, Pontiac T1000, and Acadian). The seven-terminal module converts the pickup coil signal into a crankshaft position signal used by the powertrain control module (PCM) to advance or retard ignition timing for optimum spark timing. HEI-EST distributors have no centrifugal or vacuum advance units.

The HEI system with EST and ESC was also introduced in 1981 and combines the electronic spark control of EST with the detonation sensor of ESC. It is used primarily with turbocharged engines.

The HEI system with EST and a Hall-effect switch combines the basic magnetic pulse generator of the HEI distributor with a Hall-effect switch and is used with CCC engine control systems. The pickup coil sends timing signals to the HEI module during cranking. Once the engine starts, the Hall-effect switch overrides the pickup coil and sends crankshaft position signals to the computer for electronic control of timing.

Figure 16-35. A primary circuit diagram of Chrysler's electronic ignition system. (Chrysler)

Chrysler

Electronic ignition

In 1971, Chrysler became the first domestic manufacturer to introduce a basic electronic ignition on some models, figure 16-35. The system became standard on all Chrysler Motors cars in 1973. The same basic system, with very few modifications, was used on most six- and eight-cylinder carbureted Chrysler engines.

The Chrysler electronic ignition system, figure 16-36, is a fixed dwell design using a magnetic pulse distributor, a remote-mounted electronic control module, and a unit-type ballast resistor. The control module is mounted on the firewall or inner fender panel and has an exposed switching transistor that controls primary current. *Don't touch the transistor when the ignition is on, because enough voltage is present to give you a shock.* The distributor housing, cap, rotor, and advance mechanisms are all similar to breaker-point components, as are the ignition coil and 7-mm spark plug cables.

All 1972-78 cars and some 1979-80 models have five-pin modules with a matching five-terminal wiring harness connector. Early five-pin module ignition systems used a dual ballast resistor that contained an exposed 0.5-ohm temperature-compensating resistor to control primary circuit current and voltage, and a 5.0-ohm temperature-compensating resistor to protect

Figure 16-36. The basic Chrysler electronic ignition system.

the module circuitry from high voltage or current surges. This part was superseded in the mid-1970s by a revised dual resistor using a sealed 1.2-ohm non-temperature-compensating resistor in place of the earlier 0.5-ohm part. The later design is the approved replacement part for all dual-resistor systems.

Some 1979-80 and all 1981 and later vehicles with basic electronic ignition have a four-pin module and matching wiring harness connector. The four-pin module contains integral protection circuitry, eliminating terminal 3, which received input voltage from the 5.0-ohm resistor. A single 1.2-ohm unit-type ballast resistor is used in four-pin module systems to regulate primary circuit current and voltage.

All early Chrysler electronic ignition systems have a single magnetic pickup in the distributor. However, the distributors used with some electronic lean burn (ELB) and electronic spark control (ESC) systems use a dual-pickup distributor containing a start pickup and a run pickup. The run pickup is positioned to advance the ignition trigger signal compared to the start pickup. Under normal engine operation, the module uses the signal from the run pickup. When the ignition switch is in the start position, however, the retarded trigger signal from the start pickup is used to ensure faster starts.

Distributors with early ELB systems have only a centrifugal advance mechanism. Those for later ESC systems have neither centrifugal nor vacuum advance mechanisms; all spark advance is controlled by the computer.

The air gap between the reluctor and pickup coil, or coils, is adjustable, but has no effect on the dwell period, which is determined by the control module. The air gap must be set to a specific clearance with a non-metallic feeler gauge when a new pickup unit is installed. Air gap specifications vary according to model year.

Hall-effect electronic ignition system

Chrysler introduced a different electronic ignition in 1978 on its first four-cylinder, front-wheel-drive (FWD) cars. A Hall-effect switch is used instead of a magnetic pulse generator. The original fixed dwell ignition on 1978 four-cylinder engines was used with an analog computer and had a 0.5-ohm ballast resistor to control primary current and voltage. The 1978 ELB and 1979 ESC system distributors had both centrifugal and vacuum advance mechanisms and were similar in operation to the six- and eight-cylinder versions described above.

A changeover to a digital spark-control computer in 1981 resulted in the electronic spark advance (ESA) system. This meant several changes to the system and its operation. Since the computer took over spark control timing, the distributor had no advance mechanisms. The system uses no ballast resistor, and dwell is variable; that is, it increases as engine speed increases. In 1984, the ESA system was incorporated into the electronic fuel injection (EFI) spark control system used on fuel-injected engines. A logic module and a power module replaced the spark control computer, but the ignition portion of this system works essentially the same as in the ESA system.

Ford (Motorcraft)

Solid-state ignition (SSI)

The Ford Motorcraft solid-state ignition system was used in three forms from 1973 through 1976. It consists of a magnetic pulse distributor, figure 16-37, an electronic control module and a special oil-filled coil that can be identified by its blue case or tower. The coil primary terminals are labeled BAT and DEC (distributor electronic control) and a standard primary circuit ballast resistor wire is used, figure 16-38.

Figure 16-37. Ford's solid-state ignition (SSI) distributor.

■ Mind Those Magnets

When you are servicing a distributor from an electronic ignition system, be sure that no metal particles or iron filings get inside. The magnetic pickup coils and pole pieces in the breakerless distributors used by many manufacturers will attract metal debris that can foul up ignition performance. Use a clean, soft-bristled brush or low-pressure compressed air to clean the inside of a distributor and keep scrap metal off of the pickup coil.

Figure 16-38. Components of Ford's solid-state ignition (SSI). (Ford)

Dura-Spark I and II

Ford introduced its second-generation electronic ignitions in 1977. They are direct descendants of the original SSI ignition. The Dura-Spark systems have higher secondary voltage capabilities and the electrical values of some components differ from the earlier Ford systems.

The Dura-Spark I system was used on some 1977-79 California engines. The system does not use a primary resistor and has a new coil with a gray tower and unique terminals that prevent its use in other systems. The Dura-Spark I module adjusts ignition dwell relative to current through the coil at the time of the spark. The module also has a stall-shutdown feature for circuit protection. If the engine stalls, the module opens the primary circuit even though the ignition switch is in the on position. The switch must be turned OFF and then back to START to close the primary circuit.

Dura-Spark II systems more closely resemble the 1976 solid-state ignition (SSI). They retain a primary resistor wire, but the resistance values are changed to provide higher secondary voltage. The coil is the same as that used with the 1973-76 systems.

Dura-Spark II systems have been produced in several variations from 1977 on. Different modules have different-colored grommets, so consult the appropriate manual to determine the proper service.

All Dura-Spark I and II distributor caps, figure 16-39, use male terminals for the 8-mm spark plug cables. The caps on six-and eight-cylinder distributors are much larger than previous models and have adapter rings to mate with the distributor housing. Large rotors are also used with the bigger caps.

Dura-Spark III

This system was introduced as part of Ford's second- and third-generation electronic engine controls (EEC-II and EEC-III) systems. The Dura-Spark III ignition module can be identified by its brown grommet. Although it appears similar to other Dura-Spark modules, many of its control circuits were eliminated and their functions incorporated into the EEC-II engine control assembly (ECA).

The Dura-Spark III distributor is essentially nothing more than a device to route spark from the coil to the proper plug. It has no centrifugal or vacuum advance mechanisms. The magnetic pulse generator was removed from the distributor and relocated to the crankshaft in the form of a crankshaft position sensor (pickup coil) and pulse ring (armature), figure 16-40.

Figure 16-39. A Dura-Spark distributor.

Figure 16-40. The EEC-III crankshaft position sensor replaced the magnetic pulse generator in the Dura-Spark III distributor. (Ford)

Figure 16-41. Ford TFI ignition system components.

Thick-film Integrated (TFI) Ignition

The TFI-I ignition system, figure 16-41, was introduced in 1982 on the 1.6-liter Escort engine. It differs in many respects from the earlier Ford systems already discussed. Instead of a remote-mounted control module, the TFI-I system uses an integrated circuit control module attached to the outside of the distributor housing. The module connects directly to the distributor stator.

Inside the distributor is the familiar magnetic pulse generator, but TFI-I is a variable dwell system that operates without a ballast resistor. The conventional oil-filled coil is replaced with a special low-resistance E-core part. The distributor cap, rotor, and spark plug cables, however, are similar to those used with Dura-Spark systems.

There are two different versions of the TFI-I control module. Early production parts were made of blue plastic and are called "non-push-start" modules. They contain protection circuitry that will shut off voltage to the coil if an ignition trigger signal is not

detected for a period of 10 to 15 seconds. When shutdown occurs, the ignition switch must be turned off and back on again before the engine will start.

All later modules are made of gray plastic and contain revised circuitry that still turns off voltage to the coil after a preset period, but switches the power back on as soon as a trigger signal is detected.

A revised TFI ignition system appeared in 1983 as part of Ford's fifth generation of electronic engine controls (EEC-IV). Called TFI-IV, this design uses a gray ignition module that appears similar to the TFI-I module, but has a six-wire connector instead of the TFI-I's three-wire connector. The additional three wires connect the module to the ECA. The TFI-IV module is used with a Universal distributor that contains a Hall-effect switch. The TFI ignitions replaced the Dura-Spark ignitions on virtually all Ford vehicles until OBD II.

The TFI module attaches to the distributor with several screws and depends on good contact with the distributor housing for its cooling. Whenever a module is replaced, silicone dielectric compound must be applied to its back to improve heat conductivity and prevent premature module burnout. The module should never be used as a handle to turn the distributor when setting the initial timing. This kind of careless handling can cause it to warp and fail soon after.

Early TFI-IV ignition systems were independent of the EEC-IV computer and are referred to as Non CCD TFI-IV (non–computer-controlled dwell). The TFI-IV ignition systems share similarities that make checking the TFI ignition easy. Here is a list of the Non CCD TFI-IV ignition system features.

1. The module is powered from the ignition switch at pin number 4, figure 16-42. This voltage is then applied to the internal module circuit and used as a reference voltage signal for the Profile Ignition Pickup (PIP) sensor at pin number 6. The 12-volt signal is toggled by a Hall-effect sensor to control the primary ignition circuit during cranking. The voltage for the Hall-effect sensor is supplied on pin number 3 during running mode. The computer receives the PIP signal at terminal number 56 and turns on the fuel pump relay and injectors. Pin number 2 controls the primary circuit and sets the dwell with the on/off (rising/falling) square waveforms.

2. Once the engine is running, power is switched to the ignition module from pin number 4 to pin number 3, allowing the SPOUT signal to control spark timing. A dual trace lab scope can monitor the SPOUT signal from pin number 5 and the PIP (rpm signal) from pin number 6, see figure 16-43. The square waveforms on the Non CCD TFI-IV ignition systems for the PIP and SPOUT contain timing bites on the falling edge on the PIP and on the rising edge on the SPOUT.

These are typical for this system and indicate that the computer is controlling spark advance but NOT primary current dwell.

3. The computer observes the firing events directly off the coil wire and corrects ignition timing. Because voltage is high, a 22K-ohm resistor buffers the signal. In the event the resistor burns out, the computer will set a Code 18, which is also preceded by a lack of ignition timing advance. The IDM signal can be observed on pin number 4. A dual trace lab scope can distinguish the primary current waveform and the PIP signal simultaneously, figure 16-44.

The TFI-IV non-CCD system uses the computer to monitor the module and the firing events but the ignition module is responsible for controlling the primary circuit switching.

Later in 1989, Ford introduced the TFI-IV CCD (computer-controlled dwell) ignition systems. These differ from the Non CCD TFI-IV systems in that the computer controls the internal dwell circuitry of the module. In figure 16-45, the 22K-ohm resistor and IDM circuit are removed and pin number 4 incorporates the Filtered Tach Output (FTO). The FTO signal represents the coil charge time and is directly monitored by the computer. The SPOUT signal controls the primary circuit switching, thereby firing the ignition coil. Here is a list of the major differences between the two TFI systems.

1. The SPOUT signal on pin number 5 lines up perfectly with the primary current waveform turn-on point and turn-off point (firing event), figure 16-46. A dual trace lab scope can monitor the SPOUT signal from pin number 5 and the primary current from pin number 2, figure 16-47. The SPOUT signal is monitored by the computer and then used to control the dwell of the primary current.

2. The FTO signal represents the coil charge time and is directly monitored by the computer on pin number 4. The FTO signal aligns with the SPOUT signal because the computer uses both signals to control the dwell and timing, figure 16-48.

ORIGINAL-EQUIPMENT DISTRIBUTORLESS IGNITIONS

This section contains brief descriptions of the distributorless electronic ignitions used by domestic manufacturers. Whenever a distributorless ignition requires

Figure 16-42. Schematic of a Ford TFI-IV non CCD ignition system.

service, you should always refer to the manufacturer's shop manual or an appropriate repair manual to determine the exact specifications and whether the system has any unique features you should know.

Principles of Distributorless Ignitions

The term distributorless ignition system (DIS) refers to any ignition system without a distributor. The DIS

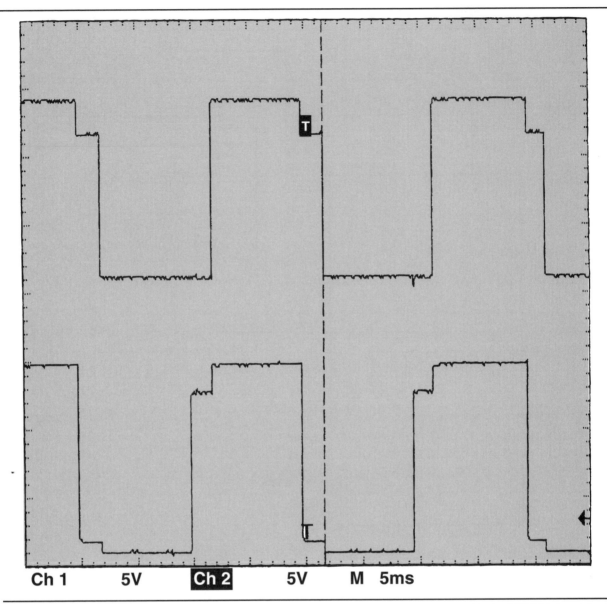

Ch 1   5V   Ch 2   5V   M   5ms

Figure 16-43. At idle, the PIP waveform (top trace) accessed on pin number 6 will align with the SPOUT signal (bottom trace) accessed on pin number 5 (TFI-IV non CCD ignition system).

system fires the spark plugs with a multiple coil pack containing two or three separate ignition coils (according to the number of engine cylinders) and an ignition control module. Control circuits in the module discharge each coil separately in sequence, with each coil serving two cylinders 360 degrees apart in the firing order. Each coil fires two plugs simultaneously in what is called a **waste spark** method. One spark goes to a cylinder near TDC on the compression stroke, while the other fires the plug in a cylinder near TDC of the exhaust stroke. The plug in the cylinder on the exhaust stroke requires very little voltage (about four kV) to fire and has no effect on engine operation.

As we learned in Chapter Fourteen, the ignition coil secondary windings in a distributor ignition generally are wound to give the spark plug center electrode positive polarity and the side electrode negative polarity. When the spark plug fires, electrons travel from the coil secondary windings to the center electrode, across the plug gap to the side electrode where they return to the coil secondary windings through the engine block. A spark plug fired in this manner is said to have forward polarity, figure 16-49. If the electrons travel to the side electrode and across the plug gap to the center electrode, the plug is said to have reverse polarity.

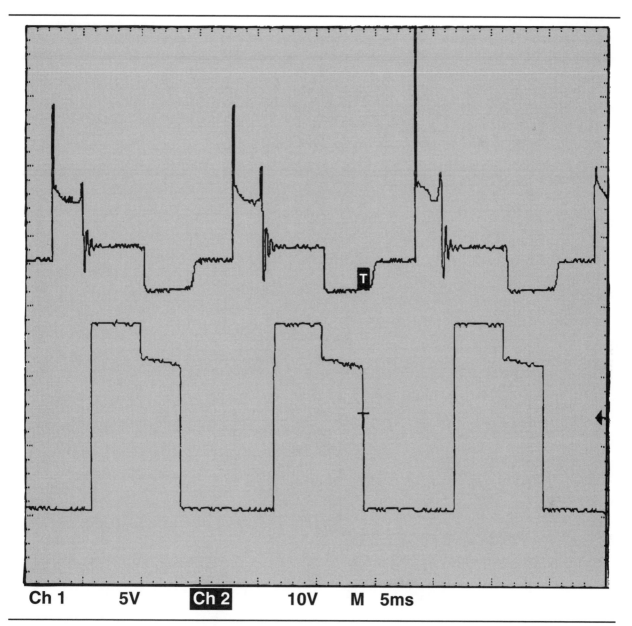

Ch 1   5V   Ch 2   10V   M   5ms

Figure 16-44. The PIP (rpm) signal does not align with the primary current turn-on signal because the TFI-IV non CCD ignition module controls the dwell, not the computer.

In a distributorless ignition, each pair of spark plugs is connected to one coil. In this system, one plug is always fired with forward polarity and the other is always fired with reverse polarity, figure 16-49. Because firing a spark plug with reverse polarity takes about 30 percent more energy, a misfire could result if the DIS coils did not have a different saturation time and primary current travel than a conventional coil. This provides more than 40 kilovolts of available energy—as much as 20 percent more than a conventional coil. Refer to the current ramping

waveform patterns at the beginning of this chapter for additional information.

Firing voltage for distributorless ignition systems exhibits a slightly different waveform pattern than distributor ignition systems because of the design of the

Waste Spark: A method of ignition in which two spark plugs are fired simultaneously. One plug fires in a cylinder near TDC of the compression stroke and ignites the air-fuel mixture; the other plug "wastes" its spark in a cylinder near TDC of the exhaust stroke.

Figure 16-45. Schematic of a Ford TFI-IV CCD ignition system.

"waste spark" secondary system. Distributorless ignition systems pair two cylinders (companion cylinders) and fire both spark plugs at the same time. One cylinder will be on the compression stroke while the other

cylinder will be on the exhaust stroke. The spark plugs are wired in series. One fires in the conventional method, from center electrode to ground electrode, while the other fires from ground electrode to center

Figure 16-46. Observe that the SPOUT signal (bottom trace) aligns with the primary current turn-on signal (falling edge) and with the spark plug firing (rising edge).

electrode. Every other cylinder has reverse polarity. The cylinder on the compression stroke will require more voltage to fire the air/fuel mixture than the other cylinder (exhaust or waste). The firing event fires two spark plugs simultaneously. One plug fires from negative to positive polarity while the other fires from positive to negative polarity. The exhaust stroke pattern will show less voltage because there is much less resistance across the spark plug gap of the waste spark, figure 16-50. Also, the distributorless ignition system fires once per engine revolution as opposed to every other revolution in a distributor-equipped engine.

The ignition control module determines and maintains the coil firing order. When it orders the coil to fire, one spark plug fires forward and the other fires backward. The voltage drop across each plug is determined by firing polarity and cylinder pressure. The ignition module controls primary current travel and limits dwell time. The low resistance of the primary coil winding, combined with an applied voltage of 14 volts, results in a theoretical current travel greater than 14 amperes, helping to decrease the coil's saturation time. Such a high current travel, however, will damage the system components unless it can be limited to a range of 8.5 to 10 amperes. Limiting of the circuit current to the safe range is done by a control circuit inside the module, figure 16-51.

Figure 16-47. A dual trace lab scope can monitor the SPOUT signal from pin 5 and the primary ignition signal from pin 2.

Some modules use a type of **closed loop dwell control,** figure 16-52. In this system, the module continuously monitors coil buildup for maximum current. If maximum current was reached during the previous buildup, the module shortens dwell time to lower the wattage used by the system. If minimum current was not reached during the previous buildup, the module lengthens dwell time to permit full saturation of the coil. When current limiting takes place before coil discharge, the module decreases dwell time for the next cycle.

Delco-Remy

Computer-controlled coil ignition C³I)

This distributorless ignition was introduced in 1984 and is used on Buick-built V6 engines. There is no distributor with signal generator, rotor, and cap in the C³I system. The ignition trigger signal is provided by Hall-effect crankshaft and camshaft position sensors. The crankshaft sensor provides a signal that indicates basic timing, crankshaft position, and engine speed. The camshaft sensor, figure 16-53, provides a firing order signal. On 3800 and 3.8-liter non-turbo engines, the camshaft sensor is mounted in the timing cover. With 3.8-liter turbocharged engines, the camshaft sensor replaces the normal distributor and is mounted in the distributor location to drive the oil pump. On 3300 and 3.0-liter engines, a synchronization ("sync") signal sensor is combined with the crankshaft sensor at the front of the engine. Regardless of their appearance or location, all camshaft sensors have the same purpose. They are used for sequential fuel injection, misfire detection, and may be used to sync the coil firing sequence. A sync signal that is on the crankshaft is used only to start the coil firing sequence.

The crankshaft and camshaft sensors use Hall-effect switches with revolving interrupter rings to synchronize and fire the coils at the required time. The ignition module sends a reference voltage through a semiconductor wafer in the Hall-effect switch. A permanent magnet mounted in line with the semiconductor wafer induces a voltage across the semiconductor, figure 16-54. As a metal blade on the interrupter ring passes between the permanent magnet and semiconductor wafer, the magnetic field is broken and Hall-effect voltage drops, figure 16-55. The 3800 and 3.8-liter non-turbo engines reverse the process. On these engines, the permanent magnet is mounted on the camshaft sprocket and the Hall-effect switch is part of the timing cover sensor, figure 16-56. As the camshaft sprocket revolves, it turns the Hall-effect switch on and off.

The camshaft sensor serves only to establish the initial ignition firing sequence during engine cranking. The ignition module synchronizes the initial cam sensor signal with one of the crankshaft sensor signals during cranking and remembers the crankshaft sensor sequence as long as the ignition remains on.

The operation of the C³I system is very similar to that of the HEI with EST system described earlier. During starting, the ignition module controls both ignition timing and spark distribution. When the engine reaches a programmed speed between 200 and 400 rpm, the PCM overrides the ignition module and assumes control of timing based on signals from the crankshaft sensor and other engine sensors. In case of PCM failure, the ignition module assumes timing control and operates the ignition with a fixed advance of 10 degrees BTDC.

Since introducing the C³I system, GM has used three different variations:

- Type 1: All three coils are molded into a single housing with a smooth exterior surface, figure 16-57. Three spark plug cable terminals are provided on each side of the housing. If one coil malfunctions, the entire coil pack must be replaced.
- Type 1 Fast Start: The coil pack can be interchanged with a Type 1, but ignition module circuitry differs and connector plugs are not compatible.
- Type 2: Similar to Type 1, but the coils can be replaced individually.

The Type 1 Fast Start system measures crankshaft sensor signals more precisely, resulting in a faster

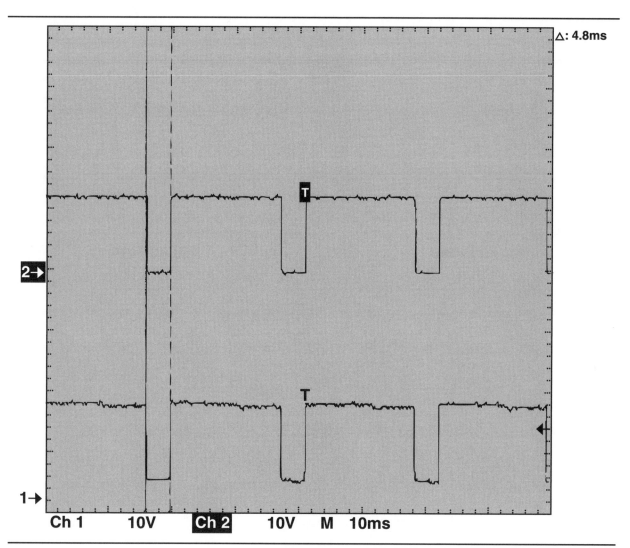

△: 4.8ms

Ch 1   10V   Ch 2   10V   M   10ms

Figure 16-48. Observe that the SPOUT and FTO signals align on the TFI-IV CCD ignition.

DIS CURRENT FLOW

Figure 16-49. In a DIS system, one spark plug in each pair always fires with forward polarity. The other plug fires with reverse polarity, with current traveling from the side to the center electrode. (GM)

startup. A dual crankshaft sensor is located beside the harmonic balancer/crankshaft pulley on the front of the engine. The harmonic balancer has two sets of interrupter rings. The outside ring consists of 18 evenly spaced interrupter blades that deliver 18 pulses every crankshaft revolution. These pulses are called the 18X signal. The inside ring consists of three blades with gaps of 10, 20, and 30 degrees spaced at 100, 90, and 110 degrees apart respectively. The inside ring pulses are called the 3X signal, figure 16-58.

Closed Loop Dwell Control: A type of distributorless ignition system in which the control module varies dwell time in response to previous coil current buildup.

SECONDARY WAVEFORM

Figure 16-50. On a DIS ignition system, the secondary waveform pattern indicates less resistance across the spark plug gap on the exhaust stroke (waste spark).

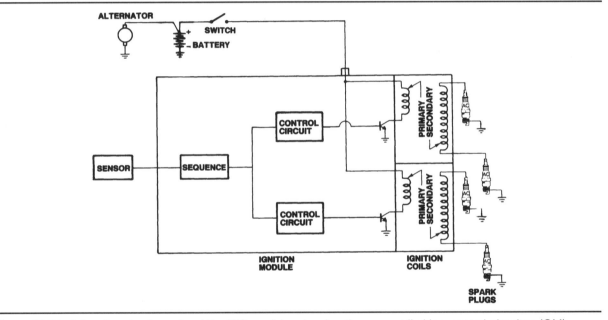

Figure 16-51. A functional schematic of the DIS module, showing the current-limiting control circuitry. (GM)

Figure 16-52. Closed loop dwell allows full saturation of the ignition coil by increasing or decreasing dwell time. (GM)

Variations in the 3X signal allow the ignition module to synchronize the correct coil without need of the camshaft signal. Since the module can determine the correct coil within 120 degrees of crankshaft rotation, it starts firing on the first coil identified. The 18X pulse acts as a "clock pulse" to measure the length of each 3X pulse. The 18X pulse changes once during the 3X 10-degree gap, twice during the 20-degree gap, and three times during the 3X 30-degree gap. Once the module determines which 3X pulse it is reading, it can energize the correct coil.

FIRING SEQUENCE — 1-6-5-4-3-2

**3.8-LITER
SFI TURBO**

**3.8-LITER
SFI NON-TURBO**

Figure 16-53. C³I Hall-effect sensors vary in appearance and location, but all use the same electrical circuitry to perform the same job. (GM)

HALL-EFFECT SWITCH ON

Figure 16-54. Hall-effect switch with unbroken field and reference voltage. (GM)

Direct ignition system (DIS)

The basic operation of the DIS system used on many Chevrolet and Pontiac four-cylinder and V6 engines is quite similar to that of the C³I system, except for

HALL-EFFECT SWITCH OFF

Figure 16-55. Hall-effect switch with broken field and voltage drop-off. (GM)

the method used to sense crankshaft position. Instead of Hall-effect switches located on the front of the engine, this DIS system uses a magnetic sensor installed in the side of the engine block. When used with the 2.5-liter engine, the sensor is installed on the back of the module. With other four-cylinder and V6

Figure 16-56. A variation of the Hall-effect switch camshaft sensor in which the magnet mounted on the camshaft sprocket rotates past the Hall-effect switch, turning it on and off. (GM)

engines, the sensor is installed in the block below the module and is connected externally, figure 16-59.

A notched wheel or reluctor is cast into the crankshaft. The crankshaft reluctor on both four-cylinder and V6 engines is machined with seven notches or slots and serves as the field interrupter. The sensor head consists of a permanent magnet with a wire winding and is positioned a specified distance from the reluctor. As the crankshaft rotates, the reluctor notches interrupt the sensor's magnetic field, causing a small ac voltage to be induced in the sensor's wire winding, figure 16-60. Because the sensor is installed in a fixed position in the engine block and the reluctor is an integral part of the crankshaft, there is no timing adjustment possible or required with this system.

Six reluctor notches are evenly spaced around the reluctor surface at 60-degree intervals; the seventh notch is spaced 10 degrees from one of the six notches. The signal from the seventh notch is used by the module to synchronize coil firing sequence to the crankshaft position. While reluctor configuration is the same for four-cylinder and V6 engines, coil firing order and determination of crankshaft position are calculated by the ignition module differently.

In the V6 engine system, figure 16-61, the synchronization notch tells the module to ignore the first notch and establish base timing for cylinders 2 and 5 with the second notch. The module ignores the third

Figure 16-57. Identifying the Type I and Type II coil and ignition module assemblies used by Delco.

notch, and relies on the fourth notch to set base timing of cylinders 3 and 6. The fifth notch also is ignored in favor of the sixth notch for cylinders 1 and 4. After the seventh or synchronization notch passes, the entire sequence is repeated. As a result, the firing order of the first crankshaft revolution is 2-5, 3-6, and 1-4.

With four-cylinder engines, figure 16-62, the module starts the firing sequence on the seventh notch. If engine speed is below a predetermined value, the module fires each coil at a specified interval based only on engine speed. The synchronization notch tells the module to ignore the first notch and use the second notch to establish 10 degrees BTDC timing for cylinders 2 and 3. The module ignores the third and fourth notches, but uses the fifth notch to establish an equivalent timing setting for cylinders 1 and 4. In this way, the 2/3 coil is fired first during startup.

The reference pulse in both systems is pulled low by the notch ahead of the one that is used to fire the cylinder, returning to its high state when the cylinder firing notch passes. The change in reference voltage is sent to the PCM for use in electronic spark timing (EST) and fuel injection.

Integrated direct ignition (IDI)

This system is used only on the Oldsmobile-built Quad 4 engine and differs from other four-cylinder DIS systems primarily in the configuration of the system components, figure 16-63. The coil pack and module are contained in a unit that connects directly to the spark plugs. This eliminates the use of spark plug cables, but the entire housing must be removed when changing spark plugs. However, the coils and housing can be replaced individually.

Figure 16-58. Dual Hall-effect switches and two sets of interrupter rings on the harmonic balancer are used in the "fast start" system to measure crankshaft sensor signals with more accuracy. (GM)

Chrysler

Direct ignition system (DIS)

Chrysler uses a direct ignition system, figure 16-64, on its 3.3-liter and 3.5-liter engines. Crankshaft timing is determined by a magneto-resistive sensor installed in the transaxle bellhousing. The single-board engine controller (SBEC) sends an eight-volt reference signal to the sensor. The transaxle drive plate contains three groups of four slots. Each group of slots is positioned 20 degrees apart and provides a signal for two spark plugs. Transaxle drive plate rotation makes and breaks the sensor's magnetic field, causing sensor output voltage to the SBEC engine controller to vary between zero and five volts. The SBEC uses this voltage signal to determine engine speed and calculate both timing advance and the required fuel delivery, as displayed in figure 16-65.

Also a magneto-resistive type, the camshaft sensor is installed in the timing chain case cover and functions in the same way as the crankshaft sensor. The camshaft timing gear contains a series of slots that

Figure 16-59. Location of DIS block-mounted crankshaft sensors to produce a crankshaft position signal. (GM)

Figure 16-60. A small ac voltage is induced in the wire winding of the magnetic sensor when its magnetic field is interrupted by the reluctor. This voltage signal is used by the ignition module to determine firing of each wheel. (GM)

Figure 16-61. The V6 ignition module recognizes notches 2, 4, and 6 as the signal to fire cylinders 2 and 5, 3 and 6, and 1 and 4, in that order. (GM)

give a one – two – three – one – two – blank sequence. The SBEC uses the signals, with the CKP signal, to determine coil firing and fuel injector sequence, figure 16-66. The proper ignition coil can be fired within one crankshaft revolution. The injectors can be pulsed at the same time.

Ford (Motorcraft)

All Ford distributorless ignitions operate on the same basic principles as those used by GM and Chrysler. Each coil fires two spark plugs, with one spark

Figure 16-62. The four-cylinder ignition module recognizes notches 2 and 5 as the signal to fire cylinders 2 and 3, and 1 and 4, in that order. (GM)

igniting the mixture at the top of the compression stroke and the other spark wasted at the top of the exhaust stroke. One plug of each pair has positive polarity; the other has negative polarity.

4-2 distributorless ignition system

Sometimes called the Dual Plug DIS, this unusual distributorless ignition was introduced on 1989 2.3-liter, four-cylinder truck engines, figure 16-67. Each cylinder uses two spark plugs, with one plug installed on each side of the combustion chamber. Those plugs on the right side of the engine form the primary system, and are responsible for engine operation at all times. The plugs on the left side of the engine form the secondary system and are switched on and off by the EEC-IV computer, according to engine speed and load requirements.

Only the primary plugs fire when the engine is cranking. Once the engine is running, the EEC-IV computer commands the DIS module through the dual plug inhibit (DPI) circuit to switch from single- to dual-plug operation. The EEC-IV computer also is responsible for ignition timing and dwell.

The 4-2 DIS uses two four-tower DIS coil packs, figure 16-68, with a single remote DIS module, figure 16-69. A dual Hall-effect crankshaft sensor bracket-mounted near the crankshaft damper, figure 16-70, completes the system. The right coil fires the primary plugs during normal operating conditions; the left coil fires the secondary plugs as directed by the EEC-IV computer and the DIS module.

The crankshaft sensor works on the same principles as other Hall-effect switches covered previously, and is very similar in operation to the dual sensor used by GM in its C^{3}I ignition. A pair of rotating vane cups on the crankshaft damper produces a profile

Figure 16-63. An exploded view of the IDI system components. (GM)

ignition pickup (PIP) signal for base timing data, and a cylinder identification (CID) signal used by the DIS module to determine which coil to fire.

The EEC-IV module sends a spark output (SPOUT) signal to the DIS module. The leading edge triggers the coil, and the trailing edge controls dwell time. This feature is called computer-controlled dwell (CCD). A buffered tach signal called Ignition Diagnostic Monitor (IDM) supplies ignition system diagnostic information used for self-test.

A CID sensor or circuit failure will not result in a no-start condition, as the DIS module randomly selects and fires one of the two coils under such circumstances. The result of the module's guess may be an engine that is hard to start. However, turning the key off and then back on to crank the engine again allows the module to make another guess. After a few tries, the module will make the right choice and select the correct firing sequence.

If an ignition failure results in the loss of the SPOUT signal, a failure-effects management (FEM) program in the EEC-IV computer memory prevents total driveability loss. The EEC-IV computer opens the SPOUT line, allowing the DIS module to fire the coils directly from the PIP output. This results in a fixed spark angle of 10 degrees BTDC and fixed dwell.

V6 distributorless ignition system (DIS)

This DIS system also was introduced in 1989 on the 3.0-liter SHO V6 engine and the 3.8-liter supercharged V6 engine. The system functions in essentially the same way as the 4-2 DIS discussed above, but its components differ, figure 16-71:

- A single six-tower coil pack contains three coils with an individual tach wire for each coil; the coil pack is serviced as an assembly.
- A single set of spark plugs is used, with one plug per cylinder.
- The 3.0-liter cylinder identification (CID) sensor is installed on the end of one camshaft.

Figure 16-64. Major components of the Chrysler DIS system. (Chrysler)

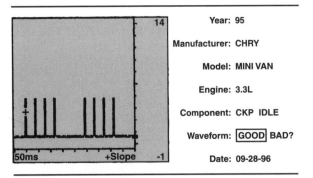

Figure 16-65. The CKP at idle. Transaxle drive plate rotation makes and breaks the magneto-resistive sensor's magnetic field, varying sensor output voltage to the SBEC. (Snap-On Vantage)

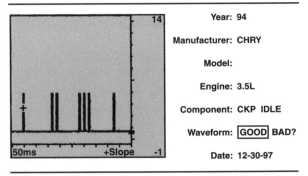

Figure 16-66. CMP sensor's signals, along with CKP signal, help the SBEC determine coil firing and fuel injector sequence. (Snap-On Vantage)

Figure 16-67. A diagram of the Ford 4-2 DIS system. (Ford)

Figure 16-68. 4-2 DIS coil pack locations. (Ford)

Figure 16-69. 4-2 DIS ignition module location. (Ford)

Figure 16-70. 4-2 DIS crankshaft sensor location. (Ford)

- The 3.8-liter CID sensor is installed in the engine block where the distributor would normally be located.
- A single Hall-effect switch is used as the crankshaft sensor.

When the engine is cranked, the DIS module looks for a change in the CID signal, from high to low or low to high. As soon as the module sees the leading or trailing edge of the CID signal, it prepares to fire coil 2 of the coil pack. Once the change in the CID signal occurs, the module looks for the trailing edge of SPOUT to turn on coil 2. When the module sees the next leading edge of SPOUT, it turns the primary current off to coil 2, which fires coil 2, figure 16-72. The DIS module always fires the coils in one coil pack in a given order. At engine start-up, the coil firing sequence is always 2, 3, 1. Because the coils continue to fire in the same order, they are synchronized with compression and remain synchronized as long as the engine is running, even if the DIS module loses the CID signal. SPOUT tells the DIS module when to fire the next coil as long as the engine is running. If the SPOUT circuit opens, the PIP signal is used by the module to fire the coils.

Electronic direct ignition system (EDIS)

A second-generation DIS system, EDIS functions faster and with greater accuracy than the V6 DIS system just described. Because the system has been used on four-cylinder, V6, and V8 engines since its introduction in 1990, the number of coils and coil packs differ according to engine application. Other EDIS components also differ in appearance and location, but the system functions essentially the same regardless of engine application. Figure 16-73 shows the EDIS components used on the 1.9-liter SEFI engine. There are other differences between EDIS and DIS:

- EDIS does not use a cylinder identification (CMP) sensor. The variable reluctance sensor is a CKP sensor with a sync signal for ignition coil firing sequence.
- EDIS crankshaft position signals are more sophisticated and complex than those used on DIS systems.
- EDIS uses a spark angle word (SAW) signal in place of the DIS SPOUT signal. The SAW signal also is more complex than a SPOUT signal.

■ Individual-Coil DIS

The distributorless ignition systems (DIS) we have detailed in this chapter commonly employ half as many coils as they have spark plugs to fire. These systems fire each pair of spark plugs simultaneously: one with forward polarity and the other with reverse polarity. Depending on piston position, one spark is a waste spark. These systems eliminate moving parts and reduce the associated friction and wear-and-tear. They are also economical to produce and quite adequate for their intended use. However, there is a better, though more expensive, way.

Many manufacturers have models with distributorless ignition systems that use a single ignition coil for each spark plug. In addition to the advantages of waste-spark DIS, individual-coil DIS fire all plugs individually with forward polarity for a hotter spark, which provides better performance at high rpm or under load. These systems further reduce the length of the secondary cable or eliminate it altogether, decreasing the chance of secondary arcing or leakage, improving the long-term reliability of the system, and eliminating the chance of cross-fire. Furthermore, shortening or eliminating the spark plug cable greatly reduces the amount of radiofrequency interference (RFI) emitted by the ignition system.

Figure 16-71. A diagram of the Ford V6 DIS. (Ford)

Figure 16-72. Coil selection with the engine cranking. (Ford)

Figure 16-73. The 1.9-liter EDIS ignition system components. (Ford)

- The EDIS module is smarter, faster, has more "thinking" ability and decision-making responsibilities, and better diagnostic ability than the earlier DIS module.

The variable reluctance sensor (VRS) is a type of crankshaft position sensor (CKP); it has a magnetic transducer containing a pole piece wrapped with fine wire, figure 16-74. If the transducer is exposed to a change in flux lines, a differential voltage will be induced across the windings. Thus, when a ferromagnetic toothed timing wheel on the crankshaft rotates in the presence of the VRS, the passing teeth cause the VRS reluctance to change, resulting in a varying analog voltage signal. The timing wheel has 35 teeth and a blank spot spaced at 10-degree increments. The

blank spot for the thirty-sixth tooth serves as a fixed reference point for No. 1 piston travel identification.

During cranking, the EEC-IV module refers to a predetermined fuel control strategy stored in its memory to supply the necessary fuel for starting the engine. At the same time, the EDIS module looks for any significant change in the VRS signal. When it recognizes the missing tooth, figure 16-75, the EDIS module has a reference point and is synchronized to fire the proper coil. While the engine continues to crank, the EDIS module fires the coil at 10 degrees BTDC (base timing). When the coil for piston No. 1 is fired, a profile ignition pickup (PIP) signal is sent from the EDIS module to the EEC-IV computer. The PIP signal provides the EEC-IV computer with

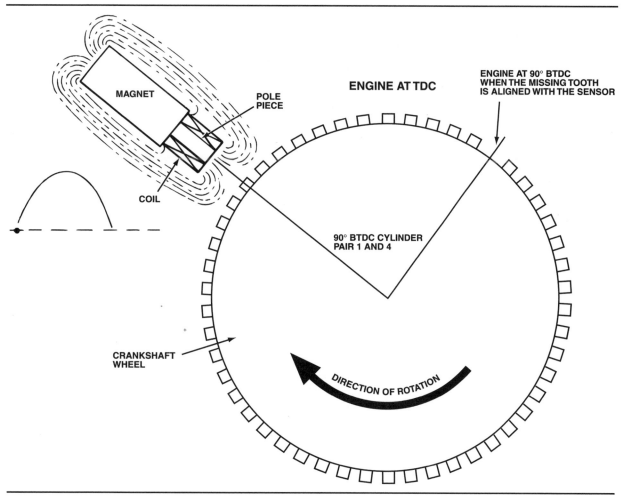

Figure 16-74. A variable reluctance sensor. (Ford)

crankshaft position and engine speed data. Because the PIP signal is synthesized by the EDIS module, it takes the form of a digital square wave with a 50-percent duty cycle, figure 16-76. When the EEC-IV computer recognizes the PIP signal, it enables fuel and spark functions. It also processes the PIP signal with other information to determine the spark angle word (SAW) signal. The spark angle word (SAW) signal replaces the former SPOUT signal on the TFI and DIS ignition systems as the signal for an ignition coil firing event (primary current turn-off). This signal is sent to the EDIS module, which uses it to determine whether ignition timing should be advanced or retarded.

Integrated electronic ignition (EI) system
Later Ford models equipped with the EEC-V OBD II system use a coil-over-plug distributorless ignition system. This system equips each cylinder with a separate coil/module assembly mounted directly over the spark plug. The EI ignition system also uses a

crankshaft position sensor (CKP) and a wiring harness to connect each coil/module assembly to the computer. This system also eliminates the need for spark plug wires but requires an input from the camshaft position sensor (CMP). Here is a list of the Integrated Electronic ignition system features:

1. Much like the EDIS system, the CKP sensor is used to detect crankshaft position and engine speed by sensing the missing tooth on a pulsed wheel mounted onto the crankshaft. The CMP sensor is used to identify top dead center (TDC) of the cylinder number 1 on compression stroke, figure 16-77.

2. On most distributorless ignition systems, each coil will fire its companion coil (waste spark) simultaneously on the exhaust stroke. Integrated electronic ignition (EI) systems fire only 1 coil/module assembly for each compression stroke.

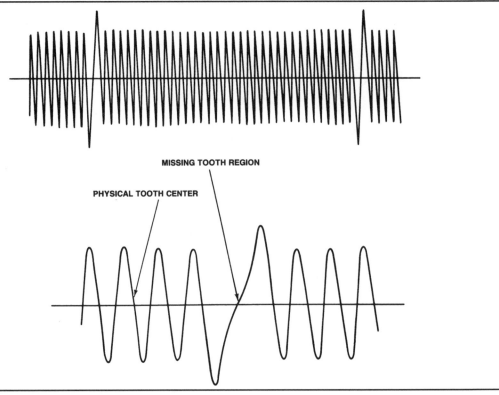

Figure 16-75. The VRS analog signal wave. (Ford)

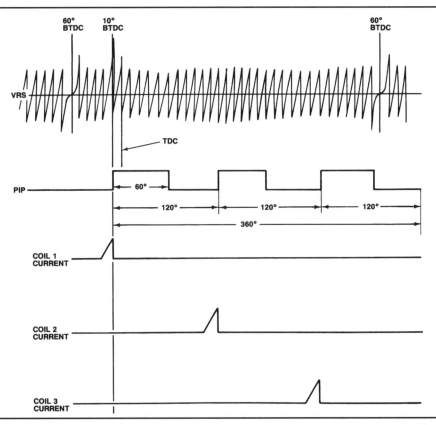

Figure 16-76. Comparison of analog CKP sensor signals with digital PIP signals created by the EDIS module. (Ford)

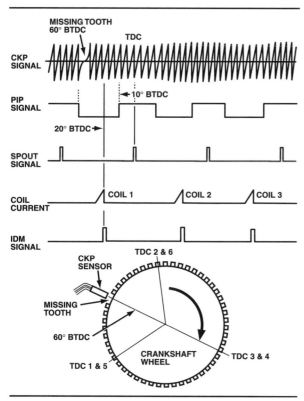

Figure 16-77. Ignition waveforms for the Ford Integrated Electronic Ignition (EI) system (coil-over-plug).

3. The PCM controls primary current to each coil/module assembly. Kickback voltage occurs when the voltage spike collapses. The PCM monitors the firing event using the ignition diagnostic monitor (IDM) circuit.

4. The EI systems require slightly less current limit amperage ratings than distributorless ignition systems. EI systems limit between 6.5 to 7.0 amps while distributorless ignition systems limit between 8.0 to 10.0 amps.

Imported Car Electronic Ignitions

Imported vehicles appeared on the automotive scene with electronic ignitions about the same time or shortly after the domestic systems we have discussed. All major imported cars now use an inductive-discharge electronic ignition. In most of these systems, timing signals are sent to the ignition module from a magnetic pulse generator in the distributor, although Bosch makes a Hall-effect distributor used by Volkswagen.

Figure 16-78. Exploded view of a Hitachi distributor installed on early model Subaru engines.

Hitachi electronic ignition systems are installed onto many Japanese import vehicles. The Hitachi system for Subaru varies with year and models. The 1977 through 1986 Subaru models use a different version for the turbocharged engines. The turbocharged models use a four-terminal igniter (module) instead of the two-terminal igniter. These Subaru Hitachi ignition systems consist of an external igniter (module) on early versions or an internal pick-up coil/control unit (module) on later versions, figure 16-78, a conventional coil, a centrifugal and vacuum advance, an external ballast resistor (early) and a 4-tooth reluctor. There are some versions that mount the igniter onto the coil.

By the middle 1980s and later, Hitachi also equipped many Subarus with a photoelectric ignition system.

Nippondenso electronic ignition systems are installed on many domestic models built overseas.

PICK-UP
COIL ASSEMBLY

GOVERNOR
WEIGHT

VACUUM
ADVANCE

CAP

ROTOR

IGNITER

IGNITION
COIL

Figure 16-79. Exploded view of a Nippondenso distributor with the integral ignition coil.

Nippondenso ignition systems are also installed onto Japanese models such as the Lexus, Subaru, Toyota, Suzuki and Mitsubishi. Later Nippondeno ignition systems equip the igniter (module) inside the distributor along with the ignition coil and pick-up coil assembly, figure 16-79.

The electronic ignition used on the Mitsubishi-built 2.6-liter engine in some Chrysler vehicles is typical of most Japanese designs, figure 16-80. The distributor contains a magnetic pickup with an integral IC igniter

(control module), although some Toyota ignitions use an external igniter mounted on the coil. The variable dwell ignition contains no ballast resistor. Full battery voltage is supplied to both the coil and igniter whenever the ignition switch is in the start or the run position.

The early Toyota had a distributor with two or three magnetic sensors. The CKP (Ne) could be either a 4- or 24-tooth sensor inside the distributor. The CMP (G) signal was a one-, two- or four-tooth signal

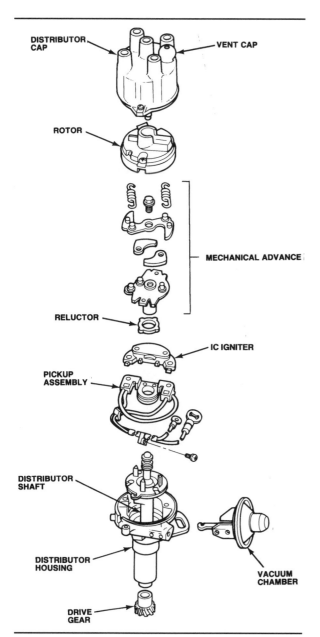

Figure 16-80. The Mitsubishi ignition system used on 2.6-liter engines is typical of the inductive-discharge ignitions used on Japanese vehicles.

to sync the Ne signal for injection and ignition firing, figure 16-81. Some systems used two (G) signals. These signals were sent to the PCM, which sent a square wave signal (IGt) to the ICM (igniter) to trigger the coil firing. The ICM monitored the inductive spike on the coil negative. If the plug fired, it sent a confirmation (IGf) signal to the PCM. The PCM required this signal for fuel injection.

With OBD II, the CKP (Ne) sensor was moved to the crankshaft for more accurate misfire detection.

The Honda distributor contains the coil, ICM, and three magnetic sensors. The CMP sensor has one tooth, the TDC sensor has four teeth, and the CKP has 24 teeth. The CKP signal is used for engine speed and crankshaft position.

The TDC signal is TDC for each cylinder. It is used for starting and as a backup for the CKP or CMP. The CMP signal is used to sync the CP and sequential fuel injection.

OBD II systems moved the CKP and TDC sensors to the crankshaft.

These signals are sent to the PCM, which controls the ICM for ignition timing. Many of the later systems use an individual coil for each cylinder. There are two basic types: one ICM for all coils and individual ICMs built into each coil.

An example of the latter is the Isuzu 3.5-liter engine. The CKP is a 58x (60-2) digital signal taken from the crankshaft. The CMP sensor is on the end of the camshaft. These signals are sent to the PCM, which controls timing and dwell with the ICM control signal to each coil, figure 16-82.

When cranking, the 58X signal is used to start ignition and fuel injection. Both companion coils are fired for a compression and waste spark effect. The fuel injectors are pulsed in groups. After the CMP signal is received, the PCM fires the coils only on compression, and the injectors are pulsed sequentially. This allows a faster start, with ignition and injection before the CMP signal is received.

Figure 16-81. Early Toyota distributors used four- or 24-tooth sensors. Different rotors generated different signals.

SUMMARY

Solid-state electronic ignition systems came into widespread use on both domestic and import vehicles in the early 1970s. Today, they are standard on all domestically built cars and light trucks, as well as imported cars and light trucks. Solid-state ignitions provide greater available voltage and reliable performance for longer periods under varying operating conditions, with decreased maintenance.

Solid-state ignitions are either the inductive discharge type or the capacitive discharge type. Original-equipment systems are the inductive discharge type. The primary circuits of solid-state ignitions can be triggered by breaker points, a magnetic pulse generator, a Hall-effect switch, a metal detector, or an optical triggering device signal. Original-equipment systems generally use a magnetic pulse generator or a Hall-effect switch in the distributor to trigger the primary circuit.

The primary circuit is switched on and off by transistors in the ignition control module. The solid-state ignition module also controls the length of the ignition dwell period. Electronic ignitions with fixed dwell use a ballast resistor; those with variable dwell have no ballast resistor.

Basic electronic ignition systems use the same centrifugal and vacuum advance devices as breaker point ignitions. Those electronic ignitions used with electronic engine control systems have no advance mechanisms. The systems computer controls spark advance.

Electronic ignitions have undergone major change and improvement since their introduction in the mid-1970s. Distributor-type ignitions are being replaced by distributorless ignitions, with increasing responsibility for their operation assigned to the electronic engine control system, which you will study in the next chapter.

Figure 16-82. Isuzu 3.5L engine uses one ICM for each coil. The PCM controls timing and dwell. (Isuzu)

Review Questions

Choose the single most correct answer.
Compare your answers with the correct answers on Page 468.

1. Which of the following is true of solid-state ignition systems?
   a. Provide less available voltage than breaker-point systems
   b. Provide greater available voltage than breaker-point systems
   c. Give less reliable system performance at all engine speeds
   d. Require more maintenance than breaker-point systems

2. Which of the following is true of inductive discharge systems?
   a. Used as original equipment by most car manufacturers
   b. A common aftermarket installation
   b. Provide about 50,000 volts of available voltage
   c. Sustain a spark for about 200 microseconds

3. Capacitive discharge systems provide _____ secondary voltage when compared to inductive discharge systems.
   a. Exactly the same
   b. About the same
   c. Greater
   d. Less

4. Transistors have:
   a. A base of one type of material and an emitter and collector of another
   b. An emitter of one type of material and a base and collector of another
   c. A collector of one type of material and a base and emitter of another
   d. A collector, base, and emitter all of the same material

5. The earliest solid-state ignition systems used which of the following triggering devices?
   a. Metal detectors
   b. Breaker points
   c. Magnetic pulse generators
   d. Light detectors

6. The most common type of original-equipment triggering devices are:
   a. Breaker points
   b. Light detectors
   c. Metal detectors
   d. Magnetic pulse generators

7. The accompanying illustration shows a:
   a. Magnetic pulse generator
   b. Metal detector
   c. Light detector
   d. Breaker point assembly

8. The dwell period of a solid-state system can be measured with:
   a. A voltmeter
   b. An ammeter
   c. An ohmmeter
   d. An oscilloscope

9. In the Delco High-Energy Ignition (HEI) system, the dwell period is controlled by the:
   a. Pole piece
   b. Timer core
   c. RFI filter capacitor
   d. Ignition control module (ICM)

10. The Delco HEI system uses:
    a. A single-ballast resistor
    b. A dual-ballast resistor
    c. No ballast resistor
    d. Calibrated resistance wire

11. The rotating component attached to the distributor shaft in the Chrysler electronic ignition is called the:
    a. Armature
    b. Reluctor
    c. Timer core
    d. Trigger wheel

12. The rotating component attached to the distributor shaft in the Ford electronic ignition is called the:
    a. Armature
    b. Reluctor
    c. Timer core
    d. Trigger wheel

13. A Hall-effect switch requires _____ to generate an output voltage.
    a. A magnetic pulse generator
    b. A varactor diode
    c. A 45-degree magnetic field
    d. An input voltage

14. Thick-film integrated (TFI) ignition modules are:
    a. Mounted inside the distributor
    b. Mounted on the side of the distributor
    c. Mounted on the vehicle fenderwell
    d. Used as a handle to rotate the distributor

15. A Hall-effect switch is used with which Chrysler electronic ignitions?
    a. Four-cylinder
    b. Inline-six
    c. V6
    d. V8

16. When a distributorless ignition coil fires its two spark plugs, one spark ignites the mixture at the _____ of the compression stroke and the other spark is wasted at the _____ of the exhaust stroke.
    a. Top, top
    b. Top, bottom
    c. Bottom, bottom
    d. Bottom, top

17. When a DIS module fires the spark plug in a cylinder on its exhaust stroke, there is _____ effect on engine operation.
    a. No
    b. A minor
    c. A stabilizing
    d. A detrimental

18. The Ford Dual Plug DIS system is used on:
    a. 3.0-liter SHO V6 engines
    b. 3.8-liter supercharged V6 engines
    c. 2.3-liter truck engines
    d. Four-cylinder, V6, and V8 engines

17

Electronic Engine Control Systems

ENGINE COMPUTERS

The computers used to control various electrical systems, including engine operation, may be called modules, assemblies, or electronic control units. Some, like the HEI module studied in Chapter Sixteen, are single-function devices that control a given system—in this case, ignition. Others are multiple-function devices that regulate more than one system. As seen in Chapter Four, such modules use input signals from various sensors to control a given system, and the output signal from one computer can act as an input signal to another computer.

Computer Functions

Every computer, regardless of its use, does four basic jobs:

- Input
- Processing
- Storage
- Output.

The voltage signals received from various sensors are the computer input. The computer then compares the input data to its operating program and makes a decision. Part of that decision can be the storage of input data for future reference or the delay of an output signal. The computer always stores its own operating instructions, and most automotive computers store additional information concerning vehicle operation. Output is the decision made by the computer and transmitted to a display unit or to a system actuator by another voltage signal.

Analog and Digital Computers

Computer systems, their input, and their output are classified into two categories:

- Analog
- Digital.

Most late-model engine control systems possess both analog and digital signals. Analog means that a voltage signal or processing action is continuously variable relative to the operation being measured or controlled. Most engine-related conditions are variable. For example, engine temperature does not change abruptly from 0°to 195°F (-18° to 91°C). It varies in an infinite number of temperatures from low to high. The same holds true for engine speed, intake airflow and many other factors.

Digital, however, means that an input or output signal or a processing action is either yes/no, high/low, or on/off. An air-conditioning compressor

Figure 17-1. The memory, or lookup tables, in electronic engine control computers contains the computer operating program. (Ford)

clutch signal is a digital input; the voltage that engages the clutch is either on or off.

Some early engine control computers, such as those in the mid-1970s Chrysler electronic lean-burn system, were analog units. However, analog computers are more susceptible to temperature changes, fluctuations in supply voltage, and signal interference than digital computers. Digital computers are also faster, simpler, and easier to build. Current engine control systems use digital computers with **analog-to-digital (AD)** converters. Digital computers can act only on digital signals, so analog inputs are changed into digital form by (AD) conversion circuits in the computer.

Computer Programs and Memory

The central processing unit of any computer is a chip called the microprocessor. This chip is responsible for performing all of the mathematical computations and decision-making logic required of the computer. By itself, a microprocessor is useless without instructions in binary form that it can use to understand input data, perform calculations, and transmit output commands. These instructions are called a program and are stored on an IC chip in the form of **lookup tables.** These tables are part of the computer memory. Figure 17-1 shows the relationship of the lookup tables to the other components of a Ford electronic control assembly (ECA).

A separate set of lookup tables in the memory contains information on fixed and variable vehicle values. This data is used to calibrate the computer for a specific engine and transmission combination and is stored in a separate IC chip called a programmable read-only memory (PROM) or calibration assembly, figure 17-2.

Two basically different types of memory are used for computer storage functions:

• Permanent, read-only memory (ROM)
• Temporary, random-access memory (RAM).

Permanent memory is called read-only because the computer can only read the contents; it cannot change the data stored in it. This data is retained even when power to the computer is shut off. Part of the ROM is built into the computer, and the rest is located in the PROM or calibration assembly just described. PROM is programmed by the chip manufacturer. If changes need to be made to the information stored in PROM, the chip must be removed from the computer and replaced by another PROM containing revised information.

PROM's are being replaced gradually by another type of read-only memory called erasable, programmable, read-only memory (EPROM). While the computer can write data into an EPROM for permanent storage, its most important feature is the ability of the EPROM to be erased and reprogrammed by the vehicle manufacturer. Since EPROM memory is erasable, it can be changed either electrically or by exposure to ultraviolet light. If the EPROM memory can be electrically reprogrammed one byte at a time, it is called an electrically erasable PROM or EEPROM. When the memory is altered by exposure to ultraviolet light, a small window on the top of the chip is exposed for 15 to 20 minutes. Once the chip's memory is clean, it

CALIBRATION ASSEMBLY (WITH SYSTEM PROM)

MOTORCRAFT

MOTORCRAFT

Nº 731879

PROCESSOR ASSEMBLY

Figure 17-2. Ford's calibration assembly is a PROM containing fixed and variable vehicle values.

can be reprogrammed with new data in less than four seconds. EPROMs are used to store data such as odometer information; EEPROMs allow a car dealership to update or change the computer memory electronically without having to replace the entire module.

Temporary memory is called random-access memory (RAM) because the computer can write or store new data into it as directed by the computer program, as well as read the data already in it. Automotive computers use two types of RAM memory: volatile and nonvolatile. Volatile RAM memory is lost whenever the ignition is turned off. However, a type of volatile RAM, called keep-alive memory (KAM) by Ford, is wired directly to battery power. This prevents its data from being erased when the ignition is turned off. Both volatile and nonvolatile RAM have the disadvantage of losing their memory when disconnected from their power source. One example of nonvolatile RAM is the loss of station settings in a programmable radio when the battery is disconnected. Since all the settings are stored in RAM, they have to be reset when the battery is reconnected. System trouble codes are commonly stored in RAM and can be erased by disconnecting the battery.

Some nonvolatile RAM memory can retain its information even when the battery is disconnected. One use for this type of RAM is the storage of odometer information in an electronic speedometer. The memory chip retains the mileage accumulated by the vehicle. When speedometer replacement is necessary, the odometer chip is removed and installed in the new speedometer unit.

Computer programs increasingly incorporate backup or fail-safe modes, as well as adaptive learning strategies. The backup or fail-safe modes

compensate for such things as sensor failure. If a sensor does fail, the computer takes its required signal from another source. For example, the most important source of information for a fuel mixture decision can be the mass airflow sensor (MAF). If the MAF fails, the computer will use engine rpm and throttle position (TP) sensor signals applied to a lookup table to calculate a replacement value for what the MAF signal should be. The process is so sophisticated that few people would notice a difference in vehicle operation. The only clues to the failure are the lighting of the malfunction indicator lamp (MIL) and the fault code stored in memory.

Adaptive strategy continually adjusts the computer's calibration strategy to correct for wear and aging of components. The adaptive strategy retains the adjustments in a nonvolatile RAM memory so it will not be lost when the ignition is turned off. A short adjustment period could occur if the battery is disconnected or the computer is replaced. However, a driving sequence of less than five miles completes the learning sequence and restores driveability.

Vehicle driveability also can be affected when a malfunctioning sensor is replaced in a system with adaptive strategy. Since the computer had modified its original calibration strategy to compensate for the unreliable sensor signals, the signals received from the new sensor are in conflict with the computer's adapted calibration strategy. This means that driveability may be unsatisfactory until the computer learns the necessary parameters.

System Operating Modes

Computer control systems use available input for decision making according to system type and operating conditions. A carbureted type system has to leave starting and warm-up fuel control in the hands of the carburetor and its components to provide the correct fuel decision for the operating conditions. When the engine is warmed and has stabilized after starting, it trims the fuel flow from the carburetor to meet the needs of the catalytic converter. It does this in what is

Analog-to-Digital (AD): An electronic conversion process for changing analog electrical signals to digital electrical signals.

Lookup Tables: Part of a computer's program, or instructions. One set of lookup tables is common to all microprocessors of a specific vehicle group. Another set of lookup tables is used for specific engine calibrations and is located in the PROM.

called a closed loop operating mode. It uses input from the exhaust oxygen sensor to do this only during closed loop. When not trimming the flow of fuel, it is considered to be in open loop, figure 17-3. The system uses engine speed, temperature and load sensor signals to know when to go to open loop and lets the carburetor circuits do their job. The system may use the engine sensors to match the proper ignition timing decision to the operating condition during open loop operation.

However, electronic fuel injection systems must be more sophisticated, because without the fuel decisions signal, no fuel flows. Different operating strategies or modes are required for each basic engine condition, including starting cold or warm, running during warm-up or normal operating temperature, or when a system failure is detected. Engine speed, temperature and airflow sensors provide the information necessary for selecting the correct mode.

During cranking, engine speed and temperature are the most important information for timing and fuel decisions. During warm-up, engine speed, temperature and airflow provide the information necessary for the correct fuel decision. Within a normal operating temperature range, at steady throttle and under light load conditions, the system will use the exhaust oxygen sensor signal in closed loop to provide fuel trim information so it can satisfy the needs of the catalytic converter. When the system is not using exhaust oxygen sensor information, it is in open-loop operation.

Open-loop control

When a vehicle is first started, the control system is in open loop. The engine sensors provide information to the computer. The computer reads these signals and orders the output actuators to operate in a specific manner. The actuators obey the orders they receive without providing any feedback to the computer. This unidirectional operating sequence is shown by the solid lines in figure 17-3.

When you turn on the windshield wipers, you are exercising open-loop control over the wiper system. The wiper blades will move across the windshield at a given rate of speed, regardless of whether the rain falling on the windshield is a light drizzle or heavy downpour. Wiper speed does not change until you readjust the wiper control. The wiper system does not receive an error feedback signal telling it that it is operating too slowly to clean the heavy downpour from the windshield. It relies on an outside force (the driver) for adjustment.

For an engine computer to determine whether the air-fuel mixture is correct, it requires a feedback signal from the exhaust gas oxygen (O2) sensor. If the computer ignores this signal, it relies on signals from other sensors to make its decision. In this case,

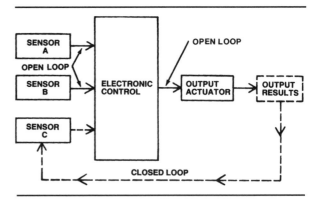

Figure 17-3. Typical open- and closed-loop control.

suppose the engine coolant sensor tells the computer that the engine is cold. The throttle position sensor also signals that the throttle opening is increasing. Based on this information, the computer tells the fuel control actuator to enrich the mixture. It does this under certain specified conditions:

- During a cold start or hot restart
- At wide-open throttle or under full load, regardless of engine speed
- During idle or deceleration conditions (some systems).

Closed-loop control

In closed-loop control, the computer responds to a feedback signal provided by the O2 sensor. This feedback signal tells the computer whether the output is too rich or too lean. In other words, the feedback signal is used to regulate the output command. This cycle is summarized by the dotted line in figure 17-3.

In our fuel-metering example above, the computer will respond to the oxygen sensor signal in closed-loop operation. If the sensor measures a low oxygen content, which indicates a rich mixture, it signals this fact to the computer. The computer then directs the fuel control actuator to lean the mixture. If the actuator makes the mixture too lean, the oxygen sensor will inform the computer, which then directs the fuel control actuator to again enrich the mixture. This is an ongoing process that occurs several times per second.

During closed-loop operation, engine speed, temperature and airflow sensors are used as modifiers to bias the timing or fuel decisions slightly. However, if one of the engine sensors signals a condition that requires more correction, the system opens loop to accommodate the corrections.

Adaptive Memory, Integrator, and Block Learn

The newer engine control systems can be programmed to learn from their own experience. This

adaptive memory feature allows the microprocessor to adjust its memory for computing open-loop operation. When the system is operating in closed loop, the microprocessor compares its open-loop calculated air-fuel ratios against the average duty cycle values in closed loop. If there is a substantial difference, the microprocessor corrects its memory so that it can match closed-loop control as closely as possible when it is in open loop. This data is stored in long-term RAM so that it can be used the next time the vehicle is started, providing more accurate air-fuel ratio control. It also allows a microprocessor to adapt to long-term changes in engine operation resulting from wear.

The electronic control module (ECM) on GM fuel-injected engine control systems contains a pair of functions called **integrator function** and **block-learn function.** These are responsible for making adjustments to the air-fuel ratio of a fuel-injected engine. As such, they eventually represent the injector on-time.

The block learn and integrator functions can be understood by seeing how the ECM calculates fuel-injection metering.

The ECM of a fuel-injected engine uses a base fuel calculation. When the oxygen sensor tells the ECM to enrich the air-fuel mixture, the ECM adds fuel to the base calculation. If the mixture needs to be leaner, the ECM subtracts fuel from the base calculation.

This information can be obtained from the ECM using a scan tool that connects to the ECM serial data transmission line through the ALCL or ALDL diagnostic connector. The scan tool monitors the inputs and outputs as received and sent by the ECM.

The scan tool reads the base fuel calculation as the number 128. If the scan tool reads a higher number, the ECM is adding fuel to the mixture. If the number is less than 128, the ECM is subtracting fuel. Such corrective action taken by the ECM is the integrator function, but it is effective only on a short-term basis. Block learn, or long-term correction, will change only if the integrator sees a condition that remains for a longer, calibrated period of time.

In summary, adaptive memory allows the engine computer to alter its program for existing conditions. The computer can adapt its program to such variables as:

- Engine wear
- Changes in fuel quality
- Changes in regular driving habits
- Changes in environmental conditions.

The integrator capability allows the computer to make short-term—second-by-second—corrections in fuel metering. Such corrections may be necessary, for example, until a vacuum leak is repaired.

Block-learn represents the long-term effects of integrator corrections. As such, it complements adaptive memory. If the computer continually must overcompensate fuel metering to maintain the stoichiometric ratio, it "learns" the correction and adapts its memory to make the correction factor part of its block-learn program.

AIR-FUEL RATIO, TIMING, AND EGR EFFECTS ON OPERATION

This is a good point to review the effects of air-fuel ratio, timing, and EGR operation on overall engine operation. This review will help you understand why only a computer can exercise the control necessary for maximum engine efficiency.

Air-Fuel Ratio

Even in an engine at normal operating temperature and light engine load, variations in air-fuel ratio have a dramatic effect on pollutants. When the ratio is richer than 14.7 to 1, HC and CO emissions are high, as would be expected with the increase in fuel consumption. However, NOx emissions are low. Torque is greatest at ratios between 12 and 16 to 1. Above 16 to 1, torque decreases, as does NOx, while HC increases. When the ratio is very lean, HC emissions also increase, as does fuel consumption. This is from engine misfiring caused by the lean mixture.

The stoichiometric air-fuel ratio

As you learned in Chapter Twelve, engine running air-fuel ratios for gasoline engines can range from 8 to 1 at the richest to about 18.5 to 1 at the leanest. With more or less fuel, the mixture will not burn. Ratios of approximately 12 to 1 to 13.5 to 1 produce maximum power. Ratios of approximately 15 to 1 to 16 to 1

Adaptive Memory: A feature of computer memory that allows the microprocessor to adjust its calibration for computing output commands, based on changes in sensor signal values over time.

Integrator Function: The ability of the computer to make short-term—immediate—corrections in fuel metering. Also called short-term fuel trim.

Block-Learn Function: The long-term effects of integrator corrections over time. If the computer continually makes the same correction, it "learns" the correction and adapts its memory to make the correction factor part of its fuel decision. Also called long-term fuel trim.

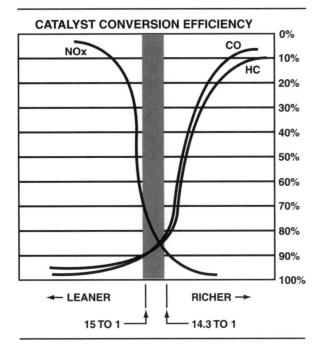

Figure 17-4. Three-way catalyst efficiency is maximized at a 14.7 to 1 air-fuel ratio. (GM)

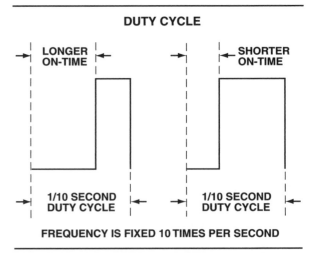

Figure 17-5. As the percentage of on-time is increased or decreased, the mixture is made leaner or richer.

produce maximum fuel economy. Between these two ranges lies the **stoichiometric air-fuel ratio** of 14.7 to 1.

"Stoichiometric" is a scientific term that indicates the air-fuel ratio which produces the most complete combustion with the fewest harmful byproducts. At a ratio of 14.7 to 1, the oxygen atoms in air and the hydrogen and carbon atoms in gasoline combine more completely for the best *compromise* of power, economy, and emission control.

Emission control is optimum at the stoichiometric ratio, if a three-way oxidation-reduction catalytic converter is used, figure 17-4. As the mixture gets richer, HC and CO conversion efficiency falls off. With leaner mixtures, NOx reduction efficiency falls off. As figure 17-4 shows, the efficiency range is very narrow—between 14.65 to 1 and 14.75 to 1. A fuel system without closed-loop control cannot maintain this narrow range.

Ratio control with carburetors and fuel injection
Two types of fuel-control actuators are used with carburetors:

- A solenoid mounted on or in the carburetor to control the fuel-metering rods, air bleeds, or both
- A solenoid-actuated air or vacuum valve to regulate float bowl pressure.

The computer uses a duty-cycle signal to control the device, varying the ratio of on-time to off-time according to the signal received from the O2 sensor, figure

17-5. As the percentage of on-time is increased or decreased, the mixture is made leaner or richer.

With fuel-injection systems, however, the computer exercises ratio control by switching one or more fuel injectors on and off. The switching rate is determined by engine speed, and the computer varies the time the injectors remain open (pulse width) to establish the air-fuel ratio. As the computer receives data from its input sensors, it lengthens the pulse width to supply additional fuel for operating conditions such as cold temperature and heavy load. In a similar manner, it shortens the pulse width to lean the mixture for operating conditions such as warm temperature or light load.

Ignition Timing

Variations in ignition timing also have a dramatic effect on fuel consumption and pollutants. When timing is correct for operating conditions, emissions are low and fuel economy is high. If timing is incorrect, fuel consumption and harmful emissions increase. Engine computers are programmed to provide the best timing for various combinations of engine speed, load and temperature conditions to lower emissions and prevent driveability problems.

Exhaust Gas Recirculation

Exhaust gas recirculation (EGR) is considered an efficient way of reducing NOx emissions without seriously affecting fuel economy, driveability, and HC emission control. Because the recirculation of exhaust gases lowers the combustion temperature, NOx emissions drop off sharply when exhaust gas is introduced into the air-fuel mixture. However, excessive use of

EGR leads to an increase in both HC emissions and fuel consumption. Again, the engine computer is programmed to deliver the percentage of exhaust gas that is the best compromise between NOx control, HC emissions, and fuel economy without detonation. On late-model cars, engineers use EGR to control detonation by lowering combustion temperatures. This allows ignition spark timing to be more advanced, for better fuel economy than would be possible without EGR.

Computer Integration

One of the primary values of a computer is its ability to integrate the operation of two or more individual, single-function systems to form a larger, more precise multiple-function system. For example, we have seen that centrifugal and vacuum advance mechanisms can control spark timing relative to engine speed and load. We know that fuel metering through a carburetor is controlled by airflow, and that ported vacuum with temperature control can manage basic EGR flow. Integrating such independent systems through a computer provides faster, more precise regulation of each system, and allows the computer to calculate the effect of changing several variables at the same time. Computer integration now is proceeding in two directions: body computer modules (BCM) with multiplexing, and smarter engine-control computers.

Body computer modules

During the mid-1980s, body computer modules and multiplexing appeared to be the trend of the future. A body computer module is one that has been designated a "master" computer in an automobile, with various other system computers functioning both on their own, and as "slaves" to the BCM. As you learned in Chapter Five, the master computer module uses multiplexing to communicate with other computer modules in the car, and acts like a traffic control officer at a four-way intersection in controlling how and when the modules communicate with each other.

Smarter computers

The trend toward multiplexing has cooled somewhat in the face of computers with faster microprocessors and larger memories. While some manufacturers continue to link separate computer modules by multiplexing, others have turned to smarter, faster engine control computers as a way of handling multiple functions and systems within a single unit. One example of this approach is the use of electronic automatic transmissions (EATs). The early EATs were controlled by their own module, which interfaced with the engine-control computer to determine torque converter clutch application and shift scheduling. More

recent EATs have their computer program integrated with that of the engine-control computer. This integration has caused some manufacturers, like GM, to redesignate their electronic control module (ECM) as a powertrain control module (PCM). In the foreseeable future, it appears that both methods of computer integration will continue to be used.

Engine Mapping

The programs for engine computers consist of three parts:

- The basic mathematical instructions for processing data
- Data on engine and vehicle fixed values such as engine displacement, number of cylinders, fuel system type, compression ratio, transmission type and gear ratios, vehicle weight, and accessories
- Variable data such as combinations of engine speed, temperature and intake airflow.

The first two groups of data are constant values and are loaded into the computer memory from engineering design information. To load the third category of variable performance values into memory, engineers use a process called engine mapping.

The car is operated on a dynamometer while speed, spark timing, fuel metering, engine load, and other factors are adjusted manually for the best combination of operating conditions. The information derived from this operation is collected by a larger computer and loaded into the vehicle computer PROM.

Engine mapping creates a three-dimensional graph of engine operation, figure 17-6. The computer PROM remembers this performance graph and responds to sensor input data to adjust ignition timing, fuel metering, and emission control for best overall performance.

ELECTRONIC FUEL-INJECTION PRINCIPLES

Gasoline fuel injection provides the fuel metering for many late-model engine-control systems. Gasoline injection systems can be classified as:

- Mechanical or electronic systems
- Continuous or intermittent injection
- Port or throttle-body injection.

Stoichiometric Air-Fuel Ratio: The air-fuel ratio of approximately 14.7 to 1 that provides the most complete combustion with the fewest harmful byproducts.

Figure 17-6. This engine mapping graph is a three-dimensional representation of ignition timing for a specific vehicle.

These categories are not always clear-cut, however. Mechanical systems have many electronic parts, for example. Most electronic systems provide intermittent (pulsed) injection, but Chrysler's V8 throttle-body system is an electronic continuous-injection system.

Air-Fuel Mixture Control

Fuel metering through a carburetor is controlled by air pressure and air volume (airflow into an engine). In a carburetor, fuel metering is controlled by the difference between air pressure in the fuel bowl and air pressure in the carburetor venturi. Airflow is determined by the pumping capacity of the engine, the airflow capacity of the carburetor, and the position of the throttle. In a fuel injection system, however, the fuel is isolated from intake airflow. All injection systems, therefore, use one of the following sensor systems to measure intake air and meter fuel accordingly:

- Airflow meter and intake air temperature sensor
- Manifold pressure sensor, intake air temperature sensor and engine speed sensor
- Air mass sensor.

Carburetors and fuel injection systems both provide rich air-fuel ratios of 12.5 to 1 to 13.5 to 1 and lean ratios of 15 to 1 to 16 to 1 for the full range of warm engine operating needs. Late-model carburetors and fuel-injection systems used with electronic control systems have fuel metering capabilities to maintain the stoichiometric air-fuel ratio of 14.7 to 1. All gasoline injection systems have three basic subsystems:

- Fuel delivery subsystem:
  - Fuel pump
  - Fuel filter, or multiple filters
  - Fuel lines, including individual lines to port-injection nozzles

Figure 17-7. Solenoid actions intermittently open the EFI nozzles. (Volvo)

  - Pressure regulator to maintain the required, constant fuel pressure at the fuel injectors
  - Fuel injectors.
- Air control subsystem:
  - Throttle
  - Idle speed (air bypass or throttle angle) control device
- Electronic control subsystem
  - Engine operating-condition sensors
  - Output drivers to fuel injectors and idle air control device.

You will study these as you progress through this chapter and learn about electronic engine control systems.

Electronic Injection Nozzles

To understand fuel injection as part of a complete engine-control system, you must understand the operation and control of electronic injection nozzles. An electronic injection nozzle is simply a specialized solenoid, figure 17-7. It has an armature and a needle or ball valve. A spring holds the needle or ball closed against the valve seat, and the armature opens the valve when it receives a current pulse from the system computer. When the solenoid is energized, it unseats the valve to inject fuel.

The injector always opens the same distance, and the fuel pressure is maintained at a constant value by the fuel pump and pressure regulator. The amount of

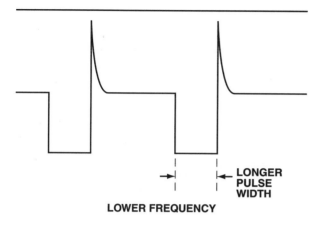

LONGER PULSE WIDTH

LOWER FREQUENCY

SHORTER PULSE WIDTH

HIGHER FREQUENCY

Figure 17-8. The longer the pulse width the longer the injector is on and consequently more fuel is delivered.

fuel delivered by the injector depends on the amount of time that the nozzle is open. This is the injector pulse width: the time in milliseconds that the nozzle is open.

The system computer varies its signal's pulse width to supply the amount of fuel that the engine needs at a specific moment. A longer pulse width delivers more fuel; a shorter pulse width delivers less fuel.

Pulse width is the amount of the time an electronic fuel injector is energized, measured in milliseconds. In figure 17-8, the waveforms show the difference between longer and shorter pulse width. The longer the pulse width, the longer the injector is on and consequently, the more fuel delivered. A shorter pulse width delivers less fuel. A cold engine's fuel injector waveform will have a longer pulse width than an engine at operating temperature. An engine under heavy load will have a longer pulse width than an engine with no load. The ability to vary or regulate

the injector's pulse width is called "modulation." The system computer calculates the necessary pulse width and duty cycle from information provided by system sensors. Modern digital computers operate fast enough to change injector pulse width in fractions of a second to maintain precise fuel metering.

Mechanical Fuel Injection

Mechanical fuel injection first entered the automobile market in the late 1940s. Stuart Hilborn designed and built one of the the first mechanical injection systems for race cars in the late 1940s. In 1957, Chevrolet installed the Rochester Ramjet mechanical injection system on Corvettes. It worked well but was dropped from the option list after 1965. A European company named Bosch built a major mechanical gasoline injection system called the Bosch K-Jetronic system, figure 17-9, introduced in the mid-1970s on several European cars. The K-Jetronic system uses fuel pressure in the injector lines to open the nozzles and continuously deliver fuel to the intake manifold. Versions of the K-Jetronic system were produced until the mid-1990s. Later versions were combined with the Bosch Motronic, or digital motor electronics (DME) system, which you will study later in this chapter.

Electronic Fuel Injection

All electronic fuel injection systems operate on the principles outlined previously, but there are two basically different system designs:

- Throttle-body injection
- Port injection.

Throttle-body injection

In a throttle-body system, one or two injectors are mounted on a throttle body located on the intake manifold, figure 17-10. The fuel pump delivers fuel to the injectors by an electric fuel pump, and a pressure regulator in the throttle body maintains constant fuel pressure at the injectors, figure 17-11. The one or two injectors deliver fuel in pulses. Pulse width and frequency are regulated by the computer. Fuel distribution from the throttle body is similar to fuel distribution from a carburetor through the intake manifold. However, the computer-controlled injection regulates fuel metering more precisely than a carburetor and improves atomization as fuel enters the intake airflow.

Throttle-body systems have been used at some time by most manufacturers since the early 1980s. Figure 17-12 shows typical throttle-body injection assemblies used by Chrysler, GM, and Ford.

Figure 17-9. The Bosch K-Jetronic mechanical gasoline injection system. (Bosch)

Figure 17-10. A throttle-body injection system resembles a carburetor.

Figure 17-11. A throttle-body injection system can use one or two injectors.

From 1981 through 1983, Chrysler used a TBI system in limited applications for V8 engines that injected fuel continuously, rather than in variable pulses, figure 17-13. A small variable-speed, constant-displacement pump in the throttle body receives a varying voltage signal from the computer. This pump speed changes to vary the fuel pressure and volume at the injectors, which regulates fuel metering.

A

FUEL INLET CHAMBER

AIR INTAKE

WIRING HARNESS CONNECTOR

AUTOMATIC IDLE SPEED (AIS) MOTOR

FUEL PRESSURE REGULATOR

THROTTLE POSITION SENSOR

CHRYSLER-HOLLEY-BENDIX HIGH-PRESSURE THROTTLE BODY ASSEMBLY

B

GM MODEL 400 CROSSFIRE INJECTION (CFI) ASSEMBLY

C

FUEL INLET

FUEL RETURN

FUEL PRESSURE SCHRADER (TEST) VALVE

FUEL INJECTORS

IDLE-SPEED CONTROL MOTOR

FORD CFI FUEL-CHARGING (THROTTLE BODY) ASSEMBLY

Figure 17-12. Examples of late-model throttle-body systems used by Chrysler, GM, and Ford.

Port injection

Some port injection systems are actually older designs than TBI systems. The first electronic port injection systems used in production were the Bosch D-Jetronic and L-Jetronic, introduced on several European cars in the late 1960s and early 1970s. The L-Jetronic system, figure 17-14, is the basis for several systems used by GM, Ford, Toyota, Nissan, and other manufacturers in the 1980s.

Port injection systems have one injector for each cylinder, mounted in the intake manifold near the cylinder head intake port, figure 17-15. This location allows each injector to deliver fuel as closely as possible to the intake valve and to ensure equal fuel distribution to all cylinders. The intake manifold has only a throttle at its inlet (and an airflow sensor on many systems). Because the manifold does not have to hold a carburetor and distribute the air-fuel mixture to all cylinders, fuel distribution and condensation problems are reduced.

Port injection systems have an injector for each cylinder, but all systems do not operate, or "fire" the injectors in the same way. Some systems fire the injectors in groups, some fire all injectors simultaneously, and others fire the injectors individually in sequence. Port injection systems can be classified in one of four ways to define injector control:

- Group, single fire
- Group, double fire
- Simultaneous, double fire
- Sequential.

In a group single-fire system, the injectors are divided into two equal groups and fired alternately. One group fires for one engine revolution; the other group fires for the next revolution. Only one injector pulse is used to deliver the entire fuel charge for each intake stroke. This kind of system is simple and economical to build, but it is not as precise as the other systems. Because only one injector in a group can fire close to the time that the intake valve opens, the fuel from the other injectors in that group must wait until the intake valve opens. Also, because a new fuel charge is delivered only once for each engine revolution, the computer must wait longer to change the air-fuel ratio.

In a grouped double-fire system, the injector groups fire alternately, but both groups fire once for each engine revolution or twice for each intake stroke. Two injector pulses make up the fuel charge for each cylinder; each pulse delivers half. The air-fuel total mixture remains in the manifold for a shorter time, and fuel-metering changes can be made faster than with a single-fire system.

Figure 17-13. This Chrysler TBI system uses continuous, rather than variable-pulse, injection.

Simultaneous double-fire systems are common on many four-cylinder engines. All injectors fire at the same time, once for each engine revolution. Because there are two revolutions between the intake strokes for each cylinder, each injector pulse delivers half of the fuel for one intake stroke. This system is easy to program and can readjust the air-fuel ratio relatively quickly for a four-cylinder engine. Figure 17-16 is a diagram of simultaneous double-fire injector operation.

Sequential injection is the newest and most precise electronic injection-control method. The computer fires each injector individually, just before the intake valve opens. The mixture does not lie in the manifold, and fuel metering can be adjusted instantly from one injector to the next. Sequential systems are electronically complex and have been expensive to build. Advances in digital microprocessor technology, however, have made these systems economically available on late-model cars.

Diagnosing Fuel Injector Problems

Fuel injectors and the circuits that control them are suspect when an intermittent problem arises. The injectors can be removed and tested individually using injector test equipment. Injectors are inspected and tested for tip damage, pintle sticking and proper spray patterns, figure 17-17. It is important to determine if there is contamination within the injector. An injector pressure drop or flow test will often show obvious problems.

Fuel injector circuits can be monitored and diagnosed using lab scopes and current probes. Lab scopes sample 1,000 times faster than digital multimeters and 100,000 times faster than scan tools. Resistance readings on injectors are not always accurate because most ohmmeters will apply only 0.5 volts into the coil windings to sample ohms values. In operational mode, fuel injectors are supplied with system or alternator voltage that creates heat throughout the windings. High resistance or open circuits can be detected with an ohmmeter. Noid lights or injector test lights should be used where recommended by the manufacturer. Noid lights will only load some circuits with less than 250 milliamps, not stressing the circuit to the limit, which peaks at 6 amps in many injector systems. In these cases, the manufacturer recommends a 12-volt test light to dynamically test the circuit for correct operation.

Figure 17-14. The Bosch L-Jetronic system has been used on various Japanese, European, and domestic vehicles. (Bosch)

Figure 17-15. Port injection systems use one injector for each cylinder.

The waveform of a fuel injector signal will vary depending upon the type of driver circuit. Some injector driver circuits contain a current limiting device that protects the injector coils from high current. To open an injector requires a considerable amount of magnetic force to overcome spring pressures. Once open, current limiting begins because it takes much less energy to hold the injector open.

Lab scopes display fuel injector waveforms that contain detailed information for fuel system diagnostics, much like ignition primary circuit patterns. The first example describes the most simple and common pattern referred to as a **Saturated Driver**. This system uses a current limiting resistor in the circuit. This example explains the sequence of events in the injector voltage pattern. Later, these voltage patterns will be compared to current ramp waveforms to further explain injector diagnosis.

Saturated Driver: A fuel injector circuit that limits current using an external resistor on the power feed side of the circuit.

Figure 17-16. Four-cylinder engine cycles, with all injectors firing at the same time. (Bosch)

Figure 17-17. Various defective injector spray patterns.

Figure 17-18. A known-good saturated driver injector pattern will have clean transitions with near vertical leading and trailing slopes.

Figure 17-19. On peak and hold type injectors, there are two distinct spikes on the injector trace.

1. Primary voltage is supplied to the injector at point 1, figure 17-18. A typical supply is 13.5 volts. This point, commonly called "open circuit voltage," is critical because injector coil saturation will fail without the necessary voltage.

2. Most injectors are controlled on the ground circuit, and it is at point 2 that the computer completes the circuit to ground. The falling edge should be clean and straight down. A "slow" falling edge indicates a driver failure while high resistance in the ground circuit will not allow the signal to drop completely to zero.

3. Current saturation takes place at this falling edge of the waveform but quickly flattens the waveform to indicate the voltage drop across the injector windings at point 3. Point 3 should come down close to zero and rise slightly. This distance is commonly called the pulse width and is measured in milliseconds.

4. Point 4 shows the electrical condition of the injector windings. The height of this voltage spike (inductive kick) is proportional to the amount of injector coil windings and the current flow through them. Different manufacturers' injectors will display slightly different voltage spikes. Most saturation type injectors will display about 35-volt peak values.

5. Point 5 shows the voltage dissipating back to supply voltage as the injector closes. Sometimes the waveform will oscillate slightly, depending upon the manufacturer, and some will display a "pintle hump" in the slope at the point the injector pintle closes. If more than one hump is visible in the slope, the pintle may be distorted and not closing properly.

The second most common injector waveform is the **Peak and Hold Driver.** Current is controlled by regulating the ground side with an internal PCM control circuit. A transistor switches the control circuit on and off and the circuit has a built-in resistor (internal) to limit current through the injector. These injectors are used on domestic TBI and some PFI systems. In most cases, peak and hold type injector windings will have between 1 to 3 ohms resistance while saturation type injectors will have from 12 to 16 ohms resistance.

1. Primary voltage is supplied to the injector at point 1, figure 17-19. A typical supply is 13.5 volts.

2. Point 2 indicates the computer completing the circuit to ground. The falling edge should be clean and straight down. A "slow" falling edge indicates a driver failure while high resistance in the ground circuit will not allow the signal to drop completely to zero.

3. Point 3 indicates the voltage drop across the injector windings. Point 3 should come down close to zero and rise slightly.

Peak and Hold Driver: A fuel injector circuit that limits current using a transistor to switch to a current limiting resistor circuit within the PCM.

4. Point 4 is the first voltage spike. The height of this voltage spike (inductive kick) is proportional to the number of injector coil windings and the current flow through them. This is the first stage in the current limiting control. Be aware, the time between injector opening and the start of the current control (first spike) is fixed and does not vary with engine speed or load. The amount of time the current limiting circuit is active determines injector pulse width.

5. Point 5 is the voltage being brought toward ground by the current limiting circuit after the circuit switching occurs. Sometimes the waveform will ring slightly. The voltage eventually levels off into the hold pattern. This line should remain flat and stable. Here, the injector waits to be shut off.

6. The second spike occurs as the transistor opens to switch off the injector. The actual on-time is measured from the beginning of point 3 to the start of point 6. The inductive spike is created by the turning off of current and the collapsing magnetic field. The injector pulse width on peak and hold injectors is indicated across Point 7. Sometimes the waveform will oscillate slightly, depending upon the manufacturer, and some will display a "pintle hump" in the slope at the point the injector pintle closes. If more than one hump is visible in the slope, the pintle may be distorted and not closing properly.

A third and less common injector waveform is the **Pulse Width Modulated (PWM) Driver.** Current is controlled by a transistor that toggles OFF and ON rather than by a current limiting resistor.

1. Point 1 is primary voltage. This injector "off" period should show steady open-circuit voltage, figure 17-20.

2. Point 2 can be ground-controlled or on some PNP systems, the switching signal is controlled by a transistor in the computer. On power-side controlled PNP systems, the waveform may appear upside down depending on the type of scope used. Expect an abrupt drop (2) to zero as the injector opens.

3. Point 3 indicates voltage drop across the injector windings. A slight rise from ground is normal.

4. Point 4 indicates transistor switching the injector OFF. This is the first voltage spike that should reach peak values.

5. Point 5 indicates the time the transistor is switching ON and OFF rapidly. This limits total current. The low points of the square wave should be close to 0 volt.

Figure 17-20. The waveform on PWM injector drivers will pulse from ground to source voltage between peaks.

6. Point 6 indicates the transistor is open, thereby allowing the injector to close. Here again, the second voltage spike should reach peak voltage.

It is best to develop a working knowledge of voltage waveforms as well as the current waveforms for the same type of systems. Current and voltage can be displayed at the same time on many dual trace Lab scopes. Figure 17-21 shows a typical voltage waveform synchronous with a current waveform for the same injector.

Each manufacturer's fuel injector is designed with windings with set resistance and magnetic inductance. This will cause the current ramp to rise at a certain rate and time base. Manufacturer's specifications can be obtained but as a general rule, the steeper the current ramp, the lower the injector resistance. For example, a low-impedance TBI injector will rise about 60° (current ramp) with a 2-millisecond interval. A higher impedance injector will display a 45-degree rise in the current ramp. Here are some examples of current waveforms and their diagnostic applications for fuel injectors.

The first example is a saturated driver ON-OFF injector circuit, used mostly on systems where the injectors are fired in groups or on sequentially fired injectors. The injector pulse width begins when the driver circuit turns on and stops when the driver circuit is turned off. Figure 17-22 shows the current ramp for a typical saturated driver circuit. Figure 17-23 shows the current ramp on a saturated driver injector on a Ford 3.0L V6 engine. Injectors number 1, 3 and 5 pulse together and then cylinder number 2, 4 and 6 are pulsed together. Known-good dynamic

MEMORY 4
20 V/div
2ms/div

MEMORY 5
200 mV/div
2ms/div

Figure 17-21. Voltage waveform (above) and a current ramp waveform (below). Viewed on a dual trace oscilloscope.

Figure 17-22. Current ramp waveform of a saturated driver injector circuit.

current draw for each group of pulsed injectors is 2 amps. The waveform clearly indicates a 2.5 amp current draw on one of the groupings. Each injector was tested and one injector displayed only 8 ohms resistance (12 ohms normal). This one bad injector created an additional 500 milliamp current draw.

The next example is a peak and hold circuit. This type of circuit is most common on throttle body injection (TBI) systems. The injector, which is mounted on the throttle body, is usually between 2 to 3 ohms (low impedance) and uses about 3 to 4 amps current to flow through the coil windings (peak) and then reduce amperage (hold) to a maximum of about 1 amp. Figure 17-24 shows the current ramp waveform for a TBI injector with the current limited at 1 amp. When GM Dual TBI systems experience injector problems

Pulse Width Modulated (PWM) Driver: A fuel injector circuit that uses a pulsing "hold" signal to keep the injector open.

Figure 17-23. The abnormally high current ramp waveform of a Ford 3.0L V6 engine with group pulsed injectors (lower waveform) indicates one injector creating excess current draw.

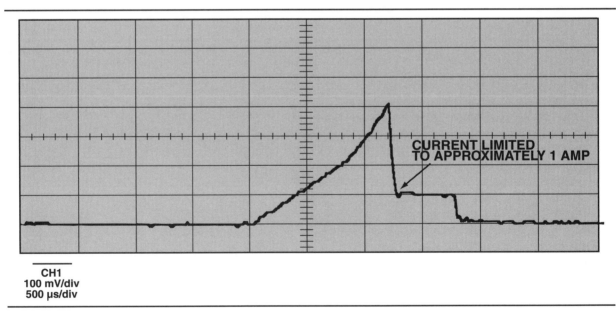

Figure 17-24. A normal current ramp waveform of a peak and hold injector circuit on a GM TBI system.

resulting in rough idle, poor fuel mileage and stalling, a weak injector driver should be suspect. Weak injector drivers cause the HOLD portion of the injector waveform to oscillate instead of holding a steady ON signal to the injector. The voltage/current waveform patterns clearly indicate vibrating and ringing in the circuit, figure 17-25.

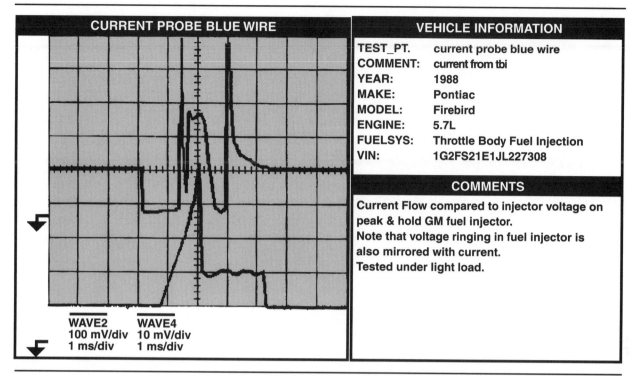

CURRENT PROBE BLUE WIRE

WAVE2
100 mV/div
1 ms/div

WAVE4
10 mV/div
1 ms/div

VEHICLE INFORMATION

TEST_PT.	current probe blue wire
COMMENT:	current from tbi
YEAR:	1988
MAKE:	Pontiac
MODEL:	Firebird
ENGINE:	5.7L
FUELSYS:	Throttle Body Fuel Injection
VIN:	1G2FS21E1JL227308

COMMENTS

Current Flow compared to injector voltage on peak & hold GM fuel injector.
Note that voltage ringing in fuel injector is also mirrored with current.
Tested under light load.

Figure 17-25. These defective peak and hold voltage and current ramp waveform patterns clearly show excess ringing in the hold portion of the sequence on both the voltage spike and the current limiting on a GM TBI system.

CURRENT PROBE HAS BEEN CLAMPED ON BACKWARDS TO INVERT THE WAVEFORM

6.25
4.68
3.12
1.56
0.00
AMPS

1.0 ms / div

Figure 17-26. The waveform of an injector that uses a switching transistor to control the power side of its circuit.

The next example is a PWM driver injector circuit. It uses a switching transistor in the computer to pulse the power side of the fuel injector instead of the negative ground activated circuits in the previous examples. These injectors are grounded all the time and the voltage pattern is upside down. As a result, it is necessary to turn the current probe upside down to flip the waveform pattern, figure 17-26. Some of these systems use an injector current limiting resistor block mounted near the radiator for cooling purposes.

The last example uses a switching transistor in the injector circuit. This type of injector circuit is used on only a select few manufacturers' vehicles including the Mazda RX-7, Subaru TBI systems and a few other models. Figure 17-27 shows a current ramp waveform for a PWM driver injector circuit. Notice that the circuit ramps much like the peak and hold injector circuit but oscillates while "holding".

SYSTEM SENSORS

As we learned in Chapter Four, a sensor is an input device used to change temperature, motion, light, pressure, and other forms of energy into voltage signals that a computer can use. Most sensors are analog; that is, they send a voltage signal proportional to the

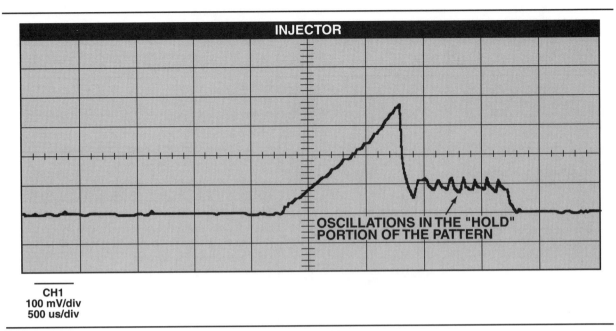

INJECTOR

OSCILLATIONS IN THE "HOLD" PORTION OF THE PATTERN

CH1
100 mV/div
500 us/div

Figure 17-27. A voltage waveform of a Bosch PWM injector driver.

variable they are measuring. Since digital computers cannot understand analog signals, the computer must convert the analog signals to a digital form for processing.

Switches and Timers

A switch is a simple form of a digital sensor. A switch is either open or closed; it can be used in a pull up or a pull down computer sensor circuit, figure 17-28. In a pull up circuit, when the switch is closed, the computer reads the available circuit voltage and when the switch is open, the computer reads 0 volts. In a pull down circuit, when the switch is closed, the available circuit voltage drops across a fixed load and the computer reads 0 volts. When the switch is open, the computer reads the available circuit voltage. In either case, the switch provides a digital off or on signal.

Resistors

Most automotive sensors are a resistor of some type. Resistors can provide an analog voltage signal proportional to the variable condition they are measuring. Since resistors cannot generate but only modify a voltage, they require a reference voltage from the computer.

A thermistor is used as a two-wire variable thermal resistor, to signal the temperature of engine coolant or air temperature, figure 17-29. The computer measures the amount of voltage drop across the thermistor. As the temperature increases, resistance and the amount of voltage drop across the thermistor decreases. The

reason the circuit works this way is that it is a series circuit that shares two loads—a fixed internal resistance in the PCM and the variable resistance of the thermistor. The computer actually is reading the voltage drop across the thermistor, not the fixed resistor.

A **potentiometer** is a three-wire variable resistor. The computer provides reference voltage to one end of the resistor; the other end is grounded. A movable contact that slides across the resistor connects to a third terminal. Since the reference voltage remains constant, the return voltage varies only relative to the position of the movable contact. Figure 17-30 shows a potentiometer connected to a vane airflow sensor used to measure the volume of airflow in a fuel-injection system. The potentiometer is activated by the moving vane and sends an analog signal to the computer.

A piezoresistive sensor is one whose signal voltage varies according to the pressure or force applied to it. Like a thermistor, most have two connections. One terminal receives the reference voltage; the second terminal returns the signal voltage to the computer. Engine detonation sensors are piezoresistive devices. Some barometric and manifold pressure sensors use a piezoresistive network.

Transformers

Transformer sensors, like resistors, receive a reference voltage and send an analog signal back to the computer. A transformer contains a movable core, allowing the coupling between the single input and dual output windings to vary according to core position. When the reference voltage is applied to the

Figure 17-28. A switch is either open or closed; it can be used in a pull up or a pull down computer sensor circuit.

input winding, the signal voltage generated in each output winding is equal as long as the core remains centered, figure 17-31. As the core moves away from center, the output voltage of one winding exceeds that of the other winding. The difference between the two output winding voltages is processed into one signal in proportion to the amount of movement. The transformer is often used as a **manifold absolute pressure (MAP)** sensor.

Potentiometer: A variable resistor with three terminals. Return signal voltage is taken from a terminal attached to a movable contact or wiper that passes over the resistor.

Manifold Absolute Pressure (MAP): Pressure in the intake manifold that is referenced to true zero at sea level instead of gauge pressure zero which is referenced to 14.7 psi absolute.

Figure 17-30. Vane-type airflow meters use a potentiometer to signal the position of the vane (amount of airflow) to the computer. (Ford).

TEMPERATURE	THERMISTOR RESISTANCE	SCANNER AND COMPARATOR VOLTAGE
HIGH	LOW	LOW
LOW	HIGH	HIGH

Figure 17-29. The PCM measures the voltage drop across the thermistor's variable resistance circuit in this engine coolant or air temperature sensor circuit.

Generators

This type of sensor does not require a reference voltage. It generates its own signal voltage. The magnetic pulse generator used in a breakerless distributor is one common example. The rotating trigger wheel varies the reluctance around a magnetic pole piece and pickup coil, figure 17-32. The signals produced can be used as a frequency reference.

Pulse generators also have been used to indicate firing order, engine speed, and crankshaft and/or camshaft position. Manufacturers have used a pulse generator to respond to a cutout or tooth on the crankshaft flywheel or harmonic balancer and camshaft.

Zirconia Exhaust Gas Oxygen Sensors (O2S)

The concept of feedback fuel-metering systems requires an exhaust gas oxygen sensor (O2S). The sensor is basically a **galvanic battery** that can generate from 0.0 to more than 1.0 volt by comparing the oxygen in the exhaust to the oxygen in the outside air.

Figure 17-31. A transformer creates a voltage differential between two output windings.

The typical oxygen sensor contains two platinum-surface electrodes separated by a ceramic zirconia element, figure 17-33. The inner surface (positive terminal) of the zirconia element is open to the atmosphere; the outer surface (negative terminal) is in contact with the exhaust gases. The zirconia element is an insulator when cold, and a semiconductor at operating temperature. The zirconia element is combined with oxides to create a porous surface. Oxygen molecules pass into the crystaline structure of the zirconia oxides and create an electrical potential. The electrical potential varies with the amount of oxygen molecules.

For comparative purposes, the atmosphere at sea level contains 21 percent oxygen; very rich exhaust gases contain approximately 0.5 percent. A large differential in the amount of oxygen contacting the inner and outer surfaces results in greater conductivity, and causes the sensor to send a voltage signal above 450 millivolts proportional to the degree of richness, up to its capacity, figure 17-34A. Very lean exhaust contains a high percentage of oxygen. This reduces the

Figure 17-32. The magnetic field expands and collapses as the trigger wheel's teeth move past. This induces a varying-strength voltage in the pickup coil.

Figure 17-33. This late-model, single-wire exhaust gas oxygen (O2) sensor uses a zirconia element. (Buick)

differential, resulting in less conductivity and a voltage signal under 450 millivolts, figure 17-34B. We can summarize the operation of an oxygen sensor as follows:

- When exhaust oxygen content is low (rich mixture), sensor voltage is high.
- When exhaust oxygen content is high (lean mixture), sensor voltage is low.

■ New Sensors

As technology advances and fuel and emissions systems become more complex, sensor design and development also advance. In the 1980s, ABS and airbags required additional sensors and actuators. The 1990s brought OBD II and a host of drivetrain sensors. The new century will require advanced technology for electronic stability control systems, collision avoidance systems, oil pressure control and climate control systems.

A yaw rate sensor determines vehicle sway around corners or during severe swerves under heavy braking. Design engineers are working on a dual rate sensor that combines yaw rate with linear acceleration. Based on silicon micro machining, the yaw rate sensor consists of two packed masses of a specialized material sandwiched in the middle with an accelerometer.

An oil viscosity sensor is being developed that senses oil viscosity based on a vibrating piezoelectric element. Oscillating viscometers measure the rate of oil degradation by the number of oscillations caused by drag.

A smaller, thimble-sized oxygen sensor is being designed to improve closed-loop status. This tiny O2 sensor uses a low resistance shield that allows the heater to warm the O2 sensor within 15 seconds thereby allowing the system to switch to closed loop very quickly.

A more sensitive fluid pressure sensor is being designed to detect high pressures in hydraulic oil, brake fluid, engine oil, transmission fluid and other fluids. This extra sensitive sensor will detect transmission oil pressure and correct for smoother shifts on the clutch packs. Other examples of the fluid high pressure sensor is using high pressure sensors in the AC refrigerant lines and power steering fluid lines to compensate the engine idle control system during activation of the AC and power steering systems.

A direct thermal detection system can deploy a child's airbag with accuracy during impact. Engineers are working on a system that detects extremely slight temperature differences in the front and rear seats to help the computer detect airbag deployment conditions.

Galvanic Battery: A battery that generates voltage based on a difference in oxygen content on either side of its two electrodes.

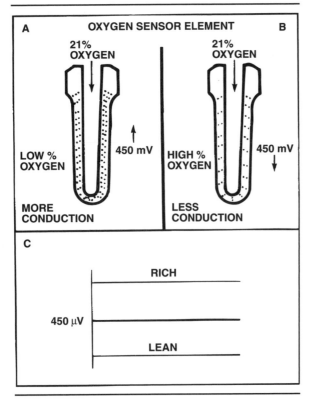

Figure 17-34. An O2 sensor measures the oxygen differential between ambient air and exhaust gases. (Buick)

Figure 17-35. The O2 sensor provides its fastest response at the stoichiometric air-fuel ratio of 14.7 to 1.

Figure 17-35 shows the operating range of a sensor at about 1,472°F (800°C). Sensor voltage changes fastest at an air-fuel ratio of 14.7 to 1, which makes it ideal for switching across the stoichiometric ratio.

Another important point about oxygen sensors is that *they measure oxygen; they do not measure air-fuel ratio.* The computer regulates feedback control of the air-fuel mixture in response to the information sent from the sensors (O2 sensor, MAF sensor, TPS, barometric pressure sensor, etc.). The oxygen sensor is simply indicating to the computer the amount of O2 molecules in the exhaust. The oxygen sensor does not control engine driveability. To accurately diagnose the system, first determine if the O2 sensor is NOT defective and then determine why the fuel, ignition, and emissions systems are malfunctioning. For example, if the engine misfires, a large amount of oxygen remains in the unburned mixture that passes out with the exhaust. In this case, the sensor will deliver a false, overly lean mixture signal. This is one example of why computer control of ignition and EGR is necessary for correct fuel-metering control.

As you learned in Chapter Four and when you studied other sensors in this chapter, the computer sends a reference voltage to resistive sensors for sensor operation. This type of oxygen sensor is a generator and does not need a reference voltage for operation. Some computers, however, use a 450 mv reference voltage as a comparison to the sensor voltage signal, figure 17-34C. This internal reference voltage is also used for fuel-metering decisions during open-loop operation when the computer ignores the oxygen sensor.

All oxygen sensors must warm to at least 572°F (300°C) before they will generate a usable signal. Oxygen sensors provide their fastest response to mixture changes at about 1472°F (800°C). This is the reason for using open-loop fuel control on a cold engine.

The oxygen sensor is installed in the exhaust manifold or header pipe directly in the path of the exhaust gas stream where it can monitor both the exhaust gas and ambient air. Some V-type engines use an oxygen sensor in each manifold. The exact location and placement of the sensor vary according to design, because engineers position it where it will be the most efficient.

All zirconium-dioxide oxygen sensors work on the principles just discussed, but they are not all built the same way. They may have one, two, or three wires that connect to the vehicle wiring harness. Some sensors, figure 17-36, had two wires and were grounded through the computer or to some point on the chassis or engine. Some sensors use a single wire for signal output and are grounded through the threads on their outer shell to the exhaust pipe or manifold.

INSULATING TUBE

SIGNAL
TERMINAL

GROUND
TERMINAL

SILICONE
BOOT

AMBIENT AIR

EXHAUST
MANIFOLD

HARNESS
CONNECTOR

PROTECTIVE SHIELD

EXHAUST GASES

Figure 17-36. An early double-wire O2 sensor.

Some oxygen sensors are equipped with heaters so they reach operating temperature quickly and are ready for closed-loop operation sooner. Heated oxygen sensors are equipped with three or four wires.

Some sensors have a silicone boot to protect the sensor and to provide a vent for ambient air circulation. The positioning of a boot (when used) is important. If the boot is seated too far down on the sensor body, it can block the air vent, resulting in an inaccurate signal to the computer. Oxygen sensors can be divided into the following basic types:

- Standard unheated
- Water-resistant unheated
- Water-resistant heated
- Waterproof heated.

To make oxygen sensors water-resistant and waterproof, it was necessary to design them with a different ambient air vent. Older designs have their ambient air vent at the sensor, but the water-resistant and waterproof sensors receive their ambient air through the sensor lead wires and connector.

Titania Exhaust Gas Oxygen Sensors

Zirconia oxygen sensors have proven themselves during more than two decades of use, but oxygen sensors containing titanium-dioxide or titania-sensing elements also are being used by Jeep, Toyota, and other

manufacturers. Both types of sensors provide a feedback signal indicating how rich or lean the exhaust is. Unlike the zirconia sensor, however, the titania sensor does not generate voltage. Instead, it reports exhaust oxygen content by acting as a variable resistor.

The computer provides a reference voltage to the sensor. As the oxygen content of the exhaust changes, the resistance of the titania-sensing element varies. Since the resistance of the sensing element also can be affected by temperature, a heating element is incorporated in the sensor to maintain a constant temperature of approximately 1,475°F (850° C).

Figure 17-37 shows the heated titania oxygen sensor as used on 1987-90 4.0-liter Jeep engines. The computer provides the sensor with a 5-volt reference voltage. The signal voltage is measured between the sensor and a fixed resistor in series with the sensor. As sensor resistance changes, the signal voltage also changes. With a rich mixture (low exhaust oxygen content), the sensor signal voltage is below 2.5 volts. With a lean mixture (high exhaust oxygen content), sensor signal voltage exceeds 2.5 volts. Although signal voltage direction, relative to oxygen content of the exhaust gas, is the opposite of that of a zirconia oxygen sensor, the computer is programmed to respond to it correctly and make the proper fuel-metering correction.

Fuel Systems and Catalytic Converter Diagnosis Using Oxygen Sensor Information

O2 sensors can be used to diagnose a variety of fuel and emission system driveability problems. Oxygen sensors should be capable of producing a waveform with peaks above 900 millivolts (RICH) and bottom values of less than 100 millivolts (LEAN) with two to four complete cycles within ten seconds at idle speed, figure 17-38. The vehicle must be at operating temperature and the transmission in Park or Neutral. Once the rpm levels are raised, oscillations will increase rapidly as the feedback control system regulates the increased air-fuel ratio for the increased engine speed. The O2 sensor will display much different waveform patterns when the engine is under load and at high rpm. The vehicle can be tested on a dynamometer or while driving with a Digital Storage Oscilloscope (DSO). Under load, with increased fuel delivery, the O2 sensor signal may increase to above 900 millivolts. Acceleration will also increase fuel delivery for more power, figure 17-39. These three waveform patterns are for a good O2 sensor reacting to normal operating conditions.

O2 sensors can degrade and eventually fail, and waveform patterns can help the technician detect

	ENGINE LEAN	ENGINE RICH
EXHAUST O2 CONTENT	↑	↓
O2 SENSOR RESISTANCE	↑	↓
VOLTAGE DROP AGAINST FIXED RESISTOR	↓	↑
SIGNAL VOLTAGE	↑	↓

Figure 17-37. The heated titania O2 sensor used by Jeep.

Figure 17-38. Typical waveform pattern of an oxygen sensor voltage signal at idle and 2,000 rpm.

failed O2 sensors. A lazy (partially operating) O2 sensor will display extremely long or delayed intervals between peak (RICH) to bottom (LEAN). Figure 17-40 displays an O2 sensor with less than two cycles in ten seconds at idle speed. Possible carbon contamination can drive the voltage values low. In this case, the O2 sensor must be replaced with a new one.

Figure 17-39. O2S waveform quickly responding to a very rich condition.

Figure 17-40. A lazy (defective) oxygen sensor will display less than two cycles in ten seconds at idle speed.

Figure 17-41. A bad injector will cause lean air-fuel ratios that will be seen as an O2S waveform indicating lean combustion events.

Figure 17-42. The high oxygen sensor voltage values indicate a rich running fuel system.

Oxygen sensor waveform patterns can indicate sticking injectors. A stuck-closed injector will display extra-low (LEAN) oscillations, figure 17-41. Problems with the fuel pump or the fuel pressure regulator can cause a RICH condition that the computer cannot correct. Increased amounts of RICH or peak oscillation values will clearly indicate the system cannot drive itself LEAN, figure 17-42. All O2 sensor signals should be tested at idle and high rpm with the vehicle stationary and under load.

O2 sensors not only sense the amount of oxygen in the exhaust system but also can indicate catalytic converter degradation in OBD II systems equipped with an upstream (before CAT) and downstream (after CAT) O2 sensors. When oxygen sensor voltages are observed on a DSO after full warm-up (closed loop), the patterns can be compared. When the catalytic converter is operating normally, the downstream oxygen sensor cycles are fewer than the upstream, figure 17-43. The downstream oxygen sensor detects less oxygen because of the lack of oxygen molecules present in the catalyzed exhaust gases. Remember, oxygen combines with hydrogen and carbon monoxide in the catalyst to form H_2O and CO_2, thus depleting oxygen from the exhaust. As the catalytic converter deteriorates, the downstream O2S cycles increase and

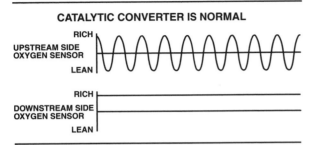

Figure 17-43. Normal waveform patterns from the upstream and downstream oxygen sensors.

Figure 17-44. Downstream oxygen sensor indicates exhaust gases are not being catalyzed efficiently.

become closer in comparison to the upstream O2S cycles, figure 17-44. OBD II systems will store a diagnostic trouble code in response to this deteriorated catalytic converter condition.

Oxygen Sensor Contamination

Oxygen sensor operation can be adversely affected by contamination. The following sources of contamination should be investigated in cases of multiple or repeated oxygen sensor failures on the same vehicle:

- An overly rich mixture can deposit black carbon or soot on the sensor tip. Mild carbon deposits, however, will not cause sensor failure and can be burned off in the engine by running it at part-throttle for at least two minutes.
- Lead deposits are more serious, as they will glaze the sensor element, making it useless. Lead deposits generally result from the use of leaded fuel, although methanol in gasoline also can cause lead contamination by dissolving the terne coat inside the fuel tank. Lead contamination is hard to detect by a visual inspection.
- Some RTV silicone gasket materials are made of sandlike particles of silica. The particles are turned into glass that attaches to the sensor element and clogs its surface. This type of contamination slows down the sensor's response time,

Figure 17-45. A vane-type airflow sensor.

Figure 17-46. A thermistor attached to the vane acts as an air temperature sensor.

affecting engine operation. Silica contamination produces a white appearance on the sensor element.
- Engine deposits can eventually affect sensor operation. Oil produces dark-brown discoloration on the element, while antifreeze causes a green discoloration.

Figure 17-47. Typical mass airflow (MAF) sensor location in the fuel injection system. (General Motors)

Other Sensors

The following is a brief description of other sensors found in electronic engine control systems.

Vane airflow sensors

Some fuel-injection systems use a vane-type airflow sensor, figure 17-45, positioned between the air filter and the intake manifold. The airflow sensor monitors the volume of air entering the intake manifold. Many systems also include a thermistor to sense air temperature. The thermistor often is an integral part of the vane, figure 17-46. Since the angular position of the vane is proportional to airflow, a potentiometer connected to the vane sends a voltage signal proportional to intake air speed to the computer.

Mass airflow sensors

A thermal measurement device, the mass airflow sensor, is installed between the air intake and the throttle body to determine the mass (weight) of air entering the engine, figure 17-47. It performs the same function as a vane-type airflow sensor, but combines the airflow speed and temperature measurement into a single sensor. Two basic types of mass airflow (MAF) sensors are used: a heated platinum wire or a heated thin-film semiconductor. Current provided by the

MAF module heats the wire or film, which is cooled by incoming airflow. As the heated wire or film cools, the module increases current to keep the sensor temperature at a specified level. As the wire or film again heats up, current decreases. The module measures current changes, and converts them into voltage signals sent to the engine control computer for use in determining injector pulse width. Figure 17-48 shows the components of a typical heated thin-film MAF; figure 17-49 shows the heated wire design.

MAF sensor waveform patterns vary according to design and manufacturer. To better grasp the waveform patterns of MAF sensors, it is best to observe waveforms on known-good operating systems to compare them with other MAF sensors. The first example is a Hitachi MAF sensor installed onto a GM 3800 engine. The Hitachi MAF sensor will produce a 5-volt signal with a frequency range of 2,400 Hz at idle to 9,000 Hz at wide-open throttle. First, observe the waveform while cranking the engine, figure 17-50. This waveform fluctuates slightly between 2,400 and 2,700 Hz while the engine is cranking. Once the engine is running, the sensor produces between 2,300 and 2,450 Hz. With the engine rpm at 2,000, the MAF sensor will produce between 3,500 and 4,000 Hz.

Figure 17-48. A heated thin-film MAF sensor consists of a screen or metal foil element to break up incoming air-flow, a ceramic resistor to measure air temperature, and an electronic module. (General Motors)

Figure 17-49. The heated wire MAF sensor places the wire directly in the path of incoming air. (General Motors)

Frequency is directly affected by the engine rpm on the Hitachi MAF sensor.

The next example details the AC-Delco MAF sensor mounted external to the throttle body. This type of AC-Delco MAF unit was prone to intermittent failure because of a defective thick-film area on the sensor body causing an open in the bridge circuit. Normally, this sensor should produce a clean square wave producing a 5-volt signal, figure 17-51. The externally mounted AC-Delco MAF sensor cycles between 10 Hz with the ignition key ON and 35 Hz at idle. These types of AC-Delco MAF sensors exhibit clean ON and OFF square waves with straight falling and leading edges.

AC-Delco MAF sensors that are built into the throttle body are called Modular MAF sensors. AC-Delco modular style MAF sensors have a high-frequency output signal with a 5-volt square wave. Notice how frequency increases noticeably from cranking speeds to 2,000 rpm, figure 17-52. With the engine running at 2,000 rpm, the signal should cycle at 3,500 Hz. Run the engine through each phase and compare the signal waveform patterns to this known-good pattern sequence.

Bosch hot wire MAF sensors produce a signal voltage between 0.8 volt at idle to about 4.5 volts at wide-open-throttle (WOT). This type of sensor is equipped with a platinum sensing wire that can easily become stained or contaminated. Notice that the Bosch MAF sensor displays 1.0 volts during idle conditions, figure 17-53. Raising the engine rpm causes the voltage signal to increase steadily to about 4.5 volts at WOT. A stained or defective hot wire will cause lower voltage values that can result in surging, stalling, and lack of power.

Ford hot-wire MAF sensors reduce voltage values similar to the Bosch hot-wire MAF sensors but with slight voltage fluctuations detected on the DSO. Figure 17-54 shows a Ford hot-wire MAF sensor at idle. Voltage values fluctuate slightly around 0.9 to 1.1 volts. Raising and lowering the engine rpm causes the signal voltage to range from 1.0 volts at idle to 4.6 volts at WOT.

Figure 17-50. Known good waveform patterns from a Hitachi MAF sensor during cranking, idle and high rpm. Note variations in the time scale.

Manifold pressure, vacuum, and barometric pressure sensors

These sensors keep the computer informed about air volume and engine load, allowing it to adjust fuel metering accordingly. Their input also is used by the computer to adjust timing and EGR flow relative to load. Speed-density fuel injection systems rely on a manifold absolute pressure (MAP) and temperature sensors as the primary input for calculating mass airflow, figure 17-55. They may be piezoresistive devices, transformers, or potentiometers operated by an **aneroid** bellows or a vacuum diaphragm. OBD II systems may use a MAP sensor to monitor EGR operation and not for fuel decisions on MAF-equipped systems.

Temperature sensors

A simple bimetal switch is used when the computer is interested only in whether air or coolant temperature is above or below one specific point. If the computer requires information about temperature in a range, a thermistor is used, figure 17-56. The computer senses voltage change as the temperature sensor warms from cold to hot.

Throttle position sensors (TPS)

Early fuel control systems used a simple ON/OFF switch to indicate wide-open throttle or idle position with a high or low voltage.

A potentiometer is commonly used to indicate the exact position and speed of throttle movement. Figure 17-57 shows a rotary-type throttle position sensor used on Bosch fuel-injection systems. A linear-type TPS is used with some carburetors. The two types differ physically, but both send the computer an analog signal proportional to the throttle opening angle. The rotary potentiometer moves on an axis with the throttle shaft, figure 17-58; the linear potentiometer uses a plunger that rides on a throttle shaft cam.

The analog voltage signal can be traced using a lab scope. The waveform pattern easily detects "flat spots" on the resistor, open circuits or defective (inaccurate) resistors. Always check the TPS with any stepper motor linkage removed to allow the throttle valve complete range from idle through wide-open throttle. Inspect the area most commonly used during acceleration. This area, from idle to about ½ throttle, is where the flat spot will most likely occur. Figure 17-59 shows a good TPS voltage sweep from idle to WOT.

Aneroid: A bellows or capsule that contains a vacuum and changes its length in response to changing atmospheric pressure.

Figure 17-51. Known good waveform pattern from an externally mounted AC-Delco MAF sensor at idle.

Figure 17-52. Known good waveform patterns from a modular style AC-Delco MAF sensor during Key On Engine Off, cranking, idle and 2000 rpm. Note selected time scale variations.

Figure 17-53. Signal voltage from a Bosch hot wire MAF sensor at idle.

Ch 1   **1V**   **M 5ms**

Ignition timing, crankshaft position, and engine speed sensors

We learned about these sensors in our discussion of electronic ignitions in Chapter Sixteen. They send the computer analog or digital signals to control timing, fuel metering, and EGR.

Vehicle Speed Sensors (VSS)

A pulse generator or an optical sensor, figure 17-60, provides the computer with vehicle speed information. This information is used by the computer in a variety of ways, including speedometer displays, torque converter lockup, transmission shift scheduling, EGR function, evaporative purging, and OBD II monitor trip criteria. As vehicle systems have become more complex, some are equipped with multiple speed sensors. For example, Chevrolet and GMC light-duty pickup trucks equipped with the Turbo Hydramatic 4L80-E transmission have both an output shaft speed sensor and an input speed sensor in addition to the main vehicle speed sensor. The PCM uses transmission input and output speeds to determine line pressure, transmission shift patterns, and torque converter clutch apply pressure, in addition to calculating turbine speed, gear ratios, and torque converter clutch slippage for diagnostic purposes.

Vehicle speed sensors display basically two different waveform patterns; an ac sine wave for magnetic pulse generator sensors or square wave for the optical switching device. The difficulty in testing vehicle speed sensors is preparing the tests by raising the vehicle and performing lab scope checks with the engine driving the wheels to simulate actual movement down the road. Once the vehicle is secured, a lab scope can be installed and waveform patterns observed. It is best to have access to known-good vehicle speed sensor waveform patterns to compare real-time data. For example, figure 17-61 displays a

Ch 1   500mV   M   5ms

Figure 17-54. Signal voltage from a Ford hot-wire MAF sensor at idle.

Figure 17-55. A speed density injection system uses manifold absolute pressure and temperature to calculate mass airflow rate. (General Motors)

Figure 17-56. A thermistor is used when the computer requires temperature information in a range.

Figure 17-58. Because a rotary potentiometer moves on an axis with the throttle shaft, it can inform the computer of any change in throttle position. (Ford)

Figure 17-57. Bosch uses a rotary potentiometer as a throttle position switch.

VSS sine wave pattern for a GM vehicle with peak-to-peak voltage values of approximately 35 volts at 35 mph. Many Ford VSS will display peak-to-peak voltage readings of approximately 9 volts at 35 mph, figure 17-62. Optical vehicle speed sensors will display clean leading and falling edges with a 12-volt amplitude, figure 17-63. Different manufacturers' VSS will have different specifications, so it is best to check factory information before testing.

EGR sensors

A sliding-contact potentiometer may be connected to the top of the EGR valve stem to inform the computer of EGR pintle position, figure 17-64. This information is used by the computer to monitor EGR valve operation.

Air-conditioning sensors

An air-conditioning compressor adds to the engine load when the compressor clutch is engaged. To allow the computer to make the necessary adjustments to compensate for the increased load, a simple on/off switch may be used to tell the computer whether the compressor clutch is engaged or disengaged. An AC pressure sensor may be used by the PCM to make control decisions for the air-conditioning clutch, radiator cooling fan, and idle speed control.

Knock sensors

Knock sensors or detonation sensors generally use a piezoresistive crystal that changes resistance whenever pressure is applied to it, figure 17-65. A reference voltage from the computer is applied to one terminal. The return signal voltage from the other terminal remains at its programmed value as long as there is no detonation, and the pressure on the crystal is uniform.

1→

Ch 1   **500mV**

Figure 17-59. Good waveform pattern of the voltage signal from a throttle position sensor (TPS).

Figure 17-60. An LED and a photocell in the speedometer act as a speed sensor. (GM)

If detonation occurs, however, the unequal pressure on the crystal changes the sensor's resistance and the return voltage signal changes.

A knock sensor is a signal-generating sensor that generates ac voltage about 3,000 Hz at idle and 7,000 Hz at 3,000 rpm. A normal amplitude on the ac scale will display peak-to-peak voltage values at idle of about 1 volt and at 3,000 rpm about 8 volt peak-to-peak voltage. The best test to determine the operation of the knock sensor is to tap the engine block near the knock sensor while the engine is running and observe the timing retard with a timing light. This test is difficult to perform on some engines with inaccessible knock sensors. Ford knock sensors operate on a 2.5-volt signal at idle until a knock is detected, then the voltage signal is increased over 3.5 volts and the computer retards the timing, figure 17-66.

SYSTEM ACTUATORS

In Chapter Four, we learned that an actuator is an output device that changes the computer's voltage signal into a mechanical action. Most engine control actuators

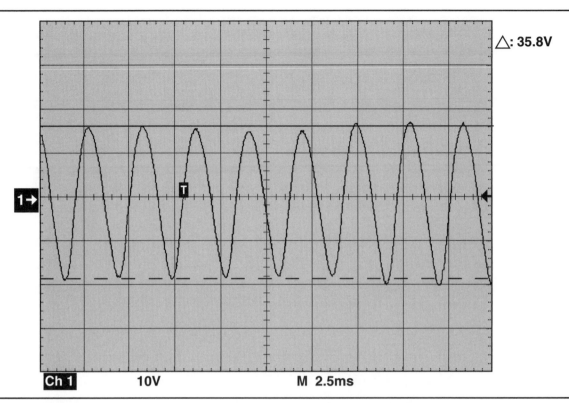

Figure 17-61. Typical waveform pattern from a magnetic pulse generator VSS on a GM vehicle at 35 mph (peak-to-peak voltage is 35.4 volts).

Figure 17-62. Typical waveform pattern from a magnetic pulse generator VSS on a Ford at 35 mph (peak-to-peak voltage is 8.9 volts).

Figure 17-63. Typical waveform pattern from an optical VSS on a GM vehicle at idle.

Figure 17-64. A potentiometer may be used to sense EGR pintle position. (Ford)

NO DETONATION—EQUAL PRESSURE

DETONATION—UNEQUAL PRESSURE

Figure 17-65. The piezoresistive crystal in a detonation sensor flexes when detonation (unequal pressure) occurs. (Audi)

Figure 17-66. The knock sensor amplitude will vary only 2 volts peak-to-peak values at idle until a knock is detected then the peak-to-peak amplitude will increase in excess of 8 volts.

Figure 17-67. The percentage of solenoid on-time can be altered to control fuel metering while duty cycle time remains constant. (GM)

are solenoids, although **stepper motors** are used in some applications.

A solenoid is an electromechanical device that operates much like a simple switch: Voltage is applied to energize it and removed to de-energize it. For this reason, it can be considered a digital actuator. Solenoids typically are used to control a vacuum signal or to control fuel flow and air bleeds.

A stepper motor is a dc motor that moves in approximately 100 to 120 incremental steps as it goes from a deenergized state (no voltage) to a fully energized state (full voltage). The stepper motor functions as an analog actuator with digital signals. Stepper motors are primarily used for idle speed and mixture control.

Solenoid Operation

Most solenoids used in a computer control system are grounded through the computer. This allows the computer to control voltage to the solenoid without having to switch system voltage. The solenoid can be energized for any length of time the computer desires, or it can pulse on and off at a given rate per second.

You learned about pulse width modulation and duty cycle in Chapter Four and earlier in this chapter when you studied fuel-injector solenoids. Duty cycle is not a concern with solenoids that simply turn something on or off. However, if a solenoid is required to modulate something, on-time and duty cycle become factors. Figure 17-67 illustrates the relationship between on-time and duty cycle for a mixture control solenoid used in a feedback carburetor.

As we saw earlier, a computer-controlled fuel system operating in open-loop ignores the oxygen sensor. It sends a predetermined, fixed duty cycle to the fuel solenoid. When the system switches into closed-loop operation, the fuel solenoid on-time is varied by the computer according to O2 sensor input to cycle back and forth close to the 14.7 to 1 air-fuel ratio.

Fuel Metering Actuators

A mixture-control solenoid or a stepper motor is designed to produce a 14.7 to 1 air-fuel ratio at the midpoint of its operational range (or at a 50-percent duty cycle). Such actuators usually have a +/- 2 ratio leeway, making them capable of producing air-fuel ratios from 12.7 to 1 to 16.7 to 1.

Stepper motors

This type of actuator is used in some Motorcraft and Carter carburetors. The motor can control the air-fuel ratio by moving the metering pins into the main circuit air bleeds to reduce air and thus enrich the mixture, or moving them outward to allow more air to enter and lean the mixture. The stepper motor used in the Motorcraft 7200 VV carburetor controls the air-fuel ratio by moving a metering valve inside the carburetor. In early models of this carburetor, the metering valve opened a passage, figure 17-68. This allows control vacuum to enter the fuel bowl, lowering the air pressure on the fuel and leaning the air-fuel ratio. Later models of the 7200 VV work differently. The valve opens air bleeds to let more air into the air-fuel mixture at the discharge jets.

The idle speed control (ISC) and idle air control (IAC) motors used on some Ford and General Motors fuel systems are other examples of stepper motors, figure 17-69.

Mixture control solenoids

All mixture-control solenoids work on the duty cycle principle, but they can manage air-fuel ratios in different ways. The mixture-control solenoid used in Rochester carburetors, figure 17-70, is an integral part of the carburetor. It operates a metering rod in the main jet. Other systems use a solenoid that controls vacuum to a diaphragm installed in the carburetor. The vacuum diaphragm controls the operation of the metering rods and air bleeds.

Figure 17-68. A stepper motor is used in early Ford 7200 VV carburetors to vary air pressure on the fuel bowl. (Ford)

Figure 17-69. GM uses a stepper motor as an idle speed control for a carburetor (top) or to control airflow in a fuel injection throttle body (bottom).

Some Carter carburetors use a solenoid with a duty cycle to control the air bleeds, figure 17-71.

EGR Actuators

Engine control computer systems that manage EGR flow use solenoids to regulate the amount of vacuum applied to the EGR valve. Although system designs differ, figure 17-72 shows a typical system, as used in Ford's EEC-II.

Figure 17-70. A mixture control solenoid used in Rochester carburetors.

Figure 17-71. A solenoid controls variable air bleeds in some Carter carburetors. (Carter)

Other System Actuators

In addition to controlling ignition timing and fuel metering, the newer integrated electronic engine systems control several other functions:

- Torque converter lockup or engine shifting— Solenoid valves in the transmission or transaxle hydraulic circuits respond to computer signals based on vehicle speed and engine load sensors.

Stepper Motor: A direct-current motor that moves in incremental steps when energized.

Figure 17-72. A typical computer-controlled EGR system. (Ford)

AIR TO EXHAUST PORTS

Figure 17-73. The Delco air switching valve uses two solenoids. (Delco-Remy)

• Air injection switching—One or more solenoids operate a valve in the vacuum line to the air switching or air control valve, figure 17-73.
• Vapor canister purge—A solenoid installed in the canister-to-carburetor or manifold vapor line opens and closes as directed by the computer.

HISTORY OF ENGINE CONTROL SYSTEMS

Electronic engine controls appeared on the domestic automotive scene with the 1977 models. The early control systems regulated only a single function: either ignition timing or fuel metering. However, they were rapidly expanded to control both systems, as well as numerous other engine functions. Most late-model engine control systems have a self-diagnostic capability, can display trouble codes for troubleshooting, and do the following:

• Open- and closed-loop fuel control
• Ignition timing control
• Idle speed control
• EGR flow control
• Air injection switching
• Vapor canister purging
• Automatic transmission or transaxle torque converter lockup and shift control.

Bosch Lambda and Motronic Systems

The Robert Bosch Company pioneered fuel injection and electronic controls used in European vehicles. The Volvo Lambda-Sond system (manufactured by Bosch) was combined with K-Jetronic fuel injection on 1977 Volvo models sold in the U.S. This was the first electronically controlled fuel-metering system using a catalytic converter and oxygen sensor, figure 17-74.

An input signal from the oxygen sensor results in an output signal to the K-Jetronic frequency valve. This valve varies the injection control pressure and regulates the fuel supplied by the continuous injection nozzles. The original Lambda-Sond system controls only fuel metering.

The Bosch Motronic or digital motor electronics (DME) system added electronic spark control to the fuel metering control of the Lambda-Sond system. In addition to the converter and oxygen sensor, the DME system receives input signals from crankshaft speed and position sensors, a magnetic pulse generator in the distributor, and the L-Jetronic sensors. This allows the computer to:

• Adjust injector pulse width for air-fuel ratio control
• Adjust ignition timing for combined speed and load conditions
• Shut off injection completely during closed-throttle deceleration.

Figure 17-74. Components of the Bosch Lambda-Sond system as used with K-Jetronic injection on the 1977 Volvo. Bottom view shows the cycles of oxygen feedback operation. (Volvo)

Figure 17-75. A Chrysler electronic lean-burn (ELB) system.

Chrysler

Chrysler introduced its electronic lean-burn (ELB) spark timing control system in 1976 on some 400-cid V8 engines, figure 17-75. The system is based on a special carburetor that provides air-fuel ratios as lean as 18:1 and a modified electronic ignition controlled by an analog spark control computer attached to the air cleaner housing. Two printed circuit boards inside the computer contain the spark control circuitry. The program schedule module receives the sensor inputs and interprets them for the ignition control module, which directs the spark timing output. The 1976 ELB distributor has dual ignition pickups and a centrifugal advance mechanism. The distributor secondary components are similar to those used with the basic Chrysler electronic ignition. A dual ballast resistor controls primary current and protects the spark control computer from voltage spikes.

In 1977, ELB became available on all Chrysler V8 engines and the centrifugal advance mechanism was eliminated. A second-generation ELB design was used on 5.2-liter V8s. The start pickup in the distributor was dropped, and the computer was redesigned so all the circuitry fit on a single board.

The second-generation system was adopted on all V8s in 1978, and a new ELB version was introduced on the Omni and Horizon 4-cylinder engine. The 4-cylinder system uses a Hall-effect distributor instead of a magnetic pickup. It has variable dwell to control primary current and does not use a ballast resistor. The 4-cylinder spark control computer is mounted on the left front fender, figure 17-76.

Figure 17-76. The Chrysler 4-cylinder ESC spark control computer.

With the introduction of 3-way converters, the ELB system was modified in 1979 to work with revised carburetors that provided air-fuel ratios closer to 14.7 to 1. The protection circuitry was integrated into the computer, and the dual ballast resistor was replaced by a single 1.2-ohm resistor to control primary current only. This third-generation system was renamed electronic spark control (ESC) and appeared on some 6-cylinder inline engines with an oxygen sensor and a feedback carburetor.

The 1980 model year was a transitional one for Chrysler. All California engines received ESC with feedback fuel control. The 5.9-liter V8 and Canadian 5.2-liter four-barrel V8s continued to use ESC without the feedback system. All other engines reverted to basic electronic ignition with mechanical and vacuum advance mechanisms. Detonation sensors were introduced on some 1980 ESC systems, but the biggest change was the switch from an analog to a digital computer. Models with the digital computer in 1980 can be identified by their return to dual ignition pickups in the distributor. Systems with digital computers also eliminate the ballast resistor completely. Since 1981, all of Chrysler's domestic, carbureted, 4-cylinder engines and all 6-cylinder and V8 powerplants have feedback fuel control and digital ESC systems without ballast resistors.

Chrysler introduced the modular control system (MCS), figure 17-77, in late 1983 on throttle-body fuel-injected 4-cylinder engines. In 1984, its use was expanded to turbocharged port-injected engines as well. The modular control system regulates vehicle functions using two separate modules whose functions are similar to the two circuit boards in the original ELB computer. The logic module handles all of the low-current tasks within the system, including receiving the inputs and making control decisions. A

Figure 17-77. Chrysler's modular engine control system (single-point injection version).

replaceable PROM is mounted in the logic module housing, and a self-test program is provided to aid in system diagnosis. The logic module is mounted inside the car to avoid underhood electrical interference.

The power module handles the high-current tasks and is located in the left front fender. It looks similar to the spark control computer used in 4-cylinder ESC systems. The power module contains the regulated power supply for the entire control system, along with the switching controls for the ignition coil, fuel injectors, and auto-shutdown (ASD) relay. The ASD supplies power to the coil, the fuel pump relay, and the power module when it detects a distributor cranking signal.

The modular control system (MCS) was replaced by the single-module engine control (SMEC) computer on some 1987 4-cylinder and V6 engines, figure 17-78, which brought the two circuit boards used in MCS logic and power modules under one housing. Its advanced microprocessor is smaller, faster, and more powerful than the earlier MCS microprocessor, with electrically erasable memory (EEPROM) that can be programmed in the assembly plant. The SMEC processes instructions twice as fast as the older MCS system. This speed is important for use on the V6 engine, as the additional cylinders require the computer to process 50 percent more information per engine revolution than a 4-cylinder engine.

The use of complementary metal oxide semiconductor (CMOS) technology improves component heat resistance. When combined with the reduction in overall size of the components, the SMEC can be installed in the engine compartment with far fewer heat-related problems than the separate logic and power modules. It also includes extensive diagnostic circuitry for use in determining and correcting problems.

Further refinement of Chrysler's engine computer came in 1989 with the introduction of the single-board engine controller (SBEC) and the SBEC II in 1992, figure 17-79. The circuitry in the SBEC and SBEC II is simplified considerably from that used by previous engine controllers. This was achieved by replacing standard integrated circuits (ICs) with application-specific integrated circuits (ASICs). The ASICs are notably smaller in size than standard ICs, while providing an expanded number of functions. One ASIC takes the place of four separate input-output ICs previously used. Circuit simplification allowed the two circuit boards to be combined, forming a single board that requires less space. This resulted in a smaller and aerodynamically designed housing with improved cooling airflow through it, and reduces the number of external wiring connections from 74 to 60.

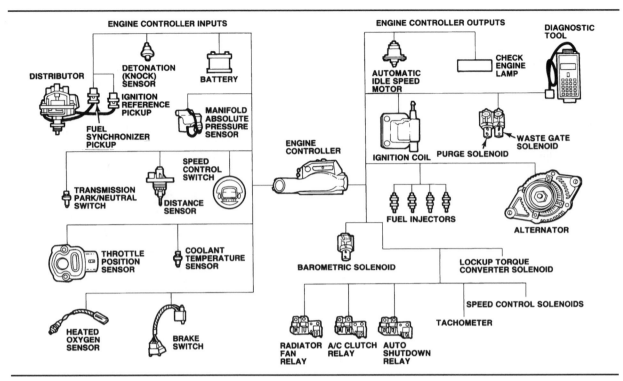

Figure 17-78. Chrysler's single module engine control (SMEC) system. Multipoint injection version shown. (Chrysler)

Figure 17-79. Chrysler's single board engine control (SBEC) system. Multipoint injection version shown. (Chrysler)

Figure 17-80. Ford's feedback electronic engine control (EEC) system.

Figure 17-81. Ford's EEC-I system was introduced in 1978.

As shown in figure 17-79, the SBEC engine controller accepts a larger number of input signals and produces more output signals than earlier controllers. In addition to the controller's increased number of functions, its enlarged memory capacity incorporates expanded diagnostic capabilities.

All of these Chrysler computer control systems are designed with an emergency "limp-in" mode. In case of a system failure, the computer reverts to a fixed set of operating values. This allows the vehicle to be driven to a shop for repair. If the failure is in the start pickup or the coil triggering circuitry, however, the engine will not start.

In an effort to standardize tailpipe emission levels, in 1994 scientists brought many changes to the fuel and emission control system designs. OBD II drivetrain computers and sophisticated sensors and actuators produced high levels of emission control. Chrysler installed the OBD II system on many of its automobiles and trucks and continued its research into gasoline and diesel technology.

Ford

Ford introduced its feedback electronic engine control system, figure 17-80, on some 1978 2.3-liter, 4-cylinder engines. The system contains a 3-way catalyst and conventional oxidation catalyst (TWC-COC) converter, an oxygen sensor, a vacuum control solenoid, and an analog computer. Its control was limited to fuel metering. In 1980, a digital computer replaced the analog unit and the system was renamed the microprocessor control unit (MCU) fuel feedback system. The major change in early applications is the addition of self-diagnostics, but later designs have expanded capabilities including control over idle speedup, canister purge, and detonation spark control. They might be considered complete engine control systems except that they lack continuous spark timing control.

Ford also introduced its first-generation electronic engine control (EEC-I) system, figure 17-81, on the 1978 Lincoln Versailles. This system controls spark timing, EGR flow, and air injection. A digital microprocessor electronic control assembly (ECA) installed in the passenger compartment receives signals from various sensors. It then determines the best spark timing, EGR flow rate, and air-injection operation and sends signals to the appropriate control devices.

All 1978-79 California EEC-I systems use a variation of the blue-grommet Dura-Spark II ignition. The 1979 Federal EEC-I system has a yellow-grommet, dual-mode Dura-Spark II module. Although these modules appear similar to their non-EEC counterparts, they are controlled through the ECA and cannot be tested with the same procedures.

The ignition switching signal on 1978 EEC-I systems is provided by a sensor at the rear of the engine

Figure 17-82. EEC-III/CFI system components.

block that detects four raised ridges on a magnetic pulse ring mounted to the end of the crankshaft. In 1979, the pickup and pulse ring were moved to the front of the engine immediately behind the vibration damper. This design is used on the later EEC-II and EEC-III systems as well.

Late in 1979, Ford's second-generation EEC-II system appeared on some 5.8-liter V8 engines. EEC-II added electronic controls for vapor canister purging and air-injection switching. In addition, dual 3-way converters are used with a feedback carburetor for precise air-fuel mixture control.

EEC-II systems have a new Dura-Spark III ignition module that can be identified by its brown grommet. This module differs from earlier Dura-Spark designs. Many of the control circuits have been eliminated and their functions incorporated into the ECA.

Ford's third-generation EEC-III system appeared in 1980 and was available in two versions through 1984. EEC-III/FBC incorporates a feedback carburetor similar to the EEC-II system; EEC-III/CFI, figure 17-82, has a throttle-body-type central fuel-injection system. All EEC-III systems use the Dura-Spark III ignition module. EEC-III is the first Ford computer engine control system to have a self-test program.

Ford's EEC-IV, figure 17-83, was introduced in 1983 and incorporates the thick-film integrated (TFI) ignition system. The two-microchip EEC-IV microprocessor is much more powerful than the four- or five-microchip ECAs used with earlier EEC systems. EEC-IV has both increased memory and the ability to handle almost one million computations per second.

Unlike earlier EEC systems, however, the EEC-IV's calibration assembly is located inside the ECA and cannot be replaced separately. All EEC-IV systems have an improved self-test capability with trouble codes that are stored for readout at a later time.

Since 1986, Ford has made continuing and significant improvements in the processing speed, memory and diagnostic capabilities of its EEC-IV microprocessor without changing the basic designation of the system. Although the original EEC-IV microprocessor is now a dinosaur compared to the one currently used, Ford discovered that technicians in the field were intimidated by the use of I, II, III, and IV designations, and discontinued the practice of redesignating the system when improvements were made. The most recent version introduced with the 1993 Mark VIII has 56 kilobytes of RAM (versus 32 kilobytes for the previous version) and processes data at a clock speed of 18 MHz (versus 15 MHz).

Unlike Chrysler and GM, Ford did not embrace the concept of multiplexing, but has relied instead on smarter computers. Most Ford vehicles equipped with electronic automatic transmissions have the transmission control functions integrated in the ECA, which has been renamed a powertrain control module (PCM).

All Ford EEC systems have a limited operating strategy (LOS) mode in case of a failure within the system. The exact nature of the LOS varies from one system to another, but generally, the timing is fixed at 10 degrees, and other ECA emission control system outputs are rendered inoperable.

The most updated version of electronic engine controls (EEC-V) was introduced on the 1994 Mustang with a V6 SFI 3.8L engine and the 1994 Cougar and Thunderbird with the 4.6L engine. This new engine management system was designed to accommodate the Environmental Protection Agency (EPA)-regulated OBD II system. This system, like others, is divided into the hardware and software categories. The hardware consists of the Powertrain Control Module (PCM), the Constant Control Relay Module (CCRM), output actuators and sensors. The software was designed to meet OBD II regulations. OBD II shares similarities with the OBD I system but it also contains sophisticated monitoring programs for misfire detection, the heated oxygen sensors, the EGR system and the fuel evaporation system. The biggest difference with OBD II software is that it is designed to not only detect component failure but also measure the working parameters of each individual system and allow the technician more access to diagnostic information.

Special test equipment is necessary to diagnose the Ford OBD II systems. Ford proprietary equipment is

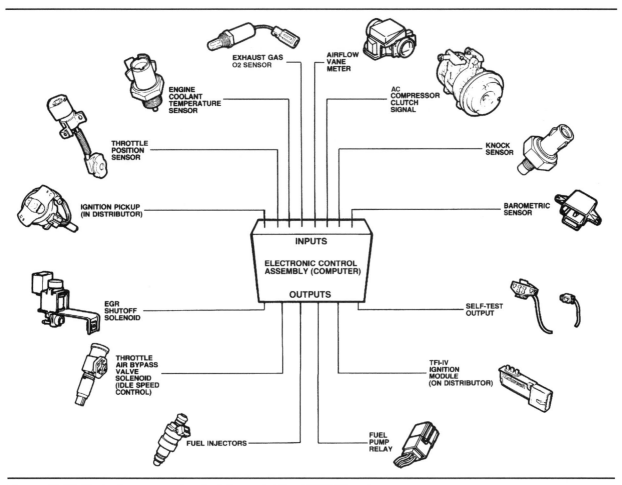

Figure 17-83. Typical components of a late-model Ford EEC-IV system.

used to access data, but there are aftermarket scan tools and software programs are available to the independent market. The scan tool is linked to the EEC-V system by attaching a special harness connector to the 16-pin OBD II test connector under the driver's side kick panel (on most vehicles). There are several different types of data that can be observed — trouble codes, real-time output actuator and sensor data, freeze frame data and various actuator data. This advanced diagnostic system allows the technician to access present and collected information from the vehicle's PCM.

Ford also introduced a new language for communicating with the electronic modules and output devices. This system is called Standard Corporate Protocol (SCP). This system allows two or more signals to be sent over the same circuit. Ford also introduced a new multiplex unit on Lincoln Continentals designed to link 10 different electronic modules to share information. The PCM can monitor information from the SRS module, the cruise control module, the ABS module, and other components to determine the

necessary information for the overall driveability of the vehicle, figure 17-84.

The PCM contains a Flash Electrically Erasable Programmable Read Only Memory (FEEPROM) within the PCM. This circuit can be reprogrammed without removing the PCM from the vehicle. If a software update is necessary because of an added sensor update, accident damage, or other changes, the scan tool can be linked to the 16-pin test connector and information exchanged.

This OBD II system is also equipped with a fuel pump monitor system spliced into the fuel pump power circuit. The purpose of this monitor system is to make sure power is supplied to the fuel pump relay and fuel pump when the system is activated. Ford designed a new modular fuel pump relay called the CCRM. The Constant Control Relay Module is designed to interface with the EEC-V system to provide control for the cooling fan, the AC clutch, and the fuel pump. This electronic relay is designed to handle the high current draws from these PCM-controlled components.

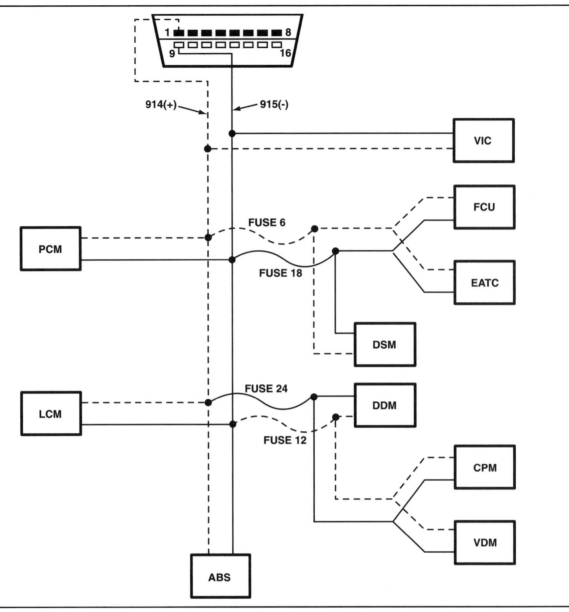

Figure 17-84. Ford's multiplex system for the Lincoln Continental.

Another new design called the Fail Safe Cooling feature was installed on 1996 Ford pickup trucks with the 4.6L engine. This system monitors cylinder head temperature and corrects overheating problems until the cooling system can be repaired. Although the engine will experience some loss of performance during Fail Safe Cooling operation, the computer can determine a safe driving speed until the proper repairs are performed. Basically, the computer stategically cuts out cylinder fuel injectors, allowing the cylinder to act as an air pump. The more injectors disabled, the quicker the engine block cools down. The Service Engine Soon light is activated and the driver is allowed to continue for a limited time. If the overheating problem continues, the computer shuts the fuel pump down and the vehicle coasts to a stop.

General Motors

The first GM spark timing control was offered on 1977-78 Oldsmobile Toronados. The 1977 system was called microprocessed sensing and automatic regulation (MISAR). MISAR is a basic spark timing system only. A rotating disc and stationary sensor on the front of the engine replaced the pickup coil and trigger wheel of the distributor. Except for this change, the 1977 MISAR system used a standard HEI distributor with a basic four-terminal ignition module.

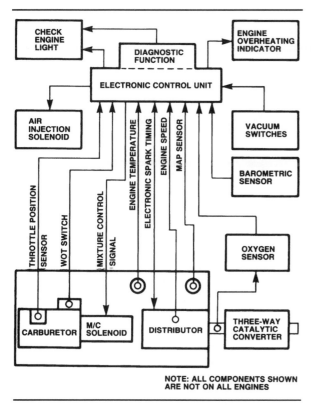

Figure 17-85. GM's computer-controlled catalytic converter (C-4) system.

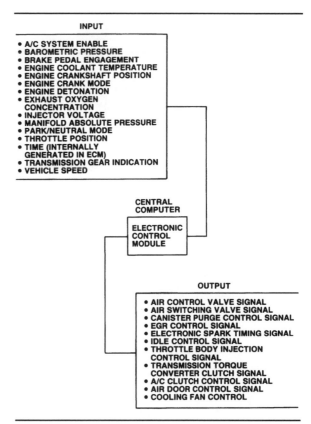

Figure 17-86. Typical CCC system sensors (inputs) and controls (outputs).

The MISAR system was modified in 1978 and renamed electronic spark timing (EST). The crankshaft-mounted disc and stationary sensor were dropped, and a conventional pickup coil and trigger wheel were again fitted in the HEI distributor. The ignition module, however, was a special three-terminal design that is not interchangeable with any other HEI system.

In mid-1979, GM introduced the computer-controlled catalytic converter (C-4) system, figure 17-85. At first, the C-4 system was purely a fuel control system used with 3-way converters. But in 1980, Buick V6 engines with C-4 were also fitted with an electronic spark timing (EST) system. Although this is the same name applied to the MISAR system just discussed, the two systems are not the same. C-4 with EST has a single electronic control module (ECM) that regulates both fuel delivery and spark timing. It was GM's first complete computer engine control system. The C-4 system was further upgraded in 1981 with EST in almost all applications, and additional control capabilities were added. The expanded system, figure 17-86, was renamed computer command control (CCC or C-3).

In 1986, GM began to update the CCC system through the introduction of a new high-speed ECM on certain vehicles. Systems using the new ECM often are called "P-4" systems. The high-speed ECM is smaller than previous models, but has more functional capabilities. It operates at twice the speed of previous ECMs, is capable of 600,000 commands per second, and contains fewer IC chips and internal connections. The high-speed ECM draws less current with the ignition off, provides more diagnostic functions, and retains memory on battery voltage as low as 6.3 volts. Service procedures for the unit allow repair and reprogramming by replacing several different integrated circuits in the controller housing.

ECMs used on vehicles with electronic automatic transmissions have the transmission control circuitry integrated in the memory and calibration (MEM-CAL) unit, and have been redesignated as powertrain control modules (PCMs). All C-4 and C-3 systems have self-diagnostic capabilities. The newer the system, the more comprehensive the diagnostic capabilities. Several GM cars provided diagnostic readouts accessible through instrument panel displays, although the trend has clearly been to make such information available only through a scan tool in late-model systems.

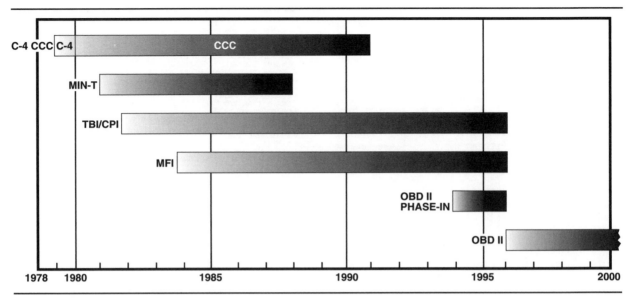

Figure 17-87. General Motors fuel and emission control systems from 1978 through 1999.

General Motors also redesigned the engine control system hardware and software as specified by the Environmental Protection Agency. This new OBD II system was introduced in several models in 1994 and then finally in 1996, all models were equipped with this updated system, figure 17-87. Many GM computers are capable of "learning" operating parameters and default patterns and then advising the computer (PCM) to correct for minor variations. If the battery is disconnected, the "learning" process begins all over again. If the vehicle is not driven and allowed to "relearn" the operating parameters, the engine may experience driveability problems for a short duration.

The OBD II computer on General Motors vehicles constantly monitors output actuators and sensors and performs diagnostic tests to determine their performance. The PCM is capable of managing various systems, analyzing data, controlling the malfunction indicator light (MIL) and managing the trip criteria and drive cycles for performance data. The PCM also records freeze frame data, trouble codes and displays Inspection/Maintenance information for the scan tool or diagnostic software programs. The OBD II computer directly accesses these emission and fuel-injection components during the testing procedure:

- Misfire detection system
- EGR system
- EVAP system
- Catalytic converter system
- Fuel-injection system
- Oxygen sensor(s) and O2 sensor heaters
- Secondary air-injection system.

The OBD II drive cycle consists of the following steps: ignition key ON, engine running at idle then under load, all criteria completed (tests performed), inspection and maintenance tests passed or failed, all information recorded and then the ignition key turned OFF. An official OBD II monitor trip occurs during the drive cycle, figure 17-88. OBD II regulations require that all systems and components that could cause tailpipe emissions levels increase be tested and the information recorded for reference. The list includes:

- Transmission turbine speed sensor
- Transmission vehicle speed sensor
- Automatic transmission temperature sensor
- Throttle position sensor (TPS)
- MAF and MAP sensors
- Knock sensors
- EVAP system vacuum sensor
- Ignition sensor high resolution (optical ignition systems)
- Ignition sensor (camshaft, crankshaft sensors)
- Fuel temperature sensor
- ECT and IAT temperature sensors
- Cruise control servo
- Brake switch for torque converter clutch system
- EVAP purge control solenoid
- 4WD low select switch
- Park/Neutral switch
- Idle air control (IAC) motor
- Ignition modules and sensors
- Transmission control solenoids.

GM OBD II DRIVE CYCLE (1998 & LATER VEHICLES)

DECEL TO 20MPH (CLUTCH OUT & NO BRAKE) THEN ACCEL TO 55 MPH 3/4 THROTTLE

STEADY STATE CRUISE (55 MPH)

ACCEL TO 55 MPH AT 1/2 THROTTLE (AC OFF)

STEADY STATE CRUISE (55 MPH)

3 MINUTES

5 MINUTES

• AIR, PURGE
• FUEL TRIM
• MISFIRE
• HO2S HEATER

• AIR, EGR
• FUEL TRIM
• HO2S
• PURGE
• MISFIRE

• EGR, PURGE
• FUEL TRIM
• HO2S
• MISFIRE

DECEL (NO BRAKE)

VEHICLE PREP:

ECT<122°F

• PURGE
• MISFIRE
• FUEL TRIM

• EGR
• PURGE
• FUEL TRIM

• PURGE
• MISFIRE
• FUEL TRIM

• EGR
• PURGE

IDLE
• CATALYST

• FUEL LEVEL
• COLD SOAK

IDLE FOR 30 SECONDS IN DRIVE

KEY OFF

0   2.5   3   6   7   12

◄─── TIME IN MINUTES ───►

IDLE IN DRIVE OR NEUTRAL FOR 2.5 MINUTES WITH AC & REAR DEFROST ON

Figure 17-88. Typical GM OBD II drive cycles.

PCMCIA CARD

COMPONENTS NECESSARY FOR PROGRAMMING

TECH 2

OFF-BOARD PROGRAMMING

SPS OFF-BOARD PROGRAMMING ADAPTER

PCM

DIAGNOSTIC LINK CONNECTOR

1 2 3 4 5 6 7 8
9 10 11 12 13 14 15 16

SAE 16/19 PIN ADAPTER

Figure 17-89. The TECH II scan tool is designed to link to the PCM using the 16-pin diagnostic link connector.

The information can be extracted from the PCM using a scan tool linked to the 16-pin OBD II test connector located under the driver's side dash, figure 17-89. The TECH 2 scan tool designed for factory technicians can access trouble codes and real-time data as well as perform certain activation and erasing functions. Aftermarket scan tools are available, but they are somewhat limited in accessing proprietary information.

Honda PGM-FI and other Asian Fuel-Injection Systems

The Acura and Honda Programmed Fuel Injection (PGM-FI) system was first introduced on the 1986 Acura Integra and Legend models. This computerized emission and emission-management system provides efficient and accurate control of the fuel and emission systems, figure 17-90. Early versions of the PGM-FI are equipped with a self-diagnosis system (OBD I) that flashes LEDs on the PCM for the coded information. In the 1990s, the CHECK ENGINE light displayed the flashing codes on most models. The PCM controls the fuel pump by grounding the PGM-FI relay for two seconds, then once the fuel pump is running, the PCM supplies a ground signal to the relay using a bypass circuit, figure 17-91. If the engine stalls with the ignition key ON, the PCM opens the ground circuit to the relay and cuts power to the fuel pump. Here is a list of the components and systems the PCM controls in the PGM-FI system:

- Alternator output
- AC compressor clutch
- Cold fast idle
- EGR valve
- EVAP purge solenoid valve
- Idle air control (IAC) valve
- Fuel cut-off system
- Fuel injector timing and duration
- Fuel pump control
- Ignition spark timing
- Intake air bypass system
- Lock-up solenoid control (transmission)
- VTEC solenoid control (valve timing).

Figure 17-90. Typical PGM-FI system on a 1998 Acura with the 3.5L V6 engine.

In 1996, Honda and Acura designed the EPA-regulated OBD II fuel and emission control system for the PGM-FI system. Like most other OBD II systems, a 16-pin test connector is located under the dash to allow scan tool diagnosis. This updated system also includes upstream and downstream heated O2 sensors, EVAP control and a more accurate EGR valve.

Toyota Computer Controlled System (TCCS)

The Toyota Computer Controlled System (TCCS) is a completely computerized fuel and emission control system, figure 17-92. Similar to the Honda and Acura system, the TCCS was designed for OBD I models but updated in 1996 for the OBD II regulations. Early systems use vane airflow meters, but later systems use MAP or MAF sensors. TCCS engines use either the Electronic Spark Advance (ESA) system or the Variable Advance Timing System (VAST). The two systems differ in the design of the crankshaft and camshaft sensors and how the signals are processed for timing, figure 17-93.

Control System Development

Engine systems have developed considerably since they first appeared a decade ago. Today's computer control systems, however, are undergoing an even more rapid development into a highly sophisticated electronic system composed of many microprocessors (computers) that will eventually manage all operational and convenience systems in a vehicle. The body computer module (BCM) concept, which appeared on some 1986 GM luxury cars, is the first generation of these "total control" systems. Their development should be rapid.

When a particular vehicle arrives for service, you will have to know the system's components, understand its operation, and use the correct procedures and specifications. As described in Chapter One of the *Shop Manual*, this information is available in service manuals available from the manufacturer or independent publishers such as Chek-Chart. It is impossible for the individual technician to carry all of this information in his or her head.

Figure 17-91. PGM-FI component locations on a Honda.

However, you should not forget that the laws of electricity, physics, and chemistry have no manufacturer's trademark on them. They remain the same, and all systems operate on the same principles.

SUMMARY

All computers must perform four basic functions: input, processing, storage, and output. Computers use various sensors to receive input data. This data is compared to lookup tables in the computer's memory. Some data may be stored in memory for future use.

Figure 17-92. Schematic of a Toyota Computer Control System (TCCS).

The computer output takes the form of voltage signals to its actuators.

A control system operates in an open-loop mode until the engine and the oxygen sensor are warm enough, then the computer switches into the closed-loop mode. In open loop, the computer ignores O2 signals and uses engine sensor data compared to a pre-determined set of values. Once the system switches into closed loop, the computer acts on the O2 signals and constantly adjusts the fuel delivery and timing while the engine is running. The most recent computers have the ability to adapt their operating strategies to account for a number of conditional changes, including the wear that results from engine operation.

System sensors generally measure analog variables. Their voltage signals are digitized by the computer, which compares the signals to its program and sends an output signal to the actuators. Actuators change the computer voltage signal into electro-mechanical motion. Sensors are generally switches, resistors, transformers, or generators. Actuators are usually solenoids, stepper motors, relay modules, or warning lights.

Computer-controlled engine systems began as a way of managing fuel metering for better mileage and emission control. Manufacturers used electronic ignitions with the fuel-metering systems to form the basis for an engine management system. Chrysler's lean-burn, the Bosch DME system, Ford's EEC-I, and GM's C-4 system are examples of early engine control systems. More recent advanced systems, such as GM's CCC and Ford's EEC-V, have self-diagnostic capabilities, control many more functions, and are far more efficient and powerful than their predecessors. 1994 brought a major change to fuel and emissions systems with the legislation and development of the Onboard Diagnostics II (OBD II) systems. These sophisticated fuel and emission control systems monitor, test and report slight changes in the operation and driveability of the vehicle.

Figure 17-93. Schematic of the VAST ignition system on the TCCS.

■ The Rise and Fall of Gaskets in a Tube

In the 1980s, auto manufacturers replaced many traditional cork gasket installations with room-temperature-vulcanizing (RTV) silicone sealants. RTV sealants quickly gained an unchallenged reign as "gaskets in a tube" for installing such parts as water pumps, valve covers, oil pans, transmission and differential covers, and other components.

Cork gaskets had been the industry standard for decades in these applications. Cork, however, dries out with age and loses its shape. Parts departments often found themselves with an inventory of unusable over-age gaskets. Moreover, car dealers and garages had to stock a variety of gaskets for different car models. RTV sealant seemed a revolutionary breakthrough.

When properly applied, RTV is an excellent sealer, but mating surfaces must be perfectly free of oil and grease because oil dissolves the RTV sealant. Additionally, RTV residue in bolt holes can cause a hydraulic effect that affects torque when a bolt is installed. These are minor problems, however, that are easily overcome by professional technicians. But, RTV also has longer-term disadvantages that took time for the service industry to discover. For example, it:

- Has a short shelf life — about one year
- Does not cure properly when the shelf life is expired
- Spoils if the cap is left off the tube, because moisture in the air causes it to cure
- Is expensive to manufacture and stock for long periods.

Despite these disadvantages, manufacturers used and specified RTV sealants and created a virtual depression in the cork gasket industry. In the mid-1980s, though, General Motors discovered that RTV sealants can cause long-term problems that had been unforeseen a decade earlier.

Although RTV sealant cures sufficiently to provide a firm seal in 24 to 48 hours, it can require as long as one year after installation to cure completely. Final curing time depends on where it is used and how thickly it is applied. During the prolonged curing time, RTV sealant gives off acidic fumes that can corrode electrical connections and sensitive electronic parts.

As solid-state electronic components increased in use during the 1980s, GM found that RTV sealant can contribute to failure of these sensitive devices. Now, GM and other manufacturers are again providing cork-based gaskets for some applications where RTV sealant had been used. The gasket makers, meanwhile, have learned new methods of leak control. In one method, they bond cork to both sides of thin metal, producing gaskets that meet the needs of modern vehicles and eliminate the shrinkage and deterioration problems that plagued the cork gaskets of a generation ago. In a more recent method, the thin metal is encased in a rubberized material to produce a gasket that is reusable for the life of the vehicle (100,000 miles).

Review Questions
Choose the single most correct answer.
Compare your answers with the correct answers on Page 468.

1. The first domestic engine control system was Chrysler's electronic lean-burn. It controls:
   a. Ignition timing
   b. Fuel metering
   c. EGR and air injection switching
   d. Throttle position

2. The engine control system used on most late-model Ford vehicles is called:
   a. Electronic Feedback Fuel Control (EFFC)
   b. Microprocessor Control Unit (MCU)
   c. Electronic Engine Control-V (EEC-V)
   d. Computerized Emission Control (CEC)

3. Technician A says engine computers receive input data, process and store data, and send output signals.
   Technician B says late-model engine computers are based on analog microprocessors.
   Who is right?
   a. A only
   b. B only
   c. Both A and B
   d. Neither A nor B

4. NOx formation may be controlled best by:
   a. Enriching the fuel mixture
   b. Lowering the engine's compression ratio
   c. Recirculating exhaust gases
   d. Retarding spark timing

5. Technician A says an oxygen sensor with two wires is grounded to the exhaust manifold.
   Technician B says the computer ignores a two-wire sensor in closed-loop operation.
   Who is right?
   a. A only
   b. B only
   c. Both A and B
   d. Neither A nor B

6. Technician A says a throttle position (TP) sensor may be either a rotary or linear potentiometer.
   Technician B says some systems may use a simple on/off switch.
   Who is right?
   a. A only
   b. B only
   c. Both A and B
   d. Neither A nor B

7. Technician A says the output signal from one computer can act as an input signal for another computer.
   Technician B says late-model computers have self-diagnostic abilities and can display trouble codes.
   Who is right?
   a. A only
   b. B only
   c. Both A and B
   d. Neither A nor B

8. Technician A says too much exhaust gas recirculation will increase HC emissions and fuel consumption.
   Technician B says the use of EGR allows for more timing advance.
   Who is right?
   a. A only
   b. B only
   c. Both A and B
   d. Neither A nor B

9. The atmosphere at sea level contains approximately 21 percent oxygen. Very rich exhaust gases may contain:
   a. 6 percent
   b. 4 percent
   c. 2 percent
   d. 0.5 percent

10. Technician A says on-time is that part of a cycle when the solenoid is energized.
    Technician B says pulse width is the length of time that a solenoid is off.
    Who is right?
    a. A only
    b. B only
    c. Both A and B
    d. Neither A nor B

11. An electronic fuel injector is a type of:
    a. Solenoid
    b. Sensor
    c. Stepper motor
    d. Control unit

12. The first electronically controlled fuel-metering system with a three-way converter and O2 sensor was the:
    a. C-4 system
    b. Lambda-Sond system
    c. Bosch Motronic system
    d. Ford FEEC system

13. Technician A says some GM microprocessors have a replaceable PROM.
    Technician B says Ford EEC-IV microprocessors have a replaceable calibration assembly.
    Who is right?
    a. A only
    b. B only
    c. Both A and B
    d. Neither A nor B

14. Technician A says a solenoid is a digital actuator.
    Technician B says a stepper motor works like an analog actuator with digital signals.
    Who is right?
    a. A only
    b. B only
    c. Both A and B
    d. Neither A nor B

15. The first engine control systems appeared on domestic cars in:
    a. 1979
    b. 1977
    c. 1974
    d. 1972

16. Technician A says EEPROMs used in a GM ECM/PCM can be erased and reprogrammed.
    Technician B says nonvolatile RAM memory is lost whenever the ignition is turned off.
    Who is right?
    a. A only
    b. B only
    c. Both A and B
    d. Neither A nor B

17. Technician A says computers can be integrated through multiplexing.
    Technician B says automatic transmission operation is controlled by the engine control computer in some late-model vehicles.
    Who is right?
    a. A only
    b. B only
    c. Both A and B
    d. Neither A nor B

PART SIX

Lighting, Accessory, and Body Electrical Systems

Chapter Eighteen
Lighting Systems

Chapter Nineteen
Horn, Windshield Wiper and Washer, Electric Cooling Fan, and Instrument Circuits

Chapter Twenty
Body Electrical Systems (Accessories)

18
Lighting Systems

Automotive lighting circuits include important safety features. For this reason, they must be properly understood and serviced. Lighting circuits follow general patterns, according to the devices they serve. Slight variations appear from manufacturer to manufacturer.

HEADLAMP CIRCUITS

The headlamp circuit is one of the most standardized automotive circuits, because headlamp use is regulated by laws that until recently have seen little change since the 1940s. There are two types of headlamp circuits:

- Two-lamp circuit
- Four-lamp circuit.

Manufacturers select the type of circuit on the basis of automotive body styling. Each circuit must provide both a high-beam and a low-beam light, a switch or switches to control the beams, and a high-beam indicator.

Circuit Diagrams

Most often, the headlamps are grounded, and switches are installed between the lamps and the power source, figure 18-1. Some circuits have insulated bulbs and a grounded switch, figure 18-2. In both cases, all lamp filaments are connected in parallel. The failure of one filament will not affect current flow through the others.

A two-lamp circuit, figure 18-3, uses lamps that contain both a high-beam and a low-beam filament. A four-lamp circuit, figure 18-4, has two double-filament lamps and two lamps with single, high-beam filaments. Lamp types are explained in more detail later in this chapter.

Switches and Circuit Breakers

The three operating conditions of a headlamp circuit are:

- Off — no current
- Low-beam — current through low-beam filaments
- High-beam — current through both the low-beam and the high-beam filaments.

These current paths are controlled by one or two switches. The switches may control other lighting circuits as well.

Most domestic cars have a three-position main headlamp switch. The positions, figure 18-5, are:

Figure 18-1. Most headlamp circuits have insulated switches and grounded bulbs.

Figure 18-2. Some headlamp circuits use grounded switches and insulated bulbs. (Oldsmobile)

- First position — off, no current
- Second position — current flows to parking lamps, taillamps, and other circuits
- Third position — current flows to both the second-position circuits and to the headlamp circuit.

The headlamp switch is connected to the battery whether the ignition switch is on or off.

A two-position dimmer switch is connected in series with the headlamp switch. The dimmer switch controls the high- and low-beam current paths. If the headlamps are grounded at the bulb, figure 18-6, the dimmer switch is installed between the main headlamp switch and the bulbs. If the headlamps are

Figure 18-3. A two-lamp headlamp circuit uses two double-filament bulbs.

Figure 18-4. A four-lamp headlamp circuit uses two double-filament bulbs and two single-filament bulbs.

remotely grounded, as shown in figure 18-2, the dimmer switch is installed between the bulbs and ground.

The dimmer switch on older cars and most light-duty trucks is foot operated and mounted near the pedals, figure 18-7. On late-model cars, it generally is mounted on the steering column and operated by a multifunction stalk, or lever, figure 18-8.

Figure 18-5. The main headlamp switch controls both the headlamp circuit and various other lighting circuits. (Chrysler)

Some imported and late-model domestic cars use a single switch to control all of the headlamp circuit operations.

Three basic types of headlamp switches are used:

- Mounted on the steering column and operated by a lever, figure 18-9
- A push-pull switch mounted on the instrument panel, figure 18-10
- A rocker-type switch mounted on the instrument panel, figure 18-11.

All systems must have an indicator lamp for high-beam operation. The indicator lamp is mounted on the instrument panel. It forms a parallel path to ground for a small amount of high-beam current and lights when the high-beam filaments light.

Because headlamps are an important safety feature, the circuitry is protected by a Type 1, self-setting circuit breaker. The circuit breaker can be built into the headlamp switch, figure 18-5, or it can be a separate unit, figure 18-1.

Headlamps

Until 1940, a small replaceable bulb mounted behind a glass lens was used to provide light for night driving. Safety standards established in the United States in 1940 made round, sealed-beam units mandatory on domestic cars. Repeated attempts to modify the

Figure 18-6. Most dimmer switches are insulated and control current flow to grounded bulbs. (Chrysler)

Figure 18-7. Until the mid-1970s, dimmer switches were usually mounted on the floor and were foot operated. (Ford)

Figure 18-8. Late-model dimmer switches are operated by a steering column-mounted multifunction stalk or lever and control other lamp circuits. (Ford)

Figure 18-9. Headlamp switches may be mounted on the steering column and operated by a stalk or lever.

standards after World War II were only partially successful, beginning with the introduction of rectangular sealed-beam units in the mid-1970s. The first major change in headlight design came with the rectangular halogen headlamp, which appeared on some 1980 models. Since that time, considerable progress has been made in establishing other types, such as composite headlamps that use replaceable halogen bulbs.

Conventional Sealed-beam Headlamps

Sealed-beam headlamps are a 1-piece, replaceable unit containing the filament, reflector, lens, and connecting terminals, figure 18-12. The position of the filament in front of the reflector determines whether the filament will cast a high or a low beam. The glass lens is designed to spread this beam in a specific way. Headlamps have **symmetrical** or **asymmetrical** beams, figure 18-13. All high beams are spread symmetrically; all low beams are spread asymmetrically.

Five types of conventional sealed-beam lamps are manufactured for normal automotive use. The type code is molded into the lens of the bulb. The different types are shown in figure 18-14.

- Type 1 lamps contain a single, high-beam filament inside a circular, 5-3/4-inch (146-mm) diameter housing.

Figure 18-10. Push-pull headlamp switches are mounted on the instrument panel. (Ford)

Figure 18-11. Rocker-type headlamp switches usually have a separate rotary rheostat control. (Ford)

Figure 18-12. A cutaway view of a conventional sealed-beam headlamp.

- Type 1A lamps contain a single, high-beam filament inside a rectangular, 4 x 6 1/2-inch (102 x 165-mm) housing.

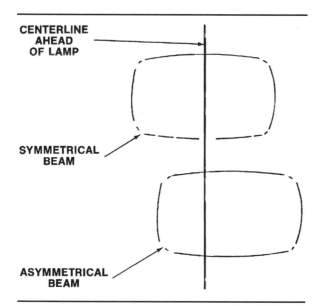

Figure 18-13. The glass lens design determines whether the beam is symmetrical or asymmetrical.

Figure 18-14. These sealed-beam bulbs used on late-model automobiles are being replaced by composite headlamps.

- Type 2 lamps contain both a high-beam and a low-beam filament inside a circular housing of either 5 3/4-inch (146-mm) or 7-inch (178-mm) diameter.
- Type 2A lamps contain the same filaments as a Type 2, inside a rectangular, 4 x 6 1/2-inch (102 x 165-mm) housing.

- Type 2B lamps contain the same filaments as a Type 2, inside a rectangular housing made to metric dimensions of 142 x 200 mm (5.6 x 7.9 inches).

All of these lamps have three aiming pads, which are small glass bumps molded into the lens at specific points. These are used when the headlamps are being aimed with a mechanical aimer, as we will learn in the *Shop Manual*.

Headlamps are installed in a circuit with multiple-plug connectors, figure 18-15. Type 1 and 1A lamps have two connecting prongs, while Type 2, 2A, and 2B lamps have three connecting prongs. One prong is a ground path; as you look at the rear of the lamp, this is the left-hand prong. The other one or two prongs conduct current from the battery to the filaments.

Halogen sealed-beam headlamps

Halogen sealed-beam headlamps first appeared as options on some 1980 domestic cars. Their illumination comes from passing current through a filament in a pressure-filled halogen capsule, instead of through a filament in conventional evacuated sealed-beam bulbs. Halogen lamps provide brighter, whiter light than conventional headlamps.

Service and adjustment procedures are the same for halogen sealed-beam lamps as they are for conventional sealed-beams. Early bulb-type halogen lamps were not interchangeable with conventional sealed-beam headlamps, but today halogen sealed-beam lamps can be used as direct replacements for their conventional counterpart in many cases. Halogen lamps are manufactured of glass or plastic. Glass

■ **Headlamp Control Levers**

Late-model cars are not the first to have a column-mounted lever controlling the headlamp circuit. The headlamps on the 1929 Reo Wolverine Model B were turned on and off by a lever mounted to the left of the horn button on the steering wheel. This lever also controlled the high-low beam switching. The Reo instruction book pointed out that, because each headlamp filament produced twenty-one candlepower, the headlamps should not be used when the car was standing still to avoid draining the battery.

Symmetrical: The same on both sides of center. In a symmetrical high-beam headlamp, the light beam is spread the same distance to both sides of center.

Asymmetrical: Different on both sides of center. In an asymmetrical low-beam headlamp, the light beam is spread farther to one side of center than to the other.

Figure 18-15. The bulbs are connected into the headlamp circuit with multiple-plug connectors.

Figure 18-16. A replaceable halogen bulb is installed through the rear of the reflector and held in place with a retaining ring. (Ford)

lamps carry an "H" prefix; plastic lamps have an "HP" prefix. Plastic lamps are less susceptible to stone damage and also weigh considerably less than glass lamps.

Halogen sealed-beam lamps are manufactured in the same sizes and types as conventional sealed-beams, with one additional type:

Type 2E lamps contain both a high-beam and a low-beam inside a rectangular, 4 x 6 1/2 inch (102 x 165-mm) housing.

Like conventional sealed-beams, the type code and aiming pads are molded into the lens of the bulb.

Composite headlamps

Composite headlamps first appeared on some 1984 models as a part of the aerodynamic styling concept that has characterized car design since the mid-1980s. Composite headlamp design uses a replaceable halogen headlamp bulb that fits into a socket at the rear of the reflector, figure 18-16. Since the headlamp housing does not require replacement unless damaged, it can be incorporated as a permanent feature of automotive styling. The housing can be designed to accept a single bulb or dual bulbs.

Composite headlamps can be manufactured by two different methods. In one, polycarbonate plastic is used to form the lens portion of the headlamp housing, figure 18-17, and the inside of the housing is completely sealed. In the other, a glass lens cover is permanently bonded with a reflector housing to form a single unit. Because this type of composite headlamp is vented to the atmosphere, water droplets may form on the inside of the glass lens cover when the headlamps are off. Such condensation disappears rapidly when the lights are turned on and does not affect headlamp performance.

Figure 18-17. Composite headlights use a polycarbonate lens and form a permanent part of the car's styling. (GM)

Replacement halogen bulbs may contain both high- and low-beam filaments for use in two-headlamp systems, or individual high- or low-beam filaments for use in four-headlamp systems. The halogen bulbs have a quartz surface that can be easily stained when handled. For this reason, the bulbs are furnished in protective plastic covers that should not be removed until the bulb has been installed. If the quartz surface is accidentally touched with bare hands, it should be cleaned immediately with a soft cloth moistened with alcohol.

Replacing the halogen bulb in a composite headlamp does not normally disturb the alignment of the headlamp assembly. There should be no need for headlamp alignment unless the composite headlamp assembly is removed or replaced. If alignment is required, however, special adapters must be used with the alignment devices.

AUTOMOTIVE HEADLAMPS

HEADLAMP TYPE AND SIZE	ID CODE①	TRADE NO.②	DESIGN WATTS @ 12.8 VOLTS	
			HIGH BEAM	LOW BEAM
5-3/4 INCH CIRCULAR SEALED-BEAM	2C1	4000	37.5	60
	2C1	4040③	37.5	60
	2C1	H5006	35	35
	1C1	4001	37.5	
	1C1	H4001	37.5	
	1C1	5001	50	
	1C1	H5001	50	
7 INCH CIRCULAR SEALED-BEAM	2D1	6014	50	50
	2D1	H6014	60	50
	2D1	6015③	60	50
	2D1	6016④	60	50
	2D1	H6017	60	35
4 X 6-12 INCH RECTANGULAR SEALED-BEAM	1A1	4651	50	
	1A1	H4651	50	
	2A1	4652	40	60
	2A1	H4656	35	35
	2A1	H4662	40	45
	2A1	H4739	40	50
	2E1	H4666	65	45
5-1/2 X 8 INCH RECTANGULAR SEALED-BEAM	2B1	6052	65	
	2B1	H6052	65	
	2B1	H6054	65	55
3 X 5 INCH RECTANGULAR	H1	H4701	65	
	H3	H4703	65	
	H4	H4704	60	55④
REPLACEMENT HALOGEN BULB		9094	65	45

NOTES:
① THE FIRST CHARACTER INDICATES THE NUMBER OF BEAMS IN THE BULB, THE SECOND INDICATES THE SIZE AND NUMBER OF BULBS USIED ON THE CAR, AND THE THIRD IS AN SAE PHOTOMETRIC SPECIFICATION. ② H INDICATES A HALOGEN SEALED-BEAM. ③ HEAVY DUTY. ④ AT 13.2 VOLTS.

Figure 18-18. Common sealed-beam headlamps and replaceable halogen bulbs.

Figure 18-18 describes the automotive headlamps currently in use.

Headlamp Location and Mounting

State and federal laws control the installation of headlamps. Automotive designers must place headlamps within certain height and width ranges. In addition, two- or four-lamp systems must follow one of the patterns shown in figure 18-19.

Headlamps are mounted so that their aim can be adjusted. Most circular and rectangular lamps have three adjustment points, figure 18-20. The sealed-beam unit is placed in an adjustable mounting which is retained by a stationary mounting. Many cars have a decorative bezel that hides this hardware while still allowing lamp adjustment, figure 18-21. Composite headlamps use a similar two-point adjustment system, figure 18-22, but require the use of special adapters with the alignment devices.

Concealed Headlamps

Another automotive styling feature is concealed headlamps. These can be either a stationary lamp behind a moveable door, figure 18-23, or a lamp that moves in and out of the car's bodywork, figure 18-24. The doors can be metal or clear plastic.

Headlamp-concealing mechanisms are operated by electric motors or vacuum actuators. Electrically operated systems usually have a relay controlling current flow to the motor. Vacuum-actuated systems work with engine vacuum stored in a reservoir, figure 18-25.

Federal law requires that the concealing mechanisms on late-model cars be controlled by the main headlamp switch and that "pop-up" headlamps that rise out of the hood must not come on until they have completed 75 percent of their travel. Switches used with electrically operated headlamp doors have additional contacts to activate the relay, figure 18-26. Vacuum-actuated systems usually have a vacuum switch attached to the headlamp switch, figure 18-27. Some older cars may have a separate switch to control the door. All concealed headlamp systems also must have a manual opening method, such as a crank or a lever, as a backup system.

Some 1967 and earlier cars have a clear plastic lens cover, or fairing, over the sealed-beam unit, figure 18-28. These are not legal on later-model cars.

FOUR-HEADLAMP SYSTEM

TYPE 1 HEADLAMP
(HIGH BEAM)

TYPE 2 HEADLAMP
(HIGH AND LOW BEAM)

TYPE 1 HEADLAMP
(HIGH BEAM)

TWO-HEADLAMP SYSTEM

TYPE 2 HEADLAMP
(HIGH AND LOW BEAM)

Figure 18-19. The law requires that headlamps be arranged in one of these patterns. The same requirements apply to rectangular lamps.

VERTICAL ADJUSTMENT SCREW

RIGHT-HAND
HORIZONTAL
ADJUSTMENT
SCREW

LEFT-HAND
HORIZONTAL
ADJUSTMENT
SCREW

Figure 18-20. Most sealed-beam headlamps have vertical and horizontal adjusting screws. (GM)

Automatic Headlamp Systems

Photocells and solid-state circuitry sometimes are used to control headlamp operation. A system either can turn the lamps on and off or can control high- and low-beam switching. Some parts can be adjusted, but defective parts cannot be repaired. All automatic systems have manual switches to override the automatic functions.

SHELL
ASSEMBLY

HEADLAMP
BODY

BULB

STATIONARY MOUNTING

HEADLAMP
ADJUSTING
SPRING

RING

ADJUSTABLE
MOUNTING

ADJUSTMENT
SLOT

BEZEL

Figure 18-21. Headlamps are held in an adjustable mounting which is generally concealed by a decorative bezel.

COMPOSITE HEADLAMP AIMERS

VERTICAL AIM
ADJUSTMENT

HORIZONTAL AIM
ADJUSTMENT

RIGHT HAND SHOWN
(REAR VIEW)

Figure 18-22. Composite headlamps also have vertical and horizontal adjustments. (GM)

On-off control

The photocell and amplifier sensor used in this system may be mounted on top of the instrument panel, figure 18-29, facing upward so that it is exposed to natural outside light. It may also be mounted to the rearview mirror assembly, figure 18-30, facing outward for exposure to outside light. The photocell voltage is amplified and applied to a solid-state control module. Photocell voltage decreases as outside light decreases. Most photocells are adjustable for earlier or later turn-on. At a predetermined low light and voltage level, the module turns the headlamps on. The module often contains time-delay circuitry, so that:

- When the vehicle is momentarily in dark or light, such as when passing under a bridge or a

Figure 18-23. Headlamps can be concealed by a moveable door. (Chrysler)

Figure 18-24. Headlamps can be concealed by moving them into and out of the car's bodywork.

Figure 18-25. Some headlamp doors are operated by engine vacuum.

streetlamp, the headlights do not flash on or off.
• When the automobile's ignition is turned off, the headlights remain on for a specified length of time and then are turned off.

High-low beam switching
In this system, the photocell is mounted behind the radiator grille, figure 18-31, so that it is exposed to the lights of oncoming vehicles. When a bright light strikes the photocell, the voltage developed acts upon a relay to switch from high- to low-beam current.

COMMON AUTOMOTIVE BULBS

Sealed-beam and composite headlamps are very specialized types of lamp bulbs. The other bulbs used in automotive lighting circuits are much smaller and less standardized. Figure 18-32 shows a representative sampling of commonly used bulb and base designs. Each specific bulb has a unique trade number that is used consistently by all manufacturers.

Most small automotive bulbs are clear, and are mounted behind colored lenses. Some applications,

however, may call for a red or an amber bulb. This is indicated by an R for red and NA for amber.

Small automotive bulbs use either a brass or a glass wedge base. Bulbs with a brass base fit into a matching socket. The single or double contacts on the base of the bulb are the insulated contacts for the bulb's filaments. A matching contact in the socket supplies current to the bulb filament, figure 18-33. A single-contact

■ Gas Lighting

Headlamps that burned acetylene gas were used on early cars, trucks, and motorcycles. The acetylene gas came from a pre-filled pressurized container or from a "gas generator".

One type of acetylene gas generator used a drip method. A tank filled with water was mounted above another tank containing calcium carbide. A valve controlled the dripping of water onto the calcium carbide. When water was allowed to drip onto the carbide, acetylene gas formed. The gas was routed through a small pipe to the headlamps. The headlamps were lit with a match or by an electric spark across a special lighting attachment.

Figure 18-26. The main headlamp switch must operate the concealing mechanism. (Chrysler)

Figure 18-27. The main headlamp switch may have a built-in vacuum switch. (Ford)

Figure 18-28. Older cars often use clear covers, or fairings, over the headlamps. (British Leyland)

Figure 18-29. This photocell is mounted near the left side of the dash panel and reacts to outside light to control the headlight on-off operation. (Ford)

bulb contains one filament; a double-contact bulb has two filaments. The ground end of the bulb filament is connected directly to the base of the bulb, which is grounded through contact with the socket. In many cases, a separate ground wire leads from the socket to a ground connection. All double-contact bulbs are indexed so that they will fit into the socket in only one way. This is called an indexed base.

Wedge-base bulbs generally have been used for instrument cluster and other interior lighting applications. The base and optical part of the bulb are a one-piece, formed-glass shell with four filament wires extending through the base and crimped around it to form the external contacts, figure 18-34. The design locates the contacts accurately, permitting direct electrical contact with the socket, which contains shoulders to hold the bulb in place. The bulb is installed by pushing it straight into its socket, with no indexing required.

Wedge-base 2358 bulbs with a new socket design were introduced in 1987 as replacements for the brass base 1157 and 2057 bulbs for exterior lighting appli-

cations. The wires of the low-profile plastic socket exit from the side instead of the rear, figure 18-35. This reduces the possibility of wire damage and permits the socket to be used in more confined areas. Since the introduction of this base-socket design, a series of these bulbs has been made available in both clear and amber versions.

AUTOMATIC DIMMER SENSOR

ELECTRONIC DAY/NIGHT MIRROR

WIRING

Figure 18-30. The photocell/amplifier assembly can be part of the rear view mirror assembly. (Ford)

TAILLAMP, LICENSE PLATE LAMP, AND PARKING LAMP CIRCUITS

The taillamps, license plate lamps, and parking lamps illuminate the car for other drivers to see.

Circuit Diagram

These lamps usually share a single circuit, because the laws of some states require that they be lit at the same time. Figure 18-36 shows a typical circuit diagram. Since the lamps are controlled by the main headlamp switch, they can be lit whether the ignition switch is on or off.

Switches and Fuses

These lamps are controlled by contacts within the main headlamp switch. They can be lit when the headlamps are off, figure 18-37. A fuse (usually 20 amperes) protects the circuit.

Bulbs

The bulb designs most commonly used as taillamps and parking lamps are G-6 single-contact bayonet and S-8 double-contact bayonet. The tail and parking lamps may be one filament of a double-filament bulb.

SENSOR AMPLIFIER

VERTICAL AIMING SCREW

BRACKET ASSEMBLY

LEVELING GAUGE

CHAMBER

Figure 18-31. This photocell reacts to the lights of oncoming cars to control the headlamp beam switching.

License plate lamps are usually G-6 single-contact bayonet or T-3 1/4 wedge bulbs.

STOP LAMP AND TURN SIGNAL CIRCUITS

Stop lamps, also called brake lamps, are always red. Federal law requires a red high-mounted brake lamp, or HMBL, on 1986 and later models. Turn signals, or directionals, are either amber or white on the front of the car and either red or amber on the rear.

Circuit Diagram

A typical circuit diagram with stop and turn lamps as separate bulbs is shown in figure 18-38A. When the brakes are applied, the brake switch is closed and the stop lamps light. The brake switch receives current from the fuse panel and is not affected by the ignition switch.

When the turn signal switch is moved in either direction, the corresponding turn signal lamps receive current through the flasher unit. The flasher unit causes the current to start and stop very rapidly, as we will see later. The turn signal lamp flashes on and off with the interrupted current. The turn signal switch receives current through the ignition switch, so that the signals will light only if the ignition switch is on.

In many cars, the stop and turn signals are both provided by one filament, figure 18-38B and figure 18-39. When the turn signal switch is closed, the filament receives interrupted current through the flasher unit. When the brakes are applied, the filament receives a steady flow of current through the brake switch and special contacts in the turn signal switch.

BULB TYPE	BASE TYPE	TRADE NO.	AMPERAGE	CANDLE POWER	COMMON USE
T 3¼	WEDGE	161①	.19	1	GENERAL
		168	.33	3	INSTRUMENT
		184	.24	1	INSTRUMENT
		193	.33	2	INSTRUMENT
		194①	.27	2	INSTRUMENT
		557	.42	2.5	WARNING
	MINIATURE BAYONET	256	.27	1.6	PARKING BRAKE
		1815	.20	1.4	INTERIOR
		1889	.27	2	INSTRUMENT
		1891	.24	2	GENERAL
		1892	.12	0.8	RADIO DIAL
		1893①	.33	2	INSTRUMENT
		1898	.33	2	INSTRUMENT
G 3½	MINIATURE BAYONET	53	.12	1	INDICATOR
		182	.18	1	GENERAL
		1445①	.135	0.7	GENERAL
G 4½	MINIATURE BAYONET	57	.24	2	INDICATOR
		257	.27	1.6	FLASHING
		293①	.33	2	GENERAL
		1895	.24	2	INDICATOR
G 6	SINGLE-CONTACT BAYONET	61	.84	2	INSTRUMENT
		67	.59	4	INDICATOR
		89	.57	6	INSTRUMENT
		97①	.69	4	MARKER
		98	.62	6	GENERAL
		631①	.63	6	GENERAL
		1293	.40	50	GENERAL
	DOUBLE-CONTACT BAYONET	68	.42	3	INDICATOR
		90①	.57	6	MARKER
		96	.69	4	GENERAL
		99	.62	6	GENERAL
		1178①	.69	4	GENERAL
S 8	SINGLE-CONTACT BAYONET	93	1.07	15	GENERAL
		199①	2.25	32	INTERIOR, SIGNAL
		1073	1.70	32	INTERIOR, SIGNAL
		1095	.51	4	GENERAL
		1141①	1.34	21	INTERIOR, SIGNAL
		1156①	1.70	32	INTERIOR, SIGNAL
		1159	1.60	21	GENERAL
		1295	3.00	0.5	SIDE MARKER
	DOUBLE-CONTACT BAYONET	94	1.07	15	INTERIOR
		1005	1.31	21	GENERAL
		1076	1.8	32	TAILLAMP
		1142	1.34	21	INTERIOR
		1176①②	1.31/.57	21/6	STOP, TAIL, SIGNAL
		1376②	1.6/.64	21/6	GENERAL
	DOUBLE-CONTACT INDEXED	198①②	2.25/.68	32/4	GENERAL
		1016②	1.26/.57	21/6	STOP, TAIL
		1034②	1.8/.51	32/3	SIGNAL, MARKER
		1157①②	1.97/.51	32/3	SIGNAL, MARKER
T 4¾	DOUBLE END CAP (FESTOON)	211	.97	12	INTERIOR
		212	.74	6	INTERIOR

① Heavy-duty bulb
② Double-filament bulb

Figure 18-32. Common automotive bulbs.

If both switches are closed at once, brake switch current is not allowed through the turn signal switch to the filament on the signalling side. The signalling filament receives interrupted current through the flasher unit and so it flashes on and off. The filament on the opposite side of the car receives a steady flow of current through the brake switch and the turn signal switch and so it is continuously lit.

Figure 18-39 shows the integration of the single filament CHMSL in a typical stop-and-turn signal circuit.

Switches, Fuses, and Flashers

Several units affect current flow through the stop lamp and turn signal circuits. The ignition switch is located between the battery and the turn signal switch, figure 18-40, so that the current cannot flow through the turn signal switch if the ignition switch is off. The brake switch is not controlled by the ignition switch. It is connected directly to battery voltage through the fuse panel, figure 18-40.

Before the mid-1960s, the brake switch was often located within the brake hydraulic system and operated by hydraulic pressure. Because of changes in braking system design, this type of switch is no longer

CURRENT FLOW

Figure 18-33. Automotive bulbs and sockets must be matched.

Figure 18-34. Wedge-base bulbs are increasingly used for interior lighting applications.

commonly used. On late-model cars, the brake switch is usually mounted on the bracket that holds the brake pedal, figure 18-41. When the pedal is pressed, the switch is closed.

The turn signal switch is mounted within the steering column and operated by a lever, figure 18-42. Moving the lever up or down closes contacts to supply current to the flasher unit and to the appropriate turn signal lamp. A turn signal switch includes cams and springs that cancel the signal after the turn has been completed. That is, as the steering wheel is turned in the signalled direction and then returns to its normal position, the cams and springs separate the turn signal switch contacts.

Figure 18-35. Wedge-base bulbs with plastic sockets are used for some external lighting applications. (Chrysler)

In systems using separate filaments for the stop and turn lamps, the brake and turn signal switches are not connected. If the car uses the same filament for both purposes, then there must be a way for the turn signal switch to interrupt the brake switch current and allow only flasher unit current to the filament on the side being signalled. To do this, brake switch current is routed through contacts within the turn signal switch, figure 18-43. By linking certain contacts, the bulbs can receive either brake switch current or flasher current, depending upon which direction is being signaled.

For example, figure 18-44 shows current flow through the switch when the brake switch is closed and a right turn is signalled. Steady current through the brake switch is sent to the left brake lamp. Interrupted current from the turn signal is sent to the right turn lamps.

Flasher units supply a rapid on-off-on current to the turn signal lamps. To do this, they act very much like a Type 1 self-setting circuit breaker. Current flows through a bimetallic arm, figure 18-45, heating the arm until it bends and opens a set of contact points. When the current stops, the arm cools and the contact

■ **Switch the Bulbs, Not the Switch**

Have you ever been stumped by a turn signal problem where the lamps on one side flashed properly, but those on the other side lit and burned steadily without flashing? The flasher checks out okay, and the panel indicator lights but doesn't flash. Both bulbs, front and rear, light; power is getting to the sockets. Sounds like trouble with the switch? Maybe it is.

However, before you tear into the steering column, try swapping the front and rear bulbs from one side to the other. Sometimes, a little corrosion on a socket and the resistance of an individual bulb can add up to cumulative resistance that unbalances the circuit and prevents flashing. Swapping the bulbs or cleaning the contacts can reduce the resistance to within limits, restore equilibrium, and get the system working correctly again.

Figure 18-36. A taillamp, license plate lamp, and parking lamp circuit diagram. (Buick)

Figure 18-37. Contacts in the main headlamp switch provide current to the taillamps, license plate lamps, and parking lamps. (Chrysler)

points close again. This cycle occurs rapidly so that the turn signal lamps flash on and off about once every second. Flasher units usually are installed in the wiring harness beneath the instrument panel, figure 18-46, or in the fuse panel.

Some manufacturers, including Ford, have used an additional control unit in series with multiple turn signal lamps, figure 18-47. This transistorized module causes the three rear turn signal lamps on either side to flash in sequence, from the center of the car outward.

The turn signal circuit must include one or more indicators to show the driver that the turn signals are operating. These indicators are small bulbs in the instrument panel that provide a parallel path to ground for some of the flasher unit current. Most systems have separate indicators for the right and left sides, although some cars use only one indicator bulb for both sides. On some models, additional indicators are mounted on the front fenders facing the driver.

The stop lamp and turn signal lamp circuits are usually protected by two separate fuses, rated at about 20 amperes.

Figure 18-38. Stop lamp and turn signal circuits. The basic drawing (A) has separate bulbs for each function. The alternate view of the rear lamps (B) has single bulbs with double filaments. One filament of each bulb works for stop lamps and for turn signals. (Buick)

Figure 18-39. A typical rear lighting circuit diagram showing the inclusion of the high-mounted brake lamp (HMBL) mandated by law on 1986 and later models. (Chrysler)

Figure 18-40. The ignition switch controls current to the turn signal switch, but does not affect current to the brake switch.

Figure 18-41. When the brake pedal is pressed, the entire brake assembly moves with it. The switch actuating pin does not move as far as the contacts do, and so it closes the contacts. (Ford)

Bulbs

The bulb types traditionally used as stop or turn signal lamps are the S-8 single- and double-contact bayonet base, although the 2358 wedge-base bulbs are being used more frequently. The stop and turn filaments may be part of a double-filament bulb.

HAZARD WARNING LAMP (EMERGENCY FLASHER) CIRCUITS

All motor vehicles sold in the United States since 1967 have a hazard warning lamp circuit. It is

Figure 18-42. The turn signal switch includes various springs and cams to control the contact points.

Figure 18-43. When the stop lamps and turn signals share a common filament, stop lamp current flows through the turn signal switch.

designed to warn other drivers of possible danger in emergencies.

Circuit Diagram

The hazard warning lamp circuit uses the turn signal lamp circuitry, a special switch, and a heavy-duty flasher unit. The switch receives battery current

Figure 18-44. When a right turn is signalled, the turn signal switch contacts send flasher current to the right-hand filament and brake switch current to the left-hand filament.

Figure 18-45. The internal components of a turn signal flasher.

through the fuse panel. When the switch is closed, all of the car's turn signal lamps receive current through the hazard flasher unit. An indicator bulb in the instrument panel provides a parallel path to ground for some of the flasher current.

Switches, Fuses, and Flashers

The hazard warning switch can be a separate unit or it can be part of the turn signal switch, figure 18-48. In both cases, the switch contacts route battery current from the fuse panel through the hazard flasher unit to all of the turn signal lamps at once. In most systems,

Figure 18-46. The turn signal flasher is often mounted beneath the instrument panel. (Oldsmobile)

Figure 18-47. When multiple rear turn signals are installed, a special sequencer module is used to control current. (Ford)

the hazard warning switch overrides the operation of the turn signal switch. The hazard warning circuit is protected by a 15- to 20-ampere fuse.

The hazard warning flasher looks like a turn signal flasher when assembled, but it is constructed differently and operates differently. This allows it to control the large amount of current required to flash all of the turn signal lamps at once.

The flasher consists of a stationary contact, a moveable contact mounted on a bimetallic arm, and a high-resistance coil, figure 18-49. The coil is connected in parallel with the contact points. The contact points are normally open. When the hazard warning switch is closed and current flows to the flasher, the high resistance of the coil does not allow enough current to light the lamps. However, the coil heats up and

Figure 18-48. The hazard warning switch is often a part of the turn signal switch. (AMC)

Figure 18-49. The hazard flasher is constructed to control a large amount of current.

causes the bimetallic strip to close the contacts. The contacts form a parallel circuit branch and conduct current to the lamps. Decreased current flow through the coil allows it to cool and the bimetallic strip opens the contacts again. This cycle repeats about 30 times per minute.

BACKUP LAMP CIRCUITS

The white backup lamps light when the car's transmission or transaxle is in reverse. The lamps have been used for decades, but have been required by law since 1971. Backup lamps and license plate lamps are the only white lamps allowed on the rear of a car.

Circuit Diagram

A typical backup lamp circuit diagram is shown in figure 18-50; figure 18-39 shows integration of the backup lamp with the stop, taillamp, and turn signals in a typical rear lighting diagram. When the transmission switch is closed, the backup lamps receive current through the ignition switch. The lamps will not light when the ignition switch is off.

Switches and Fuses

The backup lamp switch generally is installed on the transmission or transaxle housing, figure 18-51, but it may be mounted near the gear selector lever, figure 18-52, on some vehicles. The backup switch may be combined with the neutral safety switch. The circuit is protected by a 15- to 20-ampere fuse, which often is shared with other circuits.

Figure 18-50. A typical backup lamp circuit. (Chrysler)

Bulbs

The bulb designs most commonly used as backup lamps are S-8 single-contact bayonet and double-contact indexed.

SIDE MARKER AND CLEARANCE LAMP CIRCUITS

Side marker lamps are mounted on the right and left sides toward the front and rear of the vehicle to indicate its length. Side marker lamps are required on all cars built since 1969, and are found on many earlier models as well. Front side markers are amber; rear side markers are red. On some vehicles, the parking lamp or taillamp bulbs are used to provide the side marker function.

Clearance markers are required on some vehicles according to their height and width. Clearance lamps, if used, are included in the side marker lamp circuitry. Clearance lamps face forward or rearward. Like side markers, front clearance lamps are amber; rear lamps are red.

Figure 18-51. The backup lamp switch can be mounted on the transmission housing. (Chrysler)

Figure 18-52. The backup lamp switch can be mounted near the gear shift lever. (Oldsmobile)

Circuit Diagrams

Side marker lamps can be either grounded or insulated, figures 18-53 and 18-54. When they are grounded, figure 18-54, the ground path for current is through the turn signal filaments. When the headlamp switch is off and the turn signal switch is on, both the turn signal and the side marker on the side being signalled will flash. When the headlamp switch is on, only enough current flows to light the side marker. The turn signal lamp does not light until the turn signal switch and flasher are closed; then the turn signal lamp will light. The side marker lamp will not light, because 12 volts are applied to each end of the filament. There is no voltage drop and no current flow. When the turn signal flasher opens, the turn signal lamp goes out. Normal headlamp circuit current lights the side marker lamp. This sequence makes the two lamps flash alternately — one is lit while the other is not.

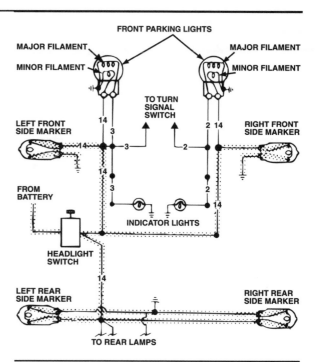

Figure 18-53. Side marker lamps can be independently grounded. (Ford)

Switches and Fuses

Side marker lamps are controlled by contacts within the main headlamp switch. Their circuit is protected by a 20-ampere fuse, which usually is shared with other circuits.

Bulbs

The G-6 and S-8 single- and double-contact bayonet base bulbs commonly are used.

■ Installing New Bulbs

If you replace a bulb in a parking light, turn signal, stop lamp, or taillamp, you may find that the bulb will not light unless you hold it against the socket. This may be due to weakened springs or flattened contacts. To solve the problem, apply a drop of solder to the contact points at the base of the bulb. Add more solder if necessary or file off the excess. The result will be a good solid connection. Also, for a weak spring, if the wires going to the socket are given slack, you may be able to gently stretch the spring.

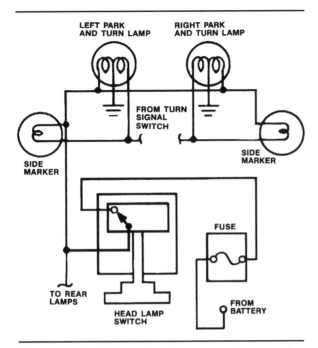

Figure 18-54. Side marker lamps can be grounded through the turn signal filaments.

INSTRUMENT PANEL AND INTERIOR LAMP CIRCUITS

Instrument Panel

The lamps within the instrument panel can be divided into three categories: indicator, warning lamps, and illumination lamps. We have seen that some circuits, such as high-beam headlamps and turn signal lamps, include an indicator mounted on the instrument panel. Warning lamps, which alert the driver to vehicle operating conditions, will be discussed in Chapter Nineteen. Lamps that simply illuminate the instrument panel are explained below.

Circuit diagram

Many late-model automobiles use a printed circuit behind the instrument panel to simplify connections and conserve space, figure 18-55. The connections can also be made with conventional wiring, figure 18-56.

Switches and rheostats

Current to the panel lamps is controlled by contacts within the main headlamp switch, figure 18-57. The instrument panel lamps receive current when the parking and taillamps are lit and when the headlamps are lit.

Rheostats and potentiometers are variable resistors that allow the driver to control the brightness of the panel lamps. The rheostat or the potentiometer for

Figure 18-55. A printed circuit board is used behind most late-model instrument panels. (Ford)

the panel lamps can be a separate unit, figure 18-58, or it can be a part of the main headlamp switch, figure 18-57.

Bulbs

The T-3 1/4 bulb with wedge or miniature bayonet base is a design commonly used in instrument panel illumination.

Interior Lamps

Interior, or courtesy, lamps light the interior of the car for the convenience of the driver and passengers.

Circuit diagram

Interior lamps receive current from the battery through the fuse panel. Switches at the doors control this current, and light the lamps when one of the doors is opened. Many manufacturers install the bulbs between the power source and the grounded switch, figure 18-59. Others, including Ford and Chrysler, install the switches between the power source and the grounded bulb, figure 18-60.

Courtesy lamp circuits also may contain lamps to illuminate the glove box, trunk, and engine compartment. Additional switches that react to glove box door, trunk lid, or hood opening control current through these bulbs.

Switches

The switches used in courtesy lamp circuits are push-pull types, figure 18-61. Spring tension closes the contacts when a door is opened. When a door is closed, it pushes the contacts apart to stop current flow. When any one switch is closed, the circuit is complete and all lamps are lit.

Figure 18-56. Multistrand wiring can be used behind the instrument panel. (Buick)

Figure 18-57. The panel lamps receive current through the main headlamp switch, which may also contain a rheostat to control the current. (Chrysler)

■ Accessory Lighting

Every car manufacturer offers unique accessory lighting circuits. These range from hand-controlled spotlights to driving and fog lamps. Each additional accessory circuit requires more bulbs, more wiring, and possibly an additional switch.

For example, cornering lamps can be mounted on the front sides of the car to provide more light in the direction of a turn. When the turn signal switch is operated while the headlamps are on, special contacts in the turn signal switch conduct a steady flow of current to the cornering lamp on the side being signalled.

Rheostat: A variable resistor used to control current.

Figure 18-58. The rheostat may be a separate unit in the panel lamp circuit. (Chrysler)

Figure 18-59. The interior (courtesy) lamp circuit may have insulated bulbs and grounded switches. (Oldsmobile)

One or more of the interior lamps may have a manually controlled switch to complete the circuit, figure 18-62. This switch allows the driver or passengers to light the bulb even when all the doors are closed.

Bulbs

The S-8 bulbs are used for trunk and engine compartment lamps, with T-3 1/4 wedge and T-3 3/4 double-end-cap bulbs used as courtesy lamps.

Figure 18-60. The interior lamps may be grounded and also have insulated switches.

Figure 18-61. Interior lamps are controlled by switches at the door jambs. (Chrysler)

ALWAYS OFF

ALWAYS ON

ON WHEN DOOR OPENS

Figure 18-62. Interior lamps often have a manual switch to override the automatic operation. (Ford)

SUMMARY

Headlamp circuits must provide low- and high-beam lights for driving, and a high-beam indicator lamp for driver use. Two or four lamps may be used. Most often, the lamps are grounded, but some circuits have insulated lamps and grounded switches. The main headlamp switch also controls other lamp circuits. The main switch sometimes controls high-low beam switching but this is usually controlled by a separate dimmer switch. A circuit breaker protects the headlamp circuit.

Conventional sealed-beam headlamps use a tungsten filament; halogen sealed-beam lamps pass current through a pressure-filled halogen capsule. Halogen headlamps provide a brighter light with less current. Sealed-beam headlamps have either a high-beam filament (Type 1) or both a high- and low-beam filament (Type 2). Headlamps are always connected with multiple-plug connectors.

Changes in Federal lighting standards have permitted sealed-beam headlamps made of plastic instead of glass. Plastic headlamps weigh considerably less and are more damage-resistant than glass. The changes also have resulted in the use of a composite headlamp in place of sealed-beams. The composite headlamp consists of a polycarbonate lens housing and a replaceable halogen bulb that contains a dual filament. Since the lens housing is not replaced, it has been integrated into vehicle styling.

Headlights are mounted so that their aim can be adjusted vertically and horizontally.

Some cars have concealed headlamps with doors or mountings that are operated by vacuum or by electric motors. The main headlamp switch controls these mechanisms, and there also is a manual control provided to open and close the mechanisms if necessary.

Photocells and solid-state modules are used to control the headlamp on-off and beam switching operation on some vehicles.

Bulbs used in other lighting circuits are smaller than sealed-beam units, and must be installed in matching sockets. These other lighting circuits include the:

- Taillamp, license plate lamp and parking lamp circuits
- Stop lamp and turn signal circuits
- Hazard warning (emergency flasher) circuit
- Backup lamp circuit
- Side marker and clearance lamp circuit
- Instrument panel and interior lamp circuits.

Review Questions
Choose the single most correct answer.
Compare your answers with the correct answers on Page 468.

1. Which of the following is true concerning headlamp circuits?
   a. The circuits can have totally insulated bulbs and grounded switches
   b. The lamp filaments are connected in series
   c. All circuits use lamps that contain both a high beam and a low beam
   d. The headlamps receive power through the ignition switch

2. Because headlamps are an important safety feature, they are protected by:
   a. Heavy fuses
   b. Fusible links
   c. Type-I circuit breakers
   d. Type-II circuit breakers

3. All high beams are spread:
   a. Symmetrically
   b. Asymmetrically
   c. Either a or b
   d. Neither a nor b

4. All types of headlamps have _____ that are used when adjusting the beam.
   a. Connecting prongs
   b. Aiming pads
   c. Filaments
   d. Reflectors

5. Concealed headlamps can be operated by all of the following methods, EXCEPT:
   a. Electric motor
   b. Vacuum actuator
   c. Manually
   d. Accessory belt

6. Which of the following is not true of automatic headlamp systems?
   a. Can turn headlamps on or off
   b. Can control high- and low-beam switching
   c. Are easily repaired when defective
   d. Can be adjusted to fit various conditions

7. On small automobile bulbs that have only one contact, the contact is:
   a. Insulated
   b. Indexed
   c. Grounded
   d. Festooned

8. Double-contact bulbs that are designed to fit into the socket only one way are called:
   a. Miniature bayonet base
   b. Single-contact bayonet
   c. Double-contact indexed
   d. Double-contact bayonet

9. The taillamps, license plate lamps, and parking lamps are generally protected by:
   a. A Type-I circuit breaker
   b. A Type-II circuit breaker
   c. A 20-amp fuse
   d. Three fusible links

10. Turn signal flasher units supply a rapid on-off-on current flow to the turn signal lamps by acting very much like:
    a. Circuit breakers
    b. Fuses
    c. Zener diodes
    d. Transistorized regulators

11. Which of the following is *not* part of the hazard warning lamp circuit?
    a. Turn signal lamps
    b. Brake lamps
    c. Flasher unit
    d. Instrument panel

12. The only white lamps allowed on the rear of a car are:
    a. Backup lamps and turn signal lamps
    b. Backup lamps and license plate lamps
    c. License plate lamps and turn signal lamps
    d. Turn signal lamps and backup lamps

13. Brightness of the instrument panel lamps is *not* controlled by:
    a. Diodes
    b. Rheostats
    c. Potentiometers
    d. Variable resistors

14. The switches used in courtesy lamp circuits are:
    a. Compound switches
    b. Push-pull switches
    c. Three-way switches
    d. Rheostats

15. Which of the following is *not* true of composite headlamps?
    a. Use replaceable bulbs
    b. Are part of the car's styling
    c. Have a polycarbonate lens
    d. May be red or amber

16. Halogen sealed-beam lamps:
    a. Are not as damage-resistant as glass
    b. Produce 30% less light
    c. May be made of plastic
    d. Have been used since the 1940.

19

Horn, Windshield Wiper and Washer, Electric Cooling Fan, and Instrument Circuits

HORN CIRCUITS

An automobile horn is a safety device operated by the driver to alert pedestrians and other motorists. Some states require two horn systems, with different sound levels for city and country use.

Circuit Diagram

Some older automobiles used a simple series horn circuit, figure 19-1A. Battery current is supplied to the horn circuit through the fuse panel, or from a terminal on the starter relay or solenoid. The normally open horn switch is installed between the power source and the grounded horn. When the driver pushes the horn button, the horn switch closes and current flows through the circuit to sound the horn. If the car has more than one horn, figure 19-1B, each horn will form a parallel path to ground.

Most horn circuits include a horn relay, figure 19-2. The normally open relay contacts are between the power source and the grounded horn. The horn switch is between the relay coil and ground. When the horn switch is closed, a small amount of current flows through the relay coil. This closes the relay coil and allows a greater amount of current to flow through the horns.

Some Chrysler front-wheel-drive (FWD) vehicles have an air horn system which uses a compressor in its circuitry, figure 19-3. Circuit operation is similar to that shown in figure 19-2, but current flows through the relay to the compressor, which is grounded at the headlamp ground. The compressor then activates the horn.

Horn Switches, Relays, and Fuses

The horn switch is normally installed in the steering wheel or steering column, figure 19-4. Contact points can be placed so that the switch will be closed by pressure at different points on the steering wheel, figure 19-5. Some cars have a button in the center of the wheel; others have a number of buttons around the rim of the wheel; or a large separate horn ring. Many imported cars and some domestic cars have the horn button on the end of a multifunction lever or stalk on the steering column. All of these designs operate in the same way. Pressure on the switch causes contacts to close. When the pressure is released, spring tension opens the contacts.

Horn relays can be mounted on the fuse panel, figure 19-6. They also can be attached to the bulkhead connector or mounted near the horns in the engine compartment. The relay is not serviceable, and must be replaced if defective.

Figure 19-1. A simple circuit with a single horn in series with the switch (A), or two horns in parallel with each other and in series with the switch (B).

Figure 19-2. Many horn systems are controlled by a relay. (Chrysler)

Figure 19-3. Chrysler's air horn system is a relay circuit but the relay activates an air horn compressor, which operates the horn. (Chrysler)

The horn circuit often shares a 15- to 20-ampere fuse with several other circuits. It may also be protected by a fusible link.

Figure 19-4. The horn switch is mounted in the steering column. (Chrysler)

Figure 19-5. Horn buttons can be placed at various locations around the steering wheel.

Horns

Except for Chrysler's air horn, which uses air pressure from the compressor, automobile horns use electromagnetism to vibrate a diaphragm and produce sound waves. A typical horn contains normally closed contact points in series with a coil. One of the contact points is mounted on a moveable armature to which the horn diaphragm is connected.

The horn coil is in series with the horn switch or horn relay contacts. When the horn switch or horn relay contacts close, current flows through the horn coil to ground. The electromagnetic field created by the coil attracts the armature, also moving the diaphragm. The armature movement opens the

30-AMP POWER
ASSIST CIRCUIT
BREAKER

POWER WINDOW
RELAY

HAZARD
WARNING
FLASHER

TIME
DELAY
RELAY

HORN
RELAY

Figure 19-6. The horn relay can be mounted on the fuse panel. (Chrysler)

contact points, which open the coil circuit. With no magnetic field to hold them, the armature and diaphragm move back to their normal positions. The points are again closed, allowing current to flow through the coil. This making and breaking of the electromagnetic circuit causes the horn diaphragm to vibrate.

Since this cycle occurs very rapidly, the resulting rapid movements of the diaphragm create sound waves. The speed or frequency of the cycling determines the pitch of the sound created. This can be adjusted by changing the spring tension on the horn armature to increase or decrease the electromagnetic pull on the diaphragm. We will learn more about this procedure in the *Shop Manual.*

WINDSHIELD WIPERS AND WASHERS

Federal law requires that all cars built in, or imported into, the United States since 1968 have both a two-windshield wiper system and a windshield washer system. Wiper systems on older vehicles may be operated by engine vacuum or by the power steering hydraulic system.

Modern wiper systems are operated by electric motors. The washer system can be manually operated, or it can have an electric pump. Many vehicles also have a single-speed wiper and washer for the rear window. This is a completely separate system, but it operates in the same way as the windshield wiper and washer system.

Circuit Diagram

A typical two-speed wiper system circuit diagram is shown in figure 19-7. The motor fields are permanent magnets. The wiper switch controls both the wiper motor speeds and the washer pump. The park switch within the wiper motor ensures that when the wiper switch is turned off, the motor will continue to turn until the wiper arms have reached the bottom edge, or park position, of the windshield. The circuit shown has a circuit breaker built into the wiper switch. However, the circuit breaker also can be a separate unit, or it can be mounted on the wiper motor.

Figure 19-8 shows low-speed current flow through the simple circuit. Current flows through the wiper switch contacts, the low-speed brush L, and the common (shared) brush C to ground. During high-speed operation, the current flows through the high-speed brush H and the common brush to ground. When the wiper switch is turned to park, or off, the park switch comes into the circuit.

The park switch is a two-position, cam-operated switch within the wiper motor. It moves from one position to the other during each motor revolution. When the wiper arms are at their park position, the park switch is at the P contact, as shown in figure 19-7. No current flows through the park switch. At all other wiper arm positions, the park switch is held against spring tension at the other contact. If the wiper switch is turned off while the wiper arms are not at

---

■ From Bell To Electric Horn

Many types of signal alarms have been used on cars:

- Mechanical bell
- Bulb horn
- Compression whistle
- Exhaust horn
- Hand-operated horn (Klaxon)
- Electric horn.

The mechanical bell was used on very early cars. The driver operated the bell with a foot pedal. The bulb horn, similar to that on a child's bicycle, proved to be inconvenient and unreliable. The compression whistle was most often used in cars with no battery or limited battery capacity. A prefilled cylinder provided the whistle's power. Exhaust horns used gases from the engine exhaust; they, too, were foot-operated. The hand-operated Klaxon horn amplified a grating sound caused by a metal tooth riding over a metal gear. This did not work well, because the horn had to be near the driver rather than at the front of the car. Over the years, the electric horn has been the most popular type of signal alarm.

Figure 19-7. A simple two-speed wiper circuit.

Figure 19-8. Low-speed current flow.

Figure 19-9. The park switch allows the motor to continue turning until the wiper arms reach their park position.

their park position, figure 19-9, current will flow through the park switch to the low-speed brush. The motor will continue to turn until the wiper arms reach their park position. At that point, the park switch moves to the P contact and all current stops.

When extra features are added to the wiper system, the circuits become more complex. For example, many manufacturers offer three-speed wiper systems. These systems use electromagnetic motor fields. The switch contacts route field current through resistors of various values, figure 19-10, to vary the wiper motor speed. Some GM two-speed wiper circuits also use this type of motor.

Many late-model vehicles have wiper arms that retreat below hood level when the switch is turned off, figure 19-11. This is called a depressed park position and is controlled by the park switch. When the wiper switch is turned off, the park switch allows the motor to continue turning until the wiper arms reach the bottom edge of the windshield. The park switch then

reverses current flow through the wiper motor, which makes a partial revolution in the opposite direction. The wiper linkage pulls the wiper arms down below the level of the hood during this motor reversal. The

Figure 19-12. Low-speed current flow in a depressed-park system. (Chrysler)

Figure 19-10. This three-speed wiper system controls motor speed by routing field current flow through various resistors. (Chrysler)

Figure 19-13. The park switch reverses current flow through the motor so that the wiper arms are pulled down into the depressed-park position. (Chrysler)

Figure 19-11. Many late-model cars have a depressed-park wiper position.

motor reversal also opens the park switch to stop all wiper motor current flow.

A depressed-park wiper system is shown in figure 19-12. During normal operation, current flows through either brush A or common brush B to ground. When the wiper switch is turned off, figure 19-13, current flows through the park switch, into brush B,

and through low-speed brush A to ground. This reverses the motor's rotation until the wiper arms reach the depressed park position, the park switch moves to the grounded position, and all current stops.

Many wiper systems have a low-speed intermittent or delay mode. This allows the wiper arms to sweep the windshield completely at intervals of three to 30 seconds. Most intermittent, or delay, wiper systems route current through a solid-state module containing a variable resistor and a capacitor, figure 19-14. Once the current passing through the variable resistor has fully charged the capacitor, it triggers a silicon-controlled rectifier (SCR), which allows current flow to the wiper motor. The park switch within the motor shunts the SCR circuit to ground. Current to the motor continues, however, until the wiper arms reach their park position and the park switch is opened. The capacitor rate of charge, and therefore the interval between the wiper arm sweeps, is controlled by the driver through the variable resistor.

Figure 19-14. An SCR in the solid-state intermittent wiper module or control unit triggers the wiper motor for intermittent wiper arm sweeps. (Chrysler)

On some imported cars, the intermittent or delay mode is sensitive to vehicle speed and varies from approximately 15 seconds (at low road speed) up to the wipers' normal low speed (at moderate road speed) as vehicle speed changes. The intermittent mode can be cancelled by pressing a cancel switch, and wiper speed can be set manually with the wiper switch.

Intermittent wiper control circuitry on many cars is contained in a separate module which is installed between the wiper switch and the wiper motor, figure 19-15.

Switches

The wiper switch is between the power source and the grounded wiper motor. The wiper switch does not receive current unless the ignition switch is turned to the Accessory or the Run position. The wiper switch may be mounted on the instrument panel, or it can be mounted in the steering column and controlled by a multifunction lever or stalk, figure 19-16.

If the system has an electric washer pump, the pump is generally controlled by contacts within the wiper switch. The washer is usually operated by a spring-loaded pushbutton that is part of the wiper switch, figure 19-16. Moving the switch to its wash position or pressing the pushbutton will operate the washer pump as long as the switch is held in position or is pressed.

Figure 19-15. The intermittent wipe governor or module is installed between the wiper switch and the wiper motor.

Figure 19-16. The washer switch is usually a spring-loaded pushbutton mounted on the instrument panel or on a multifunction lever. (Ford)

Motors

Most two-speed wiper motors use permanent ceramic magnets as pole pieces. Three brushes ride on the motor's commutator. One brush is a common, or shared, brush and conducts current whenever the wiper motor is operating. The other brushes are placed at different positions relative to the motor armature. Current through one brush produces a different motor speed than current through the other brush. The wiper switch contacts route current to one of these two brushes, depending upon which wiper motor speed the driver selects.

In many wiper motors, the high-speed brush is placed directly opposite the common brush, figure 19-17. The low-speed brush is offset to one side. This placement of the low-speed brush affects the interaction of the magnetic fields within the motor and makes the motor turn slowly. The placement of the high-speed brush causes the motor to turn rapidly. Chrysler and some GM two-speed motors vary from this pattern, figures 19-14 and 19-18. The low-speed brush is directly opposite the common brush and the high-speed brush is offset. A resistor wired in series with the low-speed brush reduces the motor's torque

Figure 19-19. In this motor with two electromagnetic fields, the motor speed is controlled by the amount of current through one of the fields. (Chrysler)

Figure 19-17. In this system, the high-speed brush is set directly opposite the common brush. The common brush is insulated, and the two speed-control brushes are grounded through the wiper switch.

Figure 19-18. This motor has an extra resistor in the low-speed circuit, and so the low-speed brush is placed directly across from the common brush. The common brush is grounded, and the two speed-control brushes are insulated.

at low speed. This extra resistance in the low-speed circuit results in a lower motor speed even with the reversed brush position.

The common brush can be grounded and the two speed-control brushes can be insulated, as shown in figure 19-18. Other motors have the speed-control brushes grounded through the wiper switch contacts and the common brush insulated, figure 19-17.

Some two-speed and all three-speed wiper motors have two electromagnetic field windings, figure 19-19. One field coil is in series with a motor brush and is called the series field. The other field coil is a separate circuit branch directly to ground and is called the shunt field. The two coils are wound in opposite directions, so that their magnetic fields oppose each other.

The wiper switch controls current through these two field coils. At low speed, about the same amount of current flows through both coils. Their opposing magnetic fields result in a weak total field, so the motor turns slowly. At medium speed (three-speed motor), current to one coil must flow through a resistor. This makes the coil's magnetic field weaker and results in a stronger total field within the motor. The motor revolves faster. At high speed, current to the coil must flow through a greater value resistor. The total magnetic field of the motor is again increased, and the motor speed increases. The resistors can act on either the shunt coil or the series coil to reduce current flow and thereby increase the motor's total field strength and speed. In figure 19-19, the resistors act on the shunt field.

Many wiper motors can be serviced to some extent, as we will learn in the *Shop Manual*.

Washer Pumps

Windshield washer pumps draw a cleaning solution from a reservoir and force it through nozzles onto the

Figure 19-20. The washer pump is often mounted on the fluid reservoir. (Chrysler)

Figure 19-21. Some GM systems have a washer pump mounted on the wiper motor.

Figure 19-22. Some vehicles use dual electric cooling fans. One system cools the radiator, while the other system cools the AC condenser. (Chrysler)

windshield. The unit can be a positive-displacement pump or a centrifugal pump that forces a steady stream of fluid, or it can be a pulse-type pump that operates valves with a cam to force separate spurts of fluid.

The washer pump is generally mounted in or on the fluid reservoir, figure 19-20. GM pulse pumps are mounted on the wiper motor, figure 19-21. Washer pumps are not usually serviceable, so they are replaced if they fail.

COOLING FAN CIRCUITS

There is no practical way to drive a cooling fan from the crankshaft pulley of a transversely mounted engine. Therefore, an electric cooling fan is used. Some manufacturers use one fan to cool the radiator and a separate system to cool the air-conditioning condenser, figure 19-22. Vehicles with a longitudinally mounted engine and the traditional crankshaft-driven fan mounted on the water pump shaft may also use one or more electric cooling fans.

Dual electric cooling fans often are used with turbocharged and air-conditioned vehicles to provide additional engine cooling and air-conditioning performance at idle. They are also used with intercooled turbocharged vehicles to cool the hot compressed intake

Figure 19-24. An air-temperature sensing switch will keep the fan running after the engine is turned off when ambient air temperature is above a certain level. (Chrysler)

temperature switch contacts, a small amount of current flows through the relay coil to close the relay contact points and allow a greater amount of current to activate the fan motor.

On air-conditioned vehicles, the circuit is also wired through the air-conditioning relay. This bypasses the coolant temperature switch and fan relay and allows the cooling fan to run in one of two modes, depending upon the particular vehicle:

- At all times when the air-conditioning compressor clutch is engaged
- When the air-conditioning system is on and compressor head pressure exceeds a specified value.

An "after-run" feature found on some vehicles incorporates an air-temperature sensing switch, figure 19-24. If the ambient temperature is above a specified value when the engine is shut off, the air-temperature sensing switch keeps the circuit closed regardless of coolant temperature to keep the fan running for a specified time. The "after-run" timer is incorporated in the fan relay. This feature is often used with turbocharged vehicles.

Toyota uses a dual "three-stage" fan system on some vehicles which automatically switches back and forth from a parallel connection at high-speed operation to a series connection for low-speed operation, figure 19-25. Switching is controlled by air-conditioning compressor operation and coolant temperature. This system reduces electrical power consumption, vibration, and noise.

Figure 19-23. Electric cooling fan circuits are controlled by a temperature switch and relay. (Ford)

air, thus increasing its density and improving cylinder charging efficiency. When two electric fans are used, each has its individual circuit with different control temperatures. Since electric fans work when needed and shut off when they are not needed, they help increase fuel efficiency.

Circuit Diagram

Electric cooling fan circuits generally incorporate a relay and temperature switch, figure 19-23. The normally open relay contacts are located between the power source and the grounded fan motor. The temperature switch is installed between the relay coil and ground. When engine coolant temperature closes the

Figure 19-25. Operational and circuit diagrams for Toyota's three-stage electrical fan system. (Toyota)

Coolant Temperature Switch

The coolant temperature switch is generally mounted in the cylinder head or in a radiator header tank where it is internally isolated from the radiator, figure 19-24. The switch contains a bimetallic contact arm that closes when coolant temperature reaches the switch's calibrated value, figure 19-26. When the contact arm closes, the switch completes the circuit to the fan relay, which turns the fan motor on. The temperature switch is usually connected to the battery side of the ignition switch to allow the fan to operate whether the engine is on or off. For this reason, you should always disconnect the fan motor when working under the hood near it, because it can turn on without warning if the coolant temperature rises.

The air-temperature sensing switch used in systems with the "after-run" feature, figure 19-24, is similar in construction to the coolant temperature switch, but it is designed to provide a quicker temperature change response time.

Computer Control

The electric cooling fan on late-model, four-cylinder Chrysler vehicles is controlled by the onboard computer instead of a temperature-sensing switch in the radiator. The computer's temperature sensor provides the input used by the computer to switch the fan circuit on and off. The computer is programmed to:

- Prevent the fan from running during cranking regardless of coolant temperature
- Allow the fan to run whenever the air-conditioning compressor clutch is engaged
- Switch the fan on at different coolant temperatures according to engine speed
- Switch the fan on for a designated length of time at idle when specified ambient air and coolant temperatures are present.

On Chrysler vehicles with onboard diagnostics, the circuitry and temperature sensor are monitored by the computer, which will set fault code 35 if the fan relay does not turn on and off when it should.

Figure 19-26. A bimetallic strip in a coolant temperature switch closes when engine coolant exceeds the switch's temperature limit. (Ford)

Some late-model GM cars use the continuously variable, dual-fan motor control circuit shown in figure 19-27. The fan control module transmits a voltage signal to the body control module (BCM), which switches the control line on and off with a pulse width modulation. The fan control module in turn switches the fan motor ground to control the fan speed. The longer the ground is intact, the longer the fan motors run during the pulse period.

The fan control module contains a current flow sensor so that it knows when the fan motors are running. The feedback generator sends a 12-volt signal to the BCM when the fans are off and drops the voltage to zero when the fans are running. This pulsing voltage from the feedback line tells the BCM that fan operation is correct.

The BCM can modify fan operation to correct a problem. For example, if a fan becomes stuck and will not rotate, it would cause an excessive current draw that might damage the system under ordinary circumstances. If this happens, however, the control module current sensor switches the feedback line high and low to tell the BCM that a problem exists. When it receives this signal, the BCM modifies the control circuit to reduce fan operation and prevent the excessive current draw.

Fan Relay and Motor

Cooling fan relays are similar in appearance to many other relays used in an engine compartment. Generally however, a cooling fan relay is mounted on the driver's side of the vehicle, on the cowl, the shock tower, or along the fenderwell. Since several relays are often located together and may be housed inside a protective cover, you should check the manufacturer's factory shop manual to determine exactly which one

Figure 19-27. The GM body control module (BCM) operates dual cooling fans through a solid-state control module by switching current on and off to provide pulse width modulation. The feedback circuit tells the BCM what the fans are doing. (GM)

controls the cooling fan. Cooling fan relays are not serviceable, and must be replaced if defective.

Cooling fan motors are small, high-torque units with permanent ceramic magnets for poles. Like relays, they are not serviceable, and are replaced if defective.

ELECTROMAGNETIC INSTRUMENT CIRCUITS

Gauges and warning lamps allow the driver to monitor a vehicle's operating conditions. These instruments differ widely from car to car but all are analog. Digital electronic instruments are explained later in this chapter. Warning lamps are used in place of gauges in many cases because they are less expensive and easier to understand, although they do not transmit as much useful information as gauges do.

The following paragraphs explain the general operation of analog gauges, lamps, and the sending units that control them.

Gauge Operating Principles

Common gauges use one of three operating principles:

- Mechanical
- Bimetallic (thermal-type)
- Electromagnetic.

Figure 19-28. The thermal-type gauge depends upon the heat of current flow bending a bimetallic strip. (Chrysler)

Figure 19-29. The D'Arsonval movement uses the field interaction of a permanent magnet and an electro-magnet.

Mechanical gauges are operated by cables, fluid pressure, or fluid temperature. Because they do not require an electrical circuit, they do not fit into our study. The cable-driven speedometer is the most common mechanical gauge.

Bimetallic gauges
A bimetallic gauge works because current flowing through the bimetallic strip will heat up one of the metals faster than the other, causing the strip to bend. A typical gauge, figure 19-28, has a U-shaped bimetallic piece anchored to the gauge body at the end of one arm. The other arm has a high-resistance wire, or heater coil, wound around it. Current flow through the heater coil bends the free bimetallic arm. Varying the current changes the bend in the arm. A pointer attached to the moving arm can relate the changes in current to a scale on the face of the gauge.

Ambient temperature could affect the gauge, but the U-shape of the bimetallic strip provides temperature compensation. While ambient temperature bends the free arm in one direction, the fixed arm is bent in the other direction and the effect is cancelled.

Electromagnetic gauges
The movement of an electromagnetic gauge depends on the interaction of magnetic fields. Three kinds of movements are commonly used:

- D'Arsonval movement
- Three-coil or two-coil movement
- Air core design.

A **D'Arsonval movement** has a moveable electromagnet surrounded by a permanent horseshoe magnet, figure 19-29. The electromagnet's field opposes the permanent magnet's field. This causes the electromagnet to rotate. A pointer mounted on the electromagnet relates this movement to a scale on the face of the gauge.

The amount of current flow through the electromagnet's coil determines the electromagnet's field strength, and therefore the amount of pointer movement.

A **three-coil movement** depends upon the field interaction of three electromagnets and the total field's effect on a moveable permanent magnet. This type of gauge is used in GM and some late-model Ford vehicles.

The circuit diagram of a typical 3-coil movement, figure 19-30, shows that two coils are wound at right angles to each other. These are the minimum-reading coil and the maximum-reading coil. Their magnetic fields will pull the permanent magnet and pointer in opposite directions. A third coil is wound so that its magnetic field opposes that of the minimum-reading coil. This is called the bucking coil.

The three coils are connected in series from the ignition switch to ground. A fixed resistor forms a circuit branch parallel to the minimum-reading coil. The variable-resistance sending unit forms a circuit branch to ground, parallel to the bucking and minimum-reading coils.

When sending resistance is high, current flows through all three coils to ground. Because the magnetic fields of the minimum-reading and the bucking coils cancel each other, the maximum-reading coil's field has the strongest effect on the permanent magnet and pointer. The pointer moves to the maximum-reading end of the gauge scale.

As sending unit resistance decreases, more current flows through the minimum-reading coil and the

Figure 19-30. In a three-coil gauge, the variable resistance sending unit affects current flow through three interacting electromagnets.

sending unit to ground than flows through the bucking and maximum-reading coils. The minimum-reading coil gains a stronger effect upon the permanent magnet and pointer, and the pointer moves to the minimum-reading end of the gauge scale.

Specific three-coil gauges may have slightly different wiring, but the basic operation remains the same. Because the circular magnet is carefully balanced, it will remain at its last position even when the ignition switch is turned off, rather than returning to the minimum-reading position, as does a bimetallic gauge.

The design of two-coil gauges varies with the purpose for which the gauge is used. In a fuel gauge, for example, the pointer is moved by the magnetic fields of the two coils positioned at right angles to each other. Battery voltage is applied to the E (empty) coil and the circuit divides at the opposite end of the coil. One path travels to ground through the F (full) coil; the other grounds through the sender's variable resistor. When sender resistance is low (low fuel), current passes through the E coil and sender resistor to move the pointer toward E on the scale. When sender resistance is high (full tank), current flows through the F coil to move the pointer toward F on the scale.

When a two-coil gauge is used to indicate coolant temperature, battery voltage is applied to both coils. One coil is grounded directly; the other grounds through the sending unit. Sender resistance causes the current through one coil to change as the temperature changes, moving the pointer.

In the **air core gauge design,** the gauge receives a varying electrical signal from its sending unit. A

pivoting permanent magnet mounted to a pointer aligns itself to a resultant field according to sending unit resistance. The sending unit resistance varies the field strength of the windings in opposition to the reference windings. The sending unit also compensates for variations in voltage.

This simple design provides several advantages beyond greater accuracy. It does not create radiofrequency interference (RFI), is unaffected by temperature, completely noiseless, and does not require the use of a voltage limiter. Like the three- and two-coil designs, however, the air core design remains at its last position when the ignition switch is turned off, giving a reading that should be disregarded.

Instrument voltage regulator

Except for the air core electromagnetic design, gauges require a continuous, controlled amount of voltage. This is usually either the system voltage of 12 volts or a regulated 5 to 6 volts. Regulated voltage is supplied by an instrument voltage regulator (IVR). The IVR can be a separate component that looks much like a circuit breaker, figure 19-31, or it can be built into one gauge, figure 19-28. Its bimetallic strip and vibrating points, figure 19-32, act like a self-setting circuit breaker to keep the gauge voltage at a specific level. Gauges that operate on limited voltage can be damaged or give inaccurate readings if exposed to full system voltage.

To prevent radiofrequency interference (RFI) from affecting other electrical components or the radio, an IVR has a **radio choke.** This is a coil wound with fine wire that soaks up the oscillations that occur when the vibrating contacts make and break the circuit.

D'Arsonval Movement: A small, current-carrying coil mounted within the field of a permanent horseshoe magnet. Interaction of the magnetic fields causes the coil to rotate. Used as a measuring device within electrical gauges and test meters.

Three-Coil Movement: A gauge design that depends upon the field interaction of three electromagnets and the total field effect on a movable permanent magnet.

Air Core Gauge: A gauge design in which there is no magnetic core. A field created by the sending unit resistance moves a pivoting permanent magnet.

Radio Choke: A coil of extremely fine wire used to absorb oscillations created by the making and breaking of an electrical circuit.

Figure 19-31. An independent instrument voltage regulator (IVR) looks like a circuit breaker and plugs into the back of the printed circuit board.

Warning Lamp Operating Principles

Warning lamps alert the driver to potentially hazardous vehicle operating conditions, such as:

- High engine temperature
- Low oil pressure
- Charging system problems
- Low fuel level
- Unequal brake fluid pressure
- Parking brake on
- Seat belts not fastened
- Exterior lighting failure.

Warning lamps can monitor many different functions but are usually activated in one of four ways:

- Voltage drop
- Grounding switch
- Ground sensor
- Fiber optics.

The first three methods are used to light a bulb or an LED mounted on the dash panel. Fiber optics is a special application of remote light.

Voltage drop

A bulb will light only if there is a voltage drop across its filament. Warning lamps can be installed so that equal voltage is applied to both bulb terminals under normal operating conditions. If operating conditions change, a voltage drop occurs across the filament, and the bulb will light. This method is often used to control charging system indicators, as we learned in Chapter Nine.

Figure 19-32. The IVR acts in the same way as a circuit breaker, but vibrates more rapidly.

Grounding switch

A bulb connected to battery voltage will not light unless the current can flow to ground. Warning lamps can be installed so that the ground path is controlled by a switch that reacts to operating conditions. Under normal conditions, the switch contacts are open and the bulb does not light. When operating conditions change, the switch contacts close. This creates a ground path for current and lights the bulb.

Ground sensor

A ground sensor is the opposite of a ground switch. Here, the warning lamp remains unlit as long as the sensor is grounded. When conditions change and the sensor is no longer grounded, the bulb lights. Solid-state circuitry generally is used in this type of circuit.

Fiber optics

Strands of a special plastic can conduct light through long, curving runs, figure 19-33. When one end of the fiber is installed in the instrument panel and the other end is exposed to a light, the driver will be able to see that light. Changing operating conditions can cause the fiber to change from light to dark, or from one color to another. Fiber optics are usually used for accessory warning lamps, such as coolant level reminders and exterior bulb monitors.

Specific Instruments

Many different instruments have appeared in automobiles, but certain basic functions are monitored in almost all cars. Normally, a car's instrument panel will contain at least:

- An ammeter, a voltmeter, or an alternator warning lamp
- An oil pressure gauge or warning lamp
- A coolant temperature gauge or warning lamp
- A fuel level gauge.

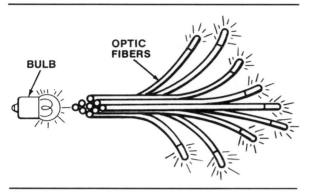

Figure 19-33. Light-carrying fibers can be used in accessory instruments.

The following paragraphs explain how these specific instruments are constructed and installed.

Charging system indicators

Ammeter, voltmeter, and warning lamp installations were studied in Chapter Nine. Ammeters usually contain a D'Arsonval movement that reacts to field current flow into the alternator and charging current flow into the battery. Many late-model cars have a voltmeter instead of an ammeter. A voltmeter indicates battery condition when the engine is off, and charging system operation when the engine is running. Warning lamps light to show an undercharged battery or low voltage from the alternator. Lamps used on GM cars with a CS charging system will light when the system voltage is too high or too low.

Some 1975 and later Chrysler rear-wheel-drive (RWD) cars with ammeters also have an LED mounted on the ammeter face. The LED works independently to monitor system voltage and lights when system voltage drops by about 1.2 volts. This alerts the driver to a discharge condition at idle caused by a heavy electrical load.

Oil pressure gauge or warning lamp

The varying current signal to an oil pressure gauge is supplied through a variable-resistance sending unit that is exposed to engine oil pressure. The resistor variation is controlled by a diaphragm that moves with changes in oil pressure, figure 19-34.

An oil pressure warning lamp lights to indicate low oil pressure. A ground switch controls the lamp, figure 19-35. When oil pressure decreases to an unsafe level, the switch diaphragm moves far enough to ground the warning lamp circuit. Current then can flow to ground and the bulb will light.

Oil pressure warning lamps can be operated by the gauge itself. When the pointer moves to the low-pressure end of the scale, it closes contact points to light a bulb or an LED.

Figure 19-34. The oil pressure sending unit provides a varying amount of resistance as engine oil pressure changes.

Figure 19-35. This oil pressure grounding switch has a fixed contact and a contact that is moved by the pressure-sensitive diaphragm.

Temperature gauge or warning lamp

In most late-model cars, the temperature gauge sending unit is a thermistor exposed to engine coolant temperature, figure 19-28. As coolant temperature increases, the resistance of the thermistor decreases and current through the gauge varies.

Temperature warning lamps can alert the driver to high temperature or to both low and high temperature. The most common circuit uses a bimetallic switch and reacts only to high temperature, figure 19-36A. A ground switch has a bimetallic strip that is exposed to coolant temperature. When the temperature reaches an unsafe level, the strip bends far enough to ground the warning lamp circuit. If the circuit also reacts to low temperature, the bimetallic strip has a second set of contacts. These are closed at low temperature, figure 19-36B, but open during normal operating temperature. The low-temperature circuit usually lights a different bulb than does the high-temperature circuit.

Figure 19-37. The fuel tank sending unit has a float that moves with the fuel level in the tank and affects a variable resistor.

Figure 19-36. Temperature grounding switches expose a bimetallic strip to engine coolant temperature to light a high-temperature lamp or both high- and low-temperature warning lamps.

A temperature warning lamp or an LED also can be lit by the action of the temperature gauge pointer, as explained for the oil pressure gauge.

Fuel gauge or warning lamp
All modern cars have a fuel level gauge. Some have an additional warning lamp or an LED to indicate a low fuel level.

Current control through the fuel gauge is provided by a variable resistor in the fuel tank. The tank sending unit has a float that moves with the fuel level, figure 19-37. As the float rises and falls, the resistance of the sending unit changes. If a low fuel level indicator is used, its switch may operate through a heater or bimetallic relay to prevent flicker.

Fuel level warning lamps are operated by the action of the fuel gauge pointer, as explained for an oil pressure gauge.

Tachometer
In addition to the other instrument panel displays, some cars have tachometers to indicate engine speed in revolutions per minute (rpm). These usually have an electromagnetic movement. The engine speed signals may come from an electronic pickup at the ignition coil, figure 19-38. Voltage pulses taken from the ignition system are processed by solid-state circuitry into signals to drive the tachometer pointer. The pointer responds to the frequency of these signals, which increase with engine speed. A filter is used to round off the pulses and remove any spikes.

Late-model vehicles with an engine control system may control the tachometer through an electronic module. This module is located on the rear of the instrument cluster printed circuit board and is the interface between the computer and tachometer in the same way the solid-state circuitry processes the ignition system-to-tachometer signals described earlier.

Turbo boost indicators
Some turbocharged engines have visual or audible indicators to inform the driver about turbo boost levels. Figure 19-39 shows the circuit diagram of the warning system used on 1979-80 Ford Mustang and Capri 2.3-liter engines with a draw-through turbocharger, where fuel is introduced upstream of the compressor. At low manifold pressure when the turbocharger starts to operate, a set of contacts in the turbo pressure switch turns on the boost indicator lamp to indicate that the turbocharger is functioning. If manifold pressure reaches approximately 8 psi (55 kPa), a second set of contacts in the switch closes while the first set opens. This turns off the boost indicator lamp and turns on the overboost buzzer and alarm indicator lamp. A high engine oil temperature warning indicator system is incorporated with the boost warning system. If this condition occurs during turbocharging, the oil temperature warning lamp also will flash.

Figure 19-38. This HEI distributor has a special connector for a tachometer. (Pontiac)

Figure 19-39. Ford's original turbo boost control circuit used a combination pressure switch to operate the boost indicator and overboost buzzer. (Ford)

Figure 19-40 shows the circuit diagram of the warning system used on 1984 and later Ford 2.3-liter engines with a blow-through turbocharger, where fuel is injected downstream of the compressor. Although this system uses separate low- and high-pressure switches, it functions in essentially the same way, but without the oil temperature warning.

Figure 19-40. The second-generation Ford turbo boost control circuit uses individual low- and high-pressure switches. (Ford)

MALFUNCTION INDICATOR LAMP (MIL)

Vehicles with electronic engine control systems generally have a computer-operated warning lamp on the instrument panel to indicate the need for service. In the past, this was called a CHECK ENGINE, SERVICE ENGINE SOON, POWER LOSS, or POWER LIMITED LAMP according to manufacturer. To eliminate confusion, all domestic manufacturers now refer to it as a MALFUNCTION INDICATOR LAMP (MIL).

■ Seatbelt-Starter Interlocks

During 1974 and early 1975, U.S. Federal safety standards required a seatbelt-starter interlock system on all new cars. The system required front-seat occupants to fasten their seatbelts before the car could be started. This particular standard was repealed by an act of Congress in 1975. Now, most interlock systems have been disabled so that only a warning lamp and buzzer remain.

Interlock systems use a solid-state or relay module to control current flow to the starter solenoid or starter relay. Switches in the front seat cushions signal the module when someone is sitting in the seat. When the seatbelts are fastened at all occupied seats, the module will complete the starter system control circuit. In case of a module failure, a bypass switch in the engine compartment can be activated by hand to close the solenoid circuit.

The MIL lamp alerts the driver to a malfunction in one of the monitored systems. In some vehicles built before 1995, the MIL is used to retrieve the faults or trouble codes stored in the computer memory by grounding a test terminal in the diagnostic connector. Like other warning lamps, the MIL comes on briefly as a bulb check when the ignition is turned on.

Antilock Brake System (ABS) Warning Lamp

Vehicles with ABS have a computer-operated amber ANTILOCK warning lamp in addition to the MIL and the standard red BRAKE lamp. The ANTILOCK lamp serves the same functions for the ABS that the MIL lamp does for engine control systems:

- Lights to warn of a system problem that inhibits ABS operation
- Retrieves trouble codes in the same way as the MIL lamp (specific vehicles only)
- Lights briefly at the beginning of an ignition cycle as a bulb check and to notify the driver that self-diagnostics are taking place.

Buzzers, Tone Generators, Chimes, and Bells

Buzzers are a special type of warning device. They produce a loud warning sound during certain operating conditions, such as:

- Seatbelts not fastened
- Door open with key in ignition
- Lights left on with engine off
- Excessive vehicle speed.

A typical buzzer, figure 19-41, operates in the same way as a horn. Instead of moving a diaphragm, the vibrating armature itself creates the sound waves.

In figure 19-41, two conditions are required to sound the buzzer: The door must be open, and the key must be in the ignition. These conditions close both switches and allow current to flow through the buzzer armature and coil.

Most warning buzzers are separate units mounted on the fuse panel or behind the instrument panel. General Motors vehicles may have a buzzer built into the horn relay, figure 19-42. When the ignition key is left in the switch and the door is opened, a small amount of current flows through the relay coil. The magnetic field is strong enough to operate the buzzer, but it is not strong enough to close the horn contacts.

Buzzers are usually activated by grounding switches. A timing circuit can be built into the buzzer by winding a heater coil around an internal circuit breaker, figure 19-43, and connecting the heater coil

Figure 19-41. Current will flow through this warning buzzer only when both switches are closed — when the door is open and the key is in the ignition switch.

Figure 19-42. General Motors cars may have a buzzer built into the horn relay. Here, the buzzer is activated because both the door switch and the key switch are closed. (Oldsmobile)

directly to ground. When current flows to the buzzer, a small amount of current flows through the heater coil to ground. When the coil is hot enough, it will open the circuit breaker and keep it open. Current through the buzzer will stop even though the grounding switch is still closed.

Some typical buzzer warning circuits are shown in figures 19-44 and 19-45. Figure 19-45 includes a prove-out circuit branch. This has a manual grounding switch that the driver can close to check that the bulb and buzzer are still working. Some prove-out circuits operate when the ignition switch is at Start, to show the driver if any bulbs or buzzers have failed.

Tone generators, chimes, and bells are mechanical devices that produce a particular sound when voltage

Figure 19-43. This buzzer will sound for only a few seconds each time it is activated because of the circuit breaker and heater coil built into the unit. (Oldsmobile)

Figure 19-44. In this circuit, one buzzer responds both to excessive speed and to driver door position. (Buick)

Figure 19-45. This warning buzzer will be activated if engine coolant temperature rises above a safe level. (Ford)

is applied across a sound bar. Various sounds are obtained by varying the voltage. Like buzzers, they are replaced if defective.

ELECTRONIC INSTRUMENT CIRCUITS

Electronic instruments used on late-model cars have the same purpose as the traditional analog instruments: They display vehicle operating information to the driver. The primary difference between the electronic and traditional systems is the way in which the information is displayed.

Like analog instruments, electronic instruments receive inputs from a sensor or a sending unit. The information is displayed in various ways, as we will see later in this chapter. Depending upon the gauge function and the manufacturer's design, the display may be digital numbers or a vertical, horizontal, or curved bar, figure 19-46.

The following paragraphs give three examples of how electronic instruments function.

The first example is in figure 19-47, which shows a block diagram of a Ford electronic speedometer system. The electronic speedometer receives a voltage signal representing vehicle speed from an optical sensor, figure 19-48. The optical sensor input comes from the speedometer cable, connected to the speedometer drive gear in the transmission case. As the cable rotates, it turns the slotted wheel through the optical sensor. This breaks the optical field and generates an electrical pulse to the speedometer display. The number of pulses generated by the optical sensor is proportional to vehicle speed. Figure 19-49 shows the electrical circuit diagram for the electronic speedometer.

The second example is shown in figure 19-50A, picturing the basic concept behind a more sophisticated electronic speedometer than the one just described. The display device used can be a quartz analog (swing needle) display or a digital readout. The speed signal in this system originates from a small ac voltage generator with four magnetic fields called a permanent magnet (PM) generator. This device usually is installed at the transmission or transaxle speedometer gear adapter and is driven like the speedometer cable on conventional systems.

As the PM generator rotates, it generates an ac voltage of four pulses per turn, with voltage and frequency increasing as speed increases. The unit pulses 4004 times per mile of travel (2488 times per kilometer) with a frequency output of 1.112 oscillations per second (Hertz) per mile per hour of travel (0.691 Hertz per kilometer per hour of travel).

Since the PM generator output is analog, a buffer is used to translate its signals into digital input for the processing unit. The processing unit sends a voltage back to the buffer, which switches the voltage on and off and interprets it as vehicle speed changes. If the

Figure 19-46. Toyota's electronic display is a digital combination meter which uses a colored liquid crystal display (LCD) panel. (Toyota)

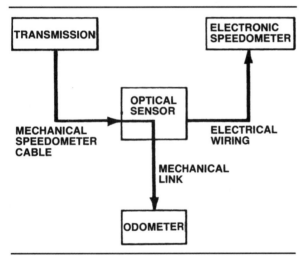

Figure 19-47. A block diagram of Ford's electronic speedometer system used in Lincolns and Mark VIs of the early 1980s. (Ford)

instrument cluster has its own internal buffer as part of the cluster circuitry, the PM generator signal will go directly to the speedometer.

On some systems, the buffer may contain more than one switching function, figure 19-50B, as it handles the ECM and cruise control systems. These secondary switching functions run at half the speed of the speedometer switching operation or 0.556 Hz/mph (0.3456 Hz/km/h).

If the instrument cluster uses a quartz analog display, figure 19-51, the gauge is similar to the two-coil electromagnetic gauge discussed earlier. This type of

Figure 19-48. The optical sensor is used to translate mechanical movement into an electrical signal for Ford's electronic speedometer. (Ford)

gauge is often called a swing needle or air-core gauge and does not return to zero when the ignition is turned off. When the car begins to move, the buffered speed signal is conditioned and sent to the central processing unit (CPU). The CPU processes the digital input using a quartz crystal clock circuit and sends it to a gain-select circuit, where it is transferred to a driver circuit. The driver circuit then sends the correct

Figure 19-49. This circuit diagram shows the electrical relationship of the optical sensor to the speedometer. (Ford)

voltages to the gauge coils to move the pointer and indicate the car's speed.

Virtually the same process is followed when a digital display is used, figure 19-52, with the following minor differences in operation:

- The CPU can be directed to display the information in either English or metric units. A select function sends the data along different circuits according to the switch position.
- The driver circuit is responsible for turning on the selected display segments at the correct intensity.

The odometer used with electronic speedometers can be electromechanical using a stepper motor, figure 19-53A, or an IC chip using a **nonvolatile RAM,** figure 19-53B.

The electromechanical type is similar to the conventional odometer, differing primarily in the way in which the numbers are driven. A stepper motor takes digital-pulsed voltages from the speedometer circuit board at half the buffered speed signal discussed

earlier. This provides a very accurate accounting of accumulated mileage.

The IC chip retains accumulated mileage in its special nonvolatile RAM which is not lost when current is removed. Since its memory *cannot* be turned back, the use of this chip virtually eliminates one of the frauds often associated with the sale of used cars.

The third example is shown in figure 19-54, which is the circuit diagram for a Ford electronic temperature gauge. The coolant temperature sensor is an NTC thermistor with high resistance at low temperatures and low resistance at high temperatures. When a cold engine is first started, the sensor's resistance is very high, resulting in a low voltage output to the gauge display, which translates into a low coolant temperature reading on the display. As coolant temperature

Nonvolatile RAM: Random access memory (RAM) that retains its information when current to the chip is removed.

Figure 19-50. GM's electronic speedometer uses a permanent magnet (PM) generator instead of an optical sensor. In A, the buffer translates the PM generator analog signals into digital signals for the processor, which activates the display driver to operate an analog or a digital display. In B, the buffer toggles voltage on and off to interpret vehicle speed to the electronic cluster. (GM)

Figure 19-51. The buffered signal passes to a signal conditioner, which transmits it to the CPU where a quartz clock circuit ensures accuracy. After processing, the signal goes to a gain-select circuit, which sends it to the driver circuit for analog display.

Figure 19-52. The digital cluster circuit is similar to the analog circuit, but an output logic circuit is used instead of a gain select circuit.

Figure 19-53. Electronic odometers may use a stepper motor or a nonvolatile RAM chip for mileage display. (GM)

increases, sensor resistance decreases. This results in a higher voltage output to the gauge display, which translates into a higher coolant temperature reading.

Trip Computers

Electronic instruments may stand alone, they may be part of a microprocessor-controlled system, figure 19-55, or they may be incorporated into an electronic "message center" often called a trip computer. Figure 19-56 shows the sensors and display devices (actuators) used in the electronic message center system on some Lincoln and Mark VI models. Figure 19-57 shows the circuit diagram for the system.

While the electronic instruments function on their own in this system, the inputs they receive are also applied to the control module, which uses them for calculations. For example, when the driver pushes the

Figure 19-54. Ford's electronic temperature gauge circuit is similar to that of an analog gauge. (Ford)

Figure 19-55. The 1986 Cadillac digital instrument cluster is a microprocessor-based system that responds to input from the ECM and BCM to provide blue-green vacuum fluorescent displays.

appropriate buttons or keys to activate such calculations, fuel gauge and speed indicator signals are used by the control module to calculate fuel consumption, mileage, and fuel remaining. The control module processes the signals and sends an appropriate signal to the message center display.

Warning indications to the control module start with a switch closing to ground. The ground signal is interpreted by the control module as an abnormal condition and processed by the microcomputer, which then sends an appropriate signal to the message center display. On engines with fuel injection, the control module receives an additional ground signal and an input from the powertrain control module (PCM). This allows the module to calculate instantaneous fuel economy when desired by the driver. Pressing the proper button brings up the trip average fuel economy, followed a few seconds later by the instantaneous fuel economy reading. This lets the driver see how engine load changes affect fuel economy.

The message center keyboard contains the pushbuttons to activate the trip computer functions. Each pushbutton is a switch connected to the control module. When a switch is pressed, it provides a ground path to the control module. The keyboard performs three functions. It lets the driver:

- Program the control module with data about time, date, and trip information
- Select the information to be displayed on the message center
- Check all systems monitored by the electronic message center system.

Body Control Module (BCM) Computers

When more than one computer is used on a vehicle, it is often desirable to link their operations. The body control module (BCM) used on some late-model GM cars is an example. The BCM manages the communications for the multiple computer system, figure 19-58, using a network of sensors, switches, and other microprocessors to monitor vehicle operating conditions. Certain components also provide the BCM with feedback signals. These tell the BCM whether the components are responding to the BCM commands properly. Like the electronic control module (ECM) which operates the engine control system, the BCM has built-in diagnostics to help locate and correct a system malfunction.

Displays

Electronic displays are used in electronic instrument clusters and other electronic readout devices. Unlike electromechanical instruments, they do not require a digital-to-analog conversion; they're compatible with the digital signals from a computer. The major types of displays that are used with electronic instruments are described in the following paragraphs.

Light-emitting diode (LED)

The light-emitting diode (LED) is a semiconductor diode that transmits light when electrical current is passed through it, figure 19-59. An LED display is composed of small dotted segments arranged to form numbers and letters when selected segments are turned on. The LED are usually red, yellow, or green. LEDs have two major drawbacks:

- Although easily seen in the dark, they are difficult to read in direct sunlight.
- They consume considerable current relative to their brightness.

Figure 19-56. These sensors, display devices (actuators), and processing units make up the electronic message center system used on Lincolns and Mark VIs of the early 1980s. (Ford)

Liquid crystal display (LCD)

The **liquid crystal display (LCD)** uses sandwiches of special glass containing electrodes and polarized fluid to display numbers and characters. Light cannot pass through the polarized fluid until voltage is applied. The display is very dense, however, and the various special filters used to provide colors create even more density. For this reason, halogen lights are generally placed behind the display, figure 19-60. Although LCDs perform slowly in cold ambient temperatures, require proper alignment, and are very delicate, they have two big advantages:

- They consume very little current relative to their brightness.
- They can be driven by a microprocessor through an interfacing output circuit.

Vacuum fluorescent display (VFD)

This is the most commonly used display for automotive electronic instruments, primarily because of its durability and bright display qualities. The **vacuum fluorescent display (VFD)** generates light similar to a television picture tube, with free electrons from a heated filament striking phosphor material that emits a blue-green light, figure 19-61.

The anode segments are coated with a fluorescent material such as phosphorous. The filament is resistance wire, heated by electrical current. The filament coating produces free electrons, which are accelerated by the electric field generated by the voltage on the accelerating grid. High voltage is applied only to the anode of those segments required to form the characters to be displayed. Since the anode is at a higher voltage than the fine wire mesh grid, the electrons pass through the grid. The phosphors on the segment anodes impressed with high voltage glow very brightly when struck by electrons; those receiving no voltage do not glow. The instrument computer determines the segments necessary to emit light for any given message and applies the correct sequences of voltage at the anodes.

VFD displays are extremely bright, and their intensity must be controlled for night viewing. This can be done by varying the voltage on the accelerating grid: the higher the voltage, the brighter the display. Intensity can also be controlled by pulse width dimming, or turning the display on and off very rapidly while controlling the duration of on-time. This is similar to the pulse-width modulation of a carburetor mixture control solenoid or a fuel injector. The on-off

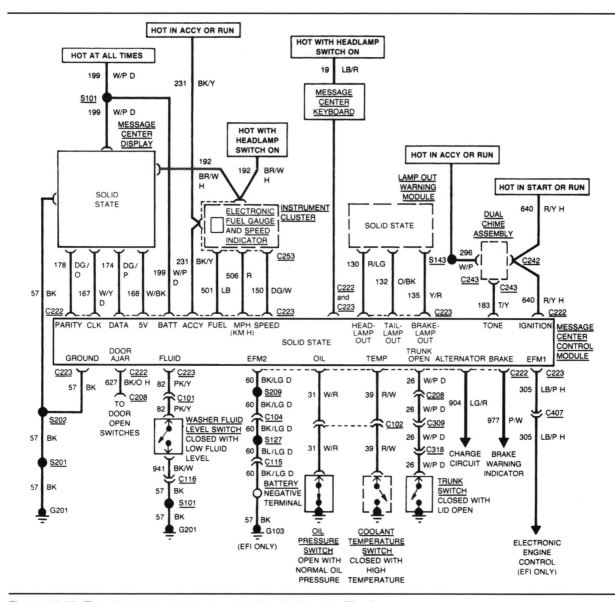

Figure 19-57. The electronic message center circuit diagram. (Ford)

action occurs so rapidly that it cannot be detected by the human eye.

Cathode ray tube (CRT)

The latest display device to be used in automotive instrumentation is the **cathode ray tube (CRT)**, as used in the 1985 Lincoln Mark VII Comtech or the 1986 Buick Riviera. The CRT is essentially the same as that used in an oscilloscope or a television set. CRTs function with an electron beam generated by an electron gun located at the rear of the tube. The CRT consists of a cathode that emits electrons and an anode that attracts them. Electrons are "shot" in a thin beam from the back of the tube. Permanent magnets around the outside neck of the tube and plates

Liquid Crystal Display (LCD): An indicator consisting of a sandwich of glass containing electrodes and polarized fluid. Voltage applied to the fluid allows light to pass through it.

Vacuum Fluorescent Display (VFD): An indicator in which electrons from a heated filament strike a phosphor material that emits light.

Cathode Ray Tube (CRT): An electron beam tube with a cathode at one end and an anode at the screen end. A "ray" of electrons shot from the cathode to the anode creates a pattern on the luminescent screen.

Figure 19-58. Sophisticated electronic systems are composed of several computers and use a central computer (GM calls it a body control module) to manage the system. (GM)

Figure 19-59. Selective application of voltage through the diodes composing a light-emitting diode (LED) results in an alphanumeric display. (GM)

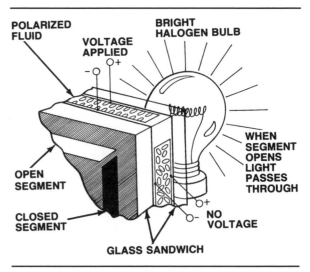

Figure 19-60. Light passes through polarized fluid to create the liquid crystal display (LCD). (GM)

Figure 19-61. In a vacuum fluorescent display, voltage applied selectively to segment anodes makes the fluorescent material glow. (Chrysler)

grouped around the beam on the inside of the tube shape the beam. A tube-shape anode that surrounds the beam accelerates it as it leaves the electron gun. The beam has so much momentum that the electrons pass through the anode and strike a coating of phosphorus on the screen, causing the screen to glow at these points. The control plates are used to move the beam back and forth on the screen, causing different parts of it to illuminate. The result is a display (oscilloscope) or a picture (television).

Menu-Driven Instrumentation

The CRT used in the 1986 and later Buick Riviera and other models has a touch-sensitive Mylar switch panel installed over its screen. This panel contains ultrathin wires which are coded by row and column. Touching the screen in designated places blocks a light beam and triggers certain switches in the panel according to

the display mode desired. The switches in turn send a signal to the control circuitry, which responds by displaying the requested information on the CRT screen. In principle, this type of instrumentation combines two personal computer attributes: It has touch-screen control and is menu-driven.

By **menu-driven,** we mean that the program operating the CRT offers the driver several choices from a list or "menu" of selections regarding many areas of vehicle operation. For example, suppose you touch DIAGNOSTICS. This brings up another menu allowing you to choose between four main (and one optional) categories: electrical, powertrain, brakes, vehicle, and

Menu-Driven: A computer program that allows the user to select choices from a list or "menu". As each choice is made, another menu allows the user to make another choice to achieve the desired end result.

Figure 19-62. A wiring schematic of the HUD system as used by Oldsmobile. (Oldsmobile)

Figure 19-63. The HUD system display image. (Oldsmobile)

lamp (optional). Each category displays a box that shows "OK" if the system is working properly. If problems exist, additional display screens can be summoned to lead you through the troubleshooting routines. In other modes, the CRT menus allow you to control or check the air conditioning, radio, trip monitor, and gauge readings.

Head-Up Display System

The Head-Up Display (HUD) was introduced by Pontiac as standard equipment on the 1990 Grand Prix Turbo. After making modifications and refinements in the system, a Generation II HUD was offered as optional equipment on certain 1991 and later GM cars.

This electronic instrumentation system, figure 19-62, consists of a special windshield, a HUD unit containing a computer module, and a system-specific dimmer switch. The HUD unit processes various inputs which are part of the instrument cluster and projects frequently used driver information on the windshield area for viewing from the driver's seat. The dimmer switch provides system power for the computer module, varies the intensity of the display unit, and can change the vertical position of the display image through a mechanical cable drive system.

When the ignition is turned on, the HUD unit performs a self-check routine and projects the following image, figure 19-63, for approximately 3.5 seconds:

- Turn signal indicators
- High-beam indicator
- Check gauges indicator
- Speed (km/h or mph) indicator
- All segments of the digital speedometer.

After completing the self-check, the system begins normal operation.

The ECM provides vehicle speed information for HUD operation by completing a ground path to the HUD unit 4,000 times per mile, figure 19-64. Each time the HUD unit recognizes a voltage drop at terminal J, it counts one pulse. By counting the pulses per second, the HUD unit can determine vehicle speed and project the corresponding figure on the windshield display.

A normal problem with the HUD system is called image ghosting. This faint secondary image appears to float above or to one side of the brighter primary image, figure 19-65. The special windshields used with HUD systems are selected by testing all production windshields for the problem and selecting those that show a minimal ghosting effect. Replacing a HUD windshield with one chosen at random will likely result in an unacceptable amount of ghosting.

SUMMARY

An automotive horn circuit can be a simple series circuit, or it can use a relay to control current through the horns. The horn switch is a normally open push-pull switch that is operated by the driver. Horns use electromagnetism to vibrate a diaphragm and to produce sound waves.

Windshield wiper and washer circuits have many variations. They can include a permanent magnet motor or one with electromagnetic fields. The park position can be at the bottom edge of the windshield or below the bottom edge. An intermittent wipe feature can be driver- or speed-controlled. Each of these variations requires slightly different circuitry. Washer pumps can be mounted at the cleaner reservoir or on the wiper motor. Pumps are not serviced, but are replaced.

Electric cooling fans are used on vehicles with transverse engine placement. They may also be used with the engine-driven pump on longitudinal mounted engines. Dual fan systems often are used with turbocharged vehicles. Cooling fan circuits work with a relay controlled by a coolant temperature switch. When used with air-conditioning systems, the air-conditioning relay also is wired into the fan circuit so the cooling fan will run whenever the air conditioning is on. Some fans have an after-run feature that keeps the fan running for a predetermined length of time after the engine is shut off. This time duration is controlled by a timer in the relay.

Instruments include gauges and warning lamps. There are various types of gauges, including mechanical, bimetallic, electromagnetic, and electronic. Warning lamps can be lit by a voltage drop, a grounding switch, a ground sensor, or fiber optics. Late-model vehicles may have a digital display instead of traditional analog gauges. Digital displays can be individual or they can be part of a more elaborate

Figure 19-64. The vehicle speed sensor circuit between the ECM and HUD module. (Oldsmobile)

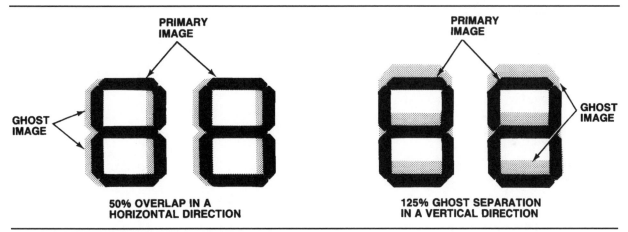

Figure 19-65. If the double image or ghosting on the windshield exceeds that shown above, the windshield should be replaced. (Oldsmobile)

vehicle electronic system, such as a trip computer or message center. Body control module (BCM) computers act as a manager of other computers in a comprehensive vehicle system.

Electronic displays may use a light-emitting diode (LED), a liquid crystal display (LCD), a vacuum fluorescent display (VFD), or a cathode ray tube (CRT) to transmit information. Some instrumentation is menu-driven, giving the user an opportunity to select the information to be displayed. Touch-sensitive screens similar to those on personal computers are used instead of keyboards or pushbuttons on late-model systems. The GM Head-Up Display (HUD) projects useful vehicle information in front of the driver near the windshield.

Review Questions

Choose the single most correct answer.
Compare your answers with the correct answers on Page 468.

1. Horn relays are sometimes included in the horn circuit to:
   a. Allow the use of two horns in the circuit
   b. Decrease the amount of current needed to activate the horn
   c. Increase the amount of current needed to activate the horn
   d. Allow the horn button to be placed on the end of a stalk on the steering column

2. Horn circuits are generally protected by a:
   a. Fuse
   b. Fusible link
   c. Either a or b
   d. Neither a nor b

3. The _____ within the wiper motor ensures that when the motor is turned off, the wiper arms will be brought to the bottom position.
   a. Wiper switch
   b. Park switch
   c. Recycle relay
   d. Park/neutral switch

4. Two-speed wiper motors generally use _____ to achieve the two speeds.
   a. Cams
   b. Reduction gears
   c. Speed-control brushes
   d. Gear reduction

5. All three-speed wiper motors have _____ fields.
   a. Electromagnetic
   b. Permanent magnet
   c. Two-series
   d. Two-shunt

6. Which of the following is *not* a reason why warning lamps have replaced gauges in automobiles?
   a. Cheaper to manufacture
   b. Cheaper to install
   c. More accurate
   d. Easier to understand

7. Temperature compensation in bimetallic gauges is accomplished by:
   a. Current flow through the heater coil
   b. The shape of the bimetallic strip
   c. An external resistor in the circuit
   d. Hermetically sealing the unit

8. Gauges with three-coil movements are most often used by:
   a. General Motors
   b. Ford
   c. Chrysler
   d. American Motors

9. An oil pressure warning lamp is usually controlled by:
   a. Voltage drop
   b. Ground switch
   c. Ground sensor
   d. Manual switch

10. The sending unit in the fuel gauge uses a:
    a. Fixed resistor
    b. Zener diode
    c. Float
    d. Diaphragm

11. Buzzers are a special type of warning device that is activated by:
    a. Voltage drop
    b. Ground switches
    c. Diaphragms
    d. Optical fibers

12. Which of the following is *not* used in the electric cooling fan circuit of an air-conditioned vehicle?
    a. Coolant temperature switch and fan relay
    b. AC relay
    c. Air temperature sensing switch and after-run timer
    d. Shuttle switch

13. In GM computer-controlled electric fan circuits:
    a. The BCM switches the control line voltage on/off with a pulse width modulation
    b. The fan control module switches the ground on/off
    c. Both a and b
    d. Neither a nor b

14. Electromagnetic gauges do *not* use a:
    a. Mechanical movement
    b. D'Arsonval movement
    c. Air core movement
    d. Two- or three-coil movement

15. Which type of gauge does *not* use an instrument voltage regulator (IVR)?
    a. D'Arsonval movement
    b. Air core movement
    c. Two-coil movement
    d. Three-coil movement

16. Technician A says GM's electronic speedometer interprets vehicle speed by using a buffer to switch the voltage on/off. Technician B says GM's electronic speedometer uses a buffer to translate the analog input of the PM generator into digital signals.
    Who is right?
    a. A only
    b. B only
    c. Both A and B
    d. Neither A nor B

17. Technician A says an electronic speedometer cannot use a stepper motor to provide the display. Technician B says the use of nonvolatile RAM prevents the odometer from being turned back.
    Who is right?
    a. A only
    b. B only
    c. Both A and B
    d. Neither A nor B

18. An electronic display device using electrodes and polarized fluid to create numbers and characters is called:
    a. LCD
    b. LED
    c. VFD
    d. CRT

19. Which electronic display device is most frequently used because it is very bright, consumes relatively little power, and can provide a wide variety of colors through the use of filters?
    a. LCD
    b. LED
    c. VFD
    d. CRT

20. Which electronic display device is difficult to read in daylight and consumes considerable power relative to its brightness?
    a. LCD
    b. LED
    c. VFD
    d. CRT

20

Body Electrical Systems (Accessories)

Electrical accessories provide driver and passenger comfort, convenience, and entertainment. New electrical accessories are introduced every year, but some systems have been common for many years. Such systems increasingly are being automated with computer control. This chapter will explain the electrical operation of some common accessory systems.

HEATING AND AIR-CONDITIONING SYSTEMS

Although heating and air-conditioning systems rely heavily on mechanical and vacuum controls, a good deal of electrical circuitry also is involved. Since the late 1970s, air-conditioning systems have become increasingly "smart", relying on solid-state modules or microprocessors for their operation. This also has complicated the job of servicing such systems.

Heater Fan

Heating systems use a fan attached to a permanent-magnet, variable-speed blower motor to force warm air into the passenger compartment, figure 20-1. The higher the voltage applied to the motor, the faster it runs. A switch mounted on the instrument panel controls the blower operation, figure 20-2. In most heating systems, the switch controls blower speed by directing the motor ground circuit current through or around the coils of a resistor block, figure 20-3, mounted near the motor.

When the switch is off, the ground circuit is open and the blower motor does not run. Some systems used in the 1970s, however, were wired so that the blower motor operated on low speed whenever the ignition was on. When the switch is turned to its low position, voltage is applied across all of the resistor coils and the motor runs at a low speed. Moving the switch to the next position bypasses one of the resistor coils. This allows more current to the blower motor, increasing its speed. When the switch is set to the highest position, all of the resistors are bypassed and full current flows to the motor, which then operates at full speed.

In some GM systems, a relay is used between the high switch position and the blower motor. Ford incorporates a thermal limiter in its resistor block, figure 20-3. Current flows through the limiter at all blower speeds. If current passing through the limiter heats it to 212°F (100°C), the limiter opens and turns off the blower motor. When this happens, the entire resistor block must be replaced.

Figure 20-1. An electric motor drives the heater fan.

Figure 20-2. The fan control switch routes current through paths of varying resistance to control motor speed. (Chrysler)

Figure 20-3. Blower motor resistors are installed on a "block" near the motor. Some resistor blocks have a thermal limiter. (Ford)

Air-Conditioning Fan and Compressor Clutch

Air-conditioning fan controls are similar to heater controls. In most cars that have both heating and air-conditioning systems, the same blower motor is shared by both systems, figure 20-4. One or more switches route current through different resistors to control the blower motor speed.

In addition to the fan switch, the control assembly in the passenger compartment contains a driver-controlled air-conditioning clutch switch and an integral clutch switch activated when the function selector lever is set to the Defrost position. These switches are used to operate the belt-driven compressor. A compressor that operates constantly wastes energy. To use energy more efficiently, the compressor has an electromagnetic clutch, figure 20-5. This clutch locks and unlocks the compressor pulley with the compressor shaft. The compressor will operate only when the clutch switch is closed and the electromagnetic clutch is engaged.

Many early air-conditioning systems use a suction throttling valve or evaporator pressure-control valve to control evaporator pressure and temperature. The compressor clutch is continuously engaged when the AC system is on. Most recent air-conditioning systems use a clutch-cycling pressure switch or a pressure-cycling switch to control compressor clutch operation. This pressure-operated electric switch generally is wired in series with the clutch field coil. The switch closes when the pressure on the low side of the refrigerant system rises to a specified value, engaging the clutch. When system pressure drops to a predetermined value, the switch opens to shut off the compressor. The switch operates to control evaporator core pressure and prevent icing of the evaporator cooling coils.

Figure 20-4. Air-conditioning and heating systems share the same fan. (Chrysler)

Air-conditioning systems may also use low- and high-pressure switches as safety devices:

- The low-pressure switch is closed during normal compressor operation and opens only when refrigerant is lost or ambient temperature is below freezing.
- The high-pressure switch is normally closed to permit compressor operation. However, if system pressure becomes excessive (generally 360 to 400 psi or 2,480 to 2,760 kPa), the switch acts as a relief valve and opens to shut off the compressor. Once pressure drops to a safe level, the switch will close again and permit the compressor to operate.
- A pressure relief valve on the compressor high-pressure side may be used instead of a high-pressure switch. Some systems have a diode installed inside the compressor clutch connector to suppress any voltage spikes that might be produced by clutch circuit interruption.

Other compressor clutch controls may include:

- A power-steering pressure or cutout switch to shut the compressor off whenever high power steering loads are encountered, as during parking. The switch senses line pressure and opens or closes the circuit to the compressor clutch accordingly.
- A wide-open throttle (WOT) switch on the carburetor or accelerator pedal to open the circuit to the compressor clutch during full acceleration.
- A pressure-sensing switch in the transmission to override the WOT switch when the transmission is in high gear.

Automatic Temperature Control (ATC)

The basic electrical components of most air-conditioning systems have already been described. As we have seen, they provide input to, and protection for, the refrigeration system.

Figure 20-5. The electromagnetic clutch in this air-conditioning compressor prevents the compressor from wasting energy.

All input to the air-conditioning system begins with the control assembly mounted in the instrument panel. Temperature control can take three forms:

- Manual control
- Semiautomatic (programmer controlled)
- Fully automatic (microprocessor or body computer controlled).

A manual temperature control system does not provide a method by which the system can function on its own to maintain a preset temperature. System input must be made by the user through the mechanical control assembly. Once the air-conditioning switch is turned on, the temperature selection made, and the blower speed set, the system functions with vacuum-operated mode door actuators and a cable-actuated air-mix door. Figure 20-6 is a block diagram of such a system.

With a semiautomatic temperature control system, the user still selects the mode, but the actuators are electrically operated. Selecting the mode does not directly control the actuator; it creates an electrical input to an independent module or programmer, figure 20-7. On Chrysler vehicles, the electronic **servomotor** performs the programmer function, figure 20-8. Two sensors are added to inform the programmer of ambient temperature and in-car temperature, figure 20-9. The programmer calculates the resistance values

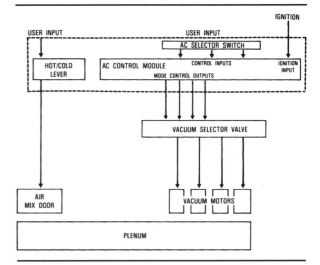

Figure 20-6. Manual air conditioning system block diagram. (GM)

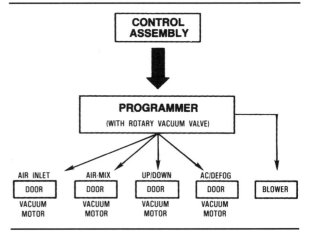

Figure 20-7. Semiautomatic AC systems use an electronic programmer to translate mechanical control movement into actuator signals. (GM)

provided by the temperature dial setting and the two additional sensors and adjusts cables or vacuum selector valves to maintain the preset temperature. The semiautomatic temperature control system differs from a manual system primarily in the use of the programmer; actuators and doors are still moved by mechanical linkage and cables.

In a fully automatic temperature control system, the control assembly is electronic instead of manual. The user selects a mode and the temperature. The control assembly microprocessor sends the appropriate signals to the programmer to operate the system. Electric servomotors are used as actuators to send a feedback signal to the electronic control assembly, figure 20-10. This lets the control assembly monitor the system and make whatever adjustments are required to maintain the desired system temperature.

- LOW AIR TEMPERATURE AT SENSORS INCREASES RESISTANCE

- HIGH TEMPERATURE COMFORT LEVER SETTING INCREASES RESISTANCE

- HIGH RESISTANCES CAUSE SERVOMOTOR TO MOVE BLEND-AIR DOOR TO HIGHER REHEAT POSITION

Figure 20-8. An electronic servomotor takes the place of a programmer in Chrysler's semiautomatic AC system. (Chrysler)

Figure 20-9. Resistance values from in-car and ambient temperature sensors are coupled with the resistance provided by the control assembly temperature dial to direct the programmer. (GM)

Since the control assembly is constantly monitoring the system, it knows when a malfunction occurs and can transmit this information to the service technician.

Semiautomatic (programmer controlled)

The GM C61 system is representative of the semiautomatic control system. Once the mode and temperature

Figure 20-10. The actuators used in fully automatic AC systems provide feedback signals that allows the control assembly to monitor system operation. (GM)

have been selected by the user, the system automatically controls blower speed, air temperature, air delivery, system turn-on, and compressor operation. It does this with a programmer inserted between the control assembly and the actuators, figure 20-7, and two temperature sensors.

The ambient sensor installed in the programmer is exposed to ambient airflow through a hole in the module wall. The in-car sensor is located under the instrument panel top cover. Figure 20-9 shows the sensor locations. Both sensors are disc-type thermistors that

Servomotor: An electric motor that is part of a feedback system used for automatic control of a mechanical device, such as in a temperature-control system.

provide a return voltage signal to the programmer based on variable resistance.

The programmer is built into the air-conditioning control assembly, figure 20-11, and contains:

- A dc amplifier that receives a weak electrical signal from the sensors and control assembly and sends a strong output signal proportional to the input signal it receives.
- A transducer that converts the amplifier signal to a vacuum signal that actuates the vacuum motor.
- A vacuum checking relay that has a check valve to maintain a constant vacuum signal to the vacuum motor and the rotary vacuum valve.
- A vacuum motor to actuate the rotary shaft that drives the air-mix door link.
- A rotary vacuum valve to route vacuum to control the mode doors and operate the heater water valve; this valve does the same job as a vacuum selector valve in a manual system.
- A feedback potentiometer to inform the programmer of system corrections required by changing temperature demands.

A circuit board electrical switch is mounted on the base of the control assembly. The rotary switch contacts are positioned by the mode-select lever to provide the correct electrical path to the compressor clutch.

The temperature dial varies the resistance of a wire-wound rheostat installed directly above it. The programmer uses the total resistance provided by the temperature dial and temperature sensors to calculate how the system should function.

To use this type of system, the driver need only set the control assembly in the Auto mode and select a temperature. From this point on, the programmer controls the system operation by automatically setting the mode and blower speed and adjusting the air-mix doors to maintain the desired air temperature.

Note that we have added nothing to the underhood portion of the air-conditioning system. We have only modified the operation of the control system by adding a device to maintain temperature within a selected narrow range.

Fully automatic (microprocessor controlled)

The GM electronic touch climate control (ETCC) system is representative of the fully automatic control system. Once the mode and the temperature have been selected by the user, the system automatically controls blower speed, air temperature, air delivery, system turn-on, and compressor operation. It does this with an electronic control assembly containing a microprocessor.

Figure 20-11. Components of the programmer used in GM's C61 AC system. (GM)

While basic operation of an ETCC system is the same regardless of the car in which it's installed, there are several different versions of the system. The primary difference between each version is the kind of actuator and the way in which each is controlled:

- All ETCC systems use an electric servomotor to control the air-mix door.
- Systems on full-size cars use electrically operated mode door actuators.
- Systems on compact and intermediate cars use vacuum-controlled mode door actuators operated by a programmer.
- Luxury full-size systems use a power module to control blower speed and have a diagnostic mode to provide trouble codes for troubleshooting.

Once the user selects the operating mode and the temperature at the climate control panel, the microprocessor looks at the selected mode and temperature, the temperatures inside and outside the car, and the positioning of the mode and air-mix doors. Based on this input, the microprocessor decides what has to be done to bring the in-car temperature in line with the selected temperature. It can:

- Turn the compressor on or off as required
- Vary the blower motor speed to create the necessary air movement inside the car
- Activate one or more vacuum or electric motors to open or close the doors that direct airflow in the passenger compartment.

In the ETCC system, compressor clutch cycling is controlled both by the underhood switches we looked at earlier and by the control assembly. On all but luxury systems, if the microprocessor decides to activate or deactivate the compressor or vary the blower speed, it

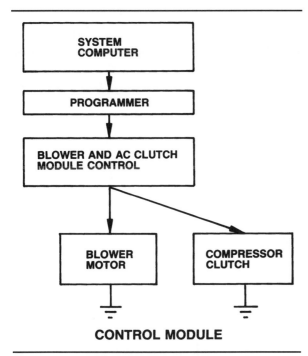

CONTROL MODULE

Figure 20-12. One ETCC system design uses a blower and AC control module to control blower motor speed and compressor clutch operation. (GM)

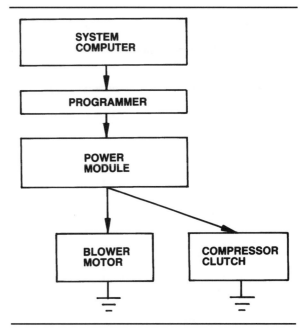

Figure 20-13. Another ETCC design controls blower motor speed and compressor clutch operation through a power module. (GM)

sends a signal through the programmer to the blower and the air-conditioning clutch control module, figure 20-12. A power transistor in the control module engages or disengages the compressor as required. A resistor strip in the temperature door actuator provides a control voltage to the microprocessor for infinitely variable blower motor speeds. When the luxury-series microprocessor decides to activate or deactivate the compressor or vary the blower speed, it sends a signal through the programmer to the power module, figure 20-13.

There also are differences in the way in which the compressor is cycled. If the system uses a power module, the compressor clutch is grounded through the low-pressure switch, figure 20-14A. The power module cycles power to the compressor clutch. In systems with a blower and air-conditioning clutch control module, the compressor clutch power is received through a fuse and the power steering cutout switch or diode; the module cycles the ground circuit to the compressor.

ETCC systems with a diagnostic mode store a trouble code if a malfunction occurs in the system, as determined by its feedback signals. For example, if the potentiometer signal from the air-mix door tells the microprocessor that the door cannot reach the position that the system requires, the microprocessor

will register a trouble code. When the service technician pushes the proper keys, the system displays a numeric code on the climate control panel. As with trouble codes in other electronic systems, the manufacturer provides a specific troubleshooting chart for each code to locate the cause of the problem.

Fully automatic (BCM controlled)

The electronic climate control (ECC) system used by Cadillac is similar to the ETCC system just described. When used with a body control computer (BCM), the control assembly contains an electronic circuit board, but the BCM acts as the microprocessor. The BCM is constantly in touch with the climate control panel on the control assembly through a **data link**, or digital signal path (serial data line) provided for communication. The panel transfers user requests to the BCM, which sends the correct data to the panel for display.

Like the other semi- and fully automatic systems we have looked at, the user selects the mode and temperature. The system automatically controls blower speed, air temperature, air delivery, system turn-on, and compressor operation. While the ECC system functions similarly to the ETCC system, there are

Data Link: A digital signal path for communications between two or more components of an electronic system.

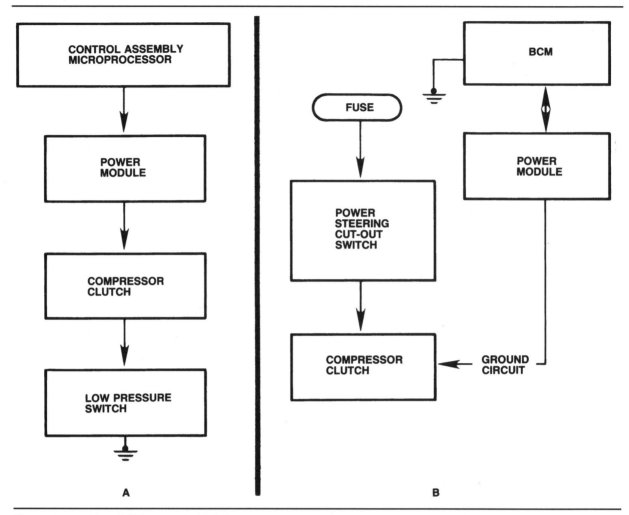

Figure 20-14. Non–BCM-controlled ECC systems ground the compressor clutch through the low-pressure switch and provide power through the power module (A). BCM-controlled ECC systems send power through a fuse and a power steering cutout switch, and cycle the ground through the power module (B). (GM)

differences in compressor cycling methods. In a system without BCM control, the compressor clutch is grounded through the low-pressure switch. The power module thus cycles power to the compressor clutch, figure 20-14A. In a BCM-controlled system, the compressor clutch current is received through a fuse and the power steering cutout switch or diode; the power module cycles the ground circuit for the compressor, figure 20-14B.

The electronic comfort control (ECC) system used by Oldsmobile is BCM-controlled and can be used as either a fully automatic or a manual system. When used manually, the driver can control blower speed and air delivery mode, but the system will continue to control temperature automatically. In addition to the BCM, power module, programmer and control panel assembly used in other BCM-controlled

systems, the ECC system uses inputs from the engine electronic control module (ECM). This allows the BCM to check several engine and compressor conditions before it turns the compressor on.

The BCM communicates with the engine ECM, the ECC panel, and the programmer on the serial data line to transmit data serially (one piece after another). The serial data line acts like a party telephone line; while the BCM is communicating with the ECM, the programmer and the ECC panel can "hear" and understand the conversation. They also can process and use the information communicated, but they cannot cut in on the transmission. For example, suppose the ECM is sending engine data to the BCM. The ECC panel computer, which needs to display engine rpm to the driver, "listens" in on the conversation, picks up the data it needs and displays it on its panel. When

Figure 20-15. The instrument panel cluster (top) and the ECC control panel (bottom) are used to enter diagnostics and access the BCM self-diagnostic system. (GM)

the ECM is finished, it momentarily transmits a five-volt signal to declare the line idle and the BCM opens a conversation with the next device it needs to talk with.

The programmer controls air delivery and temperature on instructions from the BCM, using a series of vacuum solenoids that control the mode door operation. The programmer also has a motor that controls the air-mix door position to regulate temperature. When directed to change blower speed by the BCM, the programmer sends a variable voltage signal to the power module, which sends the required voltage to the blower motor.

The ECC system is the most complex of the ones we've discussed, and this is reflected in the diagnostic sequence designed into the overall system network. When any subsystem exceeds its programmed limits, the system sets a trouble code and in some cases provides a backup function. The instrument panel cluster and the EEC panel, figure 20-15, are used to access and control the self-diagnostic features. When the technician accesses the diagnostic mode, any stored BCM and ECM codes are displayed, along with various BCM and ECM parameters, discrete inputs and outputs, and any BCM output-override information.

RADIOS AND SOUND SYSTEMS

The inner circuitry of radios, tape players, power amplifiers, and graphic equalizers is beyond the scope of this text. However, a technician must understand the external circuitry of sound systems in order to troubleshoot them.

Most sound units and speakers are grounded. In a few four-speaker systems, the speakers are insulated from their mountings. Current flows from the sound unit, through all of the speakers, and back to ground.

In addition to resistance-type spark plugs and cables, automobiles use capacitors and ground straps to suppress radio static or interference caused by the ignition and charging systems. Capacitors may be mounted:

- Inside the alternator, figure 20-16
- Behind the instrument panel near the radio, figure 20-17
- At the ignition coil with the lead connected to the coil primary + terminal, figure 20-18A
- In a module mounted at the wiper motor and connected in series between the motor and wiring harness, figure 20-18B.

Figure 20-16. RFI capacitors can be installed inside the alternator. (Chrysler)

Figure 20-17. An RFI capacitor may be installed near the radio. (Buick)

Ground straps are installed to conduct small, high-frequency electrical signals to ground. They require a large, clean, surface-contact area. Such ground straps are installed in various locations depending upon the vehicle. Some common locations are:

- Radio chassis to cowl
- Engine to cowl
- Across the engine mounts
- From air-conditioning evaporator valve to cowl.

The small bulb that lights the sound unit controls may be part of the instrument panel circuitry, figure 20-19, or part of the sound unit's internal circuitry.

Some cars use electrically extended radio antennas, figure 20-20. The antenna motor may be automatically activated when the radio is turned on, or it may be controlled by a separate switch, figure 20-21. A relay may control current to the antenna motor.

Figure 20-18. RFI capacitors may be installed on the ignition coil or on the wiper motor. (Chrysler)

Figure 20-19. This radio illumination lamp is controlled by the panel illumination circuitry. (Chrysler)

Figure 20-20. The motor of an electrically extended radio antenna is usually installed inside the wheelwell under a protective cover. (Oldsmobile)

Figure 20-21. Power antennas can be controlled by a separate switch. (Chrysler)

REAR WINDOW DEFOGGER AND DEFROSTER

Some older vehicles have a rear window defogger, which is a motor-driven fan similar to that used in the heating system but mounted behind the rear seat near the rear window. It is controlled by a separate switch that routes current through circuits of varying resistance (like a heater fan) to change motor speed. Heat is provided electrically by a length of resistance wire

Figure 20-22. The grid of conductors on this rear window will heat the glass and evaporate any condensation.

Figure 20-23. Defroster circuits often use a separate relay to control current. (Chrysler)

in the defogger unit. The resistance heater is connected in parallel with the motor so that it heats when the motor is running at either high or low speed.

A defroster is a grid of electrical heating conductors that is bonded to the rear window glass, figure 20-22. The defroster grid is sometimes called a defogger. Current through the grid may be controlled by a separate switch and a relay, figure 20-23, or by a switch-relay combination, figure 20-24. In both designs, when the switch is closed, the relay is energized and an indicator lamp is lit. The relay contact points conduct current to the rear window grid.

FUSE
SWITCH/RELAY
TO BATTERY
B
L
TO IGNITION
SWITCH
I
G
INDICATING LIGHT
(INTERNAL)

POWER
CONNECTOR

MIDPOINT "C"
(TYPICAL)
POINT "A"
POINT "B"
GROUND
CONNECTOR

REAR WINDOW GRID LINE STRUCTURE

Figure 20-24. Defroster circuits can also use a combined switch and relay to control current flow. (Chrysler)

Most late-model systems have a solid-state timing module that turns off the defroster current automatically. In the system shown in figure 20-23, the switch "On" position energizes the relay's pull-in and hold-in coils. The switch "Normal" position keeps the hold-in coil energized so that the relay points remain closed.

Cleaning the inside rear glass should be done carefully to avoid scratching the grid material and causing an open in the circuit.

HEATED WINDSHIELD

Some late-model cars have a windshield containing a conductive material that can be heated to melt frost and ice rapidly. The standard three-layer laminated windshield has a silver and zinc oxide layer applied to the back of the outer glass layer, to form an electrical conductor within the windshield. Silver buss bars at the top and bottom of the windshield connect the conductive layer to the power and the ground circuit.

Figure 20-25 shows the components of the system used by Ford:

- Conductive windshield
- Alternator output relay
- Control module
- On/off switch
- Sensing resistor.

Three conditions must be met before the heated windshield system will operate:

- The system must be on.
- The engine must be running (alternator output).
- The interior temperature of the vehicle must be under 40°F (4°C).

The control module contains a thermistor to sense in-car temperature and to prevent system operation when it exceeds 40°F (4°C). It also contains a timing function to limit system operation to four-minute cycles. When the three operational conditions are met, the module signals the driver by turning on an indicator lamp. At the same time, it turns off the charging system voltage regulator and switches alternator output from the car's electrical system to the windshield power circuit to energize the power relay, then turns the regulator back on to restore alternator output. This connects the windshield power circuit to the alternator output terminal through the power relay.

Once the battery is disconnected from the alternator, its voltage will drop to about 12 volts. Sensing this drop, the voltage regulator will full-field the alternator. Since the battery is out of the charging circuit and the alternator is providing full-field power, alternator output voltage increases to from 30 to 70 volts, depending upon engine rpm. The control module prevents alternator output from rising above 70 volts. While the system is operating, the module also monitors battery voltage. If battery voltage drops below 11 volts, the module denies power to the power relay and reconnects the car's electrical system to the alternator.

The module also is linked to the EEC-IV engine control microprocessor by the same wiring that transmits the air-conditioning compressor On signal. If the heated windshield system is turned on and the vehicle is not in gear, the module signals the EEC-IV module to increase engine speed to approximately 1,400 rpm, ensuring enough output from the alternator. Once the vehicle is shifted into gear, the EEC-IV module resumes its normal idle speed control function. Since they are both carried on the same circuitry, an air-conditioning signal will override a heated windshield signal if they occur at the same time.

A sensing resistor connected to the module prevents system operation with a cracked or damaged windshield. The module monitors the voltage across the resistor and shuts the system off if it detects a voltage drop. A 15-ampere fuse in the fuse panel protects the low-voltage control circuit; a fusible link at the alternator output control relay protects the high-voltage power circuit.

Figure 20-25. The components used in Ford's heated windshield system. (Ford)

Figure 20-26. The motor within this car door can raise and lower the window glass. (Ford)

POWER WINDOWS

Car doors can contain motors to raise and lower the window glass, figure 20-26. The motors usually are the permanent-magnet type and are insulated at their mounting and grounded through the control switch, figure 20-27, or the master switch. Each control switch operates one motor, except for the driver's door switch. This is a master switch that can control any of the motors. Some systems have a mechanical locking device that allows only the driver's switch to control any of the motors.

The single-motor control switches each have one terminal that is connected to battery voltage. Each of the other two switch terminals is connected to one of the two motor brushes. The window is moved up or down by reversing the direction of motor rotation. Motor rotation is controlled by routing current into one brush or the other.

Each individual window switch is connected in series with the driver's master switch. Current from the motor must travel through the master switch to reach ground.

POWER SEATS

Electrically adjustable seats can be designed to move in several ways:

- Two-way systems move forward and backward.
- Four-way systems move forward, backward, and front edge up and down.

Figure 20-27. A typical power window circuit. (Chrysler)

Figure 20-28. GM's two-way power seat has a motor with electromagnetic fields; current through the fields determines the direction of motor rotation. (Oldsmobile)

Figure 20-29. This switch controls the Ford four-way power seat circuit. (Ford)

• Six-way systems, used in most late-model applications, move the entire seat forward, backward, up, and down; tilt the upper cushion forward and backward, and move the lower cushion front edge up and down, and rear edge up and down.

A typical two-way power seat system, figure 20-28, was made by GM. The series-connected motor has two electromagnetic field windings that are wound in opposite directions. One winding receives current from the forward switch position. The second winding receives current from the rear switch position. Current through one winding will make the motor turn in one direction; current through the opposite winding will make the motor turn in the opposite direction. The motor armature is linked to the seat mounting by a transmission that translates this rotary motion into seat motion.

Ford and GM have made four-way power seat systems that contain two reversible motor armatures in one housing. Ford's motors have permanent-magnet fields, while GM's motors have series-connected electromagnetic fields. One motor is linked to a transmission that moves the seat forward and backward. The other motor's transmission tilts the front edge of the seat. Both motors are controlled by a single four-position switch, figure 20-29. The switch contacts shift current to different motor brushes (Ford) or to different field windings (GM) to control motor reversal.

Early GM six-way power seat systems use one reversible motor that can be connected to one of three

Figure 20-30. GM's early six-way power seat uses a single motor and three transmissions controlled by three solenoids. (Oldsmobile)

Figure 20-31. Late-model GM and Ford six-way power seats use a triple-armature motor similar to this Chrysler unit. (Chrysler)

transmissions. Transmission hookup is controlled by three solenoids, figure 20-30. The control switch is similar to that used by Ford and Chrysler, but the circuitry differs. Current must flow through one of the

Figure 20-32. The GM power door lock system.

solenoids to engage a transmission, then through a relay to ground. The relay points conduct current to the motor brushes. Additional switch contacts conduct current to the electromagnetic motor windings.

Chrysler, Ford, and late-model GM six-way power seat systems use three reversible motor armatures in one housing, figure 20-31. The control switches have two two-position knobs that control edge tilt and a four-position knob that controls forward, backward, up and down seat movement. The switch contacts shift the current to different motor brushes to control motor reversal. The permanent-magnet motors are grounded through the switch and may contain an internal circuit breaker.

POWER DOOR LOCKS, TRUNK LATCHES, AND SEAT BACK RELEASES

Solenoids and motors are used to control door, trunk, and seat back latches, and locks. Door and trunk systems are usually controlled by separate switches mounted near the driver. Seat back latches are usually controlled by door-jamb switches.

In some GM door lock systems, current flows through a solenoid winding to ground, figure 20-32, when the driver closes the switch. The solenoid core movement either locks or unlocks the door, depending upon which switch position is selected.

Some Ford and Chrysler electric door locks use a relay-controlled circuit, figure 20-33. Current from the control switch flows through the relay coil, closing the relay contacts. The contacts route current directly from the fuse panel to the solenoid windings.

Other Ford, Chrysler, and GM power door locks use an electric motor to move the locking mechanism. The electric motor receives current through a relay, figure 20-34.

Power trunk latches use an insulated switch and a grounded solenoid coil, figure 20-35.

Power seat back releases can be automatically controlled by grounding door jamb switches, figure 20-36. Opening one of the front doors energizes a relay. The relay contacts conduct current to solenoids which unlatch both seat backs.

Figure 20-33. The Chrysler power door lock system. (Chrysler)

AUTOMATIC DOOR LOCK (ADL) SYSTEM

General Motors and Ford both use an automatic door lock (ADL) system in the power door lock system on some of their models as a safety and convenience feature. Ford ADL systems are an integral part of the keyless entry system, while General Motors ADL systems are available on vehicles regardless of whether they have keyless entry.

On GM vehicles with automatic transaxles, placing the gear selector in Drive automatically locks all vehicle doors when the ignition is ON. All doors unlock automatically when the gear selector is returned to the Park position. Individual doors can be unlocked manually from the inside, the front doors can be unlocked with the key from outside, or all the doors can be unlocked electrically while in Drive.

System Operation

The ADL feature may be a function of the chime module, an ADL controller, or a multifunction alarm module, depending on the vehicle model. In a typical General Motors ADL circuit, voltage is applied to the

Figure 20-34. Some Ford power door lock systems use motors rather than solenoids for movement. (Ford)

chime module, ADL controller, or alarm module. When the doors are closed, the ignition is in the run position, and the gear selector is placed in Drive, the module or controller sends current to ground through the lock relay coil in the ADL relay, figure 20-37. Current passes through the relay, door lock motors, and unlock relay to ground, locking the doors. The module or controller then removes current from the relay coil to prevent damage to the lock motors. When the vehicle stops and the gear selector is returned to Park, voltage is sent to the unlock relay coil in the ADL relay. The doors are unlocked by current passing through the relay, door lock motors, and lock relay to ground.

KEYLESS ENTRY SYSTEMS

The first keyless entry system used on domestic vehicles was developed by Ford in the late 1970s. Chrysler and GM both offer keyless entry options on some current models. Since their applications differ substantially in design, concept, and operation, we will look at the Ford version first.

Figure 20-35. A typical power trunk lid latch system. (Ford)

Ford

Ford's present keyless entry system has remained substantially unchanged since its introduction. It provides a convenient entry method when the vehicle keys have been forgotten, or accidentally locked inside. The system consists of a five-button keypad secured to the outer panel on the driver's door, a microprocessor-relay control module, and connecting wiring, figure 20-38.

The keyless entry system incorporates two additional subsystems: one for illuminated entry and the other for automatic door locks. Operating as a single system, it performs the following functions:

- Unlocks the driver's door
- Unlocks other doors or the deck lid when a specific keypad button is depressed within five seconds after unlocking the driver's door
- Locks all doors from outside the vehicle when the required keypad buttons are depressed simultaneously
- Turns on the interior lamps and the illuminated keyhole in the driver's door
- Automatically locks all doors when they are closed, the driver's seat is occupied, the ignition switch is on, and the gear selector is moved through the reverse position.

A linear keypad using calculator-type buttons is installed in the driver's door and used to input a numerical code to the control module. The five keypad buttons are numbered 1-2, 3-4, 5-6, 7-8, and 9-0 from left to right. The numerical code used to open the door, however, is a derivative of a five-digit keypad code stamped on the control module and printed on a sticker attached to the inside of the deck lid. This code refers to the location of the five buttons on the keypad, not the keypad button number. For example, if the module number is 23145, the doors will unlock only if the keys are depressed in that order. If the module

Figure 20-36. In this power seat back release system, the grounding of either door jamb switch energizes both seat back release solenoids. (Chrysler)

requires replacement, a sticker bearing the new module number is applied over the old sticker on the deck lid.

The control module's program operates the keyless entry, illuminated entry, and ADL systems. Two 14-pin connectors (one brown and one gray) connect the wiring harness to the control module; the brown connector also connects the keypad harness to the module. The following components provide inputs to the control module:

- Keypad buttons
- Door handles
- Courtesy lamp switch
- Driver's seat sensor
- Transmission backup lamp switch
- Ignition switch
- Door lock and unlock switches
- Door ajar switch.

The following components receive output signals from the control module:

- Keypad lamps
- Interior courtesy lamps
- Door lock LEDs
- Deck lid release solenoid
- Door lock solenoids.

Figure 20-37. This ADL circuit diagram shows how the multifunction alarm module is integrated with the power door lock system. (Oldsmobile)

Figure 20-39 shows a typical Ford keyless entry circuit diagram. Ford added a remote keyless entry feature on some 1993 models. This uses a handheld radio transmitter with three buttons for door lock control from outside the vehicle. If the vehicle is equipped with the Ford antitheft system, a four-button transmitter is used. The additional button is marked PANIC and allows the driver to activate the alarm in

Figure 20-38. The Ford keyless entry system components and wiring harness. (Ford)

Figure 20-39. A typical schematic of the Ford keyless entry system. (Ford)

an emergency. The system operates essentially the same as the Delco RKE system described below.

Delco

In 1993, GM introduced a Passive Keyless Entry (PKE) system on the Corvette. In this system, a key-fob transmitter locks the doors as the person carrying it walks away from the car, and unlocks them when the carrier comes close to the car again. The owner does not even need to push a button.

Other GM vehicles use the Delco Remote Keyless Entry (RKE) or Remote Lock Control (RLC) system. The key fob contains a radio transmitter with three buttons, figure 20-40, that allows the driver to lock or unlock the doors and trunk lid from outside the car. The transmitter contains a random 32-bit access code stored in a PROM. The same code is stored in a receiver module located in the trunk. This receiver detects and decodes UHF signals from the transmitter within a range of approximately 33 feet (10 meters).

Figure 20-40. RKE or RLC transmitters differ in design from one application to another, but all have three buttons and attach to a key ring. (Oldsmobile)

Depressing the DOOR button on the transmitter sends a signal to the receiver. If the signal contains a valid access code (VAC), the receiver supplies battery voltage to the lock relay coil. This energizes the lock relay, which sends current to the door lock motors. The LH door lock motor is grounded through receiver terminal B and internal contacts; all other motors are grounded through the unlock relay contacts in the door lock relay, figure 20-41. When the lock function is used, the receiver grounds circuit 156, turning on the interior lights for two seconds to indicate that the doors are locked.

If the transmitter UNLOCK button is depressed once, the receiver sends battery voltage to the LH door lock motor, which is grounded through the lock relay contacts in the door lock relay, and only the LH door is unlocked. To unlock all doors, the UNLOCK button must be depressed twice. At this signal, the receiver also sends battery voltage to the unlock relay coil in the door lock relay. This energizes the unlock relay, which sends current to the other three door lock motors. The lock relay contacts in the door lock relay provide ground for the motors, which unlock the doors. When the unlock function is used, the receiver also grounds circuit 156 to turn on the interior lights

for approximately 40 seconds, or until the ignition switch is turned to the Run position.

Depressing the trunk lid release button on the transmitter signals the receiver to supply battery voltage at terminal H. This current energizes the trunk lid release solenoid, allowing the trunk lid to be opened. However, if the ignition is on and the transaxle position switch is not in Park, battery voltage is not supplied and the trunk lid cannot be opened.

Chrysler

The Chrysler keyless entry system also uses a key fob–style radio transmitter, figure 20-42, to unlock and lock the vehicle doors and deck lid. This multi-purpose system is similar to many aftermarket theft-deterrent systems, since it turns on the interior lamps, disarms the factory-installed theft-security system, and chirps the horn whenever it is used.

The transmitter attaches to the key ring and has three buttons for operation within 23 feet (7 meters) of the vehicle module receiver. The transmitter has its own code stored in the module memory. If the transmitter is lost, stolen, or an additional one is required, a new code also must be stored in module memory. Figure 20-43 shows the integration of the keyless entry, illuminated entry, vehicle theft security, and power door lock systems with the body control module (BCM).

THEFT-DETERRENT SYSTEMS

Antitheft systems are usually aftermarket installations, although in recent years, some manufacturers have offered factory-installed systems on the luxury vehicles in their model line. Basic antitheft systems provide a warning when a forced entry is attempted through the car doors or the trunk lid. A starter interlock feature is incorporated on some models.

System functioning relies on strategically located switches installed in the door jambs, the door lock cylinders, and the trunk lock cylinder, figure 20-44. After the system is armed, any tampering with the lock cylinders or an attempt to open any door or the trunk lid without a key causes the alarm controller to trigger the system.

Once a driver has closed the doors and armed the system, an indicator lamp in the instrument cluster comes on for several seconds, then goes out. The system is disarmed by unlocking a front door from the outside with the key or turning the ignition on within a specified time. If the alarm has been set off, the system can be disarmed by unlocking a front door with the key.

Figure 20-41. Oldsmobile Cutlass remote keyless entry circuit diagram. (Oldsmobile)

■ When to Degauss?

Have you run into this problem yet? A customer complains that the vehicle's compass in the overhead console is malfunctioning. It either indicates North in every direction, or it constantly rotates even when the car is heading in a straight line. Should you replace the compass with a new one?

No. Chances are, the problem is not the compass.

Compasses installed in overhead consoles should never be exposed to any magnetic field, or their accuracy will be affected. A magnetic field can be generated by various sources. It may happen if an aftermarket sunroof is installed. The saw used to cut the opening in the roof can magnetize the metal around the sunroof and alter the compass operation. It may occur when the service technician troubleshooting a radio malfunction temporarily mounts a test antenna on the roof, or when someone works on the console with a magnetized screwdriver.

Diagnosing the problem may not be easy, since there is no record of a magnetic field having been near the compass, and few technicians realize the effect of a saw, test antenna, magnetized screwdriver, or the like on a compass.

But once you realize the cause of the problem, the answer is quite simple: Have the roof of the vehicle "degaussed" by a radio or TV serviceman. This is similar to erasing an audio or a video tape with a bulk tape eraser. It neutralizes the magnetic field in the area of the compass and will return most "defective" compasses to working order in just a few minutes.

Figure 20-42. The Chrysler remote keyless entry transmitter is very similar in design and operation to the Delco RKE transmitter.

The trend in factory-installed antitheft systems is to combine the operation of the exterior lights, starter, horn, power door locks, and keyless entry system with a computer module to create an integrated system of multiple circuits. Such systems are complex and require the correct circuit schematic and wiring diagrams to troubleshoot.

Delco UTD System

The Delco universal theft deterrent (UTD) system was introduced on some 1980 GM models and offered as an option until it was superseded by the personal automotive security system (PASS). The circuitry, logic, and power relays that operate the system are contained within a controller module.

When the system is armed by the driver, a security system warning lamp in the instrument panel glows for four to eight seconds after the door have been closed, then shuts off. The system can be disarmed without sounding the alarm by unlocking a front door from the outside with a key, or by turning the ignition switch on. If the alarm has sounded, it can be shut off by unlocking one of the front doors with a key.

If the system is armed and a door is opened forcibly, a two-terminal doorjamb switch activates the alarm through one terminal. The other switch terminal operates the interior lights. On vehicles with power door locks, the circuits are separated by a diode. Tamper switches are installed in all door locks and the trunk lid lock, figure 20-45. The switches are activated by any rotation or in-and-out movement of the lock cylinders during a forced entry. A disarm switch in the LH door cylinder, figure 20-46, allows the owner to deactivate the system without sounding the alarm before entering the vehicle. All tamper switches should be kept clean, as corrosion can cause the system to activate without apparent reason.

Exact wiring of the UTD system depends on the particular vehicle and how it is equipped. To understand just how the system works on a given vehicle, you must have the proper wiring diagram.

Delco VATS/PASS-Key II™ System

The Delco vehicle antitheft system (VATS) introduced as standard equipment on the 1986 Corvette, figure 20-47, functions as an ignition-disable system. It is not designed to prevent a forced entry, but to protect the steering column lock if an intruder breaks into the vehicle. When used on Corvettes with the UTD system, the combination was called the forced entry alarm system (FES). When used on other GM vehicles, VATS is called PASS-Key II™. The system, figure 20-48, consists of the following components:

- Resistor ignition key
- Steering column lock cylinder with resistor-sensing contact
- VATS or PASS-Key II™ decoder module
- Starter enable relay
- PCM
- Wiring harness.

A small resistor pellet embedded in the ignition key contains one of 15 different resistance values. The key is coded with a number that indicates which resistor pellet it contains. Resistor pellet resistance values vary according to key code and model year. To operate the lock, the key must have the proper mechanical code (1 of 2,000); to close the starter circuit, it must also have the correct electrical code (1 of 15).

Inserting the key in the ignition lock cylinder brings the resistor pellet in contact with the resistor sensing contact. Rotating the lock applies battery power to the decoder module, figure 20-48. The sensing contact sends the resistance value of the key pellet to the decoder module, where it is compared to a fixed resistance value stored in memory. If the resistor code and the fixed value are the same, the decoder module energizes the starter enable relay, which closes the circuit to the starter solenoid and allows the engine to crank. At the same time, the module sends a pulse-width modulated (PWM) cranking fuel enable signal to the PCM.

If the key resistor code and the module's fixed resistance value do not match, the module shuts down

Figure 20-43. A block wiring diagram of the Chrysler remote keyless entry system shows its interrelationship with the vehicle theft security system and BCM. (Chrysler)

for two to four minutes. Repeating the attempt to start the vehicle with the wrong key will result in continued module shutdowns. During vehicle operation, the key resistor pellet inputs are continually read. If the module sees an open, short, or incorrect resistance value for 60 consecutive seconds, a SECURITY indicator lamp comes on and remains lighted until the fault is corrected. The lamp also comes on for five seconds when the ignition is first turned on. This serves as a bulb check and indicates that the system is functioning properly.

Figure 20-44. A theft-deterrent system uses strategically placed switches in the door jambs, door lock, and trunk lock cylinders. (GM)

Figure 20-45. Cylinder tamper switches are activated by the lock cylinders when a forced entry is attempted. (GM)

Chrysler Antitheft Security System

This passive arming theft-deterrent system, figure 20-49, is factory installed on high-line Chrysler models and functions like many aftermarket alarm installations. When combined with the Remote Keyless Entry, figure 20-43, the system becomes an active arming system. Once armed, the doors, hood, and trunk lid all are monitored for unauthorized entry.

The system is passively armed by activating the power door locks before closing the driver's door; it will not arm if the doors are locked manually. The system is actively armed if the doors are locked with the RKE transmitter. A SET lamp in the instrument cluster

Figure 20-46. The UTD disarm switch is a part of the LH front door lock cylinder. (GM)

Figure 20-47. The Delco VATS system has a resistor key circuit and a PCM-controlled starter interlock with the UTD system to foil would-be thieves. (GM)

flashes for 15 seconds during the arming period. If a forcible entry is attempted while the system is armed, it responds by sounding the horn, flashing the park and tail lamps, and activating an engine kill feature.

The system is passively disarmed by unlocking either front door with the key, or actively disarmed by using the RKE transmitter. If the alarm has been activated during the driver's absence, the horn will blow three times when the vehicle is disarmed as a way of informing the driver of an attempted entry or tampering.

Ford Antitheft System

This antitheft system, figure 20-50, bears many similarities to the Delco UTD theft-deterrent system. It is installed on luxury models, uses many of the same components, and functions in essentially the same way. Once the system is armed, any tampering with the doors, hood, or trunk lid signals the control module. Once triggered, the system flashes the low-beam

Figure 20-48. A circuit diagram of the PASS-Key II™ system. (Oldsmobile)

headlamps, the parking lamps, and alarm indicator lamp on and off; sounds the horn; and interrupts the starter circuit. The system is composed of the following components:

- Antitheft control module
- Antitheft warning indicator
- Door key unlock switches
- Hood switch
- Trunk lid lock cylinder tamper switch
- Ignition key lock cylinder sensor.

It also incorporates the following components from other systems:

- Power door lock switches
- Door ajar switches
- Horn relay
- Low-beam headlamps
- Parking lamps
- Keyless entry module
- Starter relay.

Figure 20-49. Components of the Chrysler antitheft security system. (Chrysler)

SUMMARY

Heating and air-conditioning systems share a motor-driven fan. The motor speeds usually are controlled by varying the resistance in the motor circuit. Air-conditioning systems also have an electromagnetic clutch on the compressor. The clutch is energized by the air conditioning system control switch. A clutch-cycling pressure switch turns the compressor clutch on and off as needed to maintain desired evaporator pressure and temperature. Other switches are used in the clutch circuit to protect the system from high or low pressure, or to shut the clutch off under certain conditions such as wide-open throttle.

Older vehicles may use a fan and motor as a rear window defogger. This system is similar to the heating system. A rear window defroster or defogger on late-model vehicles is a grid of conductors attached to the rear window. A relay usually controls current to the conductors. Ford's heated windshield system uses current directly from the alternator.

The parts of a sound system that will concern most service technicians include the way the sound unit and the speakers are mounted, interference capacitors, panel illumination bulbs, and power antennas.

Power windows are moved by a reversible motor. Motor direction is controlled by current through different brushes. The driver's side master switch controls all of the windows, because each individual switch is grounded through the master switch.

Power seats can be moved by one, two, or three motors and various transmission units. Permanent-magnet motors or electromagnetic field motors can be used. Current to the motors sometimes is controlled by a relay.

Figure 20-50. A typical Ford antitheft system circuit schematic. (Ford)

Power door locks, trunk latches, and seat back releases can be moved by solenoids or motors. Relays are often used to control current to the solenoid or motor.

ADL systems are a safety feature integrated with the power door locks. They automatically lock all doors before the vehicle is driven. Keyless entry systems are both convenience and safety features. They allow a driver access to a vehicle by entering a code through a keypad on the driver's door, or by depressing a button on a key chain transmitter.

Theft-deterrent systems such as the Delco UTD and Ford Antitheft System are factory installed on luxury cars. Such systems use other vehicle systems to sound an alarm when the car is tampered with. The Delco VATS/PASS-Key II™ system uses a resistor ignition key that is "read" by the lock cylinder when inserted. If the resistance and the memory value do not match, the system shuts down the ignition and the starter.

Review Questions

Choose the single most correct answer.
Compare your answers with the correct answers on Page 468.

1. Technician A says an electronic climate control (ECC) system with BCM control cycles the power to the compressor clutch. Technician B says an electronic climate control (ECC) system without BCM control cycles the ground circuit to the compressor clutch.
   Who is right?
   a. A only
   b. B only
   c. Both A and B
   d. Neither A nor B

2. Technician A says Ford's heated windshield system uses a conductive grid bonded to the outside surface of the glass. Technician B says the conductive grid is applied to the back of the outer glass layer before it is laminated to the inner glass layer.
   Who is right?
   a. A only
   b. B only
   c. Both A and B
   d. Neither A nor B

3. Constant operation of the compressor in automotive air-conditioning systems is prevented by:
   a. A solenoid
   b. A servomagnet
   c. An electromagnetic clutch
   d. A one-way clutch

4. Individual switches on automobile power window circuits must be connected in _____ with the driver's master switch.
   a. Series
   b. Shunt
   c. Parallel
   d. Series-parallel

5. The air-conditioning compressor clutch can be controlled by:
   a. A power steering cutout switch
   b. A pressure cycling switch
   c. Both a and b
   d. Neither a nor b

6. Technician A says the user selects the mode in a semiautomatic temperature control system, but the actuators are electrically operated. Technician B says a semiautomatic temperature control system uses in-car and ambient temperature sensors.
   Who is right?
   a. A only
   b. B only
   c. Both A and B
   d. Neither A nor B

7. Technician A says the body control module (BCM) talks to other computers in an ECC system on a serial data line. Technician B says the ECC system programmer activates the actuators on a serial data line.
   Who is right?
   a. A only
   b. B only
   c. Both A and B
   d. Neither A nor B

8. GM power seat system motors use:
   a. Permanent-magnet fields
   b. Electromagnetic fields
   c. Both A and B
   d. Neither A nor B

9. The Delco vehicle antitheft system (VATS) uses a _____ in the ignition key.
   a. Thermistor
   b. Potentiometer
   c. Magnet
   d. Resistor

10. Power window systems use:
    a. Unidirectional motors
    b. Reversible motors
    c. Stepper motors
    d. Servomotors

11. Technician A says Ford's heated windshield system will work only if the in-car temperature is above 40°F (4°C). Technician B says the heated windshield module can control the EEC-IV module under certain circumstances.
    Who is right?
    a. A only
    b. B only
    c. Both A and B
    d. Neither A nor B

12. Technician A says a keyless entry system incorporates the function of an illuminated entry system. Technician B says moving the gear selector into Drive with the ignition on activates an ADL system.
    Who is right?
    a. A only
    b. B only
    c. Both A and B
    d. Neither A nor B

13. Technician A says the Delco Remote Keyless Entry (RKE) and the Remote Lock Control (RLC) are different keyless entry systems. Technician B says the RKE and RLC systems are subsystems of the VAT and PASS systems.
    Who is right?
    a. A only
    b. B only
    c. Both A and B
    d. Neither A nor B

14. Technician A says if the resistance value of the ignition key in the PASS system does not match the UHF value stored in the receiver's memory, the vehicle will not start. Technician B says a factory-installed theft-deterrent system is a complex multiple-circuit system.
    Who is right?
    a. A only
    b. B only
    c. Both A and B
    d. Neither A nor B

Glossary of Technical Terms

Actuator: A device that translates an electrical command into a mechanical action.

Adaptive Memory: A feature of computer memory that allows a microprocessor to adjust its calibration for computing output commands, based on changes in its sensor's signal values over time.

After Top Dead Center (ATDC): The position of a piston after it has passed the top of its stroke. Usually expressed in camshaft degrees of rotation, such as 5° ATDC.

Air Core Gauge: A gauge design in which there is no magnetic core. A field created by the sending unit resistance moves a pivoting permanent magnet.

Air-Fuel Ratio: The amount of air by weight mixed with one pound of gasoline, as in 14.7 lbs. of air to 1 lb. of gasoline, or a 14.7 to 1 air-fuel ratio.

Alternating Current: A flow of electricity through a conductor, first in one direction and then in the opposite direction.

Ambient Temperature: The temperature of the air surrounding a particular device or location.

Ammeter: A meter used to measure electrical current in amperes.

Ampere: The unit for measuring the rate of electric current flow.

Analog: A signal or command that varies without interruption relative to the action being measured or controlled.

Analog-to-Digital (AD): An electronic conversion process for changing analog electrical signals to digital (on-off) electrical signals.

Aneroid: A sealed bellows or capsule that contains a partial vacuum and changes its length or size in response to a change in atmospheric pressure.

Armature: The movable part in a relay. The revolving part in a generator or motor.

Asymmetrical: Different on both sides of center. In an asymmetrical low-beam headlamp, the light beam is spread farther to one side of center than to the other.

Atom: The smallest part of a chemical element that still has all the characteristics of that element.

Available Voltage: The peak voltage that an ignition coil can produce.

Bakelite: A synthetic plastic material that is a good insulator. Distributor caps are often made of Bakelite.

Ballast Resistor: A resistor in the primary circuit that limits ignition primary system voltage and consequently current flow. Also known as a primary resistor.

Base: The center layer of semiconductor material in a transistor.

Battery Element: A complete assembly of positive plates, negative plates, and separators making up one cell of a battery.

Before Top Dead Center (BTDC): The position of a piston before it reaches the top of its stroke. Usually expressed in camshaft of degrees of rotation, such as 5° BTDC.

Biasing: Applying current to a junction of semiconductor materials.

Binary System: A mathematical system containing only two digits (0 and 1), which allows a computer to read and process digital input voltage signals.

Bipolar: Having two opposite and opposing forces.

Bits: Digital input or output signals. One bit roughly equals one computer keystroke, or one discrete piece of information. The word comes from *B*inary Dig*its*.

Block-Learn Function: Generically known as long-term fuel trim. Fuel delivery adjustments to the injector pulse width based on closed-loop feedback. Short-term fuel trim is based on rapidly switching oxygen sensor values, while long-term fuel trim is a learned value used to compensate for continual deviation of the short-term fuel trim from its central value.

Bottom Dead Center (BDC): The exact bottom of a piston stroke.

Bound Electrons: When there are five or more electrons in an atom's valence ring, they are tightly held. This is characteristic of an insulator.

Breakdown Voltage: The voltage above which a zener diode will allow a reverse current to flow.

Breaker Points: The metal contact points that act as an electrical switch in a distributor to open and close the ignition primary circuit.

Burn Time: The duration of ignition spark, usually indicated in milliseconds.

Buss Bar: A solid metal strip, or bar, used as a conductor in a multiple-fuse panel.

Capacitance: The ability of two conducting surfaces, separated by an insulator, to store an electric charge.

Capacitive-Discharge Ignition: A method of igniting the air-fuel mixture in an engine cylinder through the storage of a voltage potential within a capacitor.

Carbon Monoxide (CO): An odorless, colorless, tasteless, and poisonous gas. A pollutant produced by an internal combustion engine.

Cathode Ray Tube (CRT): An electron beam tube with a cathode at one end and an anode at the screen end. A "ray" of electrons shot from the cathode to the anode creates a pattern on the luminescent screen.

Cell: A case enclosing one element in an electrolyte. In an automotive battery (collection of cells) each cell produces approximately 2.1 to 2.2 volts. Cells are connected in series.

Central Processing Unit (CPU): The processing and calculating portion of a microcomputer.

Centrifugal (Mechanical) Advance: A method of advancing ignition timing in proportion to engine speed using weights in the distributor that react to centrifugal force, moving the top portion of the distributor shaft.

Centrifugal Force: The natural tendency of objects, when rotated, to move away from the center of rotation.

Circuit: An unbroken path through which an electric current can flow.

Circuit Number: The number, or number and letter, that manufacturers use to identify a specific electrical circuit in a diagram.

Closed Loop: An operational mode in which the computer reads and responds to feedback signals from an exhaust gas oxygen sensor, adjusting its fuel decisions accordingly.

Clutch Start Switch: A starter safety switch that prevents starter operation unless the clutch pedal is depressed.

Collector: The conductive outside layer of semiconductor material in a transistor.

Color Coding: The use of colored insulation on wire to identify an electrical circuit.

Commutator: A segmented ring attached to one end of an armature in a dc generator or a motor, providing an electrical connection between the armature's windings and the brushes. In a generator, it rectifies the current. In a motor, it provides a direct current path to the armature.

Compound Motor: A motor that has both series and shunt field windings. Often used as a starter motor.

Concentric: Having the same center, such as two circles drawn around a common centerpoint.

Condenser: A capacitor. Usually refers to an automotive capacitor constructed of two pieces of tinfoil, separated by an insulator, within a metal can.

Conductors: Materials that have atoms with three or fewer electrons, and because their electrons are not bound, allow easy electron flow.

Continuity: Continuous, unbroken. Used to describe a working electrical circuit or component that is not open or broken.

Conventional Theory: The current-flow theory that says electricity flows from positive to negative. Also called the hole theory of current flow.

Counterelectromotive Force (CEMF): An induced voltage that opposes the source voltage and any change (increase or decrease) in the charging current.

Cranking Performance Rating: A battery rating based on the amperes of current that a battery can supply for 30 seconds at 0°F, with no battery cell falling below 1.2 volts. Sometimes referred to as cold cranking amperage, or CCA.

Crossfiring: Ignition voltage jumping from the distributor rotor to the wrong spark plug electrode inside the distributor cap. Also, ignition voltage jumping from one spark plug cable to another due to insulation that is damaged or degraded.

Current Limiting Hump: The portion of the waveform that indicates the exact point in the dwell when a current limiting device is switched ON.

Current Ramping: The shape of the waveform of a circuit as coil saturation builds and then collapses.

Cycling: Battery electrochemical action and operation from charged to discharged and back. One complete cycle is operation from fully charged to discharged and back to fully charged.

D'Arsonval Movement: A small, current-carrying coil mounted within the field of a permanent horseshoe magnet. Interaction of the magnetic fields causes the coil to rotate and move the indicator needle of an electrical gauge or meter.

Data Link: A digital signal path for communications between two or more components of an electronic system.

Delta-Type Stator: An alternator stator design in which the three windings of a three-phase alternator are connected end-to-end. The beginning of one winding is attached to the end of another winding. Delta-type stators are used in alternators that must provide high-current output.

Depletion Region: An area near the junction of two semiconductors, one P-material and one N-material, where P-material is depleted of holes and N-material is depleted of electrons.

Detented: Describes positions in a switch that hold it in that position unless moved by the vehicle operator. In an ignition switch, the On, Off, Lock, and Accessory positions are detented.

Diaphragm: A thin flexible wall separating two cavities, such as the diaphragm in a vacuum advance unit.

Dielectric: The insulating material between the two conductive plates of a capacitor.

Digital: A voltage signal or processing function that has only two levels, on/off or high/low.

Digital-to-Analog (DA): An electronic conversion process for changing digital electrical signals to analog electrical signals.

Diode: An electronic device made of P-material and N-material bonded at a junction. A diode allows current flow in one direction and blocks it in the other.

Direct Current: A flow of electricity in one direction through a conductor.

Discrete Device: A complete, separately manufactured, individual component with wire leads for connection into a circuit.

Distributor Ignition System: An ignition system, either mechanical or electronic, that incorporates a distributor in the design.

Doping: The addition of a small amount of a second chemical element to a semiconductor to change its electrical properties.

Drain: The field-effect transistor (FET) layer which collects current carriers (similar to the collector of a bipolar transistor).

Duty Cycle: Duty cycle is a specific number of on-off cycles in a given length of time, for example, ten times per second.

Dwell: Period of time when a switching device (points, transistor, etc.) is closed and current is traveling through the primary circuit.

Dwell Time: The duration or actual time of the dwell period, usually expressed in degrees of distributor rotation or milliseconds.

Electrochemistry: In a battery, voltage caused by the chemical action of two dissimilar materials in the presence of a conductive chemical solution.

Electrolyte: The chemical solution in a battery that conducts electricity and reacts with the plate materials.

Electromagnet: A soft iron core wrapped in a coil of a current-carrying conductor.

Electromagnetic Induction: The creation of a voltage within a conductor when relative motion exists between the conductor and a magnetic field.

Electromagnetic Interference (EMI): An undesirable form of electromagnetism created by rapid changes in field strength whenever current stops and starts.

Electromagnetics: The study of the relationship of magnetic energy to electrical energy.

Electron: A negatively charged particle within an atom.

Electron Theory: The current flow theory that says electricity flows from negative to positive.

Electronic Ignition System: Any type of ignition system that uses electronic components to switch the primary current on and off. In OBD II vehicles, a system in which the ignition coil secondary circuit is dedicated to specific spark plugs without the use of a distributor.

Electrostatic Field: The area around an electrically charged body resulting from the difference in voltage between two points or surfaces.

Elements: Chemical building blocks that make up all types of matter in the physical universe.

Emitter: The conductive outside layer of semiconductor material in a transistor.

Engine Mapping: A process of vehicle and engine simulation used to establish a library of values for the computer to work with in determining system commands.

Equivalent Resistance: The total resistance of a parallel circuit. The single mathematical equivalent of all the parallel resistance.

Extended-Core Spark Plug: The insulator core and the electrodes in this type of spark plug extend farther into the combustion chamber than they do on other types. Also called power tip.

Farad: The unit of measurement of capacitance.

Field Circuit: The charging system circuit that controls current to the alternator field, thereby controlling alternator output.

Field Relay: A magnetic switch used to open and close the alternator field circuit or, in a charging circuit with a warning lamp, to control the lamp circuit.

Firing Line: The section of an ignition waveform trace showing the effect of the ignition coil's primary windings' magnetic field collapsing across the secondary windings.

Firing Order: The order of cylinders in which spark should occur in the combustion sequence of an engine.

Firing Voltage (Required Voltage): The voltage level that must be reached to overcome all resistance, ionize and create a spark in the air gap between the spark plug electrodes.

Fixed Dwell: The ignition dwell period begins when the switching device (points, transistor, etc.) turns on and ends when it turns off, but remains constant, specified in distributor degrees, throughout all engine speeds.

Flux Density: The number of flux lines in a magnetic field area. The more flux lines in a unit of area, the stronger the magnetic field at that point.

Flux Lines: Another term for magnetic flux.

Forward Bias: The application of a voltage to produce current flow across the junction of a semiconductor. The direction of current flow allowed by a diode.

Four-Stroke Cycle: One complete operating cycle in a four-stroke engine. The four strokes of the cycle are: intake, compression, power, and exhaust.

Free Electrons: Three or fewer loosely held electrons in an atom's valence ring; characteristic of a good electrical conductor.

Full-Wave Rectification: A process by which all of an ac sine wave voltage is rectified and allowed to flow as dc.

Galvanic Battery: A battery that generates voltage based on a difference in oxygen content on either side of its two electrodes.

Gate: The field-effect transistor (FET) layer that creates a capacitive field that lets current flow from the source to the drain (similar to the base of a bipolar transistor).

Ground Cable: The battery cable that provides a ground connection from the vehicle chassis to the battery.

Group Number: A battery identification number that indicates battery dimensions, terminal design, holddown location, and other physical features.

Half-Wave Rectification: A process by which only one-half of an ac sine wave voltage is rectified to dc.

Hall-Effect Switch: A signal switching device that develops a transverse voltage across a current-carrying semiconductor when subjected to a magnetic field. A Hall-device switches a constant voltage, digital, dc signal that varies in frequency according to speed of rotation.

Hardware: The mechanical and electronic components that physically make up a computer.

Heat Range: The measure of a spark plug's ability to dissipate heat away from its firing end.

Hold-In Winding: The coil of small-diameter wire in a solenoid that is used to create a magnetic field to hold the solenoid plunger in position inside the coil.

Hole: The space in a valence ring where another electron could fit.

Hydrocarbon: A chemical compound of hydrogen and carbon. A major pollutant from an internal combustion engine. Gasoline itself is made of hydrocarbon compounds.

Ignition Interval (Firing Interval): The number of degrees of crankshaft rotation between ignition sparks.

Impurities: The doping elements (usually arsenic and boron) added to pure silicon or germanium to form semiconductor materials.

Induced Voltage: The voltage that appears in a conductor when relative motion and proximity exists between it and magnetic flux lines.

Inductive-Discharge Ignition: A method of igniting the air-fuel mixture in an engine cylinder through the induction of a high voltage in the secondary winding of a coil.

Installation Diagram: A drawing that shows where the wires, switches, loads, attachment hardware, and other parts of an electrical circuit are located on a vehicle.

Insulated, or Hot, Cable: The battery cable that conducts battery current to the automotive electrical system.

Insulators: Materials that oppose electron flow because their electrons are bound.

Integrated Circuit (IC): A very small, complex electronic circuit that contains hundreds or thousands of transistors and other devices on a tiny silicon chip.

Integrator Function: The ability of the computer to make short-term—immediate—corrections in fuel metering in response to exhaust gas oxygen sensor input. Also called short-term fuel trim.

Ion: An atom that has become unbalanced by losing or gaining an electron. It can be positively or negatively charged.

Ionize: To break up molecules into two or more oppositely charged ions. The air gap between the spark plug electrodes is ionized when the air-fuel mixture is changed from a nonconductor to a conductor.

Junction: The area where two types of semiconductor materials (P- and N-material) are joined.

Lap Winding: A method of wiring a motor armature. The two ends of a conductor are attached to two commutator bars that are next to each other.

Left-Hand Rule: A method of determining the direction of the magnetic flux lines surrounding a current-carrying conductor, when the electron theory of current flow (− to +) is used. If the conductor is grasped with the left hand so the thumb points in the direction of current flow, the fingers will point in the direction of magnetic flux.

Light-Emitting Diode (LED): A gallium-arsenide diode that emits energy as light. Often used in automotive indicators.

Liquid Crystal Display (LCD): An indicator consisting of a sandwich of glass containing electrodes and polarized fluid. Voltage applied to the fluid allows light to pass through it.

Logic Gates: Circuit switching functions within a computer that act as routes for output voltage signals according to differing combinations of input signals.

Logic Symbol: A symbol identifying the type of electronic gate in a digital or logic circuit.

Lookup Tables: Part of a computer's program, or instructions. One set of lookup tables is common to all microprocessors of a specific vehicle group. Another set of lookup tables is used for specific engine calibrations and is located in the PROM.

Magnetic Field: The area surrounding a magnet that is influenced by the magnet's energy.

Magnetic Flux: The invisible directional lines of force that make up a magnetic field.

Magnetic Pulse Generator: A signal generating device that creates a voltage pulse as magnetic flux changes around a pickup coil. The device transmits an analog ac signal voltage that varies in frequency and amplitude according to speed of rotation.

Magnetic Saturation: The condition when a magnetic field reaches full strength and maximum flux density.

Magnetism: A form of energy caused by the alignment of atoms within certain materials. The ability of a metal to attract iron.

Manifold Absolute Pressure (MAP): Pressure in the intake manifold that is referenced to true zero at sea level instead of gauge pressure zero, which is actually 14.7 psi absolute.

Manifold Vacuum: Low pressure, less than atmospheric, in an engine's intake manifold, below the throttle.

Mechanical Ignition System: Any type of ignition system that uses a mechanical set of points to switch the primary current on and off.

Menu Driven: A computer program that allows the user to select choices from a list or "menu" is menu driven. As each choice is made, another menu allows the user to make another choice to achieve the desired end result.

Module: A self-contained, sealed unit that houses the solid-state circuits that control certain electrical or mechanical functions.

Multiplex Wiring System: An electrical circuit in which several devices share signals on a common conductor. Signals may be transmitted in parallel form by a solid-state switching device or in serial form over a peripheral data bus or fiber-optic cable.

Mutual Induction: Creation of voltage in one conductor by the rise and collapse of a magnetic field surrounding another conductor.

Negative Polarity: A correct polarity of the ignition coil connections. Coil voltage is connected to the spark plugs so that the center electrode (tip) of the plug is negatively charged and the grounded electrode (cylinder head) is positively charged.

Negative Temperature Coefficient (NTC): The property of a thermal resistor (also called a thermistor) to have less resistance as its temperature increases.

Neutral Junction: The center connection of the three windings in a Y-type stator.

Neutron: A particle in an atom that is considered to have no charge and is therefore electrically neutral.

N-Material: A semiconductor material that has excess (free) electrons because of the type of impurity added. It has a negative charge and will not attract additional electrons.

No-Load Oscillation: The rapid, back-and-forth, peak-to-peak oscillation of voltage in the ignition secondary circuit when the circuit is open.

Nonvolatile RAM: Random access memory (RAM) that retains its information when the vehicle's ignition is off.

Nucleus: The center core of an atom that contains the protons and neutrons.

Ohm: The unit for measuring electrical resistance. When one volt can push one ampere through a circuit, the resistance present is one ohm.

Ohmmeter: A meter used to measure resistance to current flow.

Open Loop: An operational mode in which the computer adjusts a system to function according to engine speed, load, and temperature input but does not respond to exhaust oxygen sensor input.

Optical Signal Generator: A switching device that uses the principle of light beam interruption to generate voltage signals from a photosensitive transistor using a light-emitting diode.

Orifice: A small opening in a tube, pipe, or valve.

Output Circuit: The charging system circuit that provides voltage to send charging current to the battery and help run other electrical systems and devices.

Oxides of Nitrogen: Chemical compounds of nitrogen and oxygen. Major pollutants produced by an internal combustion engine that combine with hydrocarbons to produce smog.

Parallel Circuit: A circuit that has more than one path through which current can flow.

Peak and Hold Driver: A fuel injector circuit that limits current using a transistor to switch to a current limiting resistor circuit within the PCM.

Peak Inverse Voltage (PIV): The highest reverse bias voltage that can be applied to a junction of a diode before its atomic structure breaks down and allows current to flow.

Permeability: A measure of the ease with which materials can be penetrated by magnetic flux lines. Iron is more permeable than air.

Photoelectricity: Voltage caused by the energy of light as it strikes certain materials.

Piezoelectricity: Voltage caused by physical pressure applied to the faces of certain crystals.

P-Material: A semiconductor material that has holes for additional electrons because of the type of impurity added. It has a positive charge and will attract additional electrons.

Polarity: Having poles, such as the north and south poles of a magnet. The poles of a battery or an electrical circuit are its positive and negative terminals.

Pole: The areas of a magnetized body where the lines of magnetic force are concentrated. One end of a magnet.

Ported Vacuum: A vacuum port immediately above a closed throttle plate in a carburetor or fuel-injection throttle body that develops vacuum when the engine is operated above idle speed.

Positive Polarity: An incorrect polarity of the ignition coil connections. Coil voltage is connected to the spark plug so that the center electrode (tip) of the plug is positively charged and the grounded electrode (cylinder head) is negatively charged.

Potential: Possible, but not yet in use. The voltage between two points before a circuit is closed (not operated).

Potentiometer: A variable resistor with three terminals. Signal voltage is taken from a terminal attached to a movable contact or wiper that passes over the resistor. The resulting signal reports the position of a device to which the wiper is attached.

Primary Battery: A battery in which chemical processes destroy one of the metals necessary to create electrical energy. Primary batteries cannot be recharged.

Primary Windings: The coil winding made of a few turns of a heavy wire, which uses battery current to create a magnetic field.

Primary Wiring: The low-voltage (or 12-volt battery voltage) wiring in an automobile electrical system.

Program: The instructions a computer uses to do its job. The program consists of mathematical instructions and may include fixed data and require data from vehicle sensors.

Programmable Read-Only Memory (PROM): An integrated circuit chip installed in the onboard computer that has been programmed with specific operating instructions and database information for a particular vehicle.

Proton: A positively charged particle within an atom.

Pull-In Winding: The coil of large-diameter wire in a solenoid that is used to create a magnetic field to pull the solenoid plunger into the coil.

Pulse Width Modulated (PWM) Driver: A fuel injector circuit that uses a pulsing "hold" signal to keep the injector open.

Pulse Width Modulation (PWM): The variation of the on-time of an automotive electronic signal to a solenoid, regulating the current flow and consequently, the work performed.

Radio Choke: A coil of extremely fine wire used to absorb oscillations created by the making and breaking of an electrical circuit. Also known as a choke coil.

Radiofrequency Interference (RFI): A form of electromagnetic interference, as created in the ignition secondary circuit, that disrupts radio and television transmission.

Random-Access Memory (RAM): Computer memory in which information can be written (stored) and read. Whatever is stored in RAM is lost whenever battery voltage is disconnected.

Reach: The length of the spark plug shell from the seat to the bottom of the shell, or length of plug threads.

Read-Only Memory (ROM): The permanent part of a computer's memory storage function. The ROM can be read but not changed and is retained when voltage to the computer is shut off.

Reciprocating Engine: Also called a piston engine. An engine in which the pistons move up and down or back and forth, as a result of combustion on the top of the cylinder. The up and down motion of the pistons is transformed into rotary motion by a crankshaft.

Recombinant: A nongassing battery design in which the oxygen released by the electrolyte recombines with the negative plates.

Rectify: To correct or change alternating current to direct current.

Reference Voltage: Voltage supplied to a sensor from a vehicle's computer. The sensor's effect on the voltage becomes a signal used by the computer as input data to judge the condition(s) at the sensor.

Relative Motion: Movement of a conductor in relation to magnetic flux lines or movement of magnetic flux lines in relation to a conductor.

Relay: An electromagnetic switch. A relay uses a small amount of control circuit current to control the flow of a larger amount of current through a power circuit.

Reluctance: The tendency of some materials to resist penetration by magnetic flux lines.

Reserve Capacity Rating: A battery rating based on the number of minutes a battery at 80°F can supply 25 amperes, with no battery cell falling below 1.75 volts.

Resistance: Opposition to electrical current flow.

Resistor-Type Spark Plug: A plug that has a resistor in the center electrode to reduce the inductive portion of the spark discharge. This reduces RFI.

Reverse Bias: The application of a voltage across the junction of a diode in a direction in which normally no current is allowed to flow.

Rheostat: A two-wire variable resistor used to control current, as in a dashlight dimmer.

Right-Hand Rule: A method of determining the direction of magnetic flux lines surrounding a current-carrying conductor, when the conventional theory of current flow (+ to −) is used. If the conductor is grasped with the right hand so the thumb points in the direction of conventional current flow, the fingers will point in the direction of magnetic flux.

Saturated Driver: A fuel injector circuit that limits current using an external resistor on the power feed side of the circuit.

Schematic Diagram: An electrical drawing that symbolically represents current flow and device function but does not necessarily contain specific wiring information or device location.

Secondary Battery: A battery in which chemical processes can be reversed. A secondary battery can be recharged so that it will continue to supply voltage.

Secondary Windings: The coil winding made of many turns of a fine wire, in which voltage is induced by the rise and collapse of the magnetic field of the primary winding.

Self-Induction: A self-induced voltage formed by the building or induction of current through a conductor, such as the primary windings in a coil.

Semiconductors: Materials that have four electrons in their valence ring and are neither good conductors nor good insulators.

Sensor: A device that provides input data in the form of voltage signals to a computer.

Series Circuit: A circuit that has only one path through which current can flow.

Series Contacts: The normally closed set of contacts in a double-contact regulator. When they open, field current must flow through a resistor.

Series Motor: A motor that has only one path for current flow through the field and armature windings. Commonly used for starter motors.

Series-Parallel Circuit: A circuit that has some parts in series with the voltage source and some parts in parallel with each other and the voltage source.

Servomotor: An electric motor that is part of a system used for automatic control of a mechanical device, such as in a temperature-control system.

Shorting Contacts: The normally open set of contacts in a double-contact regulator. When closed, they short-circuit the field to ground.

Shunt: Parallel. An electrical connection or branch circuit in parallel with another branch circuit or connection.

Shunt Motor: A motor that has its field windings wired in parallel with its armature. Not used as a starter motor, but often used to power vehicle accessories.

Sine Wave Voltage: The constant change, from zero volt to a positive peak, and then across zero to a negative peak, and back to zero, of an induced alternating voltage in a conductor.

Single-Phase Current: Alternating current created by a single-phase winding.

Single-Phase Voltage: The sine wave voltage induced within one phase of winding by one revolution of an alternator rotor.

Sintered: Welded together without using heat to form a porous material, such as the metal disc used in some vacuum delay valves.

Software: The programs and logic functions that are stored in the computer.

Solenoid-Actuated Starter: A starter that uses a solenoid both to control current flow in the starter circuit and to mechanically engage the starter motor with the engine flywheel.

Source: The field-effect transistor (FET) layer which supplies current-carrying holes or electrons (similar to the emitter of a bipolar transistor).

Spark Voltage: The inductive portion of a spark that maintains the spark in the air gap between a spark plug's electrodes, usually about one-quarter of the firing voltage level.

Specific Gravity: The weight of a volume of liquid divided by the weight of the same volume of water at a given temperature and pressure. Water has a specific gravity of 1.000.

Starting Bypass: A parallel circuit branch that bypasses the primary ignition circuit's ballast resistor during engine cranking (starter operation).

Starting Safety Switch: A neutral start switch. It keeps the starting system from operating when a car's transmission is engaged in a forward or reverse gear.

Static Electricity: Voltage resulting from the transfer of electrons from the surface of one material to the surface of another material. The electrons are "static", meaning at rest.

Stepper Motor: A direct-current motor that moves in specific incremental steps when energized.

Stoichiometric Air-Fuel Ratio: The air-fuel ratio of approximately 14.7 to 1 that provides the most efficient combustion of oxygen and hydrocarbon molecules under steady speed, light load conditions.

Stroboscopic Effect: The effect caused by a rapidly flashing light as it makes moving objects appear stationary.

Stroke: One complete top-to-bottom or bottom-to-top movement of an engine piston.

Sulfation: The crystallization of lead sulfate on the plates of a constantly discharged battery.

Symmetrical: The same on both sides of center. In a symmetrical high-beam headlamp, the light beam is spread the same distance to both sides of center.

System Diagram: A drawing of a circuit or any part of a circuit that shows circuit numbers, wire size and color coding, and how it works.

Television-Radio-Suppression (TVRS) Cables: High-resistance, carbon-conductor ignition cables that suppress radiofrequency interference (RFI).

Thermistor: A resistor specially constructed so that its resistance changes as its temperature changes. Also called a thermal resistor.

Thermoelectricity: Voltage resulting from an unequal transfer of electrons from one metal to another, when one of the metals is heated.

Three-Coil Movement: A gauge design that depends upon the field interaction of three electromagnets and the total field effect on a movable permanent magnet.

Three-Phase Current: Three overlapping, evenly spaced, single-phase currents that make up the total ac output of an alternator.

Top Dead Center (TDC): The exact top of a piston stroke. Also a specification used when tuning an engine.

Torque: Twisting or rotating force; usually expressed in foot-pounds, inch-pounds, or Newton-meters.

Total Ignition Advance: The sum of centrifugal advance, vacuum advance, and initial timing; usually expressed in crankshaft degrees of rotation, but sometimes in distributor degrees of rotation.

Transducer: A device that converts (transduces) one form of energy to another. A sensor is such a device, converting mechanical or other energy into a voltage signal.

Vacuum: A pressure less than atmospheric.

Vacuum Advance: The use of engine vacuum to advance ignition spark timing by moving the distributor breaker plate.

Vacuum Fluorescent Display (VFD): An indicator in which electrons from a heated filament strike a phosphor material that emits light.

Valence Ring: An electron shell or orbit of an atom.

Valley Forge Diagram: A type of system wiring diagram in which current travels from top to bottom and only relevant information is given.

Valve Timing: A method of coordinating camshaft rotation and crankshaft rotation so that the valves open and close at the right times during each phase of combustion.

Variable Dwell: An ignition dwell period that varies in distributor degrees of rotation proportional to engine speed.

Venturi: A restriction in an airflow, such as in a carburetor, that increases the airflow speed and creates a reduction in pressure across a tube at a right angle to airflow. Also known as the "Bernoulli effect."

Volt: The unit for measuring the amount of electrical pressure.

Voltage: The electromotive force that causes current flow. The potential difference in electrical pressure between two points when one is negatively charged and the other is positively charged.

Voltage Creep: Excessive voltage at high speeds due to excessive field current flow through a single-contact regulator. Also called voltage drift.

Voltage Decay: The rapid oscillation and dissipation of secondary voltage after the spark in a spark plug air gap has stopped.

Voltage Drop: The measurement of the loss of voltage caused by the resistance of a conductor or a circuit device.

Voltage Reserve: The amount of ignition coil voltage available in excess of the voltage required to fire the spark plugs under no-load conditions. Available for use when the engine is under heavier load conditions.

Voltmeter: A meter used to measure electromotive force or pressure in volts.

Waste Spark: A method of ignition without the use of a distributor in which two spark plugs are fired simultaneously. One plug fires in a cylinder near TDC of the compression stroke and ignites the air-fuel mixture; the other plug "wastes" its spark in a cylinder near TDC of the exhaust stroke.

Watt: The unit of measurement for electric power. One way to measure the amount of work. The wattage equals the voltage times the amperage.

Wave Winding: A method of wiring a motor armature. The two ends of a conductor are attached to two commutator bars that are opposite each other.

Wire Gauge: Wire size numbers based on the cross section area or diameter of the conductor. Larger wires have lower numbers by American Wire Gauge standards but have higher numbers in metric or ISO standards.

Wiring Harness: A bundle of wires, sometimes enclosed in a plastic cover, routed to various areas of the vehicle. Most harnesses end in plug-in connectors. Harnesses are also called looms.

Y-Type Stator: An alternator stator design in which one end of each of the three windings in a three-phase alternator is connected at a common junction. This design is used in alternators that require high voltage at low alternator speed.

Zener Diode: A junction of semiconductor materials that has been heavily doped so that the junction will allow reverse current flow without damage at any voltage above a predetermined value.

Answers to Review Questions

Chapter 1: Basic Electricity and Circuits

1-B 2-A 3-A 4-D 5-B 6-C 7-B 8-C 9-A 10-C 11-D 12-D 13-A 14-B 15-C 16-B 17-A 18-C 19-A 20-B 21-D 22-A 23-B 24-C 25-C

Chapter 2: Magnetism, Electromagnetism, and EMI Suppression

1-C 2-A 3-A 4-B 5-A 6-A 7-A 8-C 9-A 10-B 11-A 12-A

Chapter 3: Semiconductors and Solid-State Electronics

1-B 2-A 3-C 4-C 5-A 6-A 7-C 8-D 9-D 10-C 11-C 12-D

Chapter 4: Automotive Computer Control Systems

1-D 2-B 3-C 4-A 5-D 6-A 7-C 8-A 9-C 10-C 11-D 12-A 13-C 14-B 15-A 16-C 17-D 18-C 19-C 20-B

Chapter 5: Automotive Wiring and Basic Circuit Components

1-A 2-D 3-C 4-C 5-B 6-D 7-A 8-C 9-B 10-D 11-D 12-A 13-B 14-B 15-A 16-D

Chapter 6: Introduction to Electrical Circuit Diagrams

1-A 2-A 3-C 4-B 5-D 6-C 7-A 8-C

Chapter 7: Batteries

1-C 2-B 3-B 4-A 5-D 6-B 7-B 8-A 9-C 10-B 11-A 12-D 13-D 14-C 15-A 16-D 17-C 18-D 19-C 20-D 21-B

Chapter 8: AC Charging Systems and Alternators

1-A 2-C 3-D 4-B 5-C 6-A 7-C 8-A 9-B 10-B 11-D 12-B 13-A 14-C 15-D

Chapter 9: Regulators and Indicators

1-C 2-D 3-D 4-D 5-B 6-B 7-C 8-C 9-D 10-B

Chapter 10: Starting System Overview

1-C 2-A 3-D 4-D 5-D 6-C 7-C 8-D 9-D

Chapter 11: Starter Motors

1-B 2-C 3-B 4-D 5-A 6-A 7-C 8-D 9-A 10-B 11-B 12-D 13-D 14-A 15-C

Chapter 12: The Ignition System and Engine Operation

1-B 2-D 3-D 4-C 5-A 6-B 7-D 8-D 9-C 10-A 11-A 12-B 13-D

Chapter 13: The Ignition Primary Circuit and Components

1-D 2-C 3-A 4-C 5-C 6-D 7-B 8-A 9-B 10-C 11-C 12-A 13-B 14-A 15-A 16-B

Chapter 14: The Ignition Secondary Circuit and Components

1-D 2-D 3-A 4-D 5-C 6-B 7-D 8-B 9-C 10-D 11-C 12-C 13-C

Chapter 15: Ignition Timing and Spark Advance Control

1-C 2-D 3-D 4-C 5-B 6-A 7-C 8-C 9-B 10-D 11-D 12-C

Chapter 16: Solid-State Electronic Ignition Systems

1-B 2-A 3-C 4-A 5-B 6-D 7-A 8-B 9-D 10-C 11-B 12-A 13-D 14-B 15-A 16-B 17-A 18-C

Chapter 17: Electronic Engine Control Systems

1-A 2-C 3-A 4-C 5-D 6-C 7-C 8-C 9-D 10-A 11-A 12-B 13-A 14-C 15-B 16-A 17-C

Chapter 18: Lighting Systems

1-A 2-C 3-A 4-B 5-D 6-C 7-A 8-C 9-C 10-A 11-B 12-D 13-B 14-A 15-D 16-C

Chapter 19: Horn, Windshield Wiper and Washer, Electric Cooling Fan, and Instrument Circuits

1-B 2-C 3-B 4-C 5-A 6-C 7-B 8-A 9-B 10-C 11-B 12-D 13-C 14-A 15-B 16-C 17-B 18-A 19-C 20-B

Chapter 20: Body Electrical Systems (Accessories)

1-D 2-B 3-C 4-A 5-C 6-D 7-A 8-C 9-D 10-B 11-B 12-C 13-D 14-B

Index